Archaeology from the Wetlands:
Recent Perspectives

Archaeology from the Wetlands: Recent Perspectives

Proceedings of the 11th WARP Conference, Edinburgh 2005

(WARP Occasional Paper 18)

EDITORS

John Barber, Dr Ciara Clark, Dr Mike Cressey,
Dr Anne Crone, Dr Alex Hale, Dr Jon Henderson,
Dr Rupert Housley, Dr Rob Sands and Dr Alison Sheridan

Edinburgh 2007
SOCIETY OF ANTIQUARIES OF SCOTLAND

Published in 2007 by the Society of Antiquaries of Scotland

Society of Antiquaries of Scotland
Royal Museum of Scotland
Chambers Street
Edinburgh EH1 1JF

Tel: 0131 247 4115
Fax: 0131 247 4163

Email: administration@socantscot.org
Website: www.socantscot.org

British Library Cataloguing-in-Publication Data
A catalogue record for this book is available from the British Library

ISBN 978 0 903903 40 0
Copyright © Society of Antiquaries of Scotland and individual authors, 2007

The Society gratefully acknowledges grant-aid towards the publication of this volume from

HISTORIC SCOTLAND

Typeset by Waverley Typesetters, Fakenham
Design and production by Lawrie Law and Alison Rae
Manufactured in Great Britain by Bath Press

Contents

Foreword

It was a great pleasure to be asked to speak to the delegates of the 11th International Wetland Archaeology Conference when they met in Edinburgh in September 2005. It is an equal pleasure to introduce the proceedings of that important gathering, now brought so promptly and attractively into print.

A significant feature of the conference was the evidence of strong and growing co-operation between official bodies such as Historic Scotland and the Royal Commission on the Ancient and Historic Monuments of Scotland; historic environment curators working with Scotland's Councils; the Universities and Research Councils, and the voluntary and commercial archaeological sectors. To build upon this strong collaborative trend I charged Historic Scotland with leading a thorough assessment of how we can develop policies which address the topics discussed: understanding and conserving the archaeology of our wetlands. That task is now well under way. We have a firm commitment to conserve and manage our historic environment and to do this we face difficult questions of how to target our efforts and resources upon what is truly important.

Wetlands archaeology is important, and not merely for archaeologists. It provides wider lessons, the clearest of which is the impossibility of fully separating human influences and natural processes. This is particularly relevant as we grapple with current concerns such as climate change and sea-level rise. The evidence for understanding human interaction with natural processes offered by wetlands archaeology can – and indeed must – make a contribution to addressing these global issues.

Seeing Scotland's world-class archaeological resource recognized and set into its international context emphasizes just how much we hold in trust: for future generations of Scots and for humankind as a whole. As we strive to protect and understand our surviving wetlands and to identify and rescue sites and information which we cannot protect, the knowledge that we are doing so in co-operation with so many partners, both at home and abroad, is a true source of inspiration and energy.

I commend this volume to everyone who cares about understanding our past and using their understanding to sustain our future.

PATRICIA FERGUSON, MSP
Minister for Tourism, Culture and Sport
The Scottish Executive

Edinburgh, October 2006

Archaeology from the Wetlands: Recent Perspectives

The 11th International Wetland Archaeology Research Project (WARP) Conference, Edinburgh 2005

The Scottish Wetland Archaeology Project (SWAP) was initiated in 1998 in response to John Coles' energetic encouragement of the Scottish delegates to the Dublin WARP Conference. Over the following years, SWAP members and others have worked on wetland materials and projects, leading to the hosting of the 11th International WARP Conference in Edinburgh in September 2005, which was attended by delegates from Europe, Australia, New Zealand, Canada and the USA, as well as those from Britain and Ireland. This conference came at a significant time for wetland studies in Scotland and its significance for us was highlighted by the attendance of the Scottish Minister for Tourism, Culture and Sport, Patricia Ferguson MSP, who announced that Historic Scotland would be tasked with re-evaluating the nation's wetland archaeology. That re-evaluation is now underway and significant projects will roll out over the next five years. The timing was also significant in that the conference came on the eve of the UK's signing of the European Landscape Convention, raising hopes that with new landscape designations it might at last prove possible to preserve wetland sites as significant elements in cultural landscapes rather than as incidental inclusions in nature reserves. The conference just preceded the publication of the first book wholly dedicated to the theoretical framework of wetland archaeology (*Rethinking Wetland Archaeology* by Van de Noort & O'Sullivan) and two papers by the authors of that book introduce a new level of intellectual analysis to the topic. Finally, and perhaps more significantly, the conference came at a time when the preoccupation with wetland archaeology as a 'separate' discipline is being supplanted by the need to integrate the evidence from wetland sites into mainstream archaeology, which, ironically, means dryland archaeology.

In addressing wetland landscapes, the proceedings of this conference not only bear witness to a *risorgimento* in Scottish wetland studies but introduce, or re-introduce, wetland sites as elements in the cultural landscapes of the world, brought theoretical considerations into full focus for the first time and contributed to the maturation of the relationship between wet and dry archaeology. If that is not sufficient to justify these proceedings, the range, quality and interest of the papers published here quite certainly does.

List of figures

THE PLENARY SESSION

THE ALLUVIAL SESSION

THE POSTERS SESSION

List of tables

List of main contributors

PATRICK ASHMORE
Historic Scotland, Longmore House, Salisbury Place, Edinburgh EH9 1ST

JOHN BARBER
AOC Archaeology Group, Edgefield Road Industrial Estate, Loanhead EH20 9LE

MACHTELD BATS
Ghent University, Department of Archaeology and Ancient History of Europe, Blandijnberg 2, B-9000 Gent, Belgium

KATHRYN BERNICK
174 West 17th Avenue, Vancouver, BC V5Y 1Z6, Canada

RICHARD BRUNNING
Historic Environment Service, Somerset County Council, The Round Tower, Taunton Castle, Taunton TA1 4AA

JANE BUNTING
Department of Geography, University of Hull, Cottingham Road, Hull HU6 7RX

EWAN N CAMPBELL
Department of Archaeology, University of Glasgow, Gregory Building, Lilybank Gardens, Glasgow G12 8QQ

GRAEME CAVERS
AOC Archaeology Group, Edgefield Road Industrial Estate, Loanhead EH20 9LE

CIARA CLARK
AOC Archaeology Group, Edgefield Road Industrial Estate, Loanhead EH20 9SY

JO COOK
Oxford Archaeology North, Storey Institute, Meeting House Lane, Lancaster LA1 1TF

DALE R CROES
Department of Anthropology, South Puget Sound Community College and Research Faculty, Washington State University, 2201 Mottman Way SW, Olympia, Washington USA 98512

ANNE CRONE
AOC Archaeology Group, Edgefield Road Industrial Estate, Loanhead EH20 9LE

ALTHEA DAVIES
School of Biological and Environmental Sciences, Stirling University, Stirling FK9 4LA

MELANIE DIEDRICH
The Evergreen State College and the Department of Anthropology, South Puget Sound Community College, 2201 Mottman Way SW, Olympia, Washington USA 98512

NICHOLAS DIXON
The Scottish Trust for Underwater Archaeology, Scottish Crannog Centre, Kenmore, Aberfeldy PH15 2HY

DENISE DRUCE
Oxford Archaeology North, Storey Institute, Meeting House Lane, Lancaster LA1 1TF

WILLIAM FLETCHER
Suffolk County Council Archaeology Service, Shire Hall, Bury St Edmunds IP33 2AR

RHONDA FOSTER
Cultural Resources Department and Tribal Historic Preservation Officer, Squaxin Island Tribe, 10 SE Squaxin Lane, Shelton, Washington, USA 98584

ANDREW HAGGART
Department of Earth and Environmental Sciences, Greenwich University

ALEX HALE
John Sinclair House, 16 Bernard Terrace, Edinburgh EH8 9NX

DENNIS HARDING
The Old High School, 12 Infirmary Street, Edinburgh EH1 1LT

FIONA HAUGHEY
11 Blenheim Road, Bedford Park, London W4 1UB

JON HENDERSON
Department of Archaeology, University of Nottingham, University Park, Nottingham NG7 2RD

MERETE HENRIKESEN
Museum of Natural History and Archaeology, Section of Archaeology and Cultural History, Erling Skakkes gate 47b, No- 7012 Trondheim

RUPERT HOUSLEY
Department of Archaeology, University of Glasgow, Gregory Building, Lilybank Gardens, Glasgow G12 8QQ

NEA HUBBARD
Department of Anthropology, South Puget Sound Community College, 2201 Mottman Way SW, Olympia, Washington USA 98512

ELIZABETH HUCKERBY
Oxford Archaeology North Storey Institute, Meeting House Lane, Lancaster LA1 1TF

ROB INGLIS
AOC Archaeology Group, Edgefield Road Industrial Estate, Loanhead EH20 9SY

KATHERINE KELLY
The Evergreen State College and the Department of Anthropology, South Puget Sound Community College, 2201 Mottman Way SW, Olympia, Washington USA 98512

LARS LARSSON
Department of Archaeology and Ancient History University of Lund, Box 117, S-221 00 Lund, Sweden

MALCOLM LILLIE
Department of Geography, University of Hull, Hull HU6 7RX

MANDY McCULLOUGH
The Evergreen State College and the Department of Anthropology, South Puget Sound Community College, 2201 Mottman Way SW, Olympia, Washington USA 98512

TOM McCULLOUGH
Department of Anthropology, South Puget Sound Community College, 2201 Mottman Way SW, Olympia, Washington USA 98512

CONOR McDERMOTT
UCD School of Archaeology, College of Arts and Celtic Studies, Belfield, Dublin 4

RICHARD MIDDLETON
Department of Geography, University of Hull, Cottingham Road, Hull HU6 7RX

ANDREW MOIR
Department of Geography and Earth Sciences, Brunel University

CAITRÍONA MOORE
22 Merville Avenue, Stillorgan, Co Dublin

KAREN MYERS
Department of Anthropology, South Puget Sound Community College, 2201 Mottman Way SW, Olympia, USA Washington 98512

ANTHONY NEWTON
School of Earth, Environmental and Geographical Sciences, University of Edinburgh

AIDAN O'SULLIVAN
UCD School of Archaeology, College of Arts and Celtic Studies, University College Dublin, Belfield, Dublin 4

ADRIAN PHILLIPS
Landscapes and Protected Areas, 2 The Old Rectory, Dumbleton, near Evesham WR11 7TG

GILL PLUNKETT
School of Geography, Archaeology and Palaeoecology, Queen's University Belfast, Belfast BT7 1NN

ANDREZ PYDYN
Bankowa 14-16/7, 87-100 Torun, Poland

JAMIE QUARTERMAINE
Oxford Archaeology North Storey Institute, Meeting House Lane, Lancaster LA1 1TF

JANE REED
University of Hull, Hull, HU6 7RX

LARRY ROSS
Cultural Resources Specialist, Cultural Resources Department, Squaxin Island Tribe, 10 SE Squaxin Lane, Shelton, Washington, USA 98584

ROB SANDS
UCD School of Archaeology, Newman Building, Belfield Campus, University College Dublin, Dublin 4

CASSANDRA SHARRON
The Evergreen State College and the Department of Anthropology, South Puget Sound Community College, 2201 Mottman Way SW, Olympia, Washington USA 98512

ALISON SHERIDAN
National Museums of Scotland, Edinburgh

THEO SKINNER
National Museums of Scotland, Edinburgh

ROBERT SMITH
University of Hull, Hull HU6 7RX

MICHAEL STANLEY
20 Foyle Road, Fairview, Dublin 3, Ireland

INGELISE STUIJTS
The Discovery Programme, 34 Fitzwilliam Place, Dublin 2

MORTON SYLVESTER
Museum of Natural History and Archaeology, Section of Archaeology and Cultural History, Erling Skakkes gate 47b, No- 7012 Trondheim

LIESBETH THEUNISSEN
ROB National Service for Archaeological Heritage (from 2006: RACM), PO Box 1600, 3800 BP Amersfoort, The Netherlands

KATRIN THIER
Oxford University Press, Great Clarendon Street, Oxford OX2 6DP

RICHARD TIPPING
School of Biological and Environmental Sciences, University of Stirling, Stirling FK9 4LA

EILEEN TISDALL
School of Biological and Environmental Sciences, University of Stirling, Stirling FK9 4LA

C L TWIDDLE
Wetland Archaeology and Environments Research Centre, Department of Geography, University of Hull, Cottingham Road, Hull HU6 7RX

ERICA UTSI
Sarek, Newton Road, Harston, Cambridge CB22 7NZ

LAUREN VALLEY
Department of Anthropology, South Puget Sound Community College, 2201 Mottman Way SW, Olympia, USA Washington 98512

ROBERT VAN DE NOORT
School of Geography, Archaeology and Earth Resources, University of Exeter

ROBERT VAN HEERINGEN
ROB National Service for Archaeological Heritage (from 2006: RACM), PO Box 1600, 3800 BP Amersfoort, The Netherlands

BARBARA VARGO
AMEC Earth and Environmental, 4825 University Square, Suite 2, Huntsville, Alabama USA 35816

REBECCA WIGEN
Laboratory Director, Department of Anthropology, Box 1700, University of Victoria, Victoria, British Columbia, Canada V8W 2Y2

CLARE WILSON
School of Biological and Environmental Sciences, University of Stirling, Stirling FK9 4LA

SUZANNE YENDELL
School of Biological and Environmental Sciences, University of Stirling, Stirling FK9 4LA

Part I
THE PLENARY SESSION

The plenary session

JOHN BARBER with ALISON SHERIDAN

In September 2005, the 11th International Conference of the Wetland Archaeology Research Programme was held under the auspices of the Scottish Wetland Archaeology Project in Edinburgh. Attended by well over 200 scholars from Europe, Australia, Japan, New Zealand, Canada and the USA, it opened with a plenary session of review papers on the general theme of wetland landscapes, and progressed in three parallel sessions themed on lacustrine, alluvial and peatland sites. This organization is reflected in the arrangement of these proceedings.

The plenary session began with a consideration by Adrian Phillips of three approaches to landscape enshrined in the World Heritage Convention, the IUCN Protected Landscapes and the European Landscape Convention. All three provide insight into the concept of cultural landscapes; landscapes formed by the interaction of people and place over time. The survival of wetland archaeological sites can be, and often is, influenced by events at some distance from their immediate location, eg drainage of wetland miles from a raised bog can spell the end of that bog and its archaeological contents. We, the archaeological profession, have a vested interest in and should support and campaign for legislation or guidance that, operating at the level of landscape units, could contribute to the survival of our most important sites.

Conor McDermott's paper on the wetland work undertaken by the Irish Archaeological Wetland Unit emphasizes just how difficult it is to identify and make value assessments on archaeology in peatlands. For those of us living in lands in which extensive mechanized stripping of peatland is not the norm the problems are even more severe. However, his recommendations of future priorities are extremely helpful and, given that IAWU recorded over 3,500 wetland sites in just 10 of Ireland's 32 counties, his recommendations are well founded.

Richard Brunning's paper raises some very pertinent questions about the value of monitoring waterlogged sites in England and Wales in the absence of clear policies (or the resources to put them into effect) for dealing with the sites being monitored. In the absence of the means or the will to intervene and preserve or excavate threatened sites of signal importance, archaeological monitoring seems, to this writer, fatuous at best. It is merely activity masquerading as action and a wholly inadequate response to endangered archaeological sites of very high cultural value.

Major infrastructural developments in Scania afforded opportunities for the investigation of wetland sites on a landscape scale. It also revealed dryland sites and facilitated a better understanding of their interrelationships. Of course, sites discovered in this way cannot be saved. Thus, although a financial burden for the development, it is wholly appropriate that the necessary works are fully prosecuted, at the expense of the development.

John Barber must admit to a bias in commenting on the report by Robert van Heeringen and Liesbeth Theunissen. He lived for a short period in the Netherlands as a younger man and conceived, while there, a deep and abiding respect and affection for Netherlanders. Their willingness to make difficult decisions and to take logical and effective remedial action was an inspiration. Read Heeringen and Theunissen and be inspired! The professionalism of their approach and their execution of a technically complex programme together with their clear exposition of the results (and enviable publication record) sets a standard for which the rest of Europe, indeed the rest of the world, should strive.

Finally, we were reminded by Aidan O'Sullivan and Robert Van de Noort that landscapes, as opposed to landforms, are structures of the mind. They presented an interesting case for considering the sense of time experienced by the makes and users of the structures and artefacts we find in waterlogged deposits. High levels of precision are available from radiocarbon and dendrochronological dating of wetland materials. These invite and facilitate consideration of much fuller site and artefact biographies that focus on the social and cultural meanings of these objects over the whole of their existences.

In a related presentation, Van de Noort and O'Sullivan argue for a revision of our thinking on the landscape dimensions of wetlands. Confirming that the term 'wetland' is of recent birth, they argue that its use in the interpretation of wetland archaeology may prove unhelpful. Further, noting the differences of perception between those within and those outwith wetlands, they emphasize the enculturation of wetlands, the significance of boundaries and the consideration of landscapes as 'taskscapes', networks of places in which humans undertook tasks.

These considerations of time and space are presented in a post-processual exercise which is, by implication, impossible in a processual framework. However, their own observations actually suggest that the differences between processual and post-processual approaches are here more apparent than real. Aidan and Robert found their thesis in some part on a rehearsal of Crone's account of the use-history of the lacustrine crannog site at Buiston. However, Crone wrote her account of Buiston innocent of any consideration of post-processual site narrative (pers comm). Is it therefore the abundance of evidence, excellence of preservation and high chronological resolution of the wetland sites that allow us to approach the hearts and minds of our

ancestors so much more closely than we can do with dryland sites? If this is the case, we may need to conclude that the lack of impact of wetland results on the interpretational models applied to dryland sites probably cannot be remedied. The exceptionally high information-content of wetland sites derives from the high volume of recoverable detail on wetland sites which is available at extremely high levels of stratigraphic and chronological resolution, levels that dryland sites can only rarely emulate.

Perhaps then we have to accept that wetland archaeology is a theatre of archaeology in its own right, neither reliant on dryland archaeology nor validated by the provision of insights to dryland studies. Certainly, with the publication of *Rethinking Wetland Archaeology* by Van de Noort and O'Sullivan (2006), the dawning of a theoretical framework for wetland archaeology is upon us. Wetland studies ought to inform and be informed by dryland archaeology but we need to drive wetland studies forward in a positive and confident manner and not await the universal acknowledgement of the debts, real or imagined, owed by one to the other. The conference in Edinburgh certainly convinced these writers that wetland archaeology is well along the track to establishing itself as a major sub-species of that wonderful animal, Archaeology. SWAP hopes that when you have had the chance to read these papers you may also agree.

Landscape: the setting to our lives (and a context for archaeology)

ADRIAN PHILLIPS

SUMMARY

This article is deliberately broad in scope and goes far beyond a focus on wetland archaeology. Part I introduces the concept of landscape to a community of wetland archaeologists. It considers landscape both as a resource in its own right and as a medium through which to pursue and assess sustainable development. It develops the argument that landscape is the context within which to understand archaeology and a means to help shape archaeological conservation. It summarizes the threats to landscape quality and diversity. Part II describes three international instruments – notably the World Heritage Convention (WHC), the Protected Landscapes (as recognized by IUCN – the World Conservation Union), and the European Landscape Convention (ELC) – which can be used to strengthen landscape policy, and in particular to encourage the better protection, management and planning of landscape. By using such instruments to give more attention to landscape issues, it should be possible to bring benefits to archaeology as well as to the many other values that the landscape contains.

PART I:
AN INTRODUCTION TO LANDSCAPE

WHAT IS LANDSCAPE?

Landscape is a rather slippery notion: it is hard to pin down and difficult to categorize. The word came from the German word *Landschaft*, via the Dutch word for the human occupation of the landscape: *Landschap*. As Simon Schama has noted, Dutch painters, with their experience of fields reclaimed from the sea, made this notion of *Landschap* the principal focus of their images, and, in contrast to Italian painters, not mere allegorical backdrops to some religious or mythical scene (Schama 1995).

But landscape is much more than scenery as viewed or imagined at one point in time by an artist: it is ever changing, it needs to be appreciated with *all* the senses and it has layers of meaning. There are of course the physical layers of nature – on the one hand, the shape of the land, the rocks, soils, water and vegetation; on the other, the things that people have done to the land. So, landscape is first of all the result of the interaction between nature and people. But the landscape can also be seen as where past and present meet. It has been described as 'a link between what we were and what we are' (Mabey 1985). It contains, and exhibits in varying degrees, the physical remnants of past occupation and utilization; it most certainly includes visible archaeological remains of every kind. Finally, landscape is as much about experience, memory and perception as it is about the physical layers that form it: thus, as well as having an objective presence, it is in the mind too, through the associations it embodies or gives rise to.

Perhaps landscape is best viewed as a dynamic meeting ground, between people and nature, between past and present and between tangible and intangible ideas. The ELC takes this notion and puts it into bureaucratic language when it defines landscape thus: 'an area, as perceived by people, whose character is the result of the action and interaction of natural and/or human factors' (Council of Europe 2000).

WHY DOES LANDSCAPE MATTER?

To understand why landscape matters, it is helpful first to distinguish its three concentric characteristics: structure, function and value. These can be presented diagrammatically in fig 1 (modified from Bergstrom 1998) and summarized thus:

- Structure: physical landform; ecological features; land use patterns; human-made objects.

- Functions: biodiversity; water supply; soil filters and sinks; other ecosystem services; agriculture, forestry and so forth; place to work; place to live; place to visit; space; scenery.

- Values: historical; recreational; tourism; spiritual; existence, scenic and aesthetic; biodiversity and ecosystem; security and stability; agricultural and so on; job satisfaction; cultural; residential property.

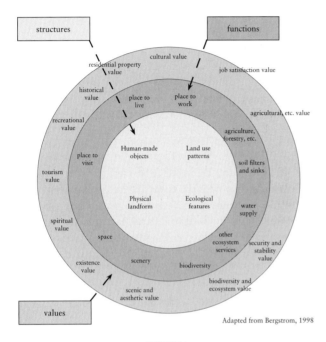

FIGURE 1
The structures, functions and values of landscape.

While landscape has these various kinds of characteristics, it looks different to different people. In particular, its significance to those who live and work within a landscape – insiders and occupiers – is very different to its significance to those who are outsiders. Table 1 sets out this contrast in telegraphic style.[1]

Because of its values, landscape is often thought of as a 'good thing' that should be protected. This view is widely held and is of course reflected in the existence of policies for landscape protection, at least for high quality landscapes. In that sense, landscape is an environmental resource, somewhat akin to biodiversity or historic buildings. But landscape has also come to be recognized as a medium through which sustainability policies can be pursued and assessed. This requires a little explanation.

As we have seen, landscape is a meeting ground: and it may therefore be viewed as a forum within which competing land-uses and other development pressures are fought out, and in which the results of this competition are recorded. A landscape that is scarred by insensitive development or damaged by polluted natural resources tells us that development has not followed a sustainable course; while one that provides good evidence of a balanced, enduring and harmonious relationship with nature, especially when that has lasted over a long period of time, can be considered more sustainable (Phillips in print). Moreover, knowledge of a landscape helps determine what kinds of future change will be acceptable, because they are in sympathy with its structures, functions and values, and those which are not because they disrupt, degrade or destroy those characteristics. It is in this sense that landscape can be considered as a medium to help promote sustainable forms of development. But we can only make sense of landscape, whether as a resource or as a medium, when we move from considering it as an abstract concept to looking at individual landscapes areas, occupying particular places.

TABLE 1
The significance of landscape to insiders and outsiders.

Significance of landscape to insiders	*Significance of landscape to outsiders*
<ul><li>quality of life</li><li>standard of living</li><li>local employment and production</li><li>facilities and services</li><li>memories and associations</li><li>way of life</li><li>symbols</li><li>living space</li><li>customary laws</li><li>safety, refuge, defence</li></ul>	<ul><li>recreation and tourism</li><li>scenic beauty</li><li>biodiversity and environmental service functions</li><li>vicarious consumption of customs and traditions</li><li>architectural significance of buildings</li><li>safe food</li><li>water, timber, minerals</li><li>military training and conquest</li></ul>

THE EMERGENCE OF LANDSCAPE CHARACTER
ASSESSMENT

An individual landscape is an area with a distinctive landscape character or type. For many years, beginning in the early 1970s, the focus of research was on assessing the value of landscapes, through a search for consensus about a hierarchy of landscape quality. This approach turned out to be a blind alley, especially as mathematical formulae were used. As noted above, landscape is a slippery idea, and it is too much imbued with cultural and emotional associations to be capable of being reduced to a computer print-out that records that one landscape is 'better' than another. But the approach was also discredited because the concept of a single, agreed hierarchy of landscape value does not recognize the way that particular individual landscapes may be important to particular groups of people.

Therefore by the mid-1980s, the former Countryside Commission, and others, had embarked on a new approach designed to identify the distinctive character of different landscapes; a few years later, it published definitive guidance (Countryside Commission 1993), updated a few years ago for the Countryside Agency and Scottish Natural Heritage (Swanwick 2002). By now, most counties and many districts in England have undertaken landscape character assessments. Work of this kind has also been undertaken at the national level by the Countryside Agency in an eight-volume series of regional studies under the title *Countryside Character* (Countryside Agency 1998).[2] Similar work has been carried out elsewhere in the British Isles (Bishop & Phillips 2004) and indeed in Continental Europe.

Swanwick (2004) says that the assessment of landscape character is about identifying:

> The distinct and recognizable pattern of elements that occur consistently in a certain type of land-scape. (Landscape character) is created by partic-ular combinations of: geology, landforms, soils, vegetation, land use, field patterns and human settlement. Character is what makes landscapes distinctive and creates a particular sense of place in a locality. Everywhere has character and all landscapes are distinctive (*ibid.*, 111).

The assessment of landscape character has involved the development of a sophisticated methodology that contains four key steps:

- Defining the scope of the exercise, so that there is a clear definition of purpose that will set the scene in terms of the detail required, the resources available and so on;

- A desk study to review available information and assemble these in a series of map overlays to help identify draft areas of common character;

- A field survey to collect data so as to: test, refine and modify draft character areas; inform written descriptions of these areas; and identify aesthetic, perceptual and cultural qualities that may not be evident at the desk study phase; and

- Classification and description of the landscape character types and areas, including mapping their boundaries.

Therefore landscape characterization is an approach designed to identify what is special about each landscape and thereby reveal what makes it distinct from the next. It is not a theoretical exercise (though academics have helped to develop a body of theory around the assessment of landscape character) but it is designed to have a practical application by providing a framework for decision-making on planning and land management issues. Thus Landscape Character Assessment (LCA) – the technique is now so well established that it merits the capital letters and acronym – involves identifying environmental and cultural features (including archaeology), under-standing sensitivity to development and change, monitoring change in the environment, and informing the conditions for any development and change (CA/SNH 2002). Latterly, LCA has gone beyond the technical and planning literature, and has been referred to in policy guidance and quoted in public enquiries. Thus Planning Policy Statement 7 (ODPM 2004) says:

> 13. Local planning authorities should prepare policies and guidance that encourage good quality design throughout their rural areas, in accordance with Annex C to PPS1, and utilizing tools such as Landscape Character Assessments and Village or Town Design Statements, and the design elements of Village or Parish Plans prepared by local Communities.

> *and*

> 24. The Government recognizes and accepts that there are areas of landscape outside nationally designated areas that are particularly highly valued locally. The Government believes that carefully drafted, criteria-based policies in LDDs, utilizing tools such as Landscape Character Assessment, should provide sufficient protection for these areas.

This is no place to get into the details of LCA, but it should be noted that landscape character areas are a little like Russian dolls: they occur at several scales, one within another. The Countryside Agency, eg, developed a fourfold hierarchy thus:

- 159 National Landscape Character Areas
- each of which is analysed by the landscape character types it contains
- which in turn form Local Landscape Character Areas
- and which can themselves be further analysed by local landscape character types.

It is to be hoped that this work will be enthusiastically pursued by the agency's successor, Natural England.

ARCHAEOLOGY AND LANDSCAPE CHARACTERIZATION

Landscape, as we have seen, is where past and present meet. It has 'time depth'. Indeed, from an archaeologist's perspective, this can be stated even more emphatically: 'the whole landscape bears the imprint of its long human history'. Or 'landscape is a complex palimpsest of influence from different periods' (Macinnes 2004). Landscapes tell us of past cultures. They become legible through the buildings, routeways, structures, land-uses and so on that they contain, including of course the archaeological heritage.

This notion is now familiar but it has only developed quite recently. Despite the writings of landscape historians like W G Hoskins, the focus of archaeology, and certainly of much conservation action relating to archaeology, has in the past tended to be on specific sites rather than on whole landscapes. In that respect, the evolution of nature conservation has gone down a rather similar route (see table 2).

It is not suggested that wildlife species and archaeological sites no longer matter, but that the focus of effort in both fields of endeavour has been progressively scaled-up over time and that they have now converged around the idea of a whole landscape approach: indeed, 'landscape scale' is the current buzzword in nature conservation circles.

Historic Landscape Characterization (HLC) is a technique that has been developed to describe the historic characteristics of landscapes as a whole. English Heritage sponsored ground-breaking research in this field between 1992 and 1994 with the aim of developing 'methods of defining historic landscape, in order to allow proper attention to its conservation' (McNab 1999). The project included pilot schemes in County Durham and Oxfordshire and was followed by pioneering work in Cornwall. Since then, a number of other projects of this kind have been developed for other counties and large areas (Clark et al 2004). The reason for applying HLC over wide areas is that historical processes are evident in the entire landscape. 'In many parts of Britain, historical influence is paramount; elsewhere it is less obvious, but it is present everywhere' (Macinnes ibid., 166, emphasis added). The quest is to identify the historic dimension of all landscapes, not simply landscapes of great historic importance.

In this, HLC has many similarities to LCA: it too involves comprehensive coverage, but also the setting of objectives, data collection, analysis and characterization, leading to identifying the policy implications. Moreover, 'it is already apparent that the product of HLC is highly valued for its role in aiding an understanding of the development and character of modern landscape and influencing decisions about its future development' (Macinnes 163). While there are some practical difficulties about merging the two data sets and linking HLC and LCA into one exercise, the logic for so doing is powerful. Landscape includes the historical dimension: indeed it cannot be fully understood without the time depth appreciation that HLC provides. At very least, the two analytical approaches should be used in combination so as jointly to inform decision-making: ideally, the two processes should merge into one.

TABLE 2
Parallel changing perspectives in nature and archaeological protection.

Form of conservation	Early focus	Later development	Current thinking
Nature conservation	Species	Habitats and ecosystems	Whole landscape approach
Archaeological conservation	Sites and monuments	Settings for sites and monuments	Whole landscape approach

WHAT IS HAPPENING TO LANDSCAPE AND WHAT
TOOLS ARE AVAILABLE?

As the product of the interaction between people
and nature, landscapes must change and evolve. But
the pace of change and the increasingly globalized,
homogenized and pervasive forces that are at work,
such as global circuits of capital, affect investment
priorities and help spread universal cultures. These
work through in a number of stresses, each of which
disrupts past relationships between people and place,
and thus impact on the landscape. The list of stresses
is a long one but includes: agricultural intensification
and abandonment; urban expansion; standardization
of materials, designs and so on; infrastructure,
especially roads; tourism and recreation; mining and
landfill; pollution impacts, to which must now be
added climate change (Stanners & Bourdeau 1998,
180–6).

As a result, the diversity and distinctiveness of
individual landscapes are being eroded and landscapes
everywhere are perceived to be under threat. This has
been well documented in Britain over many years (eg
Countryside Agency 1998). These trends are also
evident in Continental Europe (Stanners & Bourdeau
1998), and concern over this has given rise to the
development of a European convention on landscape
(see below).

Counteracting such powerful forces requires action
at national and international levels, and indeed some
of this is being put in place as part of strategies to
deal with some of the underlying issues, like loss
of biodiversity and climate change. But action can
also be taken locally, through measures like area-
based protection, local economic development and
sensitive local planning, all of which can ameliorate
negative trends, and help to reinforce the diversity
and distinctiveness of landscape. The emergence of
landscape strategies based upon advice from the
former Countryside Agency, and more recently from
Scottish Natural Heritage as well, provides a basis for
pulling together local landscape-focused action in the
fields of land-use planning, land management, public
awareness and so on (CA/SNH 2002).

SUMMARY

This article therefore provides a sequence of argument
thus:

- Landscape = a meeting ground of nature +
  people, past + present, tangible + intangible;

- Landscape has many structures, functions and
  values;

- An understanding of landscape is helped by
  landscape characterization;

- Archaeology should be an element in landscape
  characterization;

- Landscape is everywhere under threat and
  needs informed action to protect it.

PART II:
LANDSCAPE AT THE INTERNATIONAL LEVEL[3]

This part of the article considers three international
instruments for landscape protection and co-
operation, which can provide guidance to us in the
UK:

- Cultural Landscapes under the World Heritage
  Convention;

- IUCN Protected Areas: Category V-Protected
  Landscapes;

- The European Landscape Convention.

THE WORLD HERITAGE CONVENTION AND CULTURAL
LANDSCAPES[4]

This treaty, the full title of which is the *Convention
Concerning the Protection of the World Cultural
and Natural Heritage* (UNESCO 1972), is one of
the oldest environmental agreements; it was adopted
in 1972, the year of the Stockholm Conference, and
came into force three years later. A total of 183 states
now (2006) belong to it – or are 'States Parties'.

The Convention aims to promote co-operation
among nations to protect and conserve natural and
cultural heritage of 'outstanding universal value'. It
does this primarily through the inscription of sites on
the List of World Heritage properties. World Heritage
sites must be endowed with exceptional natural and/
or cultural values. The World Heritage List currently
includes 830 sites: 644 of these are cultural sites (such
as the Pyramids of Egypt, the Taj Mahal of India, the
Great Wall of China or Westminster Abbey); 162 are
natural sites (such as the Grand Canyon, Serengeti in
Tanzania or the Dorset and East Devon Coast); 24
sites are mixed (such as Machu Picchu in Peru or St
Kilda in Scotland) (UNESCO 2005a). World Heritage
sites are to be found in all parts of the world, although
there is a concentration of 376 of them in Europe.

Although the Convention brings together cultural
and natural sites within one framework, until quite
recently there was no way of recognizing sites which

were important, precisely because of the interplay between cultural and natural values – that is, outstanding landscapes. However, the unsuccessful proposal of the United Kingdom to inscribe the Lake District as a natural World Heritage site initiated a long debate about the place of landscape under the Convention. As a result, criteria were adopted in 1992 to allow 'cultural landscapes' of outstanding universal value to be recognized as World Heritage sites. The criteria have been drawn up under the cultural side of the Convention, and represent the 'combined works of nature and of man' (Article 3 of the Convention). (It is this Article that explains the use of the adjective 'cultural', which many may feel is redundant since virtually all landscapes have been affected to some extent by people, and even those that have not, have cultural significance; and so all landscapes may therefore be considered 'cultural'.) However, the committee recognized the great importance of the natural values in many such areas. Several sub-categories were identified:

- designed landscapes;
- organically evolved landscapes (sub-divided in turn into living and 'fossil' landscapes of this type);
- associative landscapes (UNESCO 2005b: paragraph 47 and Annex 3).

In the 13 years since the adoption of the relevant criteria in 1992, 53 sites have been inscribed as World Heritage Cultural Landscapes (UNESCO 2005a). The UK has four cultural landscapes – the Blaenavon Industrial Landscape of South Wales (inscribed in 2000), the Royal Botanic Gardens, Kew (2003), St Kilda (inscribed first as a natural site but designated as a cultural landscape as well in 2005) and the Cornwall and West Devon Historic Mining Landscape (2006). Down House, including the gardens and surrounding countryside that were an outdoor research laboratory for Charles Darwin, was nominated in 2006 (for decision in 2007). There is also a strong possibility that the Lake District will be re-nominated.

The inclusion of cultural landscapes in the World Heritage Convention has been significant for several reasons. First, it enables landscapes of outstanding universal value to take their place on the list alongside the world's great cultural monuments and natural sites. In the language of economists, it recognizes them as part of the world's environmental capital. Secondly, it sends a signal to all concerned with the better understanding and protection of

the environment that landscapes merit attention at the international, and – by extension – the national level, too: and that World Heritage sites can be used to raise landscape protection standards in general. Thirdly, through its threefold division of landscape types, the Convention is encouraging the recognition of three kinds of landscapes: those that are designed; those that evolve organically; and those that are to be found in the mind.

This very brief account highlights a few important messages:

- World Heritage Cultural Landscapes are more than the sum of nature plus people – they are the result of the interaction between them;
- Many such areas are of great archaeological value, too;
- The three types of World Heritage Cultural Landscapes can be a helpful way to think about landscape as a whole;
- World Heritage sites (including Cultural Landscapes) should be managed as exemplars and standard setters.

IUCN CATEGORY V-PROTECTED LANDSCAPES

IUCN – the World Conservation Union – is the leading international body for nature conservation and the sustainable use of natural resources (and an advisor to the World Heritage Convention). IUCN defines a 'protected area' as 'an area of land or sea especially dedicated to the protection and maintenance of biological diversity, and of natural and associated cultural resources, and managed through legal or other effective means' (IUCN 1994). Information about more than 102,000 sites that meet this definition is held on the database of the United Nations Environment Programme's World Conservation Monitoring Centre (UNEP-WCMC) at Cambridge, UK, and listed in the so-called United Nations List of Protected Areas (Chape *et al* 2003).

Within the overall definition, protected areas are set up for many purposes: the protection of species or ecosystems; scenic or landscape reasons; tourism and recreation; education, science or research; watersheds, forest and fisheries protection; and increasingly for the sustainable use of natural resources by local people. To bring some logic to this complex situation, and as a basis for listing of protected areas and for its other work, IUCN has developed and promoted definitions of management categories of protected areas (IUCN 1994). This system contains the following six categories:

I Protected area managed mainly for (Ia) science or (Ib) wilderness protection (Strict Nature Reserve/ Wilderness Area);

II Protected area managed mainly for ecosystem protection and recreation (National Park);

III Protected area managed mainly for conservation of specific natural features (Natural Monument);

IV Protected area managed mainly for conservation through management intervention (Habitat/ Species Management Area);

V Protected area managed mainly for landscape/ seascape conservation and recreation (Protected Landscape/Seascape);

VI Protected area managed mainly for the sustainable use of natural ecosystems (Managed Resource Protected Area).

At the risk of over-simplification, Categories I to III focus on areas which are in a broadly natural state (subject to the important proviso entered above that in practice there is little if any truly natural environment remaining anywhere, and that many protected areas in these categories contain a resident human population). Categories IV and VI are subject to rather greater manipulation, that of Category IV sites for conservation purposes and that of Category VI sites so that the local communities can derive natural resources sustainably. Category V involves the greatest degree of modification: it represents the idea of protecting humanized, managed landscapes – landscapes in which people live, work and exploit natural resources. This fifth category is also of especial interest in the context of landscape protection as it specifically recognizes a class of protected area established for this purpose.

Category V-protected areas are lived-in, working landscapes, which have special natural and cultural values deserving recognition and protection. As with World Heritage Cultural Landscapes, the concept is based on the links between nature and culture, not their separation. Local communities are central to the management of protected landscapes. The economic, social, cultural and environmental aims for the landscape embody the community's traditions and values. Historical, archaeological and cultural values are all embodied. To make this relevant to the British reader, all the National Parks, Areas of Outstanding Natural Beauty (AONBs) and National Scenic Areas of the United Kingdom are classified by IUCN as Category V-protected areas (Chape *et al* 2003).

So far, the protected landscape approach has been most used in Europe, but there is much evidence around the world to show that it has potentially wider application, eg island communities in the Pacific and Caribbean, the mountains of the Andes and Himalayas, the rice landscape of East and South East Asia and the long-settled landscapes of New England. What is emerging is a new kind of protected area, in which people live and work, to complement the stricter categories of protected area. In the words of the former President of IUCN: 'Protected landscapes are an idea whose time has come' (Yolanda Kakabadse in Phillips 2002).

THE EUROPEAN LANDSCAPES CONVENTION (ELC)

The text of this Convention took several years to prepare and was presented to governments at a ceremony in the glorious Medici Palace in Florence in October 2000. It came into force in March 2004 when the required number of ten signatories was attained.

The ELC (Council of Europe 2000) does not take a protectionist view of landscape but recognizes that landscape will and should evolve to meet society's changing needs. It acknowledges that landscape reflects the way that human needs are pursued in the environmental context: 'it is always a cultural product' (*ibid.*, 4). Apart from a very few 'museum landscapes', it is therefore unrealistic to try to 'freeze' a landscape at some particular point in its long evolution. Rather, the goal should be to manage the process of change. This means aiming to reduce the damaging effect of activities on the landscape, and on the natural and cultural values which it contains, and at the same time encouraging the creation of new landscape values. The objective should be to sustain and enrich the diversity and quality of Europe's landscapes within the context of social and economic development. This is the challenge the ELC seeks to address.

The preamble of the Convention lists a number of principles, from which three central propositions emerge:

- A democratic appreciation of the value and importance of landscapes to the people of Europe;
- An optimistic conviction that it is possible to guide the process of change affecting landscapes so that variety, diversity and quality are enhanced; and
- An unqualified belief that people must be involved in making this happen.

To expand, although formally acknowledging the principle of subsidiarity in deference to national sensibilities, the preamble seeks to establish the legal principle that 'landscape is an important part of the quality of life of people everywhere: in urban areas and in the countryside; in degraded areas as in areas of high quality; in areas recognized as being of outstanding beauty as well as everyday areas'. Landscape is seen as a people's issue: everyone's quality of life is affected by the landscapes around, and everyone – farmer, forester, house-owner or industrialist – can, by their own actions, make an impact on the landscape in their care. Landscape is a 'key element of individual and social well-being'.

The operational part of the Convention contains: (Chapter I) a set of General Provisions, (Chapter II) a group of National Measures, (Chapter III) Measures for European Co-operation, and (Chapter IV) Final Clauses. The full text of the ELC is on the Council of Europe web site: *http://conventions.coe.int/Treaty /EN/cadreprincipal.htm*.

The General Provisions define landscape thus: 'an area, as perceived by people, whose character is the result of action and interaction of natural and/or human factors'. In other words, landscape is seen – once more – as a meeting ground between nature and people, past and present, and tangible and intangible values. This section also sets out the key ideas that the convention aims to promote: landscape protection, landscape management and landscape planning.

Landscape protection means 'actions to conserve or maintain the significant or characteristic features of a landscape (of) heritage value'. *Landscape management* means 'action ... to ensure the regular upkeep of a landscape, so as to guide and harmonize changes'. *Landscape planning* means 'strong forward-looking action to enhance, restore and create landscapes' (Article 1(d),(e),(f)).

Of course, in any single area it is likely that a mix of these approaches will be appropriate but in general the scale of 'landscape protection/landscape management/landscape planning' is appropriate to 'outstanding/moderate/degraded landscapes'. Thus, the point is reinforced that all landscapes are appropriate for landscape policies, from the finest scenery of remote mountains and coastal areas to the degraded environments in and around our cities.

The core of the National Measures is the requirement that Parties: recognize landscape in law; adopt policies for landscape protection, management and planning; establish procedures for public involvement in landscape policies; and integrate landscape into other policy areas. It also commits Parties to provide information and raise awareness about landscape among the public, and develop programmes of training and education in landscape-related studies at school and university. Throughout this section, the text is brief and to the point.

The ELC acknowledges that 'the quality and diversity of European landscapes constitute a common resource, and that it is important to co-operate towards its protection, management and planning' (Preamble). It therefore reinforces the National Measures with a commitment to co-operate in this field, setting out various ways in which that might be done: technical and scientific aspects of landscape protection, management and planning; exchanges amongst staff engaged in landscape work around Europe; exchange of experience on the implementation of the Convention itself; and sharing of knowledge about public awareness of, and involvement in, landscape issues.

Many European countries share common areas of landscape with their neighbours, mountain ranges or river valleys in particular. It is desirable that work on one side of the boundary should be co-ordinated with that on the other. This may be done through the framework of established agreements between neighbouring protected areas (Sandwith *et al* 2000). But the scope for collaboration extends far beyond that, and the ELC therefore encourages such trans-frontier co-operation. It also commits States' Parties to monitoring the implementation of the Convention. Finally, this section introduces the Council of Europe's Landscape award in recognition of excellence in line with the ELC's aims.

The final clauses deal with a range of technical matters, including the requirement that ten Parties must ratify the convention before it comes into force.

REFLECTIONS ON THE ELC

As the world's first landscape treaty, the ELC represents an innovation in international discourse. Moreover progress towards its implementation has been good. Nonetheless, the treaty is not as strong a measure as some were hoping for.

Three areas have been particularly difficult to negotiate, and in all cases the outcome has erred towards the minimalist rather than the bold solution. First, the language in terms of international obligations has been watered down. For example, the draft of the treaty talked of the European landscape being 'a common resource for the protection, management and planning of which (parties) have a duty to co-operate'. As can be seen above, the key word 'duty' has gone.

Second, the draft version foresaw the introduction of a European level of landscape designation – 'Landscapes of European Significance'. Many European governments, already under pressure from EU measures (eg Natura 2000), and fearful of a backlash from their rural public about too many designations, were unhappy with this idea and it was removed in the final negotiations. Its removal weakens somewhat the idea that landscape is a European concern. Also, it leaves a gap between nationally recognized landscapes (Category V) and those that merit inclusion on the World Heritage List as cultural landscapes of global significance.[5] However, the author, having campaigned for the inclusion of such a European designation, now accepts that the strength of the Convention may lie in the very fact that it is not just about the best of landscapes, but is concerned with all of them. The ELC takes a deliberately comprehensive view of landscape that is relevant to the setting of everyone's life. Its philosophy can be captured in the phrase 'nowhere is nowhere, and everywhere is somewhere'.

But, most seriously, the ELC has no real 'engine' to drive the Convention forward. It lacks an effective secretariat and any financing mechanism, and is dependent instead on established units and funds from within the over-stretched Council of Europe secretariat at Strasbourg. Nor is there an unambiguous assignment at the political level for taking the treaty forward: instead, this is entrusted to two existing committees of the council (dealing with nature and culture respectively), who are required to co-operate in work related to the ELC. It is a common experience of many multilateral environmental treaties that they struggle without the staff and funds to make an impact. The ELC will struggle even more without a dedicated committee to oversee progress. It is to be hoped that Member States will eventually take action to rectify these deficiencies.

Maybe because the agreement is not particularly onerous, progress towards implementation has been quite rapid. As of February 2007, 26 countries had agreed to be bound by its requirements and 8 more were in the process of adhering to the Convention – see table 3. Through a series of technical meetings organized by the Council of Europe staff, the exchange of experience across Europe has been taking place and the ELC is gradually becoming better known. British experts played a key part in the drafting of the convention, and the decision of the UK to adhere to it in 2006 was widely welcomed.

CONCLUDING THOUGHTS

The case made in this article is that landscape is a concept within which archaeology – including wetland archaeology – can and should find a place and through which the protection of archaeological features can be pursued and secured. The work done on developing an understanding of landscape character now provides a robust, well-tested intellectual and practical foundation upon which can be built policies for landscape protection, management and planning. In other words, landscape character has now been operationalized.

However, there remains a lingering suspicion – or deliberate misunderstanding – in some quarters that landscape is a rather insubstantial concept, or a concern only to a privileged elite: the stuff of 'Nimbyism'. Those who hold this view believe that landscape can only be an obstacle to economic progress, and it may be that the initial reluctance of the UK Government to sign up to the ECL was due in part to this attitude. A suspicious view of landscape may have been encouraged by the way that some groups have used landscape protection as a cover to resist any change or development in the local environment. But both the forces of extreme protection and those of unbridled development misunderstand what landscape is, and what it has to offer.

As we have seen, landscape is an environmental resource and in some places it does indeed need to be protected against change. World Heritage Cultural Landscapes and Category V protected areas are examples of where the emphasis must be on landscape protection (as per the ELC). However, landscape protection is not landscape preservation; indeed, it may be undertaken with the aim of providing a foundation for economic recovery. It is interesting, for example, that economic revival and community pride were behind the nomination of sites for World Heritage Cultural Landscape status, such as the former colliery and iron town of Blaenavon in South Wales and the former tin and copper mining areas of Cornwall and West Devon. These have been important factors, too, with several other recent World Heritage nominations, such as the Liverpool waterfront, the Derwent Valley in Derbyshire and the Jurassic Coast of Dorset and East Devon (all areas that might be considered as cultural landscapes, though not designated as such).

However, in many places the principal role of landscape is to act as a medium through which to assess the impact of change and to guide it, helping

TABLE 3
Table of signatories to the European Landscape Convention (as of February 2007).

States	Signature	Ratification	Entry into force
Albania			
Andorra			
Armenia	14/5/2003	23/3/2004	1/7/2004
Austria			
Azerbaijan	22/10/2003		
Belgium	20/10/2000	28/10/2004	1/2/2005
Bosnia and Herzegovina			
Bulgaria	20/10/2000	24/11/2004	1/3/2005
Croatia	20/10/2000	15/1/2003	1/3/2004
Cyprus	21/11/2001	21/6/2006	1/10/2006
Czech Republic	28/11/2002	3/6/2004	1/10/2004
Denmark	20/10/2000	20/3/2003	1/3/2004
Estonia			
Finland	20/10/2000	16/12/2005	1/4/2006
France	20/10/2000	17/3/2006	1/7/2006
Georgia			
Germany			
Greece	13/12/2000		
Hungary	28/9/2005		
Iceland			
Ireland	22/3/2002	22/3/2002	1/3/2004
Italy	20/10/2000		
Latvia	29/11/2006		
Liechtenstein			
Lithuania	20/10/2000	13/11/2002	1/3/2004
Luxembourg	20/10/2000	20/9/2006	1/1/2007
Malta	20/10/2000		
Moldova	20/10/2000	14/3/2002	1/3/2004
Monaco			
Netherlands	27/7/2005	27/7/2005	1/11/2005
Norway	20/10/2000	23/10/2001	1/3/2004
Poland	21/12/2001	27/9/2004	1/1/2005
Portugal	20/10/2000	29/3/2005	1/7/2005
Romania	20/10/2000	7/11/2002	1/3/2004
Russia			
San Marino	20/10/2000	26/11/2003	1/3/2004
Serbia			
Slovakia	30/5/2005	9/8/2005	1/12/2005
Slovenia	7/3/2001	25/9/2003	1/3/2004
Spain	20/10/2000		
Sweden	22/2/2001		
Switzerland	20/10/2000		
the former Yugoslav Republic of Macedonia	15/1/2003	18/11/2003	1/3/2004
Turkey	20/10/2000	13/10/2003	1/3/2004
Ukraine	17/6/2004	10/3/2006	1/7/2006
United Kingdom	21/2/2006	21/11/2006	1/3/2007

to set the right conditions on buildings, infrastructure, land management activities and so forth. This is where landscape management (as per the ELC) comes into play, with its purpose of guiding and harmonizing change, and thus making it sustainable. Landscape management of this kind must be based on a full understanding of the components – including the archaeological components – that go to make up landscape character.

Finally, there are other areas where a new landscape resource needs to be created, which will be the vehicle for large-scale environmental change and to underpin economic recovery and revitalization. The example of the National Forest in the English Midlands is a case in point. Two hundred square miles of forested landscape is being created, with tree cover already up from 6 per cent to 17 per cent, and planned to double again, increasing annually at about 500ha. The forest area is attracting investment and there are signs that people want to live there. To date, some £32.5m of forest-related inward investment has been secured, 500 forest-related jobs have been created, and there are 750,000 new visitors. The National Forest is a powerful demonstration of the benefits of landscape planning (as per the ELC) and of how the landscape itself can generate economic activity, restore community pride and improve people's living and working environment. But even here, change needs to be informed by a knowledge of the existing landscape, with all its historical and other values: it is to the credit of the National Forest team that their tree planting and habitat strategy is based on such an understanding of landscape character.[6]

The author's plea to archaeologists is to engage in landscape issues. Archaeologists have much to contribute to the landscape characterization process; they should learn to engage with it as a tool to help explain time depth in the environment to a wider public; and they should ensure that the planning and land management policies that are based on this work take their interests fully into account.

NOTES

1 My thanks to Paul Selman, Department of Landscape, Sheffield University for the use of this table.
2 As Swanwick has noted, the concepts of 'landscape character' and 'countryside character' are nearly synonymous, with only subtle differences (Swanwick 2004, 109).
3 Part II on international measures draws heavily on Phillips (in print).

4 World Heritage data in this section are correct as of December 2006 and taken from the UNESCO World Heritage website: *http://whc.unesco.org/*.
5 This was a particular source of disappointment to staff in UNESCO who had hoped that the inclusion of a European level of landscape recognition under the ELC would reduce demands for more European World Heritage Cultural Landscapes, and thereby make it easier to redress the geographical imbalance of World Heritage sites towards Europe (pers comm).
6 Information in this paragraph is taken from the National Forest website: *www.nationalforest.org/forest/*.

REFERENCES

Bergstrom, J 1998 *Exploring and Expanding the Landscape Values Terrain*. Faculty Paper Series 98–20. University of Athens, Georgia, USA.

Bishop, K & Phillips, A 2004 *Countryside Planning: New Approaches to Countryside Planning and Management*. London.

Chape, S, Blyth, S, Fish, L, Fox, P & Spalding, M (compilers) 2003 *2003 United Nations List of Protected Areas*. IUCN, Cambridge, UK and Gland, Switzerland, and UNEP-WCMC, Cambridge, UK.

Clark, J, Darlington, J & Fairclough, G 2004 *Using Historic Landscape Characterization*. London and Lancaster.

Council of Europe 2000 *The European Landscape Convention*. Strasbourg.

Countryside Commission 1993 *Landscape Assessment Guidance (CCP423)*. Cheltenham.

Countryside Agency 1998 *Countryside Character* (8 vols). Cheltenham.

IUCN 1994 *Guidelines for Protected Area Management Categories*. Cambridge and Gland, Switzerland.

Mabey, R 1985 *In a Green Shade*. London.

Macinnes, L 2004 'Historic Landscape Characterization', in Bishop & Phillips (qv).

McNab 1999 'Introduction to the Project' in Fairclough, G (ed) *Historic Landscape Characterisation: Papers Presented at an English Heritage Seminar (11 December, 1998)*. London, 51–63.

Office of the Deputy Prime Minister (ODPM) 2004 *Planning Policy Statement 7: Sustainable Development in Rural Areas*. London.

Phillips, A (in print) 'International Policies and Landscape Protection', in Benson, J & Roe, M *Landscape and Sustainability (revised edition)*. London.

Sandwith, T, Shine, C, Hamilton, L & Sheppard, D 2001 *Transboundary Protected Areas for Peace and Co-operation*. Cambridge and Gland, Switzerland.

Schama, S 1995 *Landscape and Memory*. London.

Stanners, D & Bordeaux, P 1995 *Europe's Environment: The Dobris Assessment*. Copenhagen.

Swanwick, C 2002 *Landscape Character Assessment: Guidance for England and Scotland*. Cheltenham and Edinburgh.

Swanwick, C 2004 'The Assessment of Landscape Character in England: An Overview', *in* Bishop and Phillips (qv).

UNESCO 1972 *Convention Concerning the Protection of the World Cultural and Natural Heritage*. Paris.

UNESCO 2005a *The World Heritage List*. Paris.

UNESCO 2005b *The Operational Guidelines for the Implementation of the World Heritage Convention*. Paris.

'Plain and bog, bog and wood, wood and bog, bog and plain!': peatland archaeology in Ireland

CONOR McDERMOTT

I am now tired of the bogs and plains of Offaly and intend to move westwards towards the Shannon in search of something like hard ground. The Plain of Offaly is thus most remarkably described in the Dinnseanchus:

Plain and bog, bog and wood,
Wood and bog, bog and plain!

John O'Donovan, Tullamore, January 5th 1838
Ordnance Survey Letters King's County No. 13

INTRODUCTION

There is a long tradition of the examination of peatland sites in Ireland and this history has been documented and commented upon previously (Raftery 1999; Stanley 2003, 64). The last 20 years have seen major developments in Irish peatland archaeology and dramatic increases in the wetland archaeological record. This has resulted from a number of initiatives including the excavation programme conducted by Barry Raftery in Co Longford (Raftery 1990 & 1996) leading to the establishment of the Irish Archaeological Wetland Unit (IAWU), the work of the Lisheen Archaeological Project (Gowen *et al* 2005) and more recently by the appointment of archaeological consultants by Bord na Móna, the state peat company.

This paper draws primarily on the surveys conducted by the IAWU since 1990 and other published bodies of work. The surveys have typically been located in the commercially exploited raised bogs of the Irish midlands and in the counties on the eastern side of the Shannon in particular (fig 1). The survey strategies adopted and the nature of the sites encountered have been outlined previously (McDermott 2001) and will only be considered here where they influence the understanding of the sites in the wider landscape. The picture that is emerging is derived from the perspective of wetland surveys during which over 15,000km of bog drains have been walked. It is increasingly apparent that despite the importance of these surveys they do not address the full range of wetlands in the region.

The approach adopted in this paper is to consider the role of wetlands in these landscapes in its broadest

sense. This incorporates an examination of the known dryland and wetland evidence that give the region a unique character. The results have highlighted a number of critical shortcomings in the evidence to date, and how it has been gathered, while at the same time pointing to productive areas and avenues of research in the future.

CHARACTER OF THE DRYLAND EVIDENCE FROM THE IRISH MIDLANDS

These counties as a whole tend to have poor evidence of settlement patterns from the prehistoric period and there are some notable absences and deficiencies in the archaeological record as a whole. In Co Offaly, just 109 of the 990 sites in the Archaeological Inventory represent the entire range of the prehistoric period. With the exception of the Early Mesolithic camp at Lough Boora, none of these is a dryland settlement (O'Brien & Sweetman 1997). In contrast, the IAWU surveys identified 1842 peatland sites in the county and did not cover all of the commercial bogs.

This lack of settlement evidence is repeated across other midland counties. It is only since 2002, with the advent of infrastructure projects such as gas pipelines and national road schemes, that the first evidence is beginning to emerge. Three settlements have been excavated in Co Westmeath including a prehistoric round house at Whitwell (Phelan 2004, 514), a Bronze Age round house at Knockdommy (Hull 2004, 511–12) and a Late Neolithic/Early Bronze Age occupation site at Demesne or Mearsparkfarm (McDermott & O'Connor 2005).

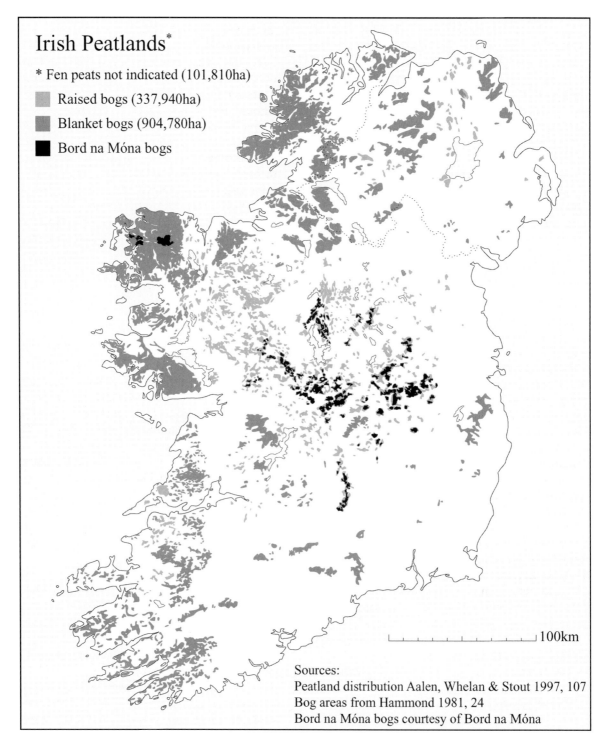

Irish Peatlands*

* Fen peats not indicated (101,810ha)

Raised bogs (337,940ha)

Blanket bogs (904,780ha)

Bord na Móna bogs

100km

Sources:
Peatland distribution Aalen, Whelan & Stout 1997, 107
Bog areas from Hammond 1981, 24
Bord na Móna bogs courtesy of Bord na Móna

FIGURE 1
Peatlands of Ireland.

It is perhaps not surprising, given the character of the midlands landscape, that few hilltop or high status sites are known in the region. The notable exceptions include important sites at the Hill of Uisneach, Ballykilleen and the Hill of Croghan. Even at these sites the evidence is ambiguous and there is little suggestion of a hierarchy of settlement in the Bronze Age or Iron Ages, again reflecting the lack of settlement evidence as a whole.

It has been argued that *fulachta fiadh* or burnt mounds played a distinct but complementary role to settlement in Bronze Age landscapes (Doody 1991, 102). These are some of the most ubiquitous sites in the Irish landscape; however, until recently, these too have been significantly underrepresented in midland counties. Just 13 are recorded in the Archaeological Inventory for Co Offaly (O'Brien & Sweetman 1997, 14–16) and none in the online Sites and Monuments Record for Co Westmeath (1999). Recent infrastructure projects have also made dramatic changes to this record and in the period 2002–2005 up to 70 such sites have been identified and excavated in Co Westmeath alone (Bennett 2004; R Swan pers comm). Almost all of these had no surface expression prior to investigation.

Monumental burial sites of the Neolithic and Early Bonze Age are almost entirely absent from the region. The Survey of the Megalithic Tombs of Ireland identified no sites from Counties Kildare, Laois and Offaly and just one in Co Westmeath and three in Co Longford (de Valera & Ó Nualláin 1972). The Archaeological Survey of Ireland did later identify two unclassified megaliths in Co Offaly (O'Brien & Sweetman 1997, 14–16) and a number of unclassified and possible tombs in Co Laois (Sweetman *et al* 1995, 1–2); however, taken together they do not represent a significant component in the archaeological record.

Of some 25,000 stone axes from Ireland just 39 are recorded from Co Offaly (Irish Stone Axe Project database) including Mesolithic and Bronze Age examples from Lough Boora (Ryan 1980) and Clonfinlough (IAWU 1993, 21). Almost all of the 1,000 Middle Bronze Age dirks and rapiers from Ireland are from wet contexts and rivers in particular (Burgess & Gerloff 1981). A preliminary examination of finds from peatlands in Offaly recorded neither artefact type (Halpin 1984, 117–224). The majority of Dowris phase hoards have also been recovered from wet contexts and almost all of these from bogs (Eogan 1983, 8; Cooney & Grogan 1994, 163) yet despite the extensive peat cover in the county just four such hoards are from Offaly (Eogan 1983; K Becker pers comm).

A number of factors are likely to have contributed to the overall pattern of dryland evidence in the midlands. Most notable are the character of the landscape and the ineffectiveness of traditional archaeological techniques. The region does not have the same tradition of antiquarian study as other parts of the country and this has resulted in a poorer foundation for later archaeological work. Agriculture in the region is predominantly pastoral rather than arable and there is little tradition of ploughzone archaeology or fieldwalking. The lack of monumentality of many of the sites does not appear to have inspired the same degree of interest, and the poor visibility of monuments continues to hinder the identification of sites on the ground. In areas adjacent to wetland the ground cover is often rough grazing and scrub vegetation that hinders aerial photography. The results that have been achieved on recent infrastructure projects have depended on extensive surface stripping using mechanical excavators as a method of blind prospection within a narrow development corridor.

All of this evidence highlights the unique character of both the landscape of Irish midlands and how it was exploited in the prehistoric period. It is also clear that patterns of activity apparent in the archaeological record today are far from complete and in some aspects very misleading. It is only by adopting an integrated approach that reflects the nature of the landscape, both wet and dry, and the distinctive evidence for its exploitation that a fuller appreciation can be achieved.

CHARACTER OF THE PEATLANDS

NATURAL BOUNDARIES AND BARRIERS

In Ireland many territorial and civil boundaries are found to coincide with or run through areas of peatland that often form the limits of historic kingdoms, counties, parishes or townlands (fig 2; McDermott 1998, 6ff). Such boundaries usually run through the centres of bogs, dividing up the peatlands such that each division contains both dryland and the adjacent wetlands. This may in part be due to peatlands being perceived as less contested landscapes with the centres of bogs forming a convenient division away from dryland and, more importantly, the wetland fringes.

The presence of large numbers of peatland sites from all periods also indicates that bogs formed barriers to communications and economic activity.

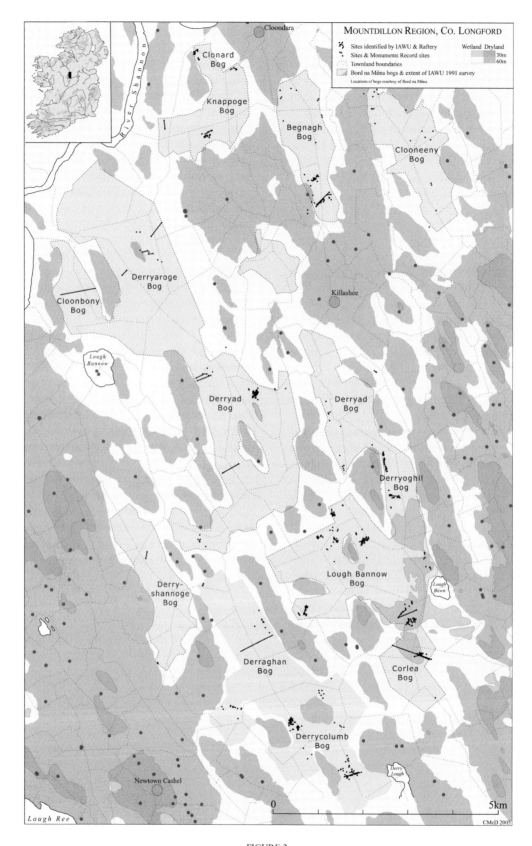

FIGURE 2
Map of the Mountdillon Region, Co Longford showing the distribution of wetlands and the results of surveys.

Peripheral fens, hollows, palaeo-channels and discharge zones often cannot be crossed and the drier surfaces do not support the regular passage of people or animals. As will be seen below, almost all peatland sites function to stabilize the surface of the bog to allow access or activity within or across a bog. It is likely that the need for such sites was dependent on local conditions, time of year, climate and the nature of the activity. Nonetheless they do demonstrate that peatlands were an obstacle that people frequently found it necessary or desirable to overcome.

ECOLOGICAL AND ECONOMIC DIVERSITY

The economic potential of wetlands has long been recognized and the importance of peatland margins and fens within a wider economy has been demonstrated at Derryville Bog, Co Tipperary (Cross *et al* 2005, 353). Many of the sites identified by peatland surveys are small structures located at or near the edge of bogs and it is likely that some of these served to exploit the ecological diversity of this zone. The wet/dry interface provided a mixture of resources and habitats ranging from mixed woodland to marsh and open water and the edges of a raised bog. This range of plant and animal habitats is seldom repeated in such close proximity and formed a natural focus for exploitation.

FOCUS OF ACTIVITY IN EVERYDAY LIFE

Such exploitation may have varied seasonally or with changes in settlement patterns; however, given the extensive nature of wetlands in these landscapes it is likely that peatlands played an almost everyday part in people's experience. Even where settlement was somewhat removed from the wetlands, or the exploitation was more occasional, the ever-present peatlands would have formed part of people's everyday existence and perception of their world. In the most extensive peatland regions people would seldom have been more than a few hours' walk from bogs in almost any direction and it would have been nearly impossible to travel directly to another settlement or territory without crossing wetlands.

SELF-ENCLOSING LANDSCAPE

Such a sense of place would be in part created by the self-enclosing nature of these landscapes. The pattern of peatlands in some areas forms many islands and peninsulas of dryland (figs 2, 3 & 4). These land blocks lend themselves to territorial or land divisions and

may well have reduced the need for land enclosure in prehistoric and early historic pastoral economies. The perception of many of these bogs has changed today as a result of extensive drainage and it is now possible to look across large bogs to the other side. During survey work in Co Longford, one farmer informed the IAWU that prior to drainage he could only see the chimney of his neighbour's house across the bog and now he can see the whole garden. This sense of enclosure would have been even more pronounced to a person standing at the edge of the wetlands looking up at the dome of a raised bog forming the horizon.

ENVIRONMENTAL AND SEASONAL CHANGE

The dynamic nature of peatlands through time is increasingly recognized in the archaeological record. With the notable exception of the Derryville Project (Casparie 2005), palaeogeographies have generally not been an integral part of archaeological projects in Irish peatlands. Despite this it has been possible to identify sites that reflect earlier peatland extents and increasing numbers of sites are now being recognized in association with buried topographic features. These highlight changes in the extent and topography of the bogs over time and demonstrate the need for considerably more work in this area. The maximum extent of the wetland transgression in Co Offaly is shown in fig 1 but we are far from being in a position to model the development of this landscape. Changes at a local scale over a period of centuries could certainly have influenced the location and movement of settlements and it is likely that extensive buried prehistoric landscapes subsumed by developing bogs remain to be explored.

The resources available in terms of plants and animals would have changed seasonally in the wetlands and this would have affected patterns of exploitation. The extents of open bodies of water such as fens and small lakes would also have fluctuated over the year thus affecting the types of activity that could be undertaken.

TRADITIONAL ARCHAEOLOGICAL TECHNIQUES

As with the dryland areas in the midlands, peatlands are not well suited to traditional archaeological techniques. Sites very rarely have a surface expression and aerial photography and geophysical techniques have limited application. It is typically only when bogs are drained and cut that sites become visible in the vertical peat faces or milled peat surfaces. Even when a site or artefact came to the attention of archaeologists

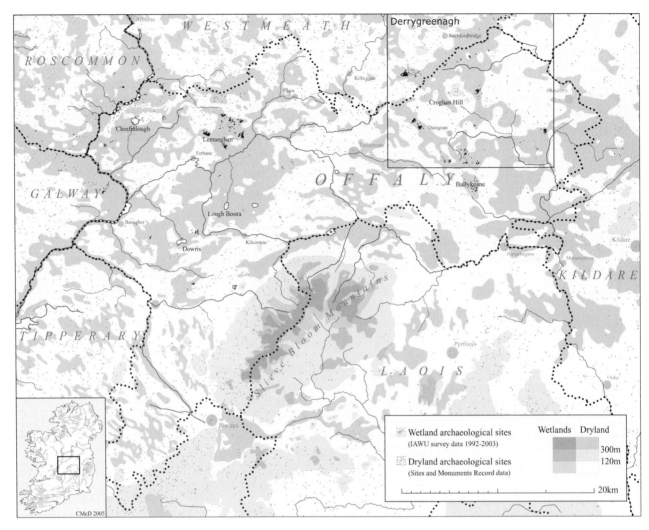

FIGURE 3
Map of Co Offaly and adjoining counties showing the distribution of wetlands and the results of surveys.

in the past they tended to be addressed on a case-by-case basis. It has only been with the advent of systematic surveys and excavations that a fuller picture of the quantity and range of material present has begun to emerge. To achieve these results it is necessary to walk thousands of kilometres of bog and the work is inherently low-tech and labour-intensive but can produce dramatic results (Moore *et al* 2003).

CHARACTER OF THE ARCHAEOLOGICAL EVIDENCE FROM PEATLANDS

COMMERCIAL PEATLANDS SURVEYED

In considering the nature of evidence from peatland surveys it is first necessary to recognize the inherent

limitations of the surveys undertaken. As outlined above, these surveys are restricted to areas where peat sections or surfaces are exposed. This has typically meant the surveys have been restricted to large-scale commercially exploited bogs. The extents of these industrial bogs tend to form large geometric shapes restricted to the areas of deeper peats. Prior to the establishment of Bord na Móna, the state peat company, most of these bogs were not subject to peat extraction as they require extensive drainage managed at a regional level. Therefore the majority of smaller bogs and the shallower edges of larger bogs are not commercially exploited (figs 2 & 4), creating a considerable bias when constructing models of the past exploitation of these landscapes.

FEW EXOTIC FINDS

Prior to the commencement of the IAWU surveys, discussions were held with bodies such as the National Museum of Ireland (NMI) regarding the types of material that were likely to be identified. An examination of the collections in the NMI suggested that, in addition to trackways and other wooden sites, occasional exotic objects such as prehistoric bronzes or even gold ornaments would be found. The subsequent peatland surveys, including the results of the excavation of the Late Bronze Age

Settlement Site at Clonfinlough (IAWU 1993) yielded only one bronze object; a single medieval stickpin. Indeed, while several hundreds of artefacts have been recovered during IAWU surveys, almost all have been wooden finds with a small number of medieval and later shoes, silver coins, bog butter and lithics. This contrasts notably with previous finds from other peatlands that include significant numbers of bronze and other objects (Halpin 1984). Most of these older finds were recovered during hand peat-cutting in smaller bogs and around the fringes of larger bogs.

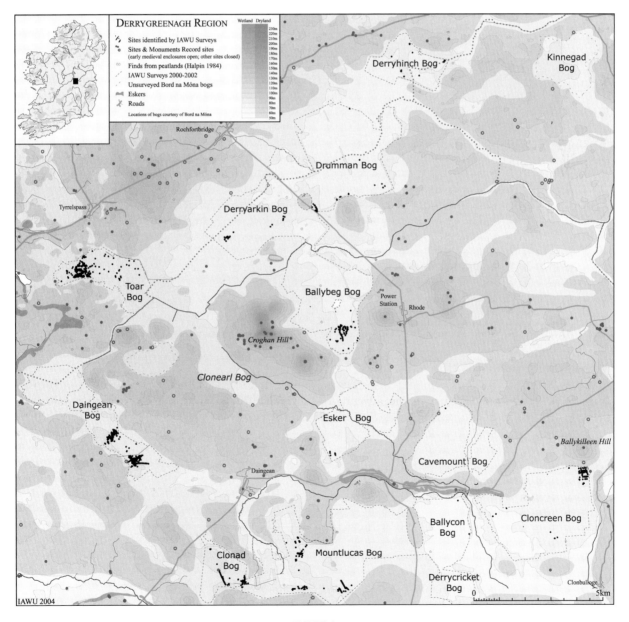

FIGURE 4
Map of the Derrygreenagh Region, Co Offaly and adjoining counties showing the distribution of wetlands and the results of surveys.

Some were found during the initial drainage works by Bord na Móna when drains were excavated by hand but these also tend to have come from near the edges of bogs rather than in the deeper areas.

PREDOMINANTLY NON-LINEAR SITES

The great majority of sites identified by surveys are not classic trackways but considerably smaller sites often with no clear structure or orientation (table 1). These sites can be seen as representing a local response to the immediate needs of those accessing or exploiting the peatlands and do not form part of a larger communication network. In drier periods it may not have been necessary to construct sites along an entire route but the unstructured, non-linear nature of most of the sites suggests they were not part of such a system. Less than 10 per cent of sites identified are greater than 15m in length with the great majority of linear sites less than that. Over half of all sites identified are 'archaeological wood' which is a classification encompassing single stakes or pieces of brushwood to large non-linear deposits of wood. These often occur in both great numbers and in close proximity and they date to all periods.

TABLE 1

Types of sites from peatland project areas including previously recorded sites such as crannogs. (Sources: IAWU Data for Cos Galway, Kildare, Kilkenny, Longford, Meath, Offaly, Roscommon, Tipperary & Westmeath; Lisheen Archaeological Project).

	Site Type	Sites	%
T	Gravel road/Pavedway/Road	29	0.8%
T	Togher – primary (>150m L)	86	2.5%
T	Togher – secondary (15–150m L)	211	6.1%
T	Togher – tertiary (<15m L)	1,077	31.1%
	Post row	57	1.6%
A	Archaeological wood	1,829	52.8%
	Platform	29	0.8%
	Complex	16	0.5%
	Burnt mounds	9	0.3%
S	Occupation site/Crannog	8	0.2%
S	Hut site/Wooden structure	2	0.1%
	Other	12	0.3%
	Unassociated artefacts	97	2.8%
	Total	3,462	

T = Trackways
A = Small deposits of wood and sites without orientation
S = Settlements/Possible settlements

Almost all sites appear to represent a single phase of deposition or construction although it may not be possible to identify the slow accumulation of material over a period of time in an unstructured deposit. The number of settlement or occupation sites is very small even when we include existing records of sites such as crannogs in the areas being surveyed.

LARGE NUMBERS OF SITES FROM ALL PERIODS

Over three hundred laboratory dates are available from IAWU surveys and programmes of excavations in Cos Longford and Tipperary. These cover all periods from the early Neolithic to the present and indicate a continuous pattern of peatland exploitation. As yet, no structures have been dated to the Mesolithic period and the earliest site is a large plank trackway from Derryarkin Bog, Co Offaly, dendrochronologically dated to 3646 ± 9 BC (fig 4; Murray *et al* 2002, 17). Surveys often identify large numbers of sites from a single period as surface milling exposes extensive peat horizons of similar date. Different bogs, however, often produce sites from different periods depending on how long each bog has been exploited. In a small number of cases bogs were resurveyed between one and five years after the initial survey and in nearly all of these new horizons of sites were identified.

BUILT-IN OBSOLESCENCE

It is important not to overestimate the longevity of the great numbers of sites identified. Each site has a form of built-in obsolescence and this is often reflected in the rudimentary nature of the construction. It is likely that smaller deposits of wood only functioned for perhaps one or two seasons with larger sites seldom surviving for more than a decade. The high quality of preservation of much of the wood indicates that it was immersed in wet conditions almost immediately. Even in bogs where large numbers of sites have been identified it is probable that only a very small proportion were in simultaneous use. Nonetheless the recurrent nature of deposition and construction demonstrates an ongoing commitment to exploiting and crossing the bogs over considerable periods of time.

LITTLE PALAEOENVIRONMENTAL WORK

The extensive surveys and excavations undertaken since the late 1980s have unfortunately not been accompanied by a corresponding degree of palaeoenvironmental work. Again, the Derryville excavations are a notable exception in this regard as were Raftery's excavations in Co Longford. However, over 45,000ha of peatland were surveyed by the IAWU alone and for almost all of this area there are no palaeoenvironmental records. Such work as has been undertaken has typically focused on the context and composition of individual sites. It is increasingly clear that future surveys must be complemented by systematic programmes to reconstruct the environment and landscape of sites in addition to the broader pattern of human settlement.

INDICATIVE OF SETTLEMENT/ACTIVITY

In the absence of prehistoric dryland evidence the very presence of these peatland sites provides the most tangible indications of settlement or other activity in these areas. The occurrence of large numbers of sites from a single period strongly suggests the presence of associated settlement on the adjacent dryland or buried beneath the margins of the peatlands. This can be seen at places such as Derryoghil, Co Longford (fig 2) where almost 40 Bronze Age sites were excavated adjacent to a large island in the bog (Raftery 1996). This pattern can also be identified in other bogs with sites dating from the Neolithic to the early historic period. It is also likely that the distribution of sites around bogs through time reflects changes in the pattern of settlement as well as changes in the environment. The available pollen evidence shows periods of woodland clearance and regeneration particularly from the later Neolithic onwards (eg Caseldine *et al* 1996; Parks & Mitchell 2000; Caseldine *et al* 2005). Each episode can last several centuries and indicates an impermanence of settlement in the longer term.

DISCUSSION

What emerges from this review is a fragmentary picture of a distinctive landscape and archaeological record. The character of the region is perhaps best evoked by the extract from the early Irish poem quoted at the outset. It suggests a landscape where rolling agricultural land melds with bog and woodlands in a repeating pattern. There seems to be no sense of division in the mind of the poet between the different facets of the landscape, nor indeed a sense of beginning or end (fig 5). The text dates to the early historic period and the picture it portrays seems to differ little from that suggested for the prehistoric period by the archaeological record.

In considering the entire landscape as a continuum across which all aspects of prehistoric settlement and society were played out, the gaps in the archaeological record become increasingly apparent. Some of these are no doubt genuine absences reflecting the character of the region. Others, however, derive from the divisions we have created in our approaches to studying these landscapes and by imbalances between these approaches. Not all existing models and methodologies are appropriate to the midlands landscape and thus far we have not succeeded in developing a suitable suite of tools to understand them.

As we increasingly populate the peatlands of the Irish midlands with archaeological sites, the lack of direct evidence for prehistoric settlement becomes increasingly striking. Ironically, the only two examples from Co Offaly are the settlements at Ballinderry 2 and Clonfinlough (Hencken 1942; IAWU 1993) and these may now be regarded as atypical of the pattern of settlement as a whole. This is supported by extensive wetland surveys in the county that have

FIGURE 5
View from the crest of Croghan Hill, Co Offaly across Ballybeg Bog east towards Co Kildare showing part of the midland plain of bogs and agricultural land.

not produced similar prehistoric sites. The evidence from these settlements clearly indicates an agrarian economy in terms of domestic animals and cereals derived from the surrounding drylands, although any expression of associated farmsteads or farming has yet to be identified. The only classic settlement identified by survey is early medieval in date and is located in Ballintemple townland (fig 6), Ballykeane Bog, Co Offaly (see Stanley this volume; fig 2 for the location of Ballintemple; McDermott *et al* 2003; Stanley & Moore 2004).

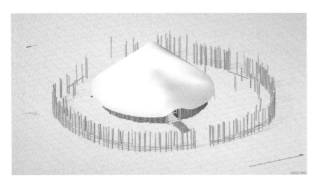

FIGURE 6
Reconstruction of a small settlement site in Ballintemple townland, Ballykeane Bog based on survey records. The site dates to AD 538–659 and consists of a single roundhouse enclosed by a palisade and is located almost 500m from the edge of the bog.

The results from some bogs indicate a remarkable degree of continuity in the use of these landscapes with sequences of sites being recorded from a number of periods. This can be seen in the excavated assemblages from Corlea and Derryoghil, Co Longford (Raftery 1996) and Derryville Bog, Co Tipperary (Gowen *et al* 2005). It is also apparent from survey results where a series of laboratory dates are available such as at Ballybeg (McDermott *et al* 2002), Mountlucas and Cloncreen Bogs, Co Offaly (Murray *et al* 2002).

However, as outlined above, the majority of sites are small in scale and, just as we may have to re-examine our recognition and understanding of dryland sites in the region, the character of the peatland sites raises issues regarding what is a 'monument'. In Ireland the term 'monument' holds particular meaning in a legal sense and in the protection of archaeological sites. In the context of peatland surveys this can cause difficulties where most of the sites are very non-monumental in character. In addition, the vagaries of classification can determine whether sites are legally protected or published as there is a reticence to protect small or ill-defined sites. The term 'entity' employed by the Sites and Monuments Record database takes on a new and useful meaning when applied to these sites where the term 'monument' may not always seem appropriate. Its suggestion of a single 'event' may prove a useful concept when considering the totality of the evidence.

This is not to underestimate the importance of the peatland evidence that has been accumulated to date by survey and excavation projects, but it can now be seen that these have often been limited in extent and detail. In adopting a broader approach it is necessary to re-evaluate the types of evidence that we look for, where we look for it and the methods we use.

Examination of figs 2 and 4 shows the very considerable parts of the wetland landscape that have not been subject to serious archaeological scrutiny and that now appear to be areas of greatest interest. The most extensive areas of peatlands remaining to be explored lie outside the limits of the commercial bogs. One-third of Co Offaly is covered by peatlands and over half of that area is formed of smaller bogs, reclaimed and cutover peatlands, forestry plantations, domestic peat-cutting and private peat companies. In other counties the proportion of unsurveyed peatlands is even greater. On current distribution maps these areas are almost devoid of archaeological features as they have not produced visible monuments and have not been subject to any form of wetland investigation.

These areas continue to produce occasional sites and finds during peat-cutting such as the recently discovered Iron Age bog body (I Mulhall pers comm) from Old Croghan townland, Clonearl Bog, at the foot of Croghan Hill in Co Offaly (fig 4). This find was located close to the edge of a bog and is in the process of being brought into production by a private company. A subsequent survey of the bog as a result of the discovery produced two small deposits of wood of recent date in the upper peat levels (IAWU 2003). However, comparison with other bogs in the area and sites on the dryland strongly suggests that this bog will contain significant archaeological features at lower levels.

In recent years there have been attempts to move away from concepts of marginality in wetland archaeology. The term may retain some validity; however, we may be applying it to the wrong parts of the landscape. In regions like the Irish midlands where the dryland evidence is apparently so sparse and impermanent, we might begin to consider woodland areas with episodic clearance and regeneration as marginal to the wet/dry interfaces where exploitation appears more constant. Where the perception of margins or marginality deters investigation we may be ignoring the very areas of greatest interest. In the case of raised bogs the great majority of the area they now cover was marginal at some point since the Mesolithic period. Some of the most important assemblages identified during surveys in recent years have been at the lower levels of bogs or near to buried land surfaces.

The early Neolithic plank trackway from Derryarkin Bog (fig 4) referred to above was discovered in an area initially suggested as unlikely to produce archaeological remains as it was mostly cut away by commercial peat production. In addition to this and other sites, the area also produced an unassociated Mesolithic bann flake (Murray *et al* 2002). Mountlucas Bog also contained extensive cutaway and overgrown areas containing archaeological sites. These included substantial Middle Bronze Age wooden platforms surviving in shallow fen peats on the flanks of two small islands in the bog and two saddle querns further to the east (*ibid.*). Significant groups of sites dating from the Late Bronze Age to the early medieval period were located in other parts of the bog including a plank walkway dating to AD 544. Cloncreen Bog produced a large number of sites adjacent to a major dryland route through the region. During the survey extensive sub-peat ridges were identified, some of which were exposed by mechanical milling. Careful examination of these surfaces produced a collection of three flint leaf-shaped arrowheads and a single chert example in addition to a flint knife (*ibid.*). In Clonad Bog (fig 4) a substantial transverse plank trackway 3.4m in width and dating to 911 ± 9 or later BC was traced for almost 600m from the edge towards the centre of the bog where it could not be traced further. More detailed examination of subsurface contours indicated that the site stopped close to a sub-peat ridge forming a peninsula into the centre of the bog. It is likely that this surface was not covered by peat growth until after the Bronze Age and may preserve other archaeological features.

LIKELY EVIDENCE

When the results of peatland surveys and recent developments in dryland areas are taken together it now seems possible to predict some of the areas of higher archaeological potential and the types of evidence likely to be identified. The categories below address a number of themes including the survival, context and character of the evidence.

PROXY INDICATORS

Indirect evidence of settlement and other activity will continue to emerge with the identification of greater numbers of sites such as burnt mounds, peatland sites, burials and artefact distributions. Other proxy indicators such as pollen evidence will contribute to this record if the necessary work is undertaken.

RIBBON ACTIVITY ALONG WET/DRY INTERFACES

All of the emerging evidence from wetlands, and increasingly from drylands, supports the identification of wet/dry interface zones as areas of higher archaeological potential. This includes dryland areas adjacent to wetlands and the wetland fringes. It is probable that increasing numbers of settlement sites will be identified dispersed along this zone.

FENS, BOGS, RIVERS, LAKES, BURIED LAND SURFACES

All wetland environments are likely to produce evidence including fens, bogs, rivers and lakes, particularly where these have encroached on former dryland. These environments can preserve both waterlogged materials within the deposits and fossilized prehistoric land surfaces preserving fragile evidence that does not survive in other environments.

ALLUVIAL DEPOSITS

To date, little work has been undertaken in alluvial sediments in the midlands and it is likely that these areas are also of considerable potential. The callow lands (seasonally flooded) along the River Shannon are up to 1km in width and there are many smaller rivers in the region. In addition to these extensive alluvial deposits, smaller rivers and streams moving through the undulating glacial topography have filled many small basins with alluvium.

COLLUVIAL SEDIMENTS

Colluvial soils are widespread in the glacial topography of the midlands where peats have not developed. The potential of these sediments has been recognized on recent infrastructure projects where archaeological features have been identified at over 1m below the surface (McDermott & O'Connor 2005). The full extent of these deposits has yet to be appreciated and it is likely that they will play an increasingly important role in future investigations.

IMPERMANENT SETTLEMENT

Where wetland resources played a significant role in the economies the associated settlements may have been impermanent in the longer term. Pollen evidence indicates that episodes of woodland clearance and agriculture may only have lasted a number of centuries and this may be linked to changes in the local wetland environment that supported the economies. This is likely to have resulted in movements in the pattern of communities over time to adjust to the changing environment.

LOW DENSITY

There is as yet no evidence of significant settlement clusters and it may not have been possible to support such large populations along the narrow wet/dry interface zone. Settlements identified in these areas are likely to be low density with noncontiguous sites dispersed along the zone.

VISIBILITY

Considering the current lack of evidence and the likely impermanence of settlement, sites are likely to be relatively low-visibility and non-monumental in character. Sites preserved in wetlands are inherently low-visibility and the dryland component of these settlement patterns are unlikely to have included earthen field banks or houses enclosed by earthworks.

PRIORITIES FOR FUTURE WORK

To realize the potential highlighted in earlier sections and to test the usefulness of the proposed model set out above it is necessary to establish priorities for future work. It will be necessary to rethink (cf Van de Noort & O'Sullivan 2006) some of the approaches employed previously and to adopt and develop new methods in examining both wetland and dryland areas.

RECURRENT SURVEY AND EXCAVATION

Each survey represents a snapshot at a single point in time of a bog that may remain in production for several decades. The condition of the bog including the point in the milling and harvesting sequence, vegetation, flooding, drain depth and weather affects the quality of the results obtained. It is therefore necessary to re-examine each bog as the peat extraction continues. The upper levels of these bogs have, typically, been irrevocably lost but the effectiveness of re-surveys in identifying new and altered site distributions as the milling continues has been demonstrated. Such surveys should be undertaken at a minimum of a five-year interval or a reduction of 0.5m in bog depth. Particular attention should be paid to the margins of bogs and buried land surfaces where evidence of the interface between dryland and wetland activity may survive.

REPRESENTATIVE INVESTIGATIONS

All levels of work from survey to excavation and analysis should represent the full range of the sites and environments identified. This includes examining sites of all types and dates in the full range of environmental and landscape contexts in which they occur. As seen above, the great majority of sites are not classic trackways and if investigations are restricted to such sites the results as a whole will be biased and unrepresentative of the communities that produced them.

REMAINING WETLAND AREAS

Opportunities should be sought and techniques developed to examine the extensive areas of wetlands not currently available for investigation. This includes privately owned bogs, as well as the areas of reclaimed wetlands used for agriculture and forestry. As has been shown, these may offer the highest potential for the identification of sites, settlements and artefact deposition. These areas also offer the potential for distributions of sites that bridge the existing gaps between sites in the larger commercial bogs and those on the dryland. Initially, it may be desirable to target selected landscape blocks to test the effectiveness of the models and methods employed and to establish priorities for further work. This will help to identify genuine gaps in the archaeological record and highlight productive avenues of approach.

INFRASTRUCTURE PROJECTS

In addition to the large-scale commercial exploitation of peatlands, opportunities have also been presented in recent years by a number of infrastructure projects in the region. It is important to exploit these opportunities as they provide a means to assess both dryland areas and wetlands outside those normally available for study. We should seek to inform the approaches adopted on such projects and to integrate those results with the peatland evidence to develop the broadest possible picture of the landscape and how it was exploited.

MODELS OF WETLAND EVOLUTION

The absence of palaeogeographies and relatively low level of palaeoenvironmental work has already been highlighted. The development of a fuller collaborative approach with other fields to undertake multidisciplinary studies will transform dramatically our understanding of these landscapes.

THEMATIC AND THEORETICAL APPROACHES

The number of sites available for study is finite and the opportunities to examine them are limited. It is therefore important to address the widest range of relevant approaches when working in peatland landscapes. Models for understanding aspects of the landscape, environment and economy must be developed and integrate concepts of society, ritual and identity to examine all aspects of life and living in the region (*ibid.*).

PUBLICATION

Publication should be the defined end product of future projects with the documentation and protection/mitigation of individual sites being integral steps in that process. The results of all levels of work including survey and excavation results, analytical and interpretative work should be made available to the widest possible audience. A single repository for the archives, digital data and reports generated by projects should be established (ideally, the Sites and Monuments Record) to facilitate access and the integration of the complete archaeological record from the region.

DRYLAND EVIDENCE

Consideration should be given to incorporating dryland evidence when undertaking wetland projects as the two assemblages represent different parts of the landscape spectrum that can only be fully appreciated in an integrated framework. It is likely that this process will also identify further gaps in our understanding and suggest new avenues of research.

SCALE OF THE RESPONSE

The scale of the threat posed to peatland sites by both commercial peat exploitation and by drainage cannot be overstated. A number of approaches have been adopted to date but all have been based on a response of fixed scale or budget. The opportunities and obligations presented by the peatlands of the Irish midlands will not be presented again and every effort should be made to ensure the scale of the response is in proportion to the scale of the threats.

> … The weather is now assuming a fierce and terrible aspect and we must hasten to a close, for this is not the season for antiquarian investigations, especially in this County of bogs and morasses …
>
> John O'Donovan, Banagher, January 9th, 1838
> Ordnance Survey Letters King's County No. 16

NOTE

The review presented in this paper was prompted by the closure of the Irish Archaeological Wetland Unit in 2005 after 15 years and I would like to express my gratitude to my colleagues throughout that period. Particular thanks go to Cathy Moore, Cara Murray, Nathalie Rynne and Michael Stanley who were there at the close and whose work and ideas contributed to this paper. The IAWU archives of almost 3,500 sites have been transferred both physically and digitally to the National Monuments Section of the Department of the Environment, Heritage and Local Government for inclusion in the Sites and Monuments Record. Credit for this achievement must go to Professor Barry Raftery, my 12 colleagues over the years and the 130 members of our field teams who made it possible.

REFERENCES

Aalen, F H A, Whelan, K & Stout, M 1977 (eds) *Atlas of the Rural Irish Landscape*. Cork.

Bennett, I 2004 (ed) *Excavations 2002: Summary Accounts of Archaeological Excavations in Ireland*. Bray.

Burgess, C & Gerloff, S 1981 *The Dirks and Rapiers of Great Britain and Ireland*. Prähistorische Bronzefunde, Abteilung IV, Band 7. Munich.

Caseldine, C, Hatton, J, Huber, U, Chiverrell, R & Woolley, N 1996 'Palaeocological work at Corlea (1992–95)', *in* Raftery, B *Trackway Excavations in the Mountdillon Bogs, Co Longford, 1985–1991*, 393–4. Transactions of the Irish Archaeological Wetland Unit 3. Dublin.

Caseldine, C, Hatton, J & Geary, B 2005 'Pollen and palaeohydrological evidence', *in* Gowen, M, Philips, M, Ó Néill J & Irish Archaeological Wetland Unit (eds) *The Lisheen Mine Archaeological Project 1996–8*, 83–136. Bray.

Casparie, W 2005 'Peat morphology and bog development', *in* Gowen, M, Philips, M, Ó Néill, J & Irish Archaeological Wetland Unit (eds) *The Lisheen Mine Archaeological Project 1996–8*, 13–53. Wordwell, Bray.

Cooney, G & Grogan, E 1994 *Irish Prehistory: A Social Perspective*. Bray.

Cross, S, Murray, C, Ó Néill, J & Stevens, P 2005 'Landscape context', *in* Gowen, M, Philips, M, Ó Néill, J & Irish Archaeological Wetland Unit (eds) *The Lisheen Mine Archaeological Project 1996–8*, 351–362. Bray.

de Valera, R & Ó Nualláin, S 1972 *Survey of the Megalithic Tombs of Ireland Vol. III: Counties Galway, Roscommon, Leitrim, Longford, Westmeath, Laoighis, Offaly, Kildare, Cavan*. Dublin.

Doody, M 1991 'Bronze Age settlements', *in* Ryan, M (ed) *The Illustrated Archaeology of Ireland*, 100–103. Dublin.

Eogan, G 1983 *The Hoards of the Irish Later Bronze Age*. Dublin.

Gowen, M, Philips, M, Ó Néill, J & Irish Archaeological Wetland Unit 2005 (eds) *The Lisheen Mine Archaeological Project 1996–8*. Bray.

Halpin, A 1984 *A Preliminary Survey of the Archaeological Material Recovered from Peatlands in the Republic of Ireland*. Unpubl report commissioned by the Office of Public Works, Dublin.

Hammond, R F 1981 *The Peatlands of Ireland*. Soil Survey Bulletin 35. Dublin.

Hencken, H O'N 1942 'Ballinderry Crannog No 2', *Proc Roy Ir Acad*, 47C, 1–77.

Hull, G 2004 'Knockdomny (BGE 1B/94/1)', *in* Bennett, I (ed), *Excavations 2002: summary accounts of archaeological excavations in Ireland*, 511–12. Bray.

IAWU 1993 *Excavations at Clonfinlough, County Offaly*. Transactions of the Irish Archaeological Wetland Unit 2. Dublin.

IAWU 2003 *Report on the rescue survey of Clonearl Bog, Co Offaly*. Unpubl report commissioned by the Department of the Environment, Heritage and Local Government, Dublin.

McDermott, C 1998 'The prehistory of the Offaly peatlands', *in* Nolan, W & O'Neill, T P (eds) *Offaly History & Society*, 1–28. Dublin.

McDermott, C 2001 'Treckers through time: recent archaeological survey results from Co Offaly, Ireland', *in* Raftery, B & Hickey, J (eds) *Recent Developments in Wetland Research*, 13–26. Seandálaíocht: Monograph 2, Department of Archaeology, University College Dublin and WARP Occasional Paper 14. Department of Archaeology, University College Dublin, Dublin.

McDermott, C & O'Connor, D 2005 *Excavations of Eight Archaeological Sites in Demesne or Mearspark Farm, Stonehousefarm and Kilbeggan South Townlands in Advance of the N6 Kinnegad to Athlone Dual Carriage*. Report commissioned by Westmeath County Council from CRDS Ltd.

McDermott, C, Moore, C, Murray, C & Stanley, M 2003 'Bog standard?', *Archaeology Ireland*, 17(4), 20–3.

McDermott, C, Murray, C, Plunkett, G & Stanley, M 2002 'Of bogs, boats and bows: Irish Archaeological Wetland Unit survey 2001', *Archaeology Ireland*, 16(1), 28–31.

Moore, C, Murray, C, Stanley, M & McDermott, C 2003 'Bogland surveys in Ireland: forty shades of brown', *in* Fenwick, J (ed) *Lost and Found: Discovering Ireland's past*, 123–37. Bray.

Murray, C, Stanley, M, McDermott, C & Moore, C 2002 'Sticks and stones: Irish Archaeological Wetland Unit Survey 2002', *Archaeology Ireland*, 16(4), 16–19.

O'Brien, C & Sweetman, P D 1997 (comp.) *Archaeological Inventory of County Offaly*. Dublin.

Parks, H & Mitchell, F J G 2000 'Vegetation history at Clonmacnoise, Co Offaly', *Proc Roy Ir Acad*, 100B, 1, 35–40.

Phelan, S 2004 'Whitwell (BGE 1/63/1)', *in* Bennett, I (ed) *Excavations 2002: summary accounts of archaeological excavations in Ireland*, 514. Bray.

Raftery, B 1990 *Trackways Through Time*. Rush.

Raftery, B 1996 *Trackway Excavations in the Mountdillon Bogs, Co Longford, 1985–91*. Transactions of the Irish Archaeological Wetland Unit 3. Dublin.

Raftery, B 1999 'The milling fields', *in* Coles, B, Coles, J & Schou Jørgensen, M (eds) *Bog Bodies, Sacred Sites and Wetland Archaeology*, 191–201. WARP Occasional Paper 12. Wetland Archaeology Research Project, Exeter.

Ryan, M 1980 'An Early Mesolithic site in the Irish midlands', *Antiquity*, 54(210), 46–7.

Stanley, M 2003 'Archaeological survey of Irish bogs: information without understanding?', *J Wetland Archaeol*, 3, 61–74.

Stanley, M & Moore, C 2004 'Medieval peatland dwellings', *Archaeology Ireland*, 18(4), 12–14.

Sweetman, P D, Alcock, O & Moran, B 1995 *Archaeological Inventory of County Laois*. Dublin.

Van de Noort, R & O'Sullivan, A 2006 *Rethinking Wetland Archaeology*. London.

Wetlands and major infrastructural programmes: prehistoric wetland sites in excavation projects in Scania, southernmost Sweden

LARS LARSSON

ABSTRACT

At the end of the 1990s, two large-scale excavation programmes were carried out in the western part of Scania, the southernmost county in Sweden (fig 1). These were salvage projects, undertaken as part of large infrastructural investments which involved major changes in the rail lines along Sweden's west coast, as well as a motorway connection linking the new bridge across the Öresund strait and the existing road network. These construction developments covered regions that were the most densely settled areas during much of prehistoric and medieval times in southern Scandinavia. In order to carry out archaeological investigations, research programmes were designed for the railroad and the motorway developments. As a result, this was the first time that wetlands were taken into serious consideration as key landscape zones for investigation. Here, the role of wetlands in the research plans, initial surveys, test excavations and final excavations will be presented.

INTRODUCTION

For a considerable time, at least in comparison to other parts of Europe, wetlands have had a central role in the study of southern Scandinavian prehistory. During the Mesolithic period, sites were located on the shores of lakes, later to be moved into the reed-belt margins of the eutrophic lakes, which were in the process of being filled with organic matter (Larsson 1998, 2001, 2006). Already from the Mesolithic, but of main importance in the Neolithic (6000–3800 cal BP), Bronze Age (3800–2500 BP) and most of the Iron Age (2500–1500 BP), bogs were used as locations for sacrificial deposits. In some cases, settlement sites were established in close contact with bodies of open water that eventually became bogs. Refuse deposited in water was covered by peat and turf, which has helped to preserve otherwise perishable artefacts made of organic materials.

Until recently, the investigation of human activities in relation to wetlands has been based on occasional finds made in association with drainage developments. In a small number of cases surveys have been carried out in order to find settlement sites in bogs. Turf and peat extraction has long been the only exception in which commercial wetland exploitation has led to archaeological investigation. For example, the turf cutting during the Second World War and somewhat later led to several excavations of bog sites in southern Scandinavia (Althin 1954; Henriksen 1976; Andersen et al 1982). Today, large-scale turf extraction is relatively rare in southern Scandinavia, but it has led to a few important excavations in the central part of Scania, the southernmost county of Sweden (Larsson 1999, 102; Sjöström 2004).

FINDS IN BOGS – SOMETHING OF A CATCH-22 SITUATION

The drainage of wetlands is still going on. Smaller bogs are also being transformed into ponds for fish and crayfish. These activities often go on under the antiquities board's radar. However, on one occasion bones and antlers together with a small number of flint artefacts were found in the dug-up peat of a former small bog. They have been interpreted as the remains of a sequence of winter hunting and butchering on ice, mainly of reindeers and horses, dating to the Late Palaeolithic (Larsson et al 2002). More sites of this kind might exist, as a number of reindeer antlers have been retrieved during turf cutting and drainage of bogs in the south-western part of the southernmost county of Sweden (Larsson et al 2002, fig 7). The risks of destruction of such sites are high when bogs are exploited for various development purposes. Moreover, the existence of such sites is often hard to recognize until most of the bog has already been destroyed, as the finds are located in the lowermost layers of the bog. This is quite another situation than for sites on firm ground but with refuse layers in

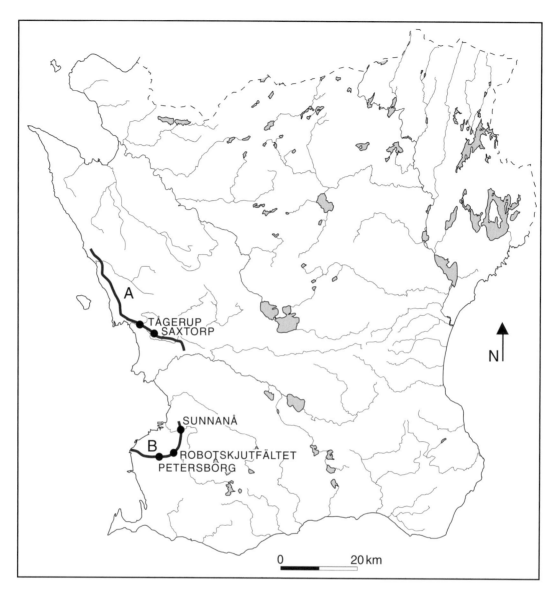

FIGURE 1
Scania, southernmost Sweden, with the areas of two major infrastructural programmes marked. A: the West
Coast Line programme; B: the beltway programme.

previous open water that might be detected by surveys around wetlands or on the surface of wetlands. It should also be added that archaeologists in Scania had a particular advantage when doing wetland archaeology, because a detailed reconnaissance map from *c* 1810 shows the locations of former wetland zones (*Skånska rekognosceringskartan* 1986) (fig 2).

Swedish law concerning the development of land for purposes other than traditional use, farming, pasture or forestry, is simple and firm. The person or the company that endorses the development has to pay for the archaeological investigations. Yet, because

archaeological sites are often difficult to recognize during bog development activities, the law offers rather poor protection. The argument for excavating a site like the one mentioned above from the Late Palaeolithic, based on the law of site protection, is somewhat of a Catch-22. This kind of site cannot be identified until the removal of the bog filling has been almost completed.

Despite the number of well-known bog finds, the former wetlands have rarely been taken into consideration in large-scale salvage projects. At best, the margins of larger bogs have been tested for prehistoric traces. In standard salvage projects, the fieldwork is carried out in stages of survey, test excavation and final full-scale excavations. On the basis of test excavations, the expense budgets are determined, and in practice it is very difficult to get additional money for excavating special sites found during subsequent research stages. The approach is well suited for sites on dry land, but it is difficult to apply to sites and finds in former wetlands. Such sites are not recovered during surveys and rarely appear during test excavations.

WETLAND SITES AND LARGE-SCALE MAJOR INFRASTRUCTURAL PROGRAMMES

Based on previous experience, the planning teams of the two major Scanian salvage projects discussed here paid extra attention to wetland areas during the large-scale rescue excavations carried out in the late 1990s (Billberg *et al* 1996–8; Karsten & Svensson 1998).

One of the archaeological projects was associated with a partly new railway construction along western Scania, covering more or less north–south oriented areas around 40km long and at a rather short distance from the coastline (fig 1A). The planned tracks were to cover areas with a number of known prehistoric monuments and settlement sites (Svensson 2003). The railway was also supposed to stretch across bogs, as well as wetlands associated with rivers and brooks. The affected zones included the narrow north–south oriented band incorporating the actual railway, plus some additional construction that included wetland zones mainly located in small river valleys. The archaeological rescue programme for *Västkustbanan* (VKB) ('the West Coast Line')

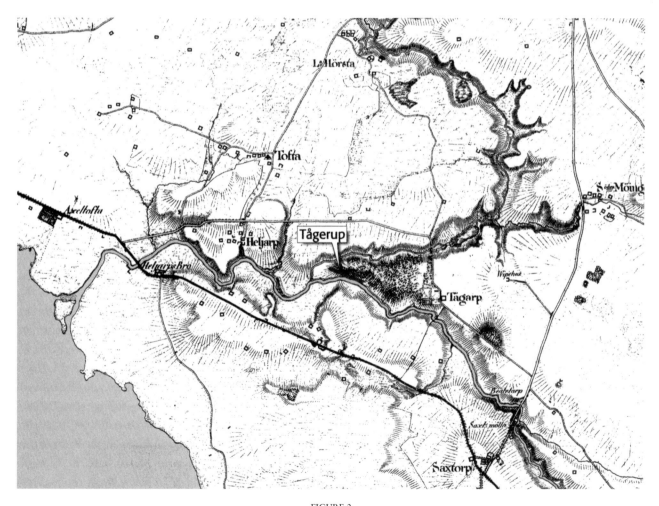

FIGURE 2
The location of the Late Mesolithic site of Tågerup projected on a map from *c* 1810. From Karsten & Knarrström 2003.

33

was carried out in several stages during the period 1995–7.

Almost contemporaneously, an archaeological salvage plan was designed for the planned motorway connection for the bridge that was then under construction to connect Denmark and Sweden across the Öresund strait (Billberg *et al* 1996–8) (fig 1B). This motorway, with a number of connecting roads, was to be a beltway around the south-west Scanian city of Malmö. It is important to emphasize that this would encompass one of the most densely populated areas in southern Scandinavia during prehistoric and medieval times. Previous salvage excavations around Malmö had already revealed an exceptionally detailed picture of prehistoric settlement.

The new beltway was to be laid down outside the urban area and would be partly connected to zones already investigated archaeologically. The beltway would more or less connect two parts of the coast. However, its inland course would run

through a substantially more hillocky landscape. In its southern part, the motorway would cross a couple of small wetlands, oriented south–north and known to be associated with prehistoric and medieval settlements. The motorway would also cross the largest river in the region, again connected to key wetlands. The plan paid special attention to the coastal plain wetlands, as well as those in the hillocky inland area.

In order to carry out investigations, the research programmes for each of the developments were formulated based upon the specific formations of the landscape in combination with known prehistoric remains as well as expected findings, and in relation to current research trends and available expertise. The rescue projects involved co-operation between archaeologists and palaeoecological specialists.

These large rescue excavation projects are of special importance as they provide an opportunity to gain insight into the distribution of different sites unbiased by the initial choice of area made by archaeologists. What is found should constitute a fair representation of different prehistoric sites.

In order to provide basic knowledge of the areas through which the long narrow development area went, intensive collection of information about sites was carried out. In a few cases this led to special analyses of regions in which wetlands have been involved (Karsten 2005).

The results of the wetland investigations from both projects may be illustrated with a few examples.

EXAMPLES FROM THE VKB PROJECT

Arguably the most important wetland site to be excavated in the VKB project was Tågerup, located on a former promontory at the confluence of a brook and the major river Saxån (Karsten & Knarrström 2001, 2003) (fig 1A). Artefacts on the southern slope indicated the existence of a large site spanning several stages of the Late Mesolithic. Because the sea level was higher during that period, the Tågerup site would have been located on the shore of a long, narrow inlet of the Öresund strait indicated by a map from *c* 1810 (fig 2). During the test excavation and subsequent final excavation, it was found that the site included settlement deposits, as well as graves from the middle Mesolithic Kongemose and late Mesolithic Ertebølle Cultures. The preservation in the refuse layers was excellent. Along more than 20m of former seashore, worked antler and wood objects were recovered. These included a perforated and ornately decorated

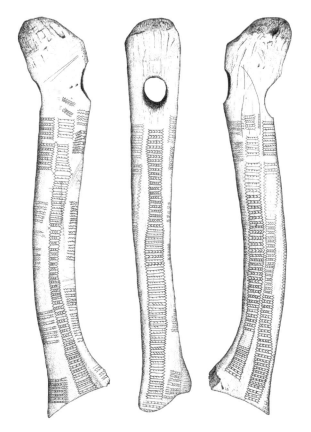

FIGURE 3
A decorated handle found at Tågerup in the refuse layer of a settlement dated to the early part of the Late Mesolithic. Length of the handle 39.5cm. From Karsten & Knarrström 2003.

shaft (fig 3). The waterlogged seashore deposits also included parts of wicker traps.

While Tågerup represents a relatively visible wetland site, it is important to highlight investigations of localities that were more challenging to trace. In Saxtorp, a still active natural spring has created a small bog, about 1,000m² in area (Nilsson & Nilsson 2003) (fig 1A). Most of the bog was excavated during the salvage project. Palaeoecological analyses show that the water flow in the small wetland varied dramatically during prehistory. Archaeological deposits in the bog date mainly to the late Early Neolithic and early Middle Neolithic periods. At least 35 ceramic vessels were deposited within a limited part of the former wetland (fig 4). Most bones, including domesticated species and bones from at least three humans, were found in the same area. Some animal bones show direct traces of butchery, but there are also examples of larger carcass parts being deposited. A small number of finds date to the Bronze Age and early Iron Age. One likely factor of importance for the bog as a place for ritual depositions is that the water is naturally coloured red by the high iron content of the surrounding sand (fig 5).

Red-coloured water or sand appears to have been favoured in ritually placing offerings in bogs (Stjernquist 1997). The use of such deposit sites may have persisted for thousands of years.

The find material from the Saxtorp bog would probably not have been recognized if it had been exploited earlier for peat extraction or today if the filling had been removed to form a pond. It appears that ceramics and bone often go unrecognized, biasing what we know about occasional bog finds towards flint axes (Larsson 2006). It is suggested that the thorough Saxtorp bog excavation gives a more complete picture of ritual depositional history in a prehistoric wetland locality.

It is important to identify in what way the results of these large rescue excavations will complement our knowledge of how wetlands were used during prehistory. Concerning the finds from the small bog at Saxtorp, the most important information, apart from the find situation, is the location of the site in relation to contemporary settlement sites. About 40m from the small bog a Neolithic settlement was found (Nilsson & Nilsson 2003, 258). At the excavation, a long-house was identified with pottery of the same date as from the small bog. The ritual activities related

to wetland seem to have taken place close to but not immediately beside the contemporaneous occupation.

During test excavations of a large number of sites, a couple of sites of Neolithic date were identified by occupation remains found in the area close to the small brook Välabäcken (Karsten 2005, 422). No settlement remains were found on the firm shore adjacent to the deposition area. These finds might have provided further information about wetland use,

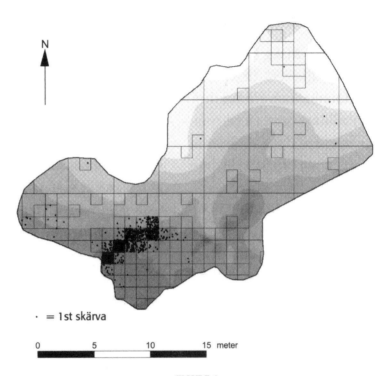

· = 1st skärva

0   5   10   15 meter

FIGURE 4
The distribution of Early Neolithic pottery at a bog in Saxtorp (skärva = sherd). From Nilsson & Nilsson 2003.

as locations of secular occupation depositions remain from settlement in the neighbourhood. Or they might have represented a special kind of ritual deposition where more or less ordinary settlement remains were used (Chapman 2000). However, these sites were excluded in the selection of sites of importance for an intensive final excavation.

SOME EXAMPLES FROM THE BELTWAY PROJECT

What may be surprising is that relatively few sites were found in the now drained wetland areas south of Malmö.

The identification of wetlands is rendered difficult by the situation that areas including wetlands have

FIGURE 5
Water from the small bog at Saxtorp which is coloured red by the iron in the surrounding sand. From Nilsson & Nilsson 2003.

been drained. If the drainage is successful the organic substances, accumulated for thousands of years, will be rapidly decomposed and in some cases where the basin has been shallow they will totally disappear. An example is the Petersborg site where axes with a patination typical of wetland environment were found in a shallow depression (Siech & Berggren 2002, 149) (fig 1B).

An excavated area at Robotskjutfältet provides an example of the difficulties of identifying prehistoric

wetlands (Ekerow & Ingwald 2002, 40ff.) (fig 1B). The area was located in a hillocky landscape with heavy erosion. A small bog was covered by 2m of colluvial layers and not identified until the final excavation started. The exploited area covered just a small part of the bog. The excavation was aimed at a survey of the exposed bog surface and involved digging a number of small trenches. The finds are similar to ordinary settlement remains mainly dated to the Neolithic. However, in several cases, artefacts were found in separate but small concentrations from two finds to thirty-three. These concentrations have been interpreted as accumulated depositions of ritual importance (Ekerow & Ingwald 2002, 52ff.).

A similar find situation was present at Sunnanå where a small bog was found below about 1m of colluvial layers (Steineke et al 2005, 61ff.) (fig 1B). The bog covered an area of about 1,000 square metres that was tested by excavating a number of small pits. Most of the finds of flint, pottery and bones were recorded close to the edge of the bog. The material is dated to the Early Neolithic and the transition from the Neolithic to the Bronze Age. Most of the finds seem to be equal to ordinary settlement refuse but they also include intact and broken tools. In this case the finds are interpreted as originating from the refuse layer of settlement combined to ritual depositions (Steineke et al 2006, 68).

The exploited area also included a crossing of the small river Sege Å at Sunnanå. This was like the river Saxån, mentioned earlier from the VKB project, a stream of importance in prehistory. Mesolithic settlement sites with a location similar to Tågerup have been found and excavated further downstream close to the estuary (Larsson 1982). However, when dredging took place further upstream, a large number of tools, mainly axes dated to the Neolithic and Early Bronze Age, were found (Forssander 1933). This seems to be the largest ritual river deposition in southern Sweden.

When the area closest to the river was investigated, a strange structure consisting of more than 1,000 postholes was revealed (Steineke et al 2005, 202ff.). The posts are rather small and covered an area 220m long and up to 15m wide (fig 6). The few finds in more than 700 postholes did not provide datable material, and just one dating of macrofossils gave a value to the Viking Age that fits well with the age of a closely situated settlement. The poles might have been part of an earth rampart used as a landing stage. The river was suitable for ship transports as far up as the excavated area, and at the site an important road known since the Bronze Age crossed the river (Samuelsson 2001).

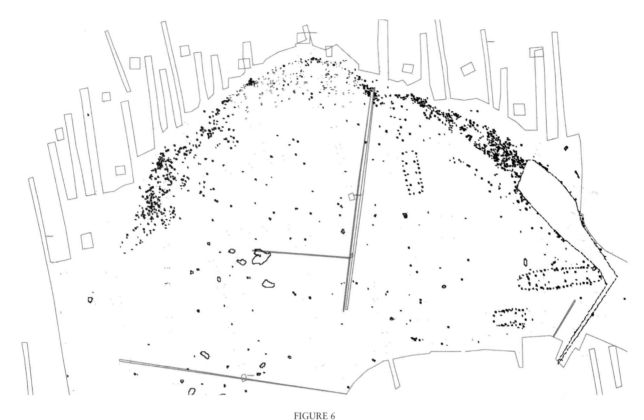

FIGURE 6
A zone filled with post-holes close to the river Sege Å. This structure is interpreted as a kind of earth rampart used as a landing stage dating to the Viking Age. From Steineke *et al* 2005.

Before the building of a bridge across the river, trenches for different purposes were dug (Steineke *et al* 2005, 27ff.). The trenching was supervised by archaeologists in order to find out whether finds and find circumstances could be linked to the depositions of mainly Neolithic tools recorded during the early part of the twentieth century (Karsten 1994, 142). However, very few artefacts were found. The most important is a fragment of a human skull that was dated to the Late Neolithic. This period is well represented in the river depositions.

When discussing ordinary refuse and its connection to features of ritual importance, one can refer to a later excavation carried out at Killäng, close to the beltway (S Siech pers comm). Most of the remains were found in the transition zone between the dry shore and a small bog. At several locations just above that zone, settlement deposits spanned from the Neolithic to an early part of the Iron Age. Excavations revealed that most of the wetland finds represent pits, which display highly variable contents. One pit held an entire lamb, while a larger pit included a large number of flint flakes from axe production, along with a finished but unpolished axe and a funnel beaker placed on

the top of the debris (fig 7). A considerable number of associated post-holes might belong to some kind of enclosure around the area with deposit pits. At a number of locations around the wetland, hearths were found in concentrations or in rows.

CONCLUSION

Major infrastructural programmes provide excellent possibilities to obtain further knowledge of how prehistoric societies used wetlands. These developments affect areas that are not primarily chosen because of their interest for archaeologists. They thereby give an insight into wetland use that should be a better representation of the importance of these parts of the landscape in prehistory. Furthermore, developments in Sweden are paid by the developers, allowing different kinds of analyses to be included in the costs.

The two Scanian development programmes presented here shed light on the prehistoric use of wetlands. Late Mesolithic settlements were found, the most well-known wetland sites in an international perspective. However, some sites date to the Neolithic

FIGURE 7
A section through the flake deposition (top) and the flint axe (bottom) found within this deposition from
Killäng, south-western Scania. Permission from Malmö kulturmiljö.

and the Early Bronze Age. The find circumstances and find combinations allow a small number to be viewed as the results of ritual depositions. However, most sites include find categories and find distribution that correspond to ordinary refuse layers from settlement. But they also include intact tools or tool fragments that one rarely finds on ordinary settlements. This is a pattern that is repeated in a way that cannot be ignored.

REFERENCES

Althin, C-A 1954 *The Chronology of the Stone Age Settlement of Scania, Sweden*. I. The Mesolithic Settlement. Acta Archaeologica Lundensia, series in 4°, N° 1, Lund.

Andersen, K, Jørgensen, S & Richter, J 1982 *Maglemose hytterne ved Ulkestrup Lyng*. Nordiske Fortidsminder, Serie B, Bind 7, København.

Billberg, I, Björhem, N, Magnusson Staaf, B & Thörn, R (eds) *Öresundsförbindelsen och arkeologin*. Malmö.

Chapman, J 2000 *Fragmentation in Archaeology: People, places and broken objects in the prehistory of South Eastern Europe*. London.

Ekerow, H & Ingwald, J 2002 *Öresundsförbindelsen. Robotskjutfältet 14A–B*. Rapport nr 26. Malmö kulturmiljö, Malmö.

Forssander, J-E 1933 'En fyndplats från stenåldern i Sege å vid Malmö', *Meddelande från Lunds universitets historiska museum*, 24–44.

Henriksen, B B 1976 *Sværdborg I. Excavations 1943–44. A Settlement of the Maglemose Culture*. Arkæologiske Studier III, Copenhagen.

Karsten, P 1994 *Att kasta yxan i sjön*. En studie över rituell tradition och förändring utifrån skånska neolitiska offerfynd. Acta Archaeologica Lundensia, series in 8°, N° 23, Stockholm.

Karsten, P 2005 'Västskånska offerfynd från 2300–500 F. Kr.', Lagerås, P & Strömberg, B (eds), *Bronsåldersbygd 2300–500 f. Kr,* 420–43. Skånska spår – arkeologi längs Västkustbanan. Lund.

Karsten, P & Knarrström, B (eds) 2001 *Tågerup special-studier.* Skånska spår – arkeologi längs Västkustbanan. Lund.

Karsten, P & Knarrström, B 2003 *The Tågerup excavations.* Skånska spår – arkeologi längs Västkustbanan. Lund.

Karsten, P & Svensson, M 1998 (eds) Projektprogram. Inför arkeologiska förundersökningar av järnvägen Västkustbanan, delen Helsingborg–Kävlinge, Malmöhus län Skåne 1996. *Riksantikvarieämbetet UV Syd Rapport 1996:50.* Lund.

Larsson, L 1982 *Segebro. En tidigatlantisk boplats vid Sege ås mynning.* Malmöfynd 4. Malmö: Malmö museer.

Larsson, L 1998 'Prehistoric Wetland Sites in Sweden', Bernick, K (ed) *Hidden Dimensions: The Cultural Significance of Wetland Archaeology,* 64–82. Vancouver.

Larsson, L 1999 'Settlement and Palaeoecology in the Scandinavian Mesolithic', Coles, J, Bewley, R & Mellars, P (eds) *World Prehistory. Studies in Memory of Grahame Clark.* Proceedings of the British Academy 99, 87–106. Oxford.

Larsson, L 2001 'South Scandinavian Wetland Sites and Finds from the Mesolithic and the Neolithic', Purdy, B A (ed) *Enduring Records. The Environmental and Cultural Heritage of Wetlands,* 158–71. Oxford.

Larsson, L 2006 'The ritual use of wetlands during the Neolithic. A local study in southernmost Sweden', Lillie, M & Ellis, S (ed) *Wetland Archaeology and Environments: Regional Issues, Global Perspectives.* In press.

Larsson, L, Liljegren, R, Magnell, O & Ekström, J 2002 'Archaeo-faunal aspects of bog finds from Hässleberga, Southern Scania, Sweden', Bratlund, B & Valentin Eriksen, B (eds) *Recent Studies in the Final Palaeolithic of the European Plain,* 61–74. Århus.

Nilsson, M-L & Nilsson, L 2003 'Ett källsprång i Saxtorp', Svensson, M (ed), *I det neolitiska rummet.* Skånska spår – arkeologi längs Västkustbanan, 243–81. Lund.

Samuelsson, B-Å 2001 'Kan gravar spegla vägars ålder och betydelse? Ett exempel på Söderslätt i Skåne', Larsson, L (ed), *Uppåkra. Centrum i analys och rapport.* Uppåkrastudier 4, 177–84. Acta Archaeologica Lundensia, Series in 8°, N° 36, Stockholm.

Siech, S & Berggren, Å 2002 *Öresundsförbindelsen. Petersborg 6.* Rapport nr. 15. Malmö kulturmiljö, Malmö.

Sjöström, A 2004 *Grävningsrapport. Rönneholm 6–10, 12, 14 och 15.* Arkeologisk undersökning av ett mesolitiskt boplatskomplex i Rönneholms mosse, Hassle 32:18, Stehags socken, Eslövs kommun, Skåne. Duplicate. Lund.

Skånska rekognosceringskartan 1986 Framställd av fältmätningsbrigaden 1812–1820. Lantmäteriet, Malmö.

Steineke, M, Ekenberg, A, Hansson, K & Ifverson, A 2005 *Öresundsförbindelsen. Sunnanå 19A–F.* Rapport nr. 34. Malmö kulturmiljö, Malmö.

Stjernquist, B 1997 *The Röekillorna Spring. Spring-cults in Scandinavian Prehistory.* Regiae Societatis Humaniorum Litterarum Lundensis LXXXII. Lund.

Svensson, M 2003 'Det neolitiska rummet' Svensson, M (ed) *I det neolitiska rummet.* Skånska spår – arkeologi längs Västkustbanan, 9–29. Lund.

Monitoring waterlogged sites in peatlands: where, how, why and what next?

RICHARD BRUNNING

SUMMARY

Waterlogged archaeological deposits are threatened with destruction across most of Europe's peatlands. In many countries attempts are being made to preserve such deposits *in situ*. Monitoring programmes are a vital part of this approach but a series of questions need to be answered before undertaking such work, including why, how, and most importantly, what happens afterwards? There are also numerous difficulties associated with interpreting the results of monitoring programmes and their implications for the survival of such deposits. Monitoring can be a worthwhile exercise but archaeologists must be clear of its purpose, aware of its limitations and unafraid of its findings.

WHY MONITOR?

Waterlogged archaeological deposits, in peatlands or elsewhere, may require monitoring if the following three conditions are met:

1. The deposit is important enough to warrant the expenditure of monitoring.
2. There is thought to be a short-term threat to the survival of the deposit.
3. There is something that can be done to prevent the destruction or otherwise mitigate the threat to the deposit.

The importance of waterlogged archaeological deposits has been stressed many times before (eg Coles 2001). Wetland burial environments preserve the most complete evidence of past material culture and structures and allow application of a wider range of analytical techniques (eg dendrochronology). Associated palaeoenvironmental remains provide evidence about local site activity and changes in the wider landscape generated by human or natural forces such as deforestation, woodland management, climate change and sea-level rise. The argument for the expenditure of money on waterlogged deposits is also strengthened by their rarity and their unique vulnerability.

Peatlands, and the archaeology within them, are threatened across Europe by a large number of factors that can be broadly divided into primarily natural forces (such as coastal erosion), the effects of agriculture (such as peat wastage) and other human development (such as peat extraction, road building and so on). Each of these forces poses a significantly different threat to the other and requires varied forms of mitigation to preserve deposits *in situ*, if such preservation is possible at all. For archaeological sites exposed in inter-tidal peat deposits, for example, there is realistically little hope of long-term preservation, unless sea-level rise or sediment movements are likely to offer them increased protection (Bird 1993; Bell *et al* 2000; Murphy & Trow 2001). In these cases a monitoring programme would only be useful to prove the speed of destruction and provide the justification for rescue recording or excavation. Monitoring programmes do not always demonstrate how deposits can be preserved; they can also suggest that complete preservation is just not feasible (eg Van de Noort *et al* 2001b).

The most important factor in the decision whether to monitor a site is usually a financial one. In many countries in Europe, including the UK, if a significant archaeological site is unavoidably threatened by a development project, the developer is usually required to provide a reasonable level of financial contribution towards measures designed to mitigate the damage (eg PPG16 1990). These measures may involve preservation *in situ* of all or part of the site, almost always with no ongoing monitoring of the burial environment. That is just as well, because if there is monitoring, what happens if it demonstrates an extant or increased threat to the waterlogged deposit? Even if rescue excavation was technically possible under a road or office development, who could be imposed upon to pay the bill, possibly decades after the development?

Preserving waterlogged archaeological deposits *in situ* on development sites is fraught with difficulty and with the present state of knowledge it is impossible to guarantee the survival of such deposits in the short term (0–15 years), let alone over a longer period. The curatorial archaeologist is therefore left either with total excavation, where much information will be gathered but the site lost to future generations, or trusting to luck that some or all of the site will survive *in situ* for future archaeologists to examine. In the latter case, monitoring will prove if the educated guess was right or wrong but will be of little other use.

Because of the practical considerations outlined above, the majority of wetland archaeological monitoring projects in Europe have taken place in rural areas where the main threat is generated by the local agricultural regime (eg Coles & Olivier 2001). In these cases the issues are usually simpler but there is less money available to carry out the work because no one expects farmers to pay for the damage they cause to the historic environment. Of all the rural wetland environments archaic peatlands are probably the most at risk because of their particular vulnerability to destruction by peat wastage caused

by arable farming and/or lowering of ground water tables through drainage or abstraction (Armstrong 1996; Richardson & Smith 1997; French 2000; Brunning 2001).

Monitoring programmes can be developed on an *ad hoc* basis for individual sites or as part of a strategic approach for dealing with a wider problem. The *ad hoc* approach is often developed in response to development proposals that require an almost immediate response (eg Peacock & Turner-Walker 2001) but also occurs where important sites are thought to be at risk (eg Brunning *et al* 2000; Matthiesen *et al* 2001 or Van de Noort 2001). In fact a strategic approach is hardly ever developed, the recent work of ROB in the Netherlands being the outstanding exception (Heeringen & Theunissen 2002; Heeringen *et al* 2004a, b) together with the recent work on Scottish crannogs that is reported elsewhere in this volume.

A strategic approach to monitoring of waterlogged archaeological deposits requires four assessments:

FIGURE 1
A sand island occupied in the Mesolithic becoming increasingly exposed as the peat that covers it wastes away through desiccation and oxidation associated with arable farming. Shapwick, Somerset, UK.

1. An assessment of the scale and nature of the threats to the known deposits.

2. An assessment of the importance of the known deposits.

3. An assessment of the survival of the known deposits.

4. An assessment of the currently unknown deposits that may be at risk.

In England the scale and nature of the threat to the known resource has been subject to desk-based assessment by the Monuments at Risk in England's Wetlands Project (*www.ex.ac.uk/marew*, Van de Noort *et al* 2001a). The MAREW report suggested that 2020 wetland monuments or 500–600 years of peat deposits have been destroyed in England during the last 50 years (Van de Noort *et al* 2001a). The series of English Heritage funded wetland surveys have also gone some way to providing the other three assessments required, although not all the surveys were fully comprehensive, especially the first one in Somerset that was largely a response to peat extraction in one area. Many river valleys and isolated waterlogged deposits have never been surveyed although they often have proven potential. Upland blanket bogs have also been overlooked until recently although their potential for preserving waterlogged sites may not be great, as none was discovered during the latest survey in the north-west of England (reported elsewhere in this volume). Regional and national surveys of materials such as waterlogged wood can also fill out the picture (Murphy 2001; Brunning 2003). Assessing the potential of currently unknown sites is obviously problematical, given the difficulties associated with locating sites in deep waterlogged deposits. It is easier to assess the potential of the palaeoenvironmental resource where systematic coring and radiocarbon dating can rapidly identify the extent and date of deposits (eg Brown *et al* 2003).

Once it is known which important waterlogged deposits are likely to survive, those thought to be potentially under short-term threat of destruction could be monitored and their present condition

assessed. Unfortunately, in England it is quite likely that all the known surviving waterlogged sites are potentially at short-term risk of destruction. Conversely, the part of the Neolithic Sweet Track that lies within Shapwick Heath National Nature Reserve in Somerset may be the only waterlogged site in England where there is evidence of the absence of such short-term risk (Brunning *et al* 2000). This obviously raises the problems of what to do with the finite financial resource available from English Heritage or how to obtain considerably more money to adequately counter the ongoing destruction. To

FIGURE 2
Monitoring a wetland burial environment using multiple redox probes and piezometers set at different depths. Sweet Track, Shapwick, Somerset, UK.

FIGURE 3
Removing palaeoenvironmental samples for condition assessment. Neolithic Chilton Track, Somerset, UK.

garner additional funding from central government or the lottery, a very public crisis would undoubtedly be required. Even with a larger pot of money, there would still be the problem of exactly what to monitor and assess.

WHAT TO MONITOR AND HOW?

On a waterlogged site there are two things to monitor, the burial environment and the condition of archaeological materials. The most important factors in the burial environment to monitor are those that regulate microbial decay of organic materials, principally the reduction-oxidation potential (Eh), ground water level fluctuations and soil and ground water chemistry (especially pH). Rainfall, temperature and ground water movements will usually affect these factors and are therefore also candidates for monitoring. The criteria to monitor and the methods to undertake the task have become increasingly standardized over the last 15 years (eg compare Capel 1992 to Heeringen *et al* 2004a) and will not be examined further in this paper.

There is much less standardization about which archaeological materials to use to assess the condition of and how to do it. Artefacts made of wood, leather, bone, bronze, iron, glass, pottery and stone will all react significantly differently to changes in the burial environment. The components of the palaeoenvironmental record will usually display a comparable variability of response. This poses a difficult strategic problem, whether to try and understand the decay process for every material in various preservation scenarios or to focus on specific materials thought to be most at risk or most indicative of increasing decay.

Organic materials are intrinsically more vulnerable to destruction by desiccation than inorganic ones but desiccation of peat deposits will also alter soil chemistry, often resulting in increased decay of inorganic materials; for example, the corrosion of metal objects (Matthiesen *et al* 2001). Unfortunately, very little is known about the degradation mechanisms of organic materials (Kars *et al* 2001). Wooden remains have been the most comprehensively studied, not least because they form a large part of the material culture of most waterlogged sites. The process of microbial decay of wood appears to be well understood (eg Kim *et al* 1996; Bjordal 2000) and examination of the patterns of decay can elucidate the long-term burial history of structures and artefacts (Bjordal *et al* 1999). However, recent investigations on several sites in Somerset (Brunning this volume) produced results that challenge some common assumptions about the vulnerability to decay of archaeological wood in peat soils.

If the purpose of monitoring is to detect the early signs of damage caused by desiccation there is growing evidence to suggest that the most susceptible parts of the archaeological resource are palaeoenvironmental remains (Brunning *et al* 2000; Kenward & Hall 2001; Heeringen *et al* 2004a, b). They are also useful because they are found on every waterlogged site in some form. In future, it may be feasible to identify a more specific environmental component such as coleopteran or plant macrofossil remains but at the moment this is not possible. Procedures for categorizing the decay of palaeoenvironmental remains are soon to be published in the UK and the Netherlands. These should help to improve the consistency of analysis and condition assessment.

For wood, plant remains, beetles or any other material chosen for condition assessment, the biggest hurdle to overcome is probably determining when the observed decay occurred. Decay will occur before deposition, when material is in a non-waterlogged deposition environment, in anoxic waterlogged conditions and often over a recent period when the anoxic conditions have begun to break down, usually as a result of human actions. In 2001 Kenward and Hall argued that 'there is barely any understanding of the relationship between ground conditions and the preservation of the full range of biological remains' (p 10). This situation has not significantly changed in the intervening years.

FIGURE 4

One advantage of excavation is that the effect of desiccation can be made visually apparent to non-archaeologists. Oak piles from an early Medieval causeway are withered and discoloured by desiccation at the top but are much better preserved towards their tips. Street, Somerset, UK.

A large part of this problem is caused by the failure to collect baseline condition data from sites that is quantifiable and can be remeasured in future assessments to determine changes over time. The few sites where quantifiable and repeatable condition assessment techniques have been applied are all fairly recent investigations and do not have a long enough period of time for significant observable changes to occur. Most other sites rely on anecdotal, descriptive or photographic records for comparisons with conditions in previous excavations.

The other choice in site condition assessment is whether to gather evidence through excavation or by less intrusive means such as coring. The benefits of the latter methodology are that the burial environment is less disturbed and that samples can be gathered quite rapidly (eg Heeringen *et al* 2002, 2004a, b). Monitoring at Nydam has shown that excavations can significantly alter water table and soil chemistry conditions over a period long enough to affect site preservation (Matthiesen *et al* 2001). This concurs with anecdotal evidence from the UK suggesting that waterlogged remains can rapidly decay after initial exposure and reburial. Contrary evidence comes from the recent reinvestigation of Glastonbury Lake Village where wooden remains exposed, possibly for a prolonged period, over 105 years ago still survive today (Brunning this volume).

The main advantages of using small-scale excavations to obtain samples for condition assessment are that you can precisely determine what you are sampling and how representative the samples are of that part of the site. In addition, small-scale excavation can provide an opportunity for useful research on sites that are sometimes only poorly understood. If intrusive excavations are rapid, do not involve significant pumping out of water and represent only a small percentage of the whole site, they are probably the best compromise between continuing preservation and increased understanding. The other factor, that should not be lightly discounted by archaeologists, is that they are a lot more fun and interesting than coring, and they can provide photographic evidence that provides a more compelling story to archaeologists, the general public and other decision makers.

WHAT NEXT?

The really hard decisions related to any monitoring programme come when the results are in and demonstrate that the waterlogged site has a burial environment that is not suitable for long-term preservation. What happens next can be divided into five possibilities:

- Preservation conditions are so poor that no further work can be justified and the site is effectively written off as a waterlogged site.

- Preservation is medium or poor and there is no likelihood that *in situ* preservation can be achieved over the short term (up to 15 years). Some scale of rescue excavation could be justified.

- Preservation is medium or poor and there is the ability to improve the burial environment conditions to achieve *in situ* preservation over at least the short term.

- Preservation is medium or poor and the burial environment conditions could be improved and might achieve *in situ* preservation over at least the short term. If there is uncertainty the case could be made for a combination of rescue excavation of part of the site and attempted preservation of the remainder.

- Nothing. The project results are filed away and the awkward conclusions discreetly ignored to avoid a potentially expensive or embarrassing situation.

CONCLUSIONS

The well-proven, extensive and rapid destruction of waterlogged archaeological deposits in European peatlands should be viewed as a significant crisis. A logical strategy to deal with this crisis would first involve the identification of the most important sites and palaeoenvironmental deposits and assessment of their present condition using methodologies that

would permit future assessments to measure the decay over the intervening period. The condition assessment should include palaeoenvironmental remains and the most important artefact or structural material present. The next stage would be to monitor the burial environment of the most important sites that were still in moderate or good condition.

The methodologies for assessing site condition and monitoring the burial environment are becoming increasingly well tested and standardized. Unfortunately, there is still a large gap in our knowledge concerning how the condition of organic materials and the burial environment interact. Only replicable condition assessments and long-term monitoring will come up with the answers. Till then there will always be an element of doubt in any preservation *in situ*.

The greatest problem with monitoring comes when the results suggest that preservation *in situ* is not sustainable. The words 'rescue excavation' appear to strike terror into the hearts of some heritage organizations because of the fear of the large cost of excavating wet sites. It is always cheaper to excavate sites where very little evidence survives. The answer is not to look the other way and wait until the waterlogged resource is almost completely gone and therefore less of a financial burden to deal with. If monitoring shows that the most important components of the archaeological resource are under unavoidable threat of destruction, the wider archaeological community should demand that adequate funds are made available to rescue by excavation what would otherwise be lost.

The perils of ploughing on the Somerset Levels

FIGURE 5
The unsustainable loss of peat soils to agricultural drainage has destroyed numerous waterlogged sites and threatens the remainder. Condition assessment and monitoring of numerous sites is urgently required to determine which can be preserved *in situ* and where rescue excavation is required.

(*Lance Jordan Photography Ltd*)

REFERENCES

Armstrong, A 1996 *The Conservation of Peat Soils on the Somerset Levels and Moors*. Mansfield.

Bell, M, Caseldine, A & Neumann, H 2000 *Prehistoric Inter-tidal Archaeology in the Welsh Severn Estuary*. CBA Research Report 120, York.

Brown, A G, Dinnin, M & Toogood, T 2003 *Peat Wastage in the Somerset Levels. A Study Based on Field Evidence*. Exeter.

Bird, E C F 1993 *Submerging Coasts: The Effects of a Rising Sea Level on Coastal Environments*. Chichester.

Björdal, C G 2001 *Waterlogged Archaeological Wood. Biodegradation and its implications for Conservation*. Uppsala.

Björdal, C G, Nilsson, T & Daniel, G 1999 'Microbial decay of waterlogged archaeological wood found in Sweden', *International Biodeterioration and Biodegradation*, 43, 63–71.

Brunning, R 2001 *Archaeology and Peat Wastage on the Somerset Moors*. Taunton.

Brunning, R 2003 *A Review of Waterlogged Prehistoric Wood in England*. Taunton.

Brunning, R, Hogan, D, Jones, J, Jones, M, Maltby, E, Robinson, M & Straker, V 2000 'Saving the Sweet Track. The *in situ* preservation of a Neolithic wooden trackway, Somerset, UK', *Conservation and Management of Archaeological Sites*, 4, 3–20.

Capel, C 1992 'Parameters for monitoring anoxic environments', *in* Corfield, M, Hinton, P, Nixon, T & Pollard, M (eds) *Preserving Archaeological Remains* in situ, 113–23. London.

Coles, B J 2001 'A past less foreign: wetland archaeology and its survival in European perspective', *in* Coles, B J & Olivier, A *The Heritage Management of Wetlands in Europe*, 1–6. WARP Occasional Paper 16, Exeter.

Coles, B J & Olivier, A (eds) 2001 *The Heritage Management of Wetlands in Europe*, 1–6. WARP Occasional Paper 16, Exeter.

French, C 2000 'Dewatering, desiccation and erosion: an appraisal of water and peat fen in the Fenlands', *in* Crowson, A, Lane, T & Reeve, J (eds) *Fenland Management Project Excavations 1991–1995*, Exeter, 4–8.

Heeringen, R M van, Smit, A & Theunissen, E M 2004 *Archaeology in the Future. Baseline Measurement of the Physical Quality of the Archaeological Monument at Broekpolder*. Nederlandse Archaeologische Rapporten 27, Amersfoot.

Heeringen, R M van, Mauro, G V & Smit, A 2004 *A Pilot Study on the Monitoring of the Physical Quality of Three Archaeological Sites at the UNESCO World Heritage Site at Schokland, Province of Flevoland, the Netherlands*. Nederlandse Archaeologische Rapporten 26, Amersfoot.

Heeringen, R M van & Theunissen, E M 2002 *Desiccation of the Archaeological Landscape at Voorne-Putten*. Nederlandse Archaeologische Rapporten 25, Amersfoot.

Kars, H, Collins, M J, Jans, M, Nord, A, Arthur, P & Kars, E 2001 'Bone as an indicator in the *in situ* degradation of archaeological heritage. Two examples: Apigliano, Italy, and Aartswoud, The Netherlands', *in* Nixon, T (ed) *Preserving archaeological remains* in situ?, 11–17. London.

Kim, Y S, Singh, A P & Nilsson, T 1996 'Bacteria as important degraders in waterlogged archaeological woods'. *Holzforschung* 50, 389–92.

Kenward, H & Hall, A 2001 'Actively decaying or just poorly preserved? Can we tell when plant and invertebrate remains in urban archaeological deposits decay?', *in* Nixon, T (ed) *Preserving Archaeological Remains* in situ?, 4–10. London.

Matthiesen, H, Gregory, D, Sørensen, B, Alstrøm, T & Jensen, P 2001 'Monitoring methods in mires and meadows: five years of studies at Nydam Mose, Denmark', *in* Nixon, T (ed) *Preserving Archaeological Remains* in situ?, 91–7. London.

Murphy, P 2001 *Review of Wood and Macroscopic Wood Charcoal from Archaeological Sites in the West and East Midlands Regions and the East of England*. CFA Report 23/2001, Portsmouth.

Murphy, P & Trow, S 2001 'Coastal change and the historic environment', *in* Nixon, T (ed) *Preserving Archaeological Remains* in situ?, 209–18. London.

Nayling, N 1989 *The Archaeological Wood Survey: A Review of the Potential and Problems of Archaeological Wood*. AM Lab Report 62/89. London.

Peacock, E & Turner-Walker G 2001 'Building for the new millennium: monitoring for the first ten years?', *in* Nixon, T (ed) *Preserving Archaeological Remains* in situ?, 65–71. London.

PPG 16 1990 *Planning Policy Guidance: Archaeology and Planning*. London.

Richardson, S J & Smith, J 1977 'Peat wastage in the East Anglian Fens', *Journal of Soil Science* 28, 485–9.

Smith, W 2002 *A Review of Archaeological Wood Analyses in Southern England*. CFA Report 75/2002, Portsmouth.

Van de Noort, R, Fletcher, W, Thomas, G, Carstairs, I & Patrick, D 2001a *Monuments at Risk in England's Wetlands*. Draft V.2, Exeter.

Van de Noort, R, Chapman, H & Cheetham, J 2001b 'Science-based Conservation and Management in Wetland Archaeology: The Example of Sutton Common, UK', *in* Purdy, B A (ed) *Enduring Records. The Environmental and Cultural Heritage of Wetlands*, 277–86. Oxford.

Archaeological monitoring of (palaeo)wetlands in the Netherlands: from best practice to guidelines

ROBERT VAN HEERINGEN and LIESBETH THEUNISSEN

SUMMARY

The favourable preservation conditions in (palaeo)-wetlands in the Netherlands have allowed archaeological organic material and structural elements to remain intact in an oxygen-poor burial environment. They include unburnt botanical macro remains, bone, wood and wooden tools, fishing weirs and fish traps, vehicles, house structures and ritual 'dimensions'. Where this highly perishable part of the archaeological resource remains well preserved, it largely determines the archaeological importance of the former wetland areas in the Holocene delta.

The vulnerability of the organic portion of the archaeological resource also makes it suitable as a parameter for archaeological monitoring, eg for tracking any decline in quality over time. The 'soft' delta sediments can be sampled relatively simply, using non-destructive methods such as 'measuring rods' and corings.

In recent years, the National Service for Archaeological Heritage (ROB; from 2006 RACM, after a merger with the Netherlands Department for Conservation) has conducted a series of projects in waterlogged areas in the Netherlands focusing on the physical quality of sites. The archaeological monitoring projects form part of a well considered whole and are aimed not only at establishing the quality of the sites (baseline measurements), but also at developing methods and standards for relating quality to the preservation capacity of the burial environment. Such a tool would allow archaeologists to give better advice about the future prospects of sites and about mitigating measures for the stable preservation of sites and landscapes.

INTRODUCTION

The 11th WARP Conference on Wetland Archaeology was held at the Royal Museum of Scotland, Edinburgh, from 20 to 23 September 2005, hosted by the Scottish Wetland Archaeological Programme (SWAP) and the Society of Antiquaries of Scotland. One of the sessions was dedicated to wetland sites in their real landscapes. This was a topical issue, in view of the European Landscape Convention (ECL) adopted by the Council of Europe's Committee of Ministers in October 2002 (Fairclough et al 2002). In the United Kingdom this issue forms part of a longer debate on the insidious erosion of the organic archaeological resource (eg Coles 1995; Coles et al 2001; Van de Noort et al 2002; Oxford Archaeological Unit 2002; English Heritage 2003). In other European countries, too, management of the underground archaeological resource, long characterized by passive protection under monuments and historic buildings legislation and planning measures, has begun to move towards an active preservation policy.

Given the nature of the Dutch coastal zone – the delta of the rivers Rhine, Meuse and Scheldt – large parts of the Netherlands can be regarded as a unique resource for archaeology. One of the main problems nowadays is the erosion of this special archive. Most archaeological monuments in the Netherlands are situated in arable landscapes, and although legislation protects them from most threats, in many cases it permits these sites to be ploughed and drained (Van Dockum & Lauwerier 2004).

Under the forthcoming new Monuments and Historic Buildings Act (revised in accordance with the 1992 Valletta Convention), assessing the current state of archaeological monuments will be a key research theme for the ROB/RACM. Over the past five years, a number of quality assessment studies have been carried out in various parts of the (palaeo)wetlands in the western Netherlands. These studies have added a great deal to our knowledge of the condition of the archaeological resource and the processes affecting it. These results will be indispensable to the new strategy for protecting threatened sites under cultivation. There is an urgent need for an integrated and active conservation policy, otherwise we will be unable to pass on the remains of previous generations to future ones.

The assessment projects, conducted in the coastal area, can be seen as baseline measurements for a number of special man-made landscapes with a long occupation history. This kind of research is fairly new (Van Dockum *et al* 2001). In this contribution, we look at some of the results obtained so far.

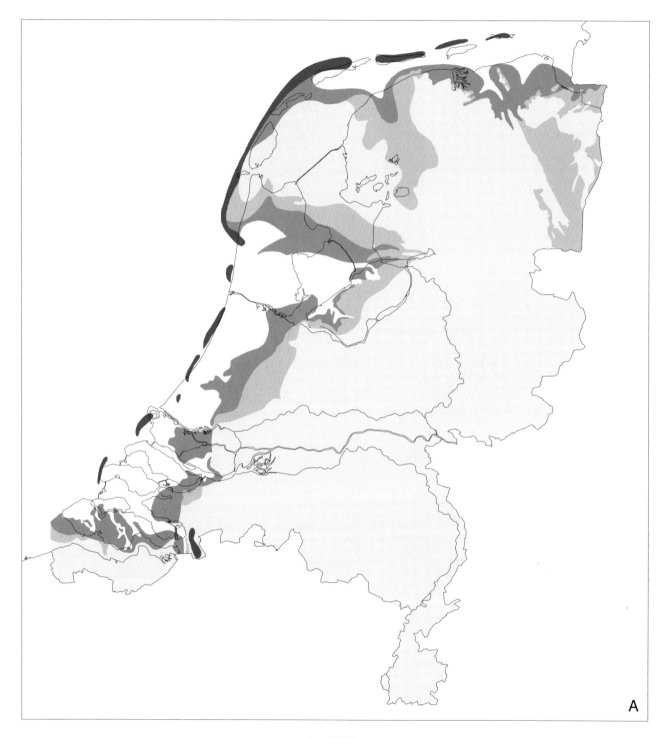

FIGURE 1A
Palaeogeographical maps of the low-lying (Holocene) deposits in the Netherlands. Legend: A. *c* 5000 BP, B. *c* 1000 BP.
1. beach barriers; 2. marine sediments; 3. river clay area; 4. peat. Adapted from Zagwijn 1986.

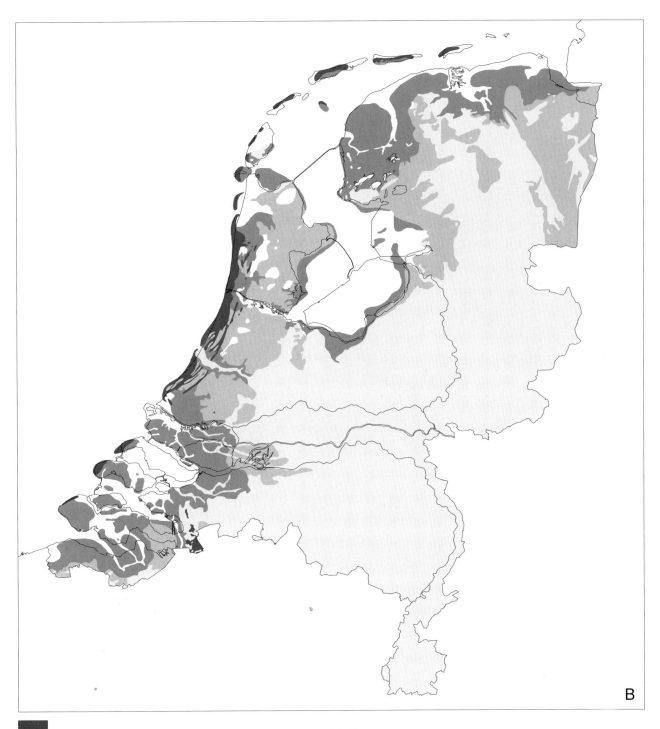

FIGURE 1B

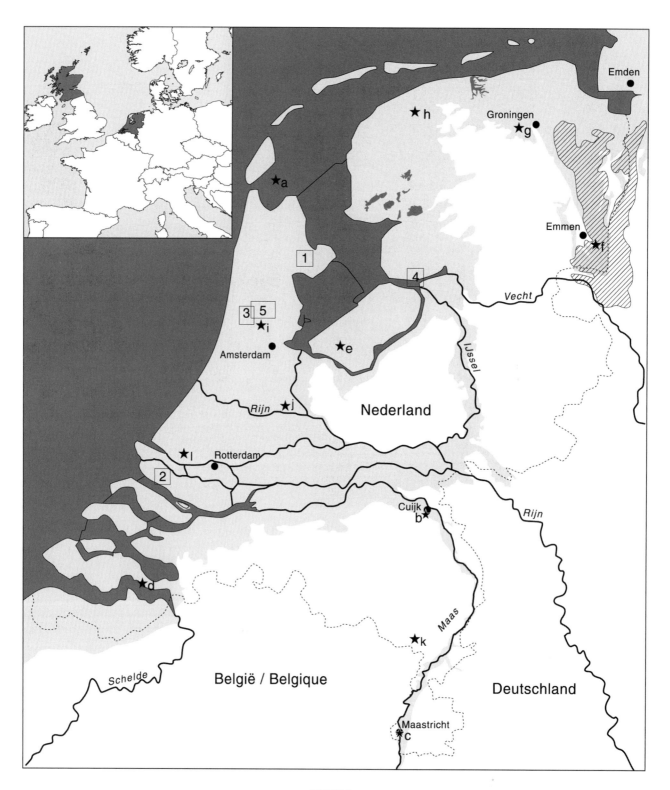

FIGURE 2

Overview map of the Netherlands showing places and sites mentioned in the text. The map has been radically simplified. For instance, only the upland peat area discussed in the text is shown: hatched = the former Bourtanger Moor; grey = area under NAP (Holocene); white = area above NAP (Pleistocene). Areas and sites: a. western Waddenzee; b. Cuijk; c. Maastricht; d. Valkenisse; e. IJsselmeerpolders; f. Nieuw-Dordrecht; g. Wierden en Waarden (Middag-Humsterland); h. Lancewad; i. Uitgeest; j. Utrecht-Leidsche Rijn; k. Stamproy; l. Vlaardingen. For project areas 1–5, see table 1.

THE NETHERLANDS AS A MAN-MADE COASTAL ZONE FROM PREHISTORIC TIMES ONWARDS

From a geological perspective, large parts of the Netherlands can be seen as a sedimentation basin. Two main river systems can be distinguished. The valley of the rivers Rhine and Meuse forms the southern system. The smaller northern system is associated with the river Vecht. In the west, near the North Sea, the Pleistocene surface is 25m below sea level. This basin slowly filled under the influence of sea-level rise following the last ice age (Holocene; from 10000 BC onwards). In around 6000 BC the sea reached the present coastline. From then on, coastal barriers were formed in a dynamic, ever-changing landscape (fig 1). From prehistoric times onwards, humans visited these landscapes and, in certain favourable circumstances, settled and made their living there. Around AD 1000 the natural landscape development process came to an end. The basin was filled with layers of sand and clay, and extensive peat areas were formed. Sea and land balanced each other. The thickness of the peat layer in central and western Holland was between 5 and 10m (see fig 10). The peat lands were colonized and brought under cultivation. This involved digging ditches and canals. The land lowered due to oxidation and settling. Dikes were constructed. Intensive land management converted the fenlands of the Low Countries into an artificial landscape below sea level, with a water regime controlled entirely by man (Van de Ven 1993).

DIFFERENT TYPES OF WET SITE

We can broadly distinguish four categories of wet or wetland site, depending on the natural and anthropogenic genesis of the landscape. The list below makes no pretence at being comprehensive, but the four categories are roughly as follows:

1. Sites in functional water bodies, such as rivers, lakes, mudflats, sea inlets (cut off or open) or the North Sea itself. Examples include sunken ships, remains of bridges and 'sunken' villages.
2. Archaeological remains in former water bodies. They include shipwrecks in poldered land and sacrificial sites in river courses that have silted up, or fens that have turned to peat.

3. Sites currently or previously situated in low-lying parts of the Pleistocene landscape, such as river and brook valleys, or in or beneath upland peat. Examples include the structures found in brook valleys (bridges, platforms) and wooden trackways.
4. Sites in former estuarine delta environments ((palaeo)wetlands). These are settlements (some of them raised) in salt marshes and on levees, gully ridges or high-lying peat areas.

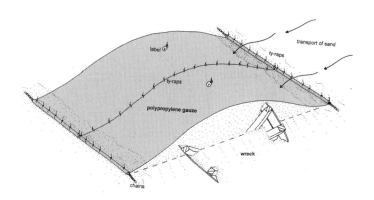

FIGURE 3
Method for physical protection of shipwrecks underwater. After Manders 2004.

1 SITES IN FUNCTIONING WATER BODIES

Most of the underwater sites are shipwrecks, found in both the North Sea and the Waddenzee, dynamic areas where wrecks are regularly uncovered and exposed to tidal flow. The management of this underwater heritage has been tackled systematically, at central government level, since around 1980. Attention was initially focused largely on legal instruments, research techniques, identification of wreck sites and the deposition environment (Maarleveld 1998). Recently, however, attention has shifted to the physical management and monitoring of the wrecks. A seventeenth-century Dutch East India Company ship was the first to be afforded provisional physical protection in 1987. Four ships are now physically protected in the western Waddenzee (fig 2a; Vos 2003). One of these ships, also a seventeenth-century merchant vessel, served as a test location for the further development of methods of physical protection and monitoring during the MoSS project (2000–04; EU Culture 2000; *www.mossproject.com*) (fig 3; Vos 2003; Vroom, Koppen 2003; Manders 2003, 2004; Mander, Lüth 2004; Palma 2004).

Bridge structures in rivers are another type of underwater site. Remains of Roman bridges in the river Maas at Cuijk and Maastricht have been investigated in recent years. It is clear that the water movements caused by high water levels and ships' propellers constitute a serious threat to these structures. An in-depth study of the physical quality and preservation potential of the remains of the Roman bridge in the Maas at Maastricht was published recently (fig 2b–c; Vos 2004).

In the province of Zeeland, in the south-western Netherlands, many villages fell victim to the sea in the Middle Ages as a result of flooding. They are known as 'sunken villages' (Kuipers 2004). Some of them lie outside the area protected by dikes, and are thus still subject to the influence of tidal movements. Rechannelling has caused the remains of these Late Medieval villages to become seriously eroded. In the face of such a threat, the former village of Valkenisse, in the Western Scheldt river, was surveyed and recorded between 1992 to 2003, and management measures were put in place (fig 2d). Two groynes were constructed to reduce the flow rate of the tidal water in the Scheldt and to cause siltation (fig 4).

2 ARCHAEOLOGICAL RELICS IN FORMER WATER BODIES

Sites in former water bodies are also a common category in the Netherlands, which has a long history of land reclamation. The shipwrecks in the IJsselmeer polders are an example of dry ship archaeology, where active preservation *in situ* is the key aim (fig 2e; Oosting 2003). Most of the 400-odd known wrecks have been excavated since the beginning of the major land reclamation operation in 1942. The wrecks still

FIGURE 4
Groynes protecting the sunken village of Valkenisse in the province of Zeeland.

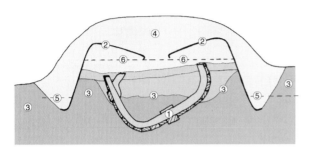

FIGURE 5
Method of protecting shipwrecks in the IJsselmeerpolders. Legend: 1. shipwreck; 2. plastic foil; 3. original sediment; 4. sediment deposited on wrecks after plastic foil applied; 5. groundwater level outside the 'plastic tub'; 6. groundwater level inside the 'plastic tub'.

present there are threatened by desiccation. A method has been developed whereby the water table at the wreck site is artificially raised to ensure that the wood remains permanently saturated (fig 5). In 2003, the quality of the timber in a sixteenth-century shipwreck 'packed' in this way was compared with that of a ship of the same age which had only been covered with a layer of earth. The timber in the first ship was found to be in better condition (Huisman & Oosting 2004; Huisman & Klaassen 2005).

Other, smaller-scale sites of this type include silted-up creeks and former lakes and fens in which peat has formed, which humans have used for ritual purposes since prehistory. For instance, the 'pingo-ruins' in Drenthe have yielded dozens of organic objects, unearthed during peat-cutting work in the eighteenth and nineteenth centuries. But former brooks and tributaries can also house unique finds, as evidenced by the discovery of an Early Iron Age canoe in the middle of a former branch of the Oer IJ estuary (fig 2i; fig 6) and of Roman ships in a silted-up branch of the Rhine at the Leidsche Rijn housing development near Utrecht (fig 2j; fig 7). Since such sites are usually discovered by chance (and are difficult to trace), it is virtually impossible to study their physical quality with a view to preservation *in situ*. However, it was decided that a Roman ship known as De Meern 4 should be preserved *in situ* and its burial environment monitored.

3 WET SITES IN LOW-LYING PARTS OF THE PLEISTOCENE LANDSCAPE

The wet, low-lying parts of the Pleistocene coversand landscape often contain a unique underground archaeological resource. Nature development projects in brook valleys, whereby channelled brooks are again

FIGURE 6
End of the canoe found at Uitgeest, showing ribs (2004). Photo © ROB/NISA.

FIGURE 7
Utrecht-Leidsche Rijn (2004). Preservation assessment of a Roman-period ship (De Meern 4). Above the water table, only the cargo (basalt blocks) has remained preserved.

allowed to meander, have uncovered some important finds in recent years, including bridge structures (fords), fishing weirs, ritual and regular dump sites, etc. These discoveries are spectacular because the fragile organic remains have been perfectly preserved under the water, cut off from oxygen. They are a major addition to the archaeology of the sandy areas of the Netherlands. However, management of these barely predictable sites is problematic. In order to come to grips with this problem, the ROB has launched a special research and conservation project (fig 2k; fig 8; Gerritsen & Rensink 2004; Rensink *et al* forthcoming).

Archaeological monuments in peat areas are another type of wet site found in the lower parts of the Pleistocene coversand landscape. One example is the former Bourtanger Moor in the north-eastern Netherlands. This once extended as far as Lower Saxony, on the other side of the German border, making it the largest contiguous area of upland peat in Europe. It contained countless prehistoric

and historic wooden trackways, among other things. Almost all the peat has now been cut, and just a few areas of the Bourtanger Moor are being maintained, with great difficulty. One example is the Oosterbos nature conservation area to the south-east of Emmen (fig 2f). Sites bordering on this include the 400m-long, legally protected remains of a Neolithic wooden trackway at Nieuw-Dordrecht, which would originally have been about a kilometre in length. The 13.4ha site in which the trackway is situated is no longer living upland peat, and is subject to desiccation. Fortunately, it is one of the few examples in the Netherlands where an active attempt is being made to improve the preservation conditions (fig 9; Mars *et al* 2004; Theunissen *et al* 2006).

SITES IN FORMER DELTA ENVIRONMENTS ((PALAEO)WETLANDS)

As a result of the dynamic genesis of large parts of the Netherlands as a delta and sedimentation basin, a number of types of (palaeo)wetland can be distinguished. The layered structure of the soil in the delta means that the remains of former habitants are embedded in layers of peat and clay, mostly situated just below the surface. Finds have included Single Grave Culture settlements in the former salt marsh landscape near Aartswoud (project area no 1 in fig 2), a creek landscape with Roman dwelling mounds near Krommenie (project area no 5 in fig 2) and a peat landscape with Iron Age farms to the west of Spijkenisse (project area no 2 in fig 2; fig 2l; fig 10).

Research in this type of landscape differs somewhat from that in the other three categories. Here, one is concerned with the site not merely as an archaeological feature, but more especially as an occupied location in a landscape setting. This landscape approach takes things onto a larger scale, including in terms of degradation. The (palaeo)wetlands are in rural areas, with dikes and a controlled water table (polder). They are continually subject to the influence of agricultural activities – ploughing up of occupation layers, desiccation as a result of the lowering of the water table. Over the past few years, initiatives have been launched to survey the archaeological resource, determine the present quality of the (palaeo)wetlands and improve the condition of the archaeological monuments situated there. Examples include the Wierden en Waarden project and the Lancewad project in the two northern provinces, Friesland and Groningen (fig 2g–h; Groenendijk 1997, 2005/2006; Volmer *et al* 2001). In the western Netherlands the ROB has

FIGURE 8
Investigation (2005) of the remains of a raised trackway, bordered by wooden posts, leading to a wooden bridge in the valley of the Tungelroysche Beek brook near Stramproy (Roman period). Photo © RAAP archaeological consultancy, Amsterdam.

FIGURE 9
Recording a redox profile by the wooden trackway at Nieuw-Dordrecht in June 2004, using equipment developed during the ROB Buried History At Risk Programme (Senter project 2003/2004, TSA02102: A Smit/A Beeker).

conducted a series of interrelated pilot projects involving quality assessment and monitoring (fig 2, 1–5). The growing insight gained from these projects is discussed in the next section.

ROB ARCHAEOLOGICAL MONITORING PROJECTS IN THE WESTERN NETHERLANDS (1999–2005)

An in-depth discussion of the series of pilot projects involving degradation processes, physical quality assessment and archaeological monitoring methods would be beyond the scope of this paper. We shall therefore restrict ourselves to three research themes and a literature reference

FIGURE 10
Vlaardingen-De Vergulde Hand (2005). Geological section of peat and clay layers showing wooden posts of a house (Iron Age).
Photo © Archaeological Service, municipality of Vlaardingen.

TABLE 1
ROB archaeological monitoring projects (1999–2005) in the western Netherlands.

No. 1
Province: Noord-Holland
Project area: West-Friesland and the Kop van Noord-Holland (de Gouw)
Project realization: 1999–2000
Number of sites: 15 (37)
Archaeological periods: Late Neolithic and Early Bronze Age
Literature: van Heeringen & Theunissen 2001a; 2001b

No. 2
Province: Zuid-Holland
Project area: Voorne-Putten
Project realization: 2000–2002
Number of sites: 18
Archaeological periods: Late Neolithic, Iron Age and Roman period
Literature: van Heeringen & Theunissen 2002

No. 3
Province: Noord-Holland
Project area: Broekpolder
Project realization: 2002–2003
Number of sites: 1
Archaeological periods: Early Bronze Age, Iron Age, Roman period and Middle Ages
Literature: van Heeringen, Smit & Theunissen 2004

No. 4
Province: Flevoland
Project area: Schokland
Project realization: 1999–2004
Number of sites: 3
Archaeological periods: Late Neolithic and Middle Ages
Literature: van Heeringen, Mauro & Smit 2004

No. 5
Province: Noord-Holland
Project area: Former Oer IJ estuary
Project realization: 2002–2005
Number of sites: 13
Archaeological periods: Iron Age and Roman period
Literature: Theunissen & van Heeringen 2006

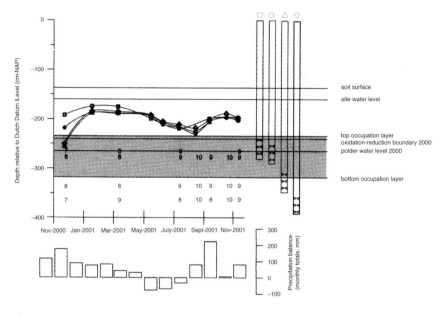

FIGURE 11

Groundwater level and redox measurements taken in 2000–2001 at the Neolithic Spijkenisse-Vriesland site in the province of Zuid-Holland. Symbols indicate recorded values, lines are interpolation. Numbers indicate redox quality at various depths, 1 (very poor quality) to 10 (very good quality).

was refined during the pilot project at Broekpolder, where the water table was measured automatically four times a day for a year using a diver, and the data transmitted to a website via a GSM modem (a so-called 'e-sense system') (see, *inter alia*, Smit 2004a, 2004b). Monitoring over a year allows the series of measurements obtained to be combined with precipitation and evaporation data to forecast the future water table after climate change, assuming a number of hydrological conditions are met.

MEASURING THE REDOX POTENTIAL

The redox potential is a measure of the total oxidizing capacity of the soil. Initially, measurements were taken in the groundwater. Later, however, for various reasons, it was decided to take measurements in the soil itself (see, *inter alia*, Smit 2002). Redox electrodes and the necessary equipment have now been developed specially for this purpose. At the moment, the preferred method is to take a series of measurements at different depths (redox profiles), to give an idea of the vertical variation in the oxidizing capacity of the soil over time. Work is also underway on digitally generated maps that can predict the archaeological preservation conditions in various hydrogeological units.

QUALITY OF BOTANICAL MACRO REMAINS AND BONE MATERIAL

Archaeobotanists and archaeozoologists have developed methods for describing the state of preservation of vulnerable organic material and the degradation processes to which it is subject (including Vernimmen 2002; Jans 2002, 2005; Jans *et al* 2004). They have devised preservation categories which allow different sites to be compared. The main thing is to consider the quality (information value) of the material compared to the quality after deposition. Human and natural formation processes play an important role here. Micromorphological analysis of thin sections can help produce an insight into these processes (Kooistra & Makaske 2002; Exaltus 2004). It might be that poor quality in a botanical sense is

presented in table 1 (see also the ROB website, *www.archis.nl*, for pdf reports). The projects have broadened our understanding of, among other things, the main parameters that allow us to view the present quality of archaeological sites (baseline measurement) in the context of the preservation potential of the burial environment. Table 2 shows the parameters examined in each project. Generally speaking, it has become clear that oxygen levels in the soil, and the partly related level of the water table, have a major impact on the quality of organic remains.

MEASURING THE GROUNDWATER LEVEL

The groundwater level, or water table, is one of the most important parameters affecting preservation conditions. Below the water table, the oxygen content of the burial environment is much lower and this slows down or halts the decay of organic remains (oxidation). Two years after the first cautious attempt at installing a dipwell and measuring the water table at three archaeological sites in De Gouw, in 1999, 13 sites on the former islands of Voorne and Putten were subjected to structural hydrological examination. The water table there was measured by hand every two months for a whole year. The method

TABLE 2
Recorded parameters during the monitoring projects 1–5 (see table 1).

Projects	1	2	3	4	5	SAM
coring						
soil profile description	x	x	x	x	x	x
oxidation–reduction boundary	x	x	x	x	x	x
occupation layer						
organic matter content	–	x	x	x	x	x
thin sections (micromorphology)	x	x	–	x	–	pm
archaeo–samples: artefacts	x	x	–	x	–	x
archaeo-samples: shell material	x	–	–	x	–	pm
archaeo-samples: botanical remains	x	x	x	x	x	x
archaeo-samples: pollen	–	–	–	–	x	pm
archaeo-samples: bone	x	x	–	x	–	pm
archaeo-samples: wood	–	–	–	–	–	pm
dipwell (water measurements)						
water level	x	x	x	x	x	x
redox potential	x	x	–	x	–	–
oxygen (O_2)	x	x	x	x	–	–
electrical conductivity (Ec)	x	x	x	x	–	–
acidity (pH)	x	x	x	x	–	x
nitrate, sulfate a.o.	–	x	x	–	–	–
chloride	x	x	–	x	–	pm
temperature	x	x	–	–	–	–
burial environment (soil measurements)						
redox potential (occupation layer)	–	–	–	–	–	–
redox potential profile	–	x	x	–	x	x
chalk presence	–	–	x	–	–	x
acidity (pH) profile	–	–	x	–	x	x
pH buffering capacity	–	–	–	–	–	pm
soil water measurements	–	–	–	–	–	pm
climate/meteorological data						
precipitation/(crop)evaporation	–	x	x	–	x	x
on surface integrity data						
(not further worked out here)	(–)	(–)	(–)	(–)	(–)	x

FIGURE 12
Aerial photograph of the Neolithic settlement (Single Grave Culture) near Aartswoud, situated in a creek landscape
with channels and levees. The occupation layer has been ploughed up and can be seen from the air and on the surface
as dark brown to black soil containing shell fragments.

the best we have available from a certain period in a certain area for monitoring purposes; and it is the monitoring potential that needs to be safeguarded for the future.

The results of the specialist studies to establish the quality of the archaeological material and the hydrological and pedological conditions were eventually combined, in line with a recently developed quality assessment system (Deeben *et al* 1999). An interdisciplinary synthesis of this kind gives us an insight into the most desirable preservation conditions and how to achieve them. An example is given in the graph in fig 11. Unfortunately, there are no conditions that provide the best guarantee for the preservation of all archaeological materials (Kars & Smit 2003). A tailor-made solution will therefore have to be found for each site, depending on the state of preservation and information value of the archaeological material and features present.

In many cases, the (palaeo)wetlands in the western Netherlands are currently close to the surface. One example is the Aartswoud Neolithic settlement site at De Gouw (fig 12). Not only is the water table there too low, the site is also subject to erosion as a result of annual ploughing. Optimum preservation would be possible if the site transformed into a meadow with a relatively high water table and ploughing was banned (figs 13–14).

PRESERVING FOR THE FUTURE

Many initiatives have been launched and projects completed in the field of quality assessment. An evaluation of all the project results mentioned above is due to commence shortly, to gather together all the knowledge acquired in this new field. The aim is to produce a standardized set of guidelines for archaeological monitoring studies (SAM, or Archaeological Monitoring Standard) in the course of 2006. The results will be presented in the form of a report at the third symposium on Preserving Archaeological Remains *In Situ* (PARIS3; Amsterdam, 7–9 December 2006). The guidelines will form part of the Dutch Archaeology Quality Standard (Kwaliteitsnorm Nederlandse Archeologie/ KNA), which is maintained under the supervision of the Infrastructure for Quality Assurance in Soil Management Foundation, which in Dutch abbreviates to SIKB (Stichting Infrastructuur Kwaliteitsborging Bodembeheer; *www.sikb.nl*).

The quality assessment studies performed in various parts of the (palaeo)wetlands in the western Netherlands have added a great deal to our knowledge of the condition of the archaeological resource and the processes affecting it. We are gradually developing a policy tool that should allow us to make better recommendations for the future about what quality we can expect to find and how sites should be managed and developed. These are the first steps on the road to the sustainable preservation *in situ* of the vulnerable wetlands in the Dutch coastal area. We still have a long way to go, but we have made a start.

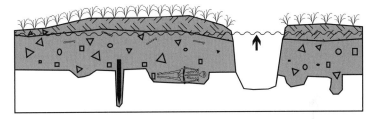

FIGURE 13

Preferred proactive policy: from insidious erosion (A) to sustainable preservation (B). Legend: A. during ploughing, the upper part of the dark shaded occupation layer is disturbed (ploughed up, and then incorporated into the topsoil); B. the site is managed in an archaeology-friendly way, arable land has been converted to meadow and the water level has been adjusted.

FIGURE 14

Active *in situ* preservation. Vlaardingen Culture settlement, Late Neolithic (Spijkenisse-Vriesland, Voorne-Putten, Zuid-Holland): One of the few protected monuments in the Netherlands where the water table is controlled. Photo © Ruurd Kok, Leiden.

REFERENCES

Coles, B 1995 *Wetland Management: A Survey for English Heritage*. Exeter (WARP Occasional Paper 9).

Coles, B, Olivier, A & Bull, D (eds) 2001 *The Heritage Management of Wetlands*. Exeter (also Europae Archaeologiae Consilium Occasional Paper 1 and WARP Occasional Paper 16).

Deeben, J, Groenewoudt, B J, Hallewar, D P & Willems, W J H 1999 'Proposals for a practical system of significance evaluation in archaeological heritage management', *European Journal of Archaeology*, 2, 177–200.

van Dockum, S G, Hallewas, D P, van Heeringen, R M & Jungerius, E 2001 'The Netherlands: Some Recent Initiatives', *in* Coles, B, Olivier, A & Bull, D (eds), 35–46.

van Dockum, S G & Lauwerier, R C G M 2004 'Archaeology in the Netherlands 2002: The national archaeology review and outlook', *European Journal of Archaeology*, 7, no. 2, 109–24 (the full report is available from *www.archis.nl*).

English Heritage 2003 *Ripping up History. Archaeology under the Plough*. Swindon (leaflet July 2003).

Exaltus, R P 2004 'Micromorphological analysis of thin sections', *in* van Heeringen, Mauro & Smit 2004 (eds), 59–71.

Fairclough, G, Rippon, S & Bull, D (eds) 2002 *Europe's Cultural Landscape: archaeologists and the management of change*. Brussels.

Gerritsen F, Rensink, E (eds) 2004 *Beekdallandschappen in archeologisch perspectief. Een kwestie van onderzoek en monumentenzorg*. Amersfoort (Nederlandse Archeologische Rapporten 28).

Groenendijk, H A 1997 'Terpen: a Shared Responsibility for a Shared Interest', *in* Willems, W J H, Kars H & Hallewas, D P (eds) *Archaeological Heritage Management in the Netherlands*. Amersfoort/Assen, 239–55.

Groenendijk, H A 2005 'Dorfwurt Ulrum (De Marne, Prov. Groningen). Eine Fundbergung aus 1995 als Anregung zur Benutzung hydrologischer Messdaten bei der Erhaltung von Großwurten', *Palaeohistoria* 47/48, 529–33.

van Heeringen, R M & Theunissen, E M 2001a 'Repeated water table lowering in the Dutch delta: a major challenge to the archaeological heritage management of pre- and protohistoric wetlands', *in* Purdy, B A (ed) *Enduring Records. The Environmental and Cultural Heritage of Wetlands*. Oxford, 271–6.

van Heeringen, R M & Theunissen, E M (eds) 2001b *Kwaliteitsbepalend onderzoek ten behoeve van duurzaam behoud van neolithische vindplaatsen in West-Friesland en de Kop van Noord-Holland*. Amersfoort (Nederlandse Archeologische Rapporten, 21).

van Heeringen, R M van & Theunissen, E M (eds) 2002 *Desiccation of the archaeological landscape of Voorne-Putten, the Netherlands*. Amersfoort (Nederlandse Archeologische Rapporten, 25).

van Heeringen, R M, Mauro, G & Smit, A 2004 (eds) *A pilot study on the monitoring of the physical quality of three archaeological sites at the UNESCO monument of Schokland, province of Flevoland, the Netherlands*. Amersfoort (Nederlandse Archeologische Rapporten, 26).

van Heeringen, R M, Smit, A & Theunissen, E M 2004 *Archaeology in the future. Baseline measurement of the physical quality of the archaeological monument at Broekpolder*, Amersfoort (Nederlandse Archeologische Rapporten, 27).

Huisman, D J & Oosting, R 2004 *Bacpoles sites 27 and 28; shipwrecks on lot Gz 80 and Kz 47 in Zuidelijk Flevoland (Southern Flevoland), The Netherlands*. Amersfoort (internal report; see also *www.bacpoles.nl*).

Huisman, D J & Klaassen, R K W M 2005 'Degradatie en bescherming van archeologisch hout', *Praktijkboek Instandhouding Monumenten* deel II–11 afl 23, 1–14.

Jans, M M E 2002 'Evaluation of the physical quality of bone material from Voorne-Putten', *in* van Heeringen & Theunissen (eds), 163–80.

Jans, M M E 2005 'Histological characterization of diagnetic alteration of archaeological bone', Amsterdam (thesis; Geoarchaeological and Bioarchaeological Studies 4).

Jans, M M E, Theunissen, E M, van Heeringen, R M, Smit, A & Kars, H 2004 'Monitoring the quality of archaeological bone *in situ*', *in* Lauwerier, R C G M & Plug, I (eds) *The Future from the Past. Archaeozoology in wildlife conservation and heritage management*. Oxford, 133–40.

Kars, H & Smit, A (eds) 2003 *Handleiding fysiek behoud archeologisch erfgoed: degradatiemechanismen in sporen en materialen. Monitoring van de conditie van het bodemarchief*. Amsterdam (Geoarchaeological & Bioarchaeological Studies 1).

Kooistra, M J & Makaske, B 2002 'Micromorphological research on site formation processes', *in* van Heeringen & Theunissen (eds), 115–36.

Kuipers, J J B 2004 (ed) *Sluimerend in slik. Verdronken dorpen en verdronken land in zuidwest Nederland*. Middelburg/Vlissingen.

Lauwerier, R C G M & Lotte, R (eds) 2002 *Archeologiebalans 2002*, Rijksdienst voor het Oudheidkundig Bodemonderzoek, Amersfoort.

Maarleveld, T 1998 *Archaeological heritage management in Dutch waters: exploratory studies*. Leiden (thesis).

Manders, M 2003 'Safeguarding: the physical protection of underwater sites', *MoSS Newsletter* 4, 18–20.

Manders, M 2004 'Combining monitoring, safeguarding and visualization to protect our maritime heritage', *MoSS Final Report*, Helsinki, 2004, 74–5.

Manders, M & Lüth, F 2004 'Safeguarding', *MoSS Final Report*, Helsinki, 63–73.

Mars, A, van der Sanden, W & Smeijers, S 2004 *Veenweg aan het infuus. Behoud in situ van de neolithische veenweg van Nieuw-Dordrecht (Drenthe)*. Assen.

NOaA in preparation: Nationale Onderzoeks Agenda Archeologie (Netherlands Research Agenda for Archaeology).

Van de Noort, R, Fletcher, W, Thomas, G, Carstairs, I & Patrick, D 2002 *Monuments at Risk in England's Wetlands*. Exeter (English Heritage).

Oosting, R 2003 'Monitoring and safeguarding wrecks in the IJsselmeerpolders', *MoSS Newsletter* no 4, 16–17.

Oxford Archaeology 2002 *The Management of Archaeological Sites in Arable Landscapes*. Oxford.

Palma, P 2004 'Final report for the monitoring theme of the MoSS project', *MoSS Final Report*, Helsinki, 8–48.

Rensink, E, Gerritsen, F & Roymans, J forthcoming *Archaeological heritage management, nature development and water management in the brook valleys of the southern Netherlands*, Berichten van de Rijksdienst voor het Oudheidkundig Bodemonderzoek.

Smit, A 2002 'The Preservation Potential of the Burial Environment', *in* van Heeringen & Theunissen (eds), 91–113.

Smit, A 2004a 'Monitoring the burial environment', *in* van Heeringen, Smit & Theunissen, 21–34.

Smit, A 2004b 'Monitoring the burial environment of terrestrial wet archaeological sites in the Netherlands', *Conservation and management of archaeological sites*, 6, 3–4, 325–32.

Theunissen, E M, Huisman, D J, Smit, A & van der Heijden, F 2006 *Kijkoperatie in het veen van de neolithische veenweg van Nieuw-Dordrecht*. Amersfoort (Rapportage Archeologische Monumentenzorg 130).

Theunissen, E M & van Heeringen, R M (eds) 2006 (in preparation) *Archaeological monitoring in the former Oer IJ estuary. A pilot study on the preservation capacity of a late prehistoric landscape*. Amersfoort (Nederlandse Archeologische Rapporten).

van Ven, G P (ed) 1993 *Man-made lowlands. History of water management and land reclamation in the Netherlands*. Utrecht.

Vernimmen, T J J 2002 'The Preservation of Botanical Remains at Archaeological Sites on Voorne-Putten', *in* van Heeringen & Theunissen (eds), 137–62.

Vollmer M, Guldberg, M, Maluck, M, van Marrewijk, D & Schlicksbier, G (eds) 2001 'Lancewad. Landscape and Cultural Heritage in the Wadden Sea Region – Project Report, Wilhelmshaven' (Wadden Sea Ecosystem 12; Common Wadden Sea Secretariat).

Vos, A D 2003 'The Burgzand-project and MoSS', *MoSS Newsletter* no. 4, 2003, 4–5.

Vos, A D 2004 *Resten van Romeinse bruggen in de Maas te Maastricht*. Amersfoort (Rapportage Archeologische Monumentenzorg 100).

Vroom, L & Koppen, F 2003 'On the use of the datalogger system WaterWatch 2681 at marine archaeological site BZN 10', *MoSS Newsletter* no 4, 12–13.

Willems, W J H & Brandt, R W 2004 *Dutch Archaeology Quality Standard*, Den Haag (version 2.1; also available from *www.archinsp.nl/publicaties/knauk/pdf*).

Zagwijn, W H 1986 *Nederland in het Holoceen*. Den Haag.

Temporality, cultural biography and seasonality: rethinking time in wetland archaeology

AIDAN O'SULLIVAN and ROBERT VAN DE NOORT

INTRODUCTION

Wetland archaeology is uniquely well placed to investigate questions of chronology, temporality, life-cycles and seasonality. Beyond the usual archaeological approaches to time (eg seriation, typology and stratigraphy), most wetland archaeological investigations have access to a ready supply of samples (ie wood, peat and organic deposits) for absolute scientific dating, particularly radiocarbon and dendrochronology. Indeed, the success of dendrochronology in revealing dynamic sequences of site and regional occupation, use and abandonment are well known. Investigating wetland archaeological sites, environmental archaeologists have used the evidence of insects, plant remains, seeds and even testate amoeba to establish the season, or months, of a site's occupation. Soil micromorphologists have carried out innovative studies of settlement deposits to reconstruct the chronological sequences of processes and events leading to their formation. In brief, wetland archaeology has become adept at calibrating past times.

However, while wetland archaeologists have traditionally made full use of scientific methods in the investigation of chronology, they have been more reluctant to rummage through the toolkits provided by theoretical archaeology, anthropology, ethnography and sociology when they think about temporal rhythms in the past. We might argue that wetland archaeologists have shown little interest in how past peoples experienced and understood time, and how this influenced the ways in which they dwelled in wetlands, or deposited objects in them. This is a pity, as wetland archaeologists often deal with the lives and works of peoples involved in landscapes that are uniquely dominated by distinctive temporal rhythms. We might imagine how a medieval fishing community attended to, and monitored, seasonal and monthly changes in ebb and flood tides, ducks, waders, geese and migratory salmon and eels.

Moving from our perception of time (inevitably western, chronological and dominated by scientific dating), we should consider then how people who inhabited and worked in wetlands understood time. Anthropologists suggest that small-scale communities think about time in quite diverse ways (Ingold 1993, 1995; Harris 2000; Bradley 2002; Lucas 2005, 62–4), variously understanding either it in terms of ancestors, historical pasts and past events (although this is rarely in western, chronological terms) or as a cyclical, unceasing rhythm of birth, life and death, with the recently dead returning to live again as newly-born children. Occasionally, people might have imagined time in terms of an eternal 'now', with all peoples, animals, places and times existing together at this time. This paper, developed from a chapter in our recent study (Van de Noort & O'Sullivan 2006, 89–118), provides some avenues for rethinking our approaches to time in wetland archaeology (fig 1).

TEMPORALITY OF THE LANDSCAPE: INTERPRETING 'LONG-TERM CONTINUITY AND CHANGE' IN WETLANDS

LONG-TERM PATTERNS AND SHORT-TERM EVENTS

Wetland archaeologists have thought often about their landscapes in terms of timelessness, persistence and endurance. For example, Coles & Hall (1998, 85), in writing about the people of the Fenlands of south-east England, referred to the 'stubbornness of the Fenlanders – resistant to change, adhering to the way of life that had its beginnings many centuries ago'. This encapsulates an idea that wetland communities are timeless, living outside the forces of historical, social and cultural change. It might be suggested that this is also a perspective similar to that of the influential French historical geographer, Fernand Braudel, who was convinced of the power of the *longue durée* or 'environmental time'; the deep, underlying economic structures that endure, unmoved by the ephemerality of politics and historical events (see Barrett 1989; Gosden 1994;

FIGURE 1

Reconstruction painting by Simon Dick of medieval fishing communities working on an estuarine fishtrap at Bunratty, Shannon estuary, Ireland (from O'Sullivan 2001, fig 68). Using archaeology, palaeoenvironmental studies, radiocarbon dating, dendrochronology, anthropology and sociology, wetland archaeologists can explore how past communities inhabited and 'dwelled' in temporal landscapes, working within evolving traditions and using their 'archaeological' knowledge of the historical past to shape their practices and social identities. We can also trace how wetland archaeological sites had cultural biographies, mirroring human lives from birth to death, with shifting historical, social and cultural meanings. Finally, we can reflect on how people's social lives resonated with temporal, seasonal rhythms of water, tides, plants, birds and fish, so that seasonality, economy and sociality should all be seen as inextricably linked.

Bintcliff 1996). This belief in the potency of long-term traditions and practices occasionally arises because wetland archaeologists do have a better chronological understanding of archaeological activities and environmental changes within their landscapes of enquiry; perhaps this also encourages a belief that similar activity across time speaks of social, cultural and economic continuity.

FROM PREHISTORIC TRACKWAYS TO EARLY MEDIEVAL PILGRIMS' TRAILS IN IRISH BOGS

Sometimes, this ability to reveal a long-term chronology of wetland activities can challenge models that are based on other, less well-dated evidence. In the Irish midlands bogs, the scanty distribution of early medieval settlements immediately around a monastic site on the bog island of Lemanaghan, Co Offaly seemed to confirm the traditional model that early monastic sites such as this were located in marginal, isolated locations (Stout 1997). However, archaeological survey and dating of wooden trackways in the wetlands demonstrated that the early medieval Lemanaghan monastic site (founded in the sixth century AD) was actually located on a long-term node of communications that had its origins in later prehistory, showing evidence for trackway building in the Middle Bronze Age, Iron Age and Early Middle Ages. Instead of being placed in a remote, ascetic location, the early medieval monastery may well have been cannily placed on a well travelled routeway, perhaps to serve as a hostel for travellers moving through the midlands bogs (McDermott 1998; O'Carroll 2001; Stanley 2003).

NEOLITHIC AND BRONZE AGE TRACKWAYS THROUGH TIME IN THE SOMERSET LEVELS

However, this general picture of long-term landscape persistence and continuity often masks the reality that human activities in wetlands may only be sporadic, occasional and interrupted by centuries of inactivity. A traditional map of 'Neolithic' or 'Bronze Age' landscapes will generally show tens or hundreds of 'dots', each representing individual settlements, burials and findspots from across several centuries. Similarly, a single map of Neolithic or Bronze Age trackways in the Somerset Levels wetlands would also show many dots and lines connecting drylands and islands and would seem to suggest long-term, continuous travel. However, Coles & Coles' critical review (1992) of the radiocarbon dating evidence for all the Neolithic and Bronze Age wooden trackways there demonstrated that in each hundred-year period, there may have been only one or two trackways. This highly visible – it is likely that a survey of wetland sites may represent a better 'cull' of all archaeological activity – and well dated archaeological evidence indicated that instead of continuous activity and stability, there were merely a few occasions of trackway construction and use (each lasting no more than a decade or so) across many centuries in the wetlands. Indeed, it might be argued that in reality we are witnessing short-term human 'decisions and events' rather than long-term patterns.

MEDIEVAL FISHTRAPS ON ESTUARIES:
RECONSTRUCTING PAST COMMUNITY KNOWLEDGE
OF THE PAST

So, we could start to think about wetland landscapes not only in terms of 'long-term continuity' but also in the context of people's decisions, the agency of the past and what we think people are doing when they work in dynamic environments. In recent years, wetland archaeologists have been able to trace surprising patterns in fishtrap use and re-use in estuarine landscapes. On the Shannon estuary (O'Sullivan 2001, 2003a, 2003b, 2005), Strangford Lough (McErlean & O'Sullivan 2002), the Severn estuary (Godbold & Turner 1994; Nayling 1997; Turner 2002) and on the Essex estuaries (Gilman 1998; Strachan 1998; O'Sullivan 2003b, 452–4), there is often significant archaeological evidence for striking continuities in location, form and character of the fishtraps.

However, wooden fishtraps are badly exposed to damage from erosion and waves and would have been repaired and rebuilt frequently. On the Blackwater estuary, Essex, there is plenty of evidence for rebuilding of fisheries over centuries, but in interesting ways (Gilman 1998; Strachan 1998; O'Sullivan 2003b, 452–4). At Collins Creek, a complex of five V-shaped fishtraps had been built on a mud island, enclosing a huge expanse of mudflats, 3km by 700m. However, these were not contemporary sites, as statistical analysis of the seemingly closely spaced radiocarbon dates indicated construction, 'piece-meal repair, minor modification and radical alteration' from the mid-seventh century to the beginning of the tenth century AD (Hall & Clarke 2000; O'Sullivan 2003b, 452–3).

On the Severn estuary, there is also interesting dating evidence for stylistic change across a fairly short period of time. At Magor Pill, at least seven V-shaped fishtraps (with densely packed post fences, 15m long, leading to baskets) were used within a small area during the twelfth century AD. Nayling's detailed dendrochronological studies (1999) indicated that some were in use about AD 1120, while a second phase of fishing began about AD 1150, almost 30 years later (a significant gap for people whose average lifespan was about 35–40 years). This actually may indicate that the first structures had been out of use, before people came back and re-built what must have been quite dilapidated structures that had been abandoned for a generation. By about AD 1170, there was a third phase of the fishery at Magor Pill, involving a different type of fishtrap that used long straight fences, along which baskets were placed at intervals (Nayling 1997, 1999).

Indeed, we might envisage that medieval fishtraps survived effectively as archaeological sites of rotten wooden posts within the early Middle Ages, actively shaping how later fishing communities lived and worked in these estuarine landscapes. Although medieval fishing communities worked within evolving traditions, the pre-existing fishtraps might have enabled or perhaps even encouraged a continuity with the past (O'Sullivan 2003b). Using theoretical jargon, we might say that material culture in these landscapes was active, structuring people's lives, identities and understanding of their worlds.

CULTURAL BIOGRAPHIES OF WETLAND DWELLINGS AND OBJECTS

THINKING ABOUT THE BIOGRAPHIES OF PLACES AND OBJECTS

Wetland archaeologists are well used to exploring the life-cycles of archaeological sites and objects. Archaeological study of a wooden bucket will usually cover such topics as the sourcing and procurement of raw materials; the production of the object through conversion, hewing and carving, followed by its use, damage, repair and ultimately its abandonment in wetlands. This approach is essentially a functionalist approach to life-cycles or use-lives of objects – exploring their changing role and forms across time with a particular emphasis on their appearance, manufacture and function. It is somewhat similar to the processualist approaches adopted to artefact production, exploring the role of commodities within production and exchange systems. Essentially though, the processual approach to object biographies envisages objects as inert, passive things to which things happen and things are done (Gosden & Marshall 1999, 169). Recent post-processual or interpretative approaches to material culture have adopted the concept of the cultural biography. This proposes that between the moment that an object is produced to the moment that it is discarded or forgotten, it goes through several phases of specific social and cultural meaning. In each phase, the function, role, status and perception of an object may change, and through use and handling by different people it acquires its own life-history, biography and social meaning.

Cultural biographical approaches can be made to both dwellings and objects. Kopytoff's anthropological description (1986, 67) of the biographies of huts among the Suku people of Zaire described how a hut initially shelters a couple or a mother and child. After some years, it may serve as a guesthouse for visitors, then as a kitchen until finally it descends to the role of a chicken coop, before its collapse. However, it is not possible for the biography to go in the other direction; for a kitchen or chicken coop to be turned into a dwelling. In recent years, archaeological studies of Neolithic houses in south-east Europe (Tringham 1991, 1995), Bronze Age houses in southern Britain (Brück 1999) and Iron Age houses and farmsteads in the Netherlands (Gerritsen 1999, 2003) have also suggested that prehistoric dwellings had biographies and life-cycles that were practically and metaphorically linked to the lives of the people, their cultural ideas, as well as the specifics of their actual social and material circumstances. Indeed, Gerritsen (2003, 38) states that wetland archaeological sites with their 'detailed evidence about successive phases of use, reconstruction and abandonment' may produce the best evidence to support the writing of a 'truly detailed archaeological biography'.

BUILDING, OCCUPYING AND ABANDONING AN EARLY MEDIEVAL CRANNOG AT BUISTON, AYRSHIRE, SCOTLAND

Wetland archaeological excavations can also enable a closer understanding of both the chronology and environmental conditions on a site – the 'muck of life' as it were. Archaeological excavations, palaeoenvironmental studies and dendrochronological dating of a crannog at Buiston, Ayrshire in south-west Scotland provide a striking example of this (Barber & Crone 1993; Crone 2000). The Buiston early medieval crannog was a small *packwerk* site, of a mound of timber, brushwood and stone dumped onto the lakebed. On this were placed layers of brushwood and turves taken from local agricultural slopes. The site was enclosed within several phases of palisades and was rebuilt and resurfaced on a number of occasions, typically extending it to an oval mound, 17m across. Early medieval Buiston, during the sixth to the seventh century AD, was the island dwelling of a fairly self-sufficient and prosperous community, with evidence for the production and use of wooden and leather objects, herding of cattle for dairying and meat, and the tending and consumption of sheep, pig and geese. They ate a range of cultivated foodstuffs, including barley, oats and linseed, as well as an array of wild foods; hazelnuts, red deer and roe deer.

Palaeoenvironmental studies reveal to a striking extent that, on Buiston crannog, people constantly struggled and coped with mucky, damp conditions, perpetual flood waters, structural collapse and buzzing flies. Insect studies revealed that the site saw only periodic or seasonal occupation, but indicated that people may have endured great swarms of house-flies that thrived in the rotting organic material lying on the floor (also indicated by beetles who inhabit rotting vegetation). Dendrochronological studies were also revealing (and, indeed, also challenging to the radiocarbon evidence that seemed to imply a long period of occupation at Buiston, from the second to the seventh century AD). The site's history of occupation and abandonment was dynamic and compressed into a relatively brief period, between AD 589–630.

The origins of the crannog lay in the Roman period, in the first to second century AD, when it was briefly occupied, abandoned and flooded over. For the next 300 years, the site lay quiet. Then, at the end of the sixth century AD, people returned to it to build an island dwelling, perhaps representing the deliberate re-activation of an antique site (see Crone 1993; Henderson 1998; O'Sullivan 1998; Fredegren 2003 for discussion of 'chronology' of crannogs).

The rebirth of the site comes then in the early medieval phases of occupation beginning in the late sixth century AD. In AD 589 (Phase III), House A was constructed and a palisade erected around the site. This house was represented only by an arc of posts from a roundhouse 5.6m in diameter (25 square metres in floor space). It was occupied for five years. Within that time, the hearth and floor were replaced three times, something like every one to two years. The site may also have been flooded on one occasion during that time also. In fact, insect studies (see below) indicate that there were such swarms of flies in House A that living conditions were sufficiently unpleasant to warrant its abandonment (as indeed happened).

The site matured and increased in scale quickly. In AD 594 (Phase IV), the entire crannog was levelled and rebuilt, extending its surface further towards the northwest. House B, a roundhouse 8m in diameter, the largest house to be used on the dwelling (with a floor area of 50sq m), was constructed of a double wall of post-and-wattle, with internal partitions. This transformation in scale would usually be taken to represent some change in the social status of the site's inhabitants or that the household group itself had grown in size (as younger family members moved in with their grandparents). House B was used as a dwelling for the next 20 years, during which time the hearth and floor were replaced four times, every five years or so, the last time being in AD 609. It is tempting to suggest that people were returning to the crannog and refurbishing it after winter floods and storms. In AD 608, the crannog dwellers had to reconstruct the palisade, after slumping and structural collapse, as waterlogged deposits settled into position and slid outwards.

The site moves towards its 'death' at the end of the next decade. In AD 620, the site's inhabitants replaced the palisade with something more substantial and a timber ringbeam palisade was constructed, to be followed by an arc of alder stakes in AD 630. However, the site was moving towards the final phases of its occupation and was certainly abandoned by AD 650. Explanations for all this structural change can of course be sought in environmental conditions, but they must also be explained by social and cultural factors; the historical changes in wealth, health and family dynamics that are specific to every household group. We also recognize here the constant choices that people had to make in creating, sustaining, transforming and ultimately abandoning a settlement over a period of a few generations.

A CULTURAL BIOGRAPHY OF AN IRON AGE VESSEL FROM TOAR BOG, IRELAND

It should be emphasized that the cultural biographical approach can be used even if precise scientific dating is not available. It is widely known that during the Iron Age people deposited human bodies, weaponry, tools and cauldrons into waterlogged places, for various cultural, ideological and ritual reasons (Raftery 1994). This understanding, as well as surviving evidence on the object itself, provides the context for interpreting the cultural biography of an Iron Age wooden trough that was recently recovered from Toar Bog, Co Westmeath, in the Irish midlands (Murray 2000; Moore *et al* 2003, 134). This marvellous Iron Age object (probably dating from the last few centuries BC) was a large, carved alder-wood trough, rectilinear in shape (1.3m in length, 60cm in width), with projecting handles at the end. The object itself and its treatment in the past provides insights into how it accumulated different meanings and values and how these changed across time.

In conception and design, this Iron Age vessel was clearly always intended to be something special. Firstly, it was carved from an unusually thick and mature alder tree (which was *c* 54 years age) suggesting that it was intended to be impressively and uniquely large. It was a work of several people who came together in its production, as toolmark analysis showed that it was carved using five axes and at least one gouge. The clarity of the toolmarks also show that the timber was green and unseasoned. It might be thought that they were hurriedly preparing an item intended for use in an upcoming event, as the unseasoned character of the wood caused a problem when a worrying split developed in the wood during the last few hours of its manufacture. Close to the handle, a very fine crack started to develop outwards from the heartwood, but its carvers ingeniously used four tiny, cleverly-spaced wooden wedges to staple this crack together, to prevent it shearing along the wood grain. This repair definitely occurred during the manufacturing phase, as subsequent carving deliberately reduced their appearance to near invisibility.

During the early years (months?) of the life of the vessel, it was probably used for some high-status activity, perhaps bathing, feasting or the display and consumption of fine foods. This is suggested by the fact that the toolmarks on its outer surface are pristine and unblurred, suggesting it was not moved around much or roughly handled. As a unique and cherished item, it is conceivable that the vessel was produced for some special event, perhaps a ritual meal associated with a marriage, or an inauguration ceremony or other significant rite of passage; early Irish kings reputedly bathed in horses' blood upon their inauguration. Indeed, bathing is a likely function as early mythological sources place great store on washing, bathing and the body itself in early Irish society.

As the Iron Age trough matured and aged, it was to shift in meaning again. After a time – unlikely to have been long – a second crack appeared along the edge of the vessel where its narrow sides reduced its strength. Perhaps this occurred as the wood was alternately wet and dried, which is something that alder wood tolerates poorly (for all its suitability of holding food and drink). This new crack was also repaired using small, carved ash-wood panels on the inner and outer surface, secured by slight wooden ties through perforations in the vessel's sides. But it seems that this crack somehow changed the meaning of the object, perhaps spoiling or tainting it in some way. For a time, it was to be employed in a more domestic or everyday context, such as salting, curing, tanning or dyeing. This is suggested by evidence for fire-scorching along the top edge, which definitely occurred after the second repair, implying that the trough was used in cooking or the heating of water; small stone chips found in the vessel might suggest the use of hot-stone technology for heating water, perhaps for washing and bathing.

The death of the vessel soon followed. By this time, the perception and social meaning of the vessel had changed once more – leading to its structured deposition in a bog pool. At the end of its life – or perhaps the life of the person most associated with it – people used a series of withy ropes, some of which were found still wrapped around the vessel, to carry the heavy object out into the bog, where environmental evidence suggests that they placed it in waterlogged, reedy conditions; plant macrofossil and beetle studies indicates a bog pool of stagnant water. They propped it upright, using long, vertical pegs driven into the peat, and also pinned it down by using a forked hazel branch – a wooden vessel would tend to float in water,

especially when dry and seasoned. Radiocarbon dating of the branch indicates that this Iron Age vessel was placed in the bog about 197 BC–AD 68. It is also interesting how closely the treatment of the Iron Age trough echoes that meted out to bog bodies recently discovered in the region. An Iron Age body recently found in Croghan Bog, Co Offaly (6km to the south-east) was of a high-status, well-fed individual who was executed and also pinned into position using hazel withies (Ahlstrom 2006). Indeed, the potential metaphorical links between the biographies of Iron Age wooden vessels and human bodies (food consumption, washing and bathing, the body as a container of fluids) are obvious and an anthropological perspective might suggest that sometimes objects are so deeply connected with people that they too must die.

SEASONALITY AND SOCIALITY: OTHER WAYS OF THINKING ABOUT RHYTHMS OF WETLAND LIFE

ANTHROPOLOGICAL PERSPECTIVES ON THE PERCEPTION AND EXPERIENCE OF SEASONAL RHYTHMS

In tracing cultural biographies of wetland dwellings, we should also reflect on how people in the past may have perceived the passage of shorter periods of time – seasons in particular. Wetland archaeologists have long been interested in seasonality and often explain their sites in terms of the perceived past use and exploitation of economic resources that vary from winter to summer, ie reeds, wood, birds, game, seasonal grazing, wild plant foods etc. Ethnographic sources do indicate that small-scale communities perceived and understood time in terms of seasonal rhythms and cycles. This may have been a calendrical knowledge, involving the recognition of the changing phases of the moon, the changing location of constellations in the starlit sky and the changes in weather, light and darkness, and springs and neaps tides that are governed by these celestial movements. However, people also monitored and 'attended to' seasonal changes in the environment around them; the rise and fall of lacustrine and riverine water levels, bird and fish migrations, the fertility and movement of animals, the cyclical growth and decay of plant life and so forth. Practices, lifeways and even our own bodies 'resonate' with such seasonal rhythms (Ingold 1993, 65; Harris 1998, 2000, 126; O'Sullivan 2005). This suggests that it is time to move beyond explanations that focus only on economic and subsistence activities and start to think about how past people's social identities, relationships and beliefs were also connected to seasonality.

ETHNOGRAPHIC STUDIES OF SEASONALITY AND SOCIALITY AMONGST RIVERINE COMMUNITIES IN THE AMAZONIAN WETLANDS

Harris's recent anthropological study (2000) of a community of *caboclo* fisherpeople who live in the village of Parú, on the banks of the River Amazon, Brazil, provides some inspiring insights. On the banks of the river, seasonality is intrinsic to the practices and social relationships of the people who dwell there; the community's social relationships have a distinctly rhythmic character that 'resonate' with changes in the seasons (Harris 1998, 2000, 125–41). Indeed, seasonality is the 'frame of life' within which people's social lives are performed. Harris's emphasis on sociality fits with recent Amazonian anthropological theory, where scholars have moved from western-oriented, cultural, ecological and subsistence economic approaches to ideas that explore indigenous collective identities and people's own emphases on 'conviviality' – their beliefs that what is important is how people live together communally (Overing & Passes 2000).

For the wetland dwelling people of Parú, there are distinct social and aesthetic differences between the 'wet season' and the 'dry season'. People find the wet season (December–June) difficult; they feel 'cold', their 'being-in-the-world' makes them feel miserable and wretched. Fish are difficult to catch, crops are impossible to cultivate, so they worry about food shortages and they observe how the flood destroys all their labours (Harris 1998, 2000). On a daily basis, people are isolated by the floods within their own houses, so they live at home, doing odd jobs, sewing, mending, teaching children. It is a time of inner family life, introversion, boredom – people swinging in their hammocks, watching the floodwaters listlessly through the floorboards or occasionally visiting close neighbours by boat.

As the seasons change, the 'dry season' comes on in June, the flood waters retreat again and the land re-appears, richly fertilized by the river's muds. People move out from their houses, wandering around the village, working and chatting together, making plans for the best months of the dry season. In reality, people's social lives are transformed. Men get away from the house, hunt in the forest, fish from boats with nets, sleep in huts by the river and gather together spontaneously to work in a relaxed way on their gardens. Women also move out into the village, connecting with their friends, helping each other with domestic work and children. Men and women use every opportunity to have a party, to go and visit distant kin. They build temporary 'specialist' huts without fireplaces by the rivers and lakes, so they can remain close to good fishing grounds without the need to return to their villages. People regard this as a 'beautiful time', a joyful time of plentiful food and partying, as well as courting and sex in the forest for unmarried couples. In other words, it is people's social and gender relations that come to the fore, not their economic activities, and all resonate with the rhythms of seasonal and environmental changes (Harris 2000, 140–1).

ETHNOGRAPHIES OF SEASONALITY AND SOCIALITY AMONGST CATTLE-HERDERS IN MEDIEVAL IRELAND AND WALES

It may be interesting to explore these ideas in the context of prehistoric dwellings in wetlands. Recent wetland archaeological projects on the estuaries of Britain and Ireland have uncovered much evidence for what seem to be Bronze Age and Iron Age houses, trackways and platforms in environmental contexts that were originally saltmarshes, raised bogs and fens (see O'Sullivan 2001, 128–33 for a review). In general, it is thought that these were houses and structures used by people herding cattle and sheep on estuarine marshes during spring and summer. There is also evidence for Bronze Age and Iron Age structures and features (eg spreads of burnt stone, charcoal and animal bone, metalwork and skulls) that suggests that some ritual activities were also carried out in these liminal spaces between land and water.

However, if we accept that it was people who were grazing cattle, hunting, trapping and 'inhabiting' the estuarine wetlands, we need to take a social as well as an economic perspective. Closer to home, we find that seasonality and sociality can also be found amongst the transhumance cattle-herders of medieval Ireland and Wales. In the cattle-obsessed culture of early medieval Ireland, from May to October, it was young women who went with the herds to the *macha samraid* – the summer milking place located in the mountains or in the marshlands – and there they tended the animals and engaged in butter making (Ó Corráin 1972, 54; Patterson 1994, 90–1; Kelly 1997, 450). Indeed, in early Irish law, distinctions were made between the home farm (*senbaile*) and the summer milking place (*áirge*). Interestingly, there is a similar distinction in medieval Welsh between the winter-dwelling (*hendref*) and the summer-house (*hafoty*) (Kelly 1997, 44). In late medieval Ireland, young women also drove the cattle herds to the summer pastures in the mountains and marshlands (Lucas 1989, 58–67). There they lived in booley huts from May to November, milking the cows and making cheeses that children would carry the short distance back down to the lowland settlements (often located only a few miles below the hills). Young men would sometimes visit the booley site and the useful social distance that these places had from the normal world enabled young courting couples to try out various conjugal relationships before the winter marrying season (Patterson 1994).

INTERPRETING SEASONALITY, SOCIAL IDENTITY AND THE IRON AGE MARSHLAND HOUSES AT GOLDCLIFF, SEVERN ESTUARY

Can we trace evidence for seasonality and sociality in Bronze Age and Iron Age marshland dwellings? Probably the best archaeological evidence we have comes from the Iron Age houses at Goldcliff West, on the Welsh shore of the Severn estuary. These buildings were large rectangular structures originally constructed on raised hummocks in a raised bog or on fen-peats at the edge of an estuary. Dendrochronological and radiocarbon dates suggest their construction and use in the fifth to the early third century BC (Bell 1993a, 1993b, 1999; Bell *et al* 2000). They were quite substantial (5–8m in length, by 4–6m in width), with walls constructed of alder roundwood and oak planking, entrances situated at the ends, and internal or axial posts suggest that they were roofed. There was occasional evidence for roundwood, reeds or straw as floors. Beetle and insect studies indicated the presence of decaying vegetation, animal dung and reeds around the houses. Palaeoenvironmental analyses suggest that the Iron Age Goldcliff houses were used during periods of increased marine transgression, when marine flooding altered the vegetation of the raised bogs, making them good seasonal grazing grounds.

Hundreds of cattle hoof prints identified in the clays of the channels around the structures clearly indicated that the animals gathered around the structures, perhaps cooling their heels in the water. Lice found in the palaeochannels also indicated the presence of cattle and the identification of fleas that prey on humans suggested that both people and cattle were sheltering inside these structures – a common feature of historical bothy huts in western Ireland (where animals provided useful warmth) (Bell & Neumann 1996, 1997, 1998; Bell 1999). The few finds (wooden withy ties and bucket fragments) recovered from the entrances or in the palaeochannels around the Goldcliff buildings suggested that people didn't bring other objects with them and both could be associated with hobbling and milking of cattle. Other structures at Goldcliff included Iron Age trackways that run for up to a hundred metres and directly approach these buildings, either from the estuary channel or bedrock islands in the levels. These may well have been built and used in the winter – tree-ring studies suggested winter cutting – to enable activities in the marshes, such as trapping ducks and geese, although, of course, this wood could have been stockpiled for use in the spring (Bell 2003, 13).

The absence of hearths, charcoal and ash within the Goldcliff houses suggest that these sites were seasonally occupied and not permanent domestic habitations. Moreover, the Goldcliff houses seem to have been used episodically, over several years (Bell 1999). Dendrochronological studies suggest that Goldcliff Buildings 1 and 2 were rebuilt over multiple phases of activity over some time, perhaps up to 17 years. Goldcliff 6 probably had a shorter life. Beetle analyses and lithological studies of lenses of clay between the occupation horizons also suggest that this episodic use was interspersed by periods of flooding under brackish water. Bell (1999, 23) concludes from the presence of neonatal calf bone – calves are typically born in the spring months – that occupation was between May and June, when tides were lowest and the bogs would not have been so regularly inundated by the monthly high spring tides.

Where did these people come from? Several substantial Iron Age hillforts dominate the Gwent Levels on the dryland hills to the north and there are also smaller Iron Age enclosed and unenclosed settlements at the edge of the levels. However, Bell (2003, 12) had noted that the Goldcliff Iron Age buildings are 'odd' in several ways. Other Iron Age houses are usually circular, whereas the Goldcliff buildings are rectangular. Other Iron Age roundhouse entrances usually face towards the rising sun, but at Goldcliff the entrances are generally oriented north-west. Bell (2003, 12) suggests that the architectural 'oddness' of these structures, the surprising lack of pottery – and indeed other finds – indicate that these were wetland communities of 'an impoverished material culture and distinctive identity from those occupying the surrounding hillforts and upland'.

SOCIAL AND AESTHETIC ASPECTS OF MARSHLAND GRAZING

The idea of a distinctively different Iron Age wetland community is certainly valid, especially if we consider that these might have been cattle-herders of low social status, responsible for activities out at the 'edge' of the Iron Age landscape. However, even if we accept that Iron Age social identity may have been linked to role and responsibility (reminding us that people's identities are not merely constructed in collective, ethnic or class terms, but also through what they did and the time of the year they did it), it is possible that the materiality of Goldcliff is expressing ideas related to time, rather than social status. Summer dwellings amongst cattle-herders are often different from the 'normal' winter dwelling. It is possible that the Goldcliff Iron Age houses are architecturally distinctive because of when they were used and that they are expressing notions of social identity, lifeways and time – precisely because they are summer dwellings. It is certainly evident that people came out here in spring and summer, stayed for a while and left again and that they did this over a period of years. It is interesting that at Goldcliff there are subtle architectural and technological differences between each building, suggesting that each of them belonged to different social groups who repaired them every year. Bell (2003) also notes that anthropological studies of cattle transhumance groups reveal that each household or extended social group is responsible for the maintenance of its own hut at the summer grazing places.

How about the social and aesthetic aspects of these seasonal economic practices? Summer saltmarshes are pleasant places to be. We might imagine that people did enjoy the sunny months out on the marshes, freed from the winter *ennui* of dryland life in a dark, smoky Iron Age roundhouse. Indeed, it seems likely that these were women and children, and that they were occasionally joined by young men. So, a social interpretation of the Iron Age houses at Goldcliff might be that their distinctive architecture is expressing specific social and gender relationships that were embedded in or intrinsic to the seasonal rhythms of economic activity in the estuarine wetlands. Obviously we cannot prove this, but it provides a social explanation that fits well with our understanding of Iron Age communities, of seasonal cattle-herders and how people dwell amongst ever changing wetlands.

CONCLUSIONS

In conclusion, amongst wetland archaeology's greatest strengths has been its ability to reveal the 'muck of life', the dirt underneath the fingernails of 'energetic commoners', the physical reality and materiality of past people's existence. We also suggest that wetland archaeology encourages us to think in different ways about time, chronology and past people's perception and experience of it. Indeed, we suggest that all archaeologists interested in the temporal and seasonal rhythms of dwelling, the phenomena of remembering and forgetting, and cultural biographies of place and objects should look again at the astonishingly detailed narratives that it enables.

REFERENCES

Ahlstrom, D 2006 'Bog find calls for new view of our Iron Age ancestors'. *The Irish Times*, January 7, 2006.

Barber, J W & Crone, B A 1993 'Crannogs; a diminishing resource? A survey of south-west Scotland and excavations at Buiston crannog', *Antiquity* 67, 520–33.

Barrett, J 1994 *Fragments from antiquity: an archaeology of social life in Britain, 2900 BC – 1200 BC.* Oxford.

Bell, M 1993a 'Intertidal archaeology at Goldcliff in the Severn estuary', *in* Coles, J, Fenwick, V & Hutchinson, G (eds) *A spirit of enquiry. Essays for Ted Wright*, 9–13. Exeter.

Bell, M 1993b 'Field survey and excavation at Goldcliff, Gwent 1993', *Archaeology in the Severn Estuary*, 81–101.

Bell, M 1999 'Prehistoric settlements and activities in the Welsh Severn Estuary', *in* Coles, B, Coles, J & Jørgensen, M S (eds) *Bog bodies, sacred sites and wetland archaeology*, 17–25. Exeter.

Bell, M 2003 'Making one's way in the world: trackways from a wetland and dryland perspective', *in* Croes, D (ed) *Wetland Archaeology Research Project: 10th International Conference: Wet sites connections, April 1–5, 2003, Olympia, Washington. Conference Pre-prints*, 1–18.

Bell, M, Caseldine, A & Neuman, H 2000 *Prehistoric Intertidal Archaeology in the Welsh Severn Estuary.* CBA Research Report 120, York.

Bell, M & Neumann, H 1996 'Intertidal survey in the Welsh Severn estuary', *Archaeology in the Severn Estuary 1995* 6, 29–33.

Bell, M & Neumann, H 1997 'Prehistoric intertidal archaeology and environments in the Severn estuary', Wales, *World Archaeology* 29(1), 95–113.

Bell, M & Neumann, H 1998 'Intertidal survey in the Welsh Severn estuary', *Archaeology in the Severn Estuary, 1997* 8, 13–28.

Bintcliff, J (ed) 1991 *The Annales School and Archaeology.* Leicester.

Bradley, R 2002 *The Past in Prehistoric Societies.* London and New York.

Brück, J 1999 'Houses, life-cycles and deposition on Middle Bronze Age settlements in southern England', *Proceedings of the Prehistoric Society* 65, 145–66.

Crone, A 1993 'Crannogs and chronologies', *Proceedings of the Society of Antiquaries of Scotland*, 123, 245–54.

Crone, A 2000 *The History of a Scottish Lowland Crannog: Excavations at Buiston, Ayrshire 1989–90*, Edinburgh.

Coles, J & Hall, D 1998 *Changing Landscapes: The Ancient Fenland.* Cambridgeshire County Council/Wetland Archaeology Research Project, Cambridge.

Coles, B J & Coles, J M 1992 'Passages of time', *Archäologische Mitteilungen aus Nordwestdeutschland* 15. Oldenburg 1992, Seite 5–21.

Fredengren, C 2002 *Crannogs: A Study of People's Interaction with Lakes, with Particular Reference to Lough Gara, in the North-west of Ireland.* Bray.

Gilman, P J 1998 'Essex fishtraps and fisheries: an integrated approach to survey, recording, and management', *in* Bernick, K (ed) *Hidden Dimensions. The Cultural Significance of Wetland Archaeology*, 273–89. Vancouver.

Godbold, S & Turner, R C 1994 'Medieval fishtraps in the Severn estuary', *Medieval Archaeology* 38, 19–54.

Gosden, C 1994 *Time and Social Being.* London and New York.

Gosden, C & Marshall, Y 1999 'The cultural biography of objects', *World Archaeology* 31(2), 169–78.

Gerritsen, F 1999 'The cultural biography of Iron Age houses and the long-term transformation of settlement patterns in the southern Netherlands', *in* Fabech, C & Ringtved, J (eds) *Settlement and Landscape. Proceedings of a Conference in Arhus, Denmark, May 4–7, 1998.* Hojbjerg, 139–48.

Gerritsen, F 2003 *Local Identities: Landscape and Community in the Late Prehistoric Meuse-Demer-Scheldt Region.* Amsterdam.

Hall, R & Clarke, C P 2000 'A Saxon intertidal timber fish weir at Collins Creek in the Blackwater estuary', *Essex Archaeology and History* 31, 125–46.

Harris, M 1998 'The rhythm of life: seasonality and sociality in a riverine village', *Journal of the Royal Anthropological Institute* 4(1), 65–82.

Harris, M 2000 *Life on the Amazon: The Anthropology of a Brazilian Peasant Village.* Oxford.

Henderson, J C 1998 'Islets through time: the definition, dating and distribution of Scottish crannogs', *Oxford Journal of Archaeology* 17(2), 227–44.

Ingold, T 1993 'The temporality of the landscape', *World Archaeology* 25(2), 152–74.

Ingold, T 1995 'Building, dwelling, living: how animals and people make themselves at home in the world', *in* Strathern, M (ed) *Shifting Contexts: Transformations in Anthropological Knowledge.* London.

Kelly, F 1997 *Early Irish Farming.* Dublin.

Kopytoff, I 1986 'The cultural biography of things: commoditization as process', *in* Appadurai, A (ed) *The Social Life of Things. Commodities in Cultural Perspective*, 64–91. Cambridge.

Lucas, A T 1989 *Cattle in Ancient Ireland.* Kilkenny.

Lucas, G 2005 *The Archaeology of Time.* London and New York.

McDermott, C 1998 'The prehistory of the Offaly peatlands', *in* Nolan, W & O'Neill, T P (eds) *Offaly History and Society*, 1–28. Dublin.

McErlean, T & O'Sullivan, A 2002 'Foreshore tidal fishtraps', *in* McErlean, T, McConkey, R & Forsythe, W *Strangford Lough: An Archaeological Survey of its Maritime Cultural Landscape*, 144–80. Belfast.

Moore, C, Murray, C, Stanley, M & McDermott, C 2003 'Bogland surveys in Ireland: forty shades of brown', *in* Fenwick, J (ed) *Lost and Found: Discovering Ireland's Past*, 123–38. Dublin.

Murray, C 2000 'A wooden vessel from Co Westmeath, Ireland', *NewsWARP* 28, 7–8.

Nayling, N 1997 'Further fieldwork and post-excavation: Magor Pill, Gwent Levels intertidal zone', *Archaeology in the Severn Estuary 1996*, 7, 85–93.

Nayling, N 1999 'Medieval and later fishweirs at Magor Pill, Gwent Levels: coastal change and technological development', *Archaeology in the Severn Estuary*, 10, 93–113.

O'Carroll, E 2001 *The Archaeology of Lemonaghan – The Story of an Irish Bog.* Dublin.

Ó Corráin, D 1972 *Ireland before the Normans.* Dublin.

O'Sullivan, A 1998 *The Archaeology of Lake Settlement in Ireland.* Dublin.

O'Sullivan, A 2001 *Foragers, Farmers and Fishers in a Coastal Landscape: An Intertidal Archaeological Survey of the Shannon Estuary.* Dublin.

O'Sullivan, A 2003a 'A day in the life of a medieval fisherman … and of intertidal archaeologists', *in* Fenwick, J (ed) *Lost and Found: Discovering Ireland's Past*, 233–46. Dublin.

O'Sullivan, A 2003b 'Place, memory and identity among estuarine fishing communities: interpreting the archaeology of early medieval fish weirs', *World Archaeology* 35(3), 449–68.

O'Sullivan, A 2005 'Medieval fishtraps on the Shannon estuary, Ireland: Interpreting people, place and identity amongst wetland communities', *Journal of Wetland Archaeology* 5, 65–77.

Overing, J & Passes, A 2000 'Conviviality and the opening up of Amazonian anthropology', *in* Overing, J & Passes, A (eds) *The Anthropology of Love and Anger: The Aesthetics of Conviviality in Native Amazonia.* London and New York.

Patterson, N 1994 *Cattle Lords and Clansmen: The Social Structure of Early Ireland*. Notre Dame.

Stanley, M 2003 'Archaeological survey of Irish bogs: information without understanding', *Journal of Wetland Archaeology* 3, 61–74.

Strachan, D 1998 'Intertidal stationary fishing structures in Essex. Some C14 dates', *Essex Archaeology and History*, 29, 274–82.

Stout, M 1997 *The Irish Ringfort*. Dublin.

Tringham, R 1991 'Households with faces: the challenge of gender in architectural remains', *in* Gero, J & Conkey, M (eds) *Engendering Archaeology: Women and Prehistory*, 93–131. Oxford.

Tringham, R 1995 'Archaeological houses, households, housework and the home', *in* Benjamin, D N, Stea, D & Saile, D (eds) *The Home: Words, Interpretations, Meanings and Environments*, 79–107. Aldershot.

Turner, R C 2002 'Fish weirs and fishtraps', *in* Davidson, A (ed) *The Coastal Archaeology of Wales*, CBA, York, 95–108.

Van de Noort, R & O'Sullivan, A 2006 *Rethinking Wetland Archaeology*. London.

Places, perceptions, boundaries and tasks: rethinking landscapes in wetland archaeology

ROBERT VAN DE NOORT and AIDAN O'SULLIVAN

INTRODUCTION

This paper is an elaboration of one of the chapters in our *Rethinking Wetland Archaeology* (Van de Noort & O'Sullivan 2006), and concerns the archaeological study of wetland landscapes. In this book, we argue that many approaches to the archaeology of wetlands have failed to influence our peers and colleagues in the broader field of landscape archaeology and, indeed, archaeology itself, and thus the great promise of wetland archaeology remains unfulfilled (Coles 2001).

This failure to influence and inform the broader archaeological debates can be attributed to three aspects of current research in the landscape archaeology of wetlands. First, many research projects remain de-contextualized geographically, as if wetlands were islands out at sea, rather than surrounded by non-wetland landscapes. Second, wetland archaeology frequently appear as being de-contextualized in time, as if wetlands were timeless landscapes, disconnected from the changes surrounding them. Third, most wetland landscape projects are disconnected from current theoretical debates in archaeology and are thus not actively attempting to contribute to contemporary archaeological debate.

This critique does not originate with ourselves, but with external commentators who, for example, when reviewing compilations of wetland research papers or conference proceedings, comment on this multi-period isolationism of wetland archaeology (eg Evans 1990). From these critiques, it is apparent that the potential benefits of wetland archaeology to broader debates are fully recognized, but that wetland archaeologists must interact fully with current theoretical debates if that potential is to be realized (eg Scarre 1989; Tilley 1991; Haselgrove *et al* 2001). Recently, similar criticism has been echoed from within the field of wetland archaeology (eg Gearey 2002).

The aim of this paper is to demonstrate how such a (re-)engagement with mainstream landscape archaeology could be achieved. We need to start with a consideration of the meaning and etymology of the words 'landscape' and 'wetland', as the way in which we understand these terms in archaeological research has been changing. We will subsequently look at how we should reconsider the archaeological study of wetland landscapes, and finally, provide a case study of how this reconsideration can be made to work.

'LANDSCAPE'

What is a 'landscape'? The *Oxford English Dictionary* defines the word as 'a view or prospect of natural inland scenery, such as can be taken in at a glance from one point of view; a piece of country scenery' and 'a picture representing natural inland scenery, as distinguished from a sea picture, a portrait, etc'. The duality of meaning can be explained by considering the origin of the word. Etymologically, the term originated in the Dutch language (*landschap* or *landscap*) sometime during the Middle Ages, it was adopted during the renaissance for a particular genre of painting and was only then adopted into English towards the very end of the sixteenth century. The *Oxford English Dictionary* names Richard Haydocke (in *Lomazzo's* (G. P.) *Tracte containing the artes of curious paintinge*) as the first person to use the word *landscape* in English in 1598 in the sentence: 'In a table donne by Cæsar Sestius where hee had painted Landskipes'.

In its original medieval meaning, however, landscape had nothing to do with painting or art, but was a geopolitical idea, or an ideological concept. In this original sense, the suffix *-schap* or *-scap* did not mean *view* or *perspective*, but *skill* or *ability* as in the modern English workman*ship* and craftsman*ship* (and surviving in its corresponding Dutch word *ambacht*schap), or in the German word *Wirt*schaft ('economy'). Thus, the original meaning of the word *landscape* was the perception of the ability to live in, on and from the land. The Dutch planner Hans

Schoen (1993) expressed this landscape as something that was not in front of one's eyes, but existed between the ears.

During the renaissance, the concept of landscape gained currency, and the philosopher Tom Lemaire (1970) argued that the development of scientific knowledge, and the growth of the market system, changed the perception of landscape into something that could be (increasingly) controlled, observed, enjoyed and used for acquiring ever greater riches. The new genre of landscape paintings was produced principally for the *nouveaux riche* who invested their earnings from manufacture and trade into land. Thus, these new paintings, with perspective and realism, expressed a new understanding of what a landscape was, as something that can be seen, owned and exploited. Nevertheless, throughout the early modern period, landscape paintings were never free of their political (and manipulated) context. Thus, in the sixteenth century, Pieter Breughel the Elder often chose as the topic of his work people resting, eating, drinking, playing music, enjoying themselves or simply being outdoors, but not manifestly working (eg *The Harvesters*, c 1565), in landscapes that were frequently as much imagined rather than real (eg *The Return of the Hunters*, c 1565), and in the nineteenth century, John Constable's landscapes (eg *The Haywain*, 1821) present the rural poor in a 'naturalized' context, justifying the social order of the countryside, with people being part of the landscape in much the same way as the farm animals (Lambert 2005, 14–16).

The academic study of the landscape (as opposed to the geographical study of nature and natural landscapes as advocated by von Humboldt in the nineteenth century) only developed around 1900, and the German geographer Otto Schlüter (1872–1952) was the first to argue that landscape was the central topic of geography. His landscape was the visible landscape as a reflection of human society. It had become disconnected from its socio-political context, and the concept of landscape was accredited a 'face value', which forms the basis for the functional analysis of landscapes. His distinction between the *Kulturlandschaft* ('cultural landscape') and *Naturlandschaft* ('natural landscape') is still commonplace in much geographical and archaeological landscape research in continental Europe, whilst similar ideas of the role of culture in the making of landscapes was advocated in the English-speaking world by the American geographer Carl Sauer (1889–1975), for example in his *The Morphology of Landscape* (1925).

In recent years, post-modern cultural geography in the English-speaking world has (unwittingly?) returned to the medieval, and wittingly to the pre-capitalist, concept of landscape. For example, the British geographer Dennis Cosgrove (1984) defines the landscape as: 'an ideological concept representing a way in which people would have signified themselves and their world through their imagined relationship with nature'. There has been a broad acceptance of the idea that, in the modern world, landscape is not the representation of a society's reality, but the environment experienced through human/native eyes which can be (actively and passively) manipulated. Landscapes always present a certain perception, which is politically biased or coloured, and every landscape has a political context. Alongside many archaeologists (eg Barrett *et al* 1991; Bradley 1993, 1998, 2000; Barrett 1994; Bradley *et al* 1994; Tilley 1994; Hill 1995; Cooney 2000; McOmish *et al* 2002), we would argue that the same is true for past landscapes.

'WETLANDS'

What is a 'wetland'? The etymology of the word shows that it is a modern, twentieth century, creation. According to the *Oxford English Dictionary* it was first defined in the *New Scientist* in 1965 (17 June, 763/3: 'Wetlands are defined to include marshes, bogs, swamps and any still water less than six metres deep') and again in *Nature* in 1969 (19 April, 239/2: 'Wetland ecosystems in the limited sense of this work are defined as ecosystems with a watertable, above, at or very near the substrate surface, the substrate remaining saturated throughout the year'). Only one earlier use of the word is recorded, dated to 1955 (*Science News Letter*, 29 October 281/2: 'The wetland partridge is about twice the size of the valley quail'), but before that date, wetlands as a word did not exist, and only emerged in the twentieth century out of a growing concern about the habitat of birds, and especially ducks, leading to a number of federal laws in the USA that used the term wetland as a generic term for such habitats. That the pressure for such laws came principally from the hunting lobby matters not, but it explains the early preoccupation with generic, rather than specific, wetland protection. During the UNESCO-sponsored International Convention on Wetlands in Ramsar, Iran, in 1970, the term became internationally recognized.

Bradley (2000) has argued that people in the past did not think in terms of environmental systems or ecosystems, but developed 'native ecologies', using their own terms to define specific topographical features or places. Recent cultural anthropological studies have come to similar conclusions (eg Lopez 1986; Ingold 1995; Harris 2000). We can assume that people in the past living within and outside the wetlands would have understood these landscapes in terms of particular landforms, rather than by using the broad, generic term 'wetlands', and proof of this is abundantly available in the form of place-names. These never include the generic term wetland as a prefix or suffix. Instead, we find plenty of English place-names (often deriving from Anglo-Saxon roots) indicating specific kinds of wet landscapes or wet features, with suffixes such as –ings, –hay, –moor, –dyke, –fen, –levels, –fleet, –pool, –mere, –beach, –ford, –bridge, or –on-the-water and –on-the-Marsh. We find the same in Irish, Dutch, German, French, Danish and many other European languages.

Rethought wetland archaeology should similarly deconstruct the concept of wetlands when attempting to understand how people in the past engaged with these landscapes. It should develop an empathy for the characteristics of the many wetlands as seen and understood by the people we study.

RETHINKING THE LANDSCAPE ARCHAEOLOGY OF WETLANDS

Examining the terms 'landscape' and 'wetland' leads us to two suppositions. First, that 'landscape' is not simply the representation of a society's reality, and that as archaeologists we cannot 'read the landscape' as a direct reflection of its daily use and function, without the awareness that landscapes represent politically biased and coloured perceptions, and that landscapes have been actively created, re-created and manipulated within political contexts. Thus, landscape studies must be hermeneutic – the (wetland) landscape does not carry innate information. Second, that the term 'wetlands' is not often a useful unit for analysis, as it meant nothing to the people we study and attempt to understand.

These suppositions form the basis from which we have developed a 'rethought' approach to wetland landscapes which, we envisage for the future, would include the following seven characteristics.

CONTEXTUALIZATION

First, the landscape archaeology of wetlands has to be contextualized. This includes geographical contextualization, as no wetlands exists within a space void of other landscapes, and interactions between wetland and non-wetland landscapes are omnipresent, both in the physical (eg the run-off of nutrients-rich water from hills into a bog) and cultural (eg the use of stone axes and non-wetland trees to build a trackway) spheres. Contextualization should extend to include the passing of time and the cultural changes surrounding the conditions, and it should also include the socio-political context of the researchers, who should make their theoretical stance explicit, as we always interpret our data 'through a cloud of theory' (Johnson 1999).

It must be acknowledged here, that more and more wetland archaeologists recognize the need for the geographical contextualization of their work, but the specialized nature of the work has frequently prevented broader theoretical explorations.

DECONSTRUCTING THE WETLAND META-NARRATIVE

Second, we must deconstruct the meta-narrative of wetlands, accepting that this term had no significance for people in the past. Where the term wetland is used as shorthand for the mosaic of ecosystems of wet and damp places, or for defining the area where wet-preserved archaeological and palaeoenvironmental remains may survive, this should not become the basis for cultural analysis.

In the study of the Humber Wetlands in north-east England, the archaeology of the later prehistoric period suggests, for example, that there was a near diametrical opposition in the perception of alluvial wetlands and peatlands (Van de Noort 2004). Archaeological survey of the former found few monumental sites, or types of sites traditionally associated with death and burial. Instead, the survey identified 'hunting camps' and 'flint production sites', field systems, settlements and sites of industrial activities, including salt winning and metal production or, if one wishes, the archaeology of 'daily life'. The palynological evidence indicates something similar; the opening up of the indigenous forest throughout the Neolithic and Bronze Ages, with little remaining woodland by the start of the Iron Age. In contrast, the archaeology of the peatlands offers a dearth of settlements and field systems, and there is also a pronounced lack of finds of flint or pottery. Instead, the antiquarian finds of bog bodies from Thorne and Hatfield Moors in the Humberhead Levels and a large number of Bronze Age and Iron Age bronze objects 'ritually deposited' in the moors and floodplain mires, testify to a perception that is strikingly different from that attributable to the minerogenic wetlands.

However, such perceptions of specific types of wetlands do not translate across cultural boundaries. A contrasting perception of peatlands is shown in the study of the lowlands of North Holland. Jan Besteman (1990) considers the early medieval socio-political context of patrons and clients. The king, occupying the top of the feudal pyramid, would have been perceived as the landowner of any wilderness such as the peatlands of North Holland. However, with the declining control of the Carolingian kings over their vassals after the middle of the ninth century, the latter usurped the peat bogs for themselves. Continuing erosion of political structures and increasing geographical distance between the seats of the local elites and the areas of reclamation in the subsequent centuries gave rise to groups of 'free farmers'. These 'free farmers' were no longer bound by oath, obligation or tax to their patrons, and these apparently marginal wetland landscapes had become fundamentally attractive places to live.

The landscape as understood by the people living within the wetlands would include a differentiation of the many landscape features, producing native ecologies, which would have included a detailed knowledge of where to fish, where to build houses and to obtain building material from, where to take cattle for grazing in the spring months, and where the spirits, gods or ancestors lived. Particular streams, hummocks, trees and fields would have been known by their individual names (eg Summerfield; Fishlake), with distinct connotations and memories attached to these features and names (eg Nelson 1983).

PERCEPTION

Third, we should approach the significance of specific landscapes from the perspective of the people we study. We cannot hope to start to understand the significance and meaning of trackways, bog bodies, lake settlements and so on if we approach wetlands from a modern, functionalist perspective. Furthermore, we must also recognize that the perception of wetlands, and other types of landscapes, differs between insiders and outsiders.

The most 'extreme' example of wetland occupation is probably provided by the Marsh Arabs of Iraq and Iran. These are best known to western observers through the writings of travellers such as Wilfrid Thesiger. He described in the 1950s a people who lived on reed islands, who built architecturally-spectacular communal meeting houses (*mudhif*) of dried reeds, fished and hunted from long canoes (*mashuf*), and grew rice and kept water buffaloes in the marshes (Maxwell 1957; Thesiger 1959, 1964; Young 1977). However, the Marsh Arabs were regarded with distrust by the Iraqi government, who saw the marshes as a refuge for bandits, smugglers and rebels disdainful of external control, and as bases for Shi'ite resistance groups (Lamb 2003). After the unsuccessful Shi'ite rebellions immediately following the First Gulf War, the Iraqi government constructed canals and drains across the marshes, while the marsh villages were bombed and their peoples expelled.

An historical example of such contradictory perspectives of wetlands comes from the Humberhead Levels region in the seventeenth century. The drainage of the Hatfield Chase by the Dutch engineer Cornelius Vermuyden was financed by external monies, and under royal authority. The Chase was described in 1608 as 'utterly wasted' as it produced little or no revenue for the crown or the big landowners, but the commoners enjoyed the myriad resources provided by the various wetlands: the higher, free-draining islands were used as arable land, typically; the minerogenic floodplains were used for grazing stock and as hay land, the meadows and ings provided the main source of food for livestock and plough animals; the lowest terrestrial areas, the carrs, moors and wastes, were extensively exploited as seasonal pastures and as such formed an essential part of the rural economy, enabling the use of some of the higher ings as hay lands. Furthermore, historical sources show that peat-cutting, for fuel and as building materials ('turves'), was an important activity by the thirteenth and fourteenth centuries. The wet parts of the landscape were also valuable for seasonal grazing throughout the Middle Ages and the post-medieval period; for providing reeds for building, thatching and basket making, but even more importantly for fishing and fowling. Unsurprisingly, the commoners sided during the English Civil War with the anti-royalists. This was not predicated in socio-political terms, but represents a choice that expressed their social identity. As part of their reformed social identities, the commoners sabotaged much of the smaller drainage works, culminating in their attack on the drainage engineers' village at Sandtoft (Van de Noort 2004).

ENCULTURATION

Fourth, we should recognize that all through the human past, and indeed in the present, the natural environment has been perceived as dynamic and sometimes even alive, and often as imbued with supernatural powers (eg Nelson 1983; Ingold 1995). Enculturing nature – and the spirits within them – forms a key theme of human behaviour, which can be favourably studied in wetland landscapes with its high-resolution dating and close association with palaeoenvironmental source material.

Christopher Tilley (1994) has argued that tracks and paths are primary human artefacts. They were one of the first modifications people made to their environment, forming a medium through which the environment could be integrated with the psyche and transformed into a landscape, that is, an environment which reflects and is interpreted by human beings. The environment thus becomes 'encultured' into landscape (Tilley 1994, 206–7). The concepts of paths and roads, and the journeys that they enable, are powerful metaphors (Tilley 1999, 178), recognized by the Romans and even by us in our modern, so-called rational culture (eg expressions such as 'taking the high road' and 'road to success' use paths as metaphors). Thus the path is not just a route from one place to another; more importantly, it transforms a wilderness full of unknowns into a cultured landscape, a known place.

Wetland archaeology is particularly well-placed to study enculturation, for example, though the contextualized research of trackways. Prehistoric trackways in mires, from the Neolithic Sweet Track through to medieval *toghers* in Ireland, were the principal cultural elements in otherwise un-encultured landscapes. The contexts of many prehistoric trackways include specific objects that can be understood as votive or ritual deposits, suggesting that the locales where these depositions had been placed were viewed as being connected with ancestors, ghosts or gods (Cosgrove 1993). Objects include the unused jade axe found adjacent the Neolithic Sweet Track (B & J Coles 1986), the wooden disc wheels beneath the Neolithic Nieuw-Dordrecht trackway in the Bourtanger Moor in the eastern Netherlands (Van der Sanden 2001, 141–2), the many bronze weapons, artefacts and skeletal remains alongside the Fag Fen stake alignment, now reinterpreted as a series of trackways (Pryor 2001), the bog bodies alongside the first century AD Valtherbrug in the Bourtanger Moor. Furthermore, many excavators have commented on the limited functionality of trackways, for example, because it did not connect two complementary regions (eg the Nieuw–Dordrecht trackway), it was only in use for a very short period (eg the Sweet Track), it was periodically extended (eg the Nieuw–Dordrecht trackway) or because the trackways had been partially destroyed soon after their construction,

as was the case for the second century BC Corlea I trackway in the Irish Midlands (Raftery 1990).

These contextual observations suggest that the function of these, invariably long, trackways was not simply linking two areas of relative dry land across a wetland. Rather, we would argue that these trackways were often constructed with the objective to enculture the wilderness landscapes in between, or to make a statement about the prowess of culture over nature. On a number of occasions, this idea was restated, through additional depositions or through extensions of a track that in fact led nowhere.

BOUNDARIES AND EDGES

Fifth, special attention should be given to the boundaries and edges of the landscapes or native ecologies. From our observations of the perceived dynamic nature of the natural environment, it follows that the boundaries and edges of these landscapes are often given particular significance, for example as 'natural places' in the sense used by Richard Bradley (2000).

Stocker and Everson's study (2003) of the Witham valley in Lincolnshire, England, offers an outstanding example of the longevity of the significance of some natural places in wetlands. In the Middle Ages, the River Witham was the boundary of the independent state of Lindsey. Research found that the medieval monasteries were located at strategic points along the valley where causeways provided access across the river and its extensive riparian wetlands. In the Middle Ages, the causeways were already of great age, and excavations of one of them, at Fiskerton, showed a predecessor of Iron Age and Roman date (Field & Parker Pearson 2003). The causeways were also associated with votive depositions, which occur in this area only at the terminals of the causeways. In turn, these votive depositions were found to be in the vicinity of Bronze Age barrow cemeteries. Stocker and Everson thus argue that specific locales within the Witham valley were perceived as places where one could cross this boundary for a period in excess of two millennia, despite the evolving nature of this wetland landscape. Bronze Age perceptions endured, in one way or another, into the Middle Ages, with the medieval monasteries effectively Christianizing pagan practices and beliefs.

MARGINALITY AND LIMINALITY

Sixth, we should distinguish clearly between marginality and liminality. The concept of liminality is frequently invoked where wetlands are traversed.

Liminality is a notoriously fluid concept. Originally proposed by Van Gennep (1908), the concept is linked to 'rites of passage' to describe the formalized rituals and practices that accompany one's transition from one particular state into another, especially the rites associated with birth, reaching adulthood, marriage and death. As part of these rituals, symbolic or real 'thresholds' needed to be crossed, with the thresholds constituting liminal zones. As economic and ritual activities are not, on a landscape level, mutually exclusive, the recurrent equation of liminality with marginality is often mistaken. Although some liminal zones were to be found in what were considered marginal landscapes, others (eg the threshold passed by newlyweds in the modern world) are located within settlements or within areas in economic use. In other words we must be very specific when identifying places that were liminal.

The lake-dwellings in the Holderness region in East Yorkshire provide an example of liminality that is unconnected from marginality. A reappraisal of the West Furze 'lake-dwelling' showed that the site was in effect a Late Neolithic or Early Bronze Age trackway across a sinuous wetland that had developed in the Bail and Low Mere complex (Van de Noort 1995; see also Fletcher & Van de Noort this volume). These elongated mires may have been seen as a boundary between the world of the living and the world of the dead, with evidence of two burial mounds to the east of the former meres, and somewhat tentatively, a settlement on their west bank. The trackway at West Furze that crossed these wetlands included several features that could have symbolized this liminal space, most notably the wicket or doorway at the eastern terminal of the short trackway. The symbolic function of this boundary was further reinforced with a number of human skulls.

TASKSCAPES

Seventh, we should not underplay the importance of many wetland landscapes as taskscapes, areas where the rhythm of daily life determines the significance of how these wetland landscapes are perceived. The phrase 'taskscape' was coined by Tim Ingold (1993) to focus on the concept that the manner in which landscapes are experienced and perceived is closely related to the activities or tasks that are undertaken in particular landscapes at particular times. With this, Ingold has effectively returned to the original concept of landscape, as in the Dutch *landschap*. As we have argued already, the insiders' view of wetlands is one that offers myriad resources, ranging

from eels, fish and shellfish, to peat for fuel, reeds for roofing, to summer pastures and hay lands. Raised bogs can also be used intermittently for short-term seasonal grazing by burning the top layer of the bog, for the preservation of butter, the seasoning of wood and the curing of leather. We should recognize that these activities, though seemingly economic practices, are things that people do every day, albeit in specific cultural and social conditions.

It is therefore not surprising that the overwhelming majority of trackways excavated from wetlands are not the long tracks described previously as playing part in enculturation processes, but are short tracks, often little more than 10m in length. In contrast to the long, over-designed and possible ceremonial tracks, these short trackways were usually simple narrow pathways, platforms or bundles of brushwood used to create passing places at especially wet and boggy places alongside existing routes through the landscape. We recognize that large linear causeways that traverse a bog from one edge to another represent a very small proportion of the total number of known sites (MacDermott 1998, 7; Stanley 2003, 65). The absence of exotic objects and bog bodies at these locations reinforces the concept that the short trackways were used functionally in everyday lives and had, in the eyes of the people that used them, little in common with the large trackways that were constructed for specific occasions.

RETHOUGHT WETLAND LANDSCAPES: A CASE STUDY INTO THE EARLY RECLAMATION OF 'INCLESMOOR'

In this case study, into the early reclamation of Inclesmoor or Thorne Moors, we want to show how a rethought landscape archaeology of wetlands can be undertaken. Long-standing research interests, into the history of reclamation and the exploitation of these wetlands, are neither forgotten nor ignored, but new, deeper, information is uncovered through contextualization: consideration of the appropriateness of the wetland concept, comparisons between insiders' and outsiders' perceptions, the introduction of the enculturation concept, special attention to boundaries and understanding the wetland landscapes as taskscapes.

'Inglesmoor' is the medieval name for the Thorne Moors, in the Yorkshire Humberhead Levels. These Levels were formed by the pro-glacial Lake Humber, a meltwater lake that expanded and retracted with the

FIGURE 1
The Inclesmoor Map, *c* 1407 (PRO MPC 56).

seasons and the glaciers. The lake ceased to exist not later than *c* 11000 cal BC, when the icesheet blocking the Humber Gap between the Yorkshire Wolds and the Lincolnshire Wolds retreated, or possibly somewhat earlier through silting of the lake itself (Bateman *et al* 2000). The Lake Humber deposits were subject to aeolian reworking during the Loch Lomond Stadial of the Devensian, *c* 11500 to 10500 cal BC, and this reworking resulted in the formation of sandy dunes or 'islands', resulting in extensive undulated flatland. Holocene sea-level rise initiated the development of expansive wetlands in the Humberhead Levels. Initially, the impact of sea-level rise was restricted to the Late-glacial river channels, but from *c* 3200 cal BC, the impeded arterial drainage resulted in widespread paludifcation, and the onset of mire formation at Thorne Moors (Buckland & Dinnin 1997).

Recent archaeological research has shown the construction of a Neolithic trackway on nearby Hatfield Moors (Gearey & Chapman this volume), and it seems likely that similar activity would have taken place at Thorne Moors. To date, however, only a very short Bronze Age brushwood trackway has been identified (Buckland 1979), alongside a number of isolated finds of stone axes, and it is unlikely that new archaeological sites will be discovered, as this former milled peatland has been converted into a nature conservation reserve (eg Van de Noort 2001).

The time-transgressive nature of the development of the mire would have initially involved a number of smaller, mesotrophic, mires developing in the lowest areas, with deciduous woodland surviving on the higher grounds. The local impact of continued sea-level rise and impeded drainage was the evolvement of a single, continuous ombrothrophic raised mire, which drowned the forest (Dinnin 1997). This raised mire appears to have survived more or less undisturbed to the first half of the second millennium

AD, when *Sphagnum imbricatum*, having formed the bulk peat up to then, disappeared (Smith 1985).

Medieval Thorne Moors was probably significantly greater than the remnants surviving today, and the Moor and its lagg areas would almost certainly have been explored and utilized by the local population, living on the hills on the edges of the wetlands. A charter from early in the fourteenth century gives the picture as one of extensively used peatlands for turves, both for fuel and as building materials, as hunting and fishing grounds, for retting of hemp and for seasonal grazing and hay making (Thirsk 1953). The open waters were used extensively as fisheries, especially for eels. By the early seventeenth century, Thorne and Hatfield Moors were considered from the point of view of outsiders as wastes, but to the commoners, the wetlands provided invaluable resources which enabled them to live self-sufficient lives.

However, the formal ownership of Thorne Moors had passed to Norman barons and institutions, even though the rights of access and use given to freemen was occasionally recorded in charters. Selby Abbey, founded in 1069 and one of the earliest ecclesiastical buildings in Norman northern England, had extensive landholdings, including Whitgift in the north of Thorne Moors, and was gifted the eastern part of the Moors by John de Mowbray, Lord of Axholme, in the early fourteenth century, albeit he retained the rights of free chase. Other owners of strips of land, from the River Ouse in the north 'as far as the moor goes towards the south', included the canons of Newhouse, St Peter's Hospital of York and the Abbey of Thoronton (Dinnin 1997, 22–3).

By the early fifteenth century, the religious houses, possibly led by Selby Abbey, had commenced with the full-scale drainage of Thorne Moors (Metcalfe 1960). The Inclesmoor Map (PRO MPC 56), dated to *c* 1407 (Beresford 1986), shows a (hand-dug) drain encircling the Moor, and in the northern third of Thorne Moors, roads, drains, bridges, a sluice, several roadside crosses and settlements with churches have appeared. The map itself is thought to have been produced as part of the ongoing disputes of rights and ownership over the Moor, and was based on documents held at the manor court at Snaith, supplemented by observations

FIGURE 2
The Inclesmoor Map,
c 1407 (PRO MPC 56):
detail of 'Stone Cros'.

FIGURE 3
The Inclesmoor Map, *c* 1407
(PRO MPC 56): detail of
wetland vegetation.

in the field (*ibid.*, 159). The latter provided the basis for the pictorial elaborations of the map, from the miniature villages to the marshland vegetation on the as yet unenclosed and unexploited Moor.

The reasons for the drainage of Inclesmoor were for its exploitation for economic benefits, and there is little doubt that from the point of view of the formal landowners, this benefit lay in the turves that were sold in towns as fuel. For example, Thornton Abbey paid Henry the Lacey 16,000 turves annually for the rent of its turbary in Inclesmoor (*ibid.*, 154–5). The regional palynological record (eg Smith 1985) indicates that woodland had become scarce aound this time, and the peat turves must have provided for an eager market. This external perception of the value of the Moor contrasts somewhat with the insiders' perception, who valued the natural diversity of the Moor.

Following the Dutch philosopher Hub Zwart (2003), we would argue that there is another layer of perception to be discerned here, and that is the moral stance of the religious houses to the uselessness of the Moor. The wilderness of Inclesmoor was an affront to the *ora et labora* ('pray and work') principle of the medieval monastic orders, and the reclamation of unproductive, ungodly land would have been seen as an act of conversion: the Christianization of the pagan wilderness. The Christian enculturation of wildernesses throughout Europe was organized and undertaken by monasteries and ecclesiastical institutions who had the organizational ability to do so, and 'regarded themselves as stewards appointed by God, as co-creators, taking active part in the management and restitution of fallen nature' (*ibid.*, 111).

In terms of the landscape archaeology of these wetlands, we can discern a cultivated or encultured taskscape with an ordered system of fields, roads, canals and villages; the latter often placed on the inside of the dike alongside the Rivers Ouse and Trent. The village churches are located at the junctions of the dike with the roads encroaching onto the Moor, and would have been visible from deep inside Thorne Moors as is, for example, the case of the church of St Mary Magdalene at Whitgift (Van de Noort 2004, 135–7). The Inclesmoor Map reinforces this reading of the landscape. The northern part shows a landscape under cultivation, with roads,

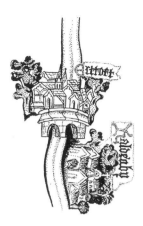

FIGURE 4
The villages of Eastoft and Haldenby on the River Don. Redrawn from The Inclesmoor Map, *c* 1407 (Keith Miller).

paths and canals, villages with churches and stone, road-side crosses on the most important landowner boundaries. This encultured part of the Moor stands in stark contrast to the Moor proper, where uncultivated and, largely, unproductive plants thrive unrestrained.

Of course, Thorne Moors is no exception in respect to the medieval reclamation of wetlands, and from the early twelfth century onwards ecclesiastical institutions across Europe were engaged in reclamation projects. In western Europe north of the Roman *limes*, Christianity was also part of the political arsenal of the kings who derived the legitimacy of their power from the divine rule of the Christian God, and it is unsurprising that one of the earliest wetland reclamations recorded, that of the marshlands east of the River Elbe, organized by the Bishop of Bremen in 1103, was undertaken in the Saxon heartland. In the case of the early reclamation of the Netherlands, Hub Zwart (2003, 111–12) described the role of Christianity '… as an ideology, [that] rendered the erection of dikes and the reclamation of wetlands morally legitimate, or even obligatory. A demarcation was introduced between the "baptized" and humanized areas on this side of the dikes, and the diffuse and unreliable realms beyond. The dike materialized a form of moral criticism, directed at previous generations of pagans who, faced with natural phenomena, had been overwhelmed by a mixture of fear and awe. They had regarded uncultivated nature as the abode of their gods and had settled for a more passive attitude. Time had come for the demystification of nature.'

CONCLUSION

This paper has argued for a rethinking of the landscape archaeology approach to wetlands, based principally on the beliefs that the concept of landscape is something that resides in people's minds, rather than being a simple reflection of culture-nature interactions, and that the concept of wetlands had little meaning to the people we study and try to understand. The paper proposes new ways of approaching wetland landscapes and has argued specifically for the need to contextualize wetland research: consider the (in-)appropriateness of the wetland name, appreciate the frequently diverging perceptions of people living and working in wetlands from the perceptions of outsiders, the importance of the enculturation concept, the need to pay particular attention to boundaries and edges, and the significance of wetland landscapes as taskscapes.

ACKNOWLEDGEMENT

Catherine Rackham, for drawing attention to the paper by Hub Zwart (2003).

REFERENCES

Barrett, J C 1994 *Fragments from Antiquity: An Archaeology of Social Life in Britain, 2900 BC – 1200 BC*. Oxford.

Barrett, J, Bradley, R & Green, M 1991 *Landscape, Monuments and Society: The Prehistory of Cranborne Chase*. Cambridge.

Bateman, M D, Murton, J B & Crowe, W 2000 'Late Devensian and Holocene depositional environments associated with the coversands around Caistor, north Lincolnshire, UK', *Boreas* 29, 1–15.

Beresford, M W 1986 'Inclesmoor, West Riding of Yorkshire', *in* Skelton, R A & Harvey, P D A (eds) *Local Maps and Plans from Medieval England*, 147–61. Oxford.

Besteman, J C 1990 'North Holland AD 400–1200: turning tide or tide turned?', *in* Besteman, J C, Bos, J M & Heidinga, H A (eds) *Medieval Archaeology in the Netherlands. Studies presented to H. H. van Regteren Altena*, 91–120. Assen/Maastricht.

Bradley, R 1993 *Altering the Earth: the origin of monuments in Britain and Continental Europe*. Edinburgh.

Bradley, R 1998 *The Significance of Monuments: on the shaping of human experience in Neolithic and Bronze Age Europe*. London.

Bradley, R 2000 *An Archaeology of Natural Places*. London.

Bradley, R 2002 *The Past in Prehistoric Societies*. London/ New York.

Bradley, R, Entwistle, R & Raymond, F 1994 *Prehistoric Land Divisions on Salisbury Plain: The Work of the Wessex Linear Ditches Project*. London.

Buckland, P C 1979 *Thorne Moors: A Palaeoecological Study of a Bronze Age Site*. Birmingham.

Buckland, P C & Dinnin, M H 1997 'The rise and fall of a wetland habitat: recent palaeoecological research on Thorne and Hatfield Moors', *Thorne and Hatfield Moors Paper* 4, 1–18.

Coles, B J & Coles, J M 1986 *Sweet Track to Glastonbury*. London.

Coles, J M 2001 'Energetic activities of commoners', *Proceedings of the Prehistoric Society* 67, 19–48.

Cooney, G 2000 *Landscapes of Neolithic Ireland*. London.

Cosgrove, D E 1984 *Social Formation and Symbolic Landscape*. Madison.

Cosgrove, D E 1993 'Landscapes and myths, gods and humans', *in* Bender, B (ed) *Landscape: politics and perspectives*, 281–305. Providence/Oxford.

Dinnin, M H 1997 'The palaeoenvironmental survey of West, Thorne and Hatfield Moors', *in* Van de Noort, R, Ellis, S (eds) *Wetland Heritage of the Humberhead Levels, An Archaeological Survey*, 157–89. Hull.

Evans, C 1990 Review of B A Purdy (ed) 1988. *Wet Site Archaeology*. New Jersey. *Proceedings of the Prehistoric Society* 56, 339–40.

Gearey, B R 2002 '"Foule and flabby quagmires"': the archaeology of wetlands', *Antiquity* 76, 896–900.

Harris, M 1998 'The rhythm of life: seasonality and sociality in a riverine village', *Journal of the Royal Anthropological Institute* 4(1), 65–82.

Haselgrove, C, Armitt, I, Champion, C, Creighton, J, Gwilt, A, Hill, J D, Hunter, F & Woodward, A 2001 *Understanding the British Iron Age: An Agenda for Action*, Salisbury.

Hill, J D 1995 *Ritual and Rubbish in the Iron Age of Wessex*, BAR British Series 242, Oxford.

Ingold, T 1993 'The temporality of the landscape', *World Archaeology* 25(2), 24–174.

Ingold, T 1995 'Building, dwelling, living: how animals and people make themselves at home in the world', *in* Strathern, M (ed) *Shifting Contexts: Transformations in Anthropological Knowledge*. London.

Johnson, M 1999 *Archaeological Theory: An Introduction*. London.

Lamb, C 2003 'The Eden project: can the arid lands of the Marsh Arabs ever be restored?', *in Sunday Times Magazine*, 27 July 2003, 20–8.

Lambert, R 2005 *John Constable and the Theory of Landscape Painting*. Cambridge.

Lemaire, T 1970 *Filosofie van het landschap*. Bilthoven.

Lopez, B 1986 *Arctic Dreams: Imagination and Desire in a Northern Landscape*. New York.

MacDermott, C 1998 'The prehistory of the Offaly peatlands', *in* Nolan, W & O'Neill, T P (eds) *Offaly: History and Society*, 1–28. Dublin.

McOmish, D, Field, D & Brown, G 2002 *The Field Archaeology of the Salisbury Plain Training Area*. Swindon.

Maxwell, G 1957 *A Reed Shaken by the Wind*. London.

Metcalfe, B 1960 *Geographic Aspects of the Reclamation and Development of the Hatfield Chase*. MA thesis, University of Leeds.

Nelson, R 1983 *Make Prayers to the Raven. A Koyukon View of the Northern Forest*. Chicago.

Pryor, F 2001 *The Flag Fen Basin: Archaeology and Environment of a Fenland Landscape*. Swindon.

Raftery, B 1990 *Trackways through Time: Archaeological Investigations on Irish Bog Roads, 1985–89*. Rush.

Sauer, C 1925 *The Morphology of Landscape*. University of California Publications in Geography 2, 19–54.

Scarre, C 1989 Review of Coles, J M & Lawson, A J (eds) 1987 *European Wetlands in Prehistory*. *Proceedings of the Prehistoric Society* 55, 274–5.

Schoen, H 1993 *De Helling* 6, 22–5.

Smith, B 1985 *A Palaeoecological Study of Raised Mires in the Humberhead Levels*. PhD thesis, University of Wales.

Stanley, M 2003 'Archaeological survey of Irish bogs: information without understanding?', *Journal of Wetland Archaeology* 3, 61–74.

Stocker, D & Everson, P 2003 'The straight and narrow way: Fenland causeways and the conversion of the landscape in the Witham valley, Lincolnshire', *in* Carver, M (ed) *The Cross goes North: Processes of Conversion in Northern Europe AD 300–1300*, 271–88. York.

Thesiger, W 1959 'Marsh dwellers of Southern Iraq', *National Geographic Magazine*, February 1959.

Thesiger, W 1964 *The Marsh Arabs*. London.

Thirsk, J 1953 'The Isle of Axholme before Vermuijden', *Agricultural History Review* 1, 16–28.

Tilley, C 1991 Review of B & J Coles (1989) *People of the Wetlands*. *Proceedings of the Prehistoric Society* 57, 214–15.

Tilley, C 1994 *A Phenomenology of Landscape: Places, Paths and Monuments*. London.

Tilley, C 1999 *Metaphors and Material Culture*. Oxford.

Van de Noort, R 1995 'West Furze: the reconstruction of a monumental wetland landscape', *in* Van de Noort, R, Ellis, S (eds) *Wetland Heritage of Holderness, an Archaeological Survey*, 323–34. Hull.

Van de Noort, R 2001 'Thorne Moors: a constested wetland in north-eastern England', *in* Coles, B & Olivier, A (eds) *The Heritage Management of Wetlands in Europe*. Earupae Archaeologiae Consilium, 133–40, Brussels.

Van de Noort, R 2004. *The Humber Wetlands: The Archaeology of a Dynamic Landscape*. Bollington.

Van de Noort, R & O'Sullivan, A 2006 *Rethinking Wetland Archaeology*. London.

Van der Sanden, W 2001 'From stone pavement to temple – ritual structures from wet contexts in the province of Drenthe, the Netherlands', *in* Purdy, B (ed) *Enduring Records: The Environmental and Cultural Heritage of Wetlands*, 132–47. Oxford.

Van Gennep, A 1908 *Les Rites de Passage*. Paris.

Young, G 1977 *Return to the Marshes: Life with the Marsh Arabs of Iraq*. London.

Zwart, H 2003 'Aquaphobia, tulipmania, biophilia: a moral geography of the Dutch landscape', *Environmental Values* 12, 107–28.

Part II
THE ALLUVIAL SESSION

The Flemish wetlands:
an archaeological survey of the valley of the River Scheldt

MACHTELD BATS

INTRODUCTION

Although well established in the surrounding countries, wetland archaeology in Belgium is nearly non-existent. Because of their low visibility, archaeological sites covered by alluvial deposits were up to now only discovered during major construction works. This makes thorough scientific research very difficult or even impossible. Therefore, earlier detection and identification of such archaeological sites is essential.

A PhD research project was begun in 2004 at Ghent University. Its main purpose was to define a reliable methodology of surveying for and the evaluation of covered prehistoric landscapes and sites in alluvial contexts. The floodplains of the River Scheldt were chosen as a test area for fieldwork. In this paper we focus on the research methods and the first results of the fieldwork.

GEOMORPHOLOGICAL DESCRIPTION OF THE SCHELDT VALLEY

Selecting the basin of the River Scheldt as the main study area offers many advantages. The Scheldt is one of Belgium's main rivers. Nevertheless, prehistoric human occupation of its floodplains remains a blind spot in Belgian archaeology. Hardly any systematic research has taken place, although some rescue excavations, mostly in unfavourable conditions but yielding well-preserved material, demonstrate the archaeological potential of the floodplain (Crombé 2006).

Coming from France, the Scheldt meanders in a north-eastern direction towards the Scheldt estuary and the North Sea, largely following the alluvial plains of its Lateglacial predecessor. In the present landscape some features still refer to this Lateglacial channel: well-developed oxbows, river dunes and sand ridges which accumulated during colder and drier periods in and along the floodplain (Kiden

1991). Others became covered, but are sometimes still detectable on detailed soil maps of the area. At the end of the Lateglacial period, the gradual infilling of the palaeochannel began, indicating a considerable decrease of fluvial activity, combined with a drop in the groundwater level. The slow aggradation continued at the beginning of the Holocene. At c 5000 BP the channels were almost completely filled with calcareous gyttja, peat and organic to peaty clay. Lateglacial features became covered with fine-grained floodplain sediments and the Holocene alluvial plain largely corresponded with the Lateglacial floodplain.

However, from 6000 BP the lower part of the river evolved differently from the part upstream. The influence of rising sea levels affected this part of the river faster and caused an accelerated rise of the groundwater level. Low sediment supply allowed the development of an extensive peat layer filling the Lateglacial palaeochannels and, from c 5000 BP onwards until 2000–1500 BP, gradually spreading over the rest of the floodplain. No distinct river channels from this period are known in this part of the floodplain. Probably here the river had an anastomosed rather than a meandering pattern.

For our project, the research area was restricted, approximately, to the floodplain between Oudenaarde and Antwerp. As described above, the dissimilar influence of the sea level rises caused an uneven geomorphological development of the Scheldt floodplain. This means that our study area can be divided roughly in two parts, in this article referred to as 'upstream' (with a considerable later tidal influence) and 'downstream' (where tidal influence started earlier). In both parts, some well-preserved archaeological sites are known, demonstrating the richness of the floodplain.

Upstream, the floodplain is relatively narrow and the alluvial sediment layer is in most places relatively thin. In the 1980s in this area a complex palaeolandscape was uncovered during major

93

sand extraction works near Oudenaarde (fig 1a). A Lateglacial channel of the Scheldt, along with at least seven scroll bars was recognized (Depredomme 1986). Several small Mesolithic and Neolithic sites were found on and in the swales between the scroll bars, all close to the palaeochannel (Parent *et al* 1986–7). Most of these sites yielded remains of small, short-term camps and settlements, focused on the exploitation of wild resources such as game, fish and plants. Finds were situated mainly on top of the

Pleistocene sediments and in the organic clay layer above. Organic preservation was poor in the sandy matrix, but extremely good in this organic clay. Tools made from bone and antler found *in situ* are rare in Flemish Stone Age archaeology.

Downstream, the river changes direction and runs through an area north of the city of Antwerp, called the Scheldepolders. Here the Lateglacial surface, consisting of large and long stretches of sand dunes and shallow wet depressions, lies buried beneath

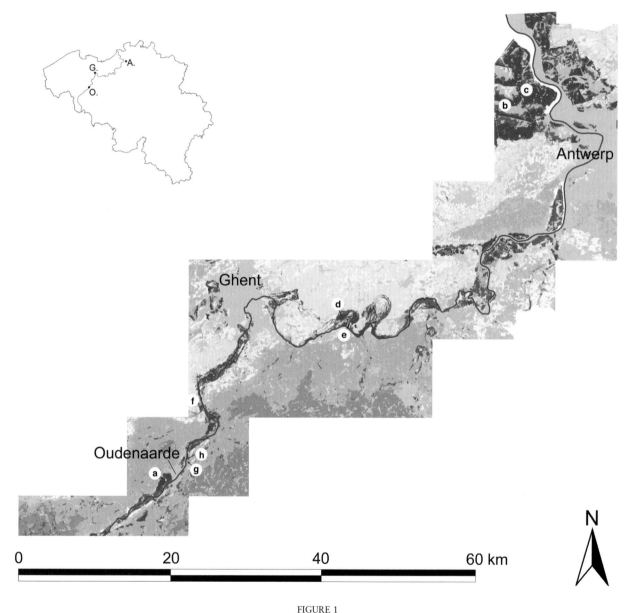

FIGURE 1
The floodplain of the River Scheldt (alluvium – dark areas) with the seven research areas: (a) Oudenaarde, (b) Verrebroek, (c) Doel, (d) Kalken, (e) Schellebelle, (f) Gavere-Donkstraat, (g) Ename and (h) Eine.

thick layers of peat and alluvial clay. It must have been an attractive landscape for Stone Age people, as is demonstrated by the high number of sites already known along these ridges (Crombé *et al* 2002). During the construction of two large harbour docks near Antwerp, numerous sites were discovered in the Verrebroek-Dok (fig 1b) and Doel-Deurganckdok (fig 1c). At both locations, extensive settlement complexes dating back to the Final Palaeolithic, the Mesolithic and the Neolithic were found on the Pleistocene sand ridges (Crombé 2005). Most sites are characterized by a high artefact density and a vast extent, but poor organic conservation. The latter is due to long exposure before peat growth and alluvial sedimentation covered the area.

Not many prehistoric sites have been excavated in the floodplain of the River Scheldt, but with the variety of site-type already apparent (such as different periods and high versus low artefact density) conservation would appear to be vast and so calls for a different survey approach.

CURRENT RESEARCH

In anticipation of the increasing destruction of the Flemish floodplains, our goal was to define the best and most efficient survey technique for the discovery and assessment of these covered prehistoric sites in the Scheldt alluvium. Because of the restricted visibility of archaeological sites in covered landscapes, 'traditional' survey techniques, such as field-walking and aerial photography, are obviously inappropriate, whereas digging test pits or trial trenches appeared to be both too destructive and too expensive in an early stage of research.

Therefore, survey by augering seems the most appropriate technique. According to Wilkinson and Bond (2001), bore hole study is an essential part of the search for buried surfaces in a dynamic sedimentary environment. Howard and Macklin

(1999) proposed useful, but general, guidelines for assessing archaeological potential in river valleys. In this procedure, a geomorphological mapping of the alluvial valley floor should lead to the identification of zones in which archaeology is (un)likely to be found through conventional prospecting techniques. Next the authors propose archaeological prospecting of the sub-surface topography, but without practical details. In his PhD thesis, Groenewoudt (1994) suggested standard techniques of systematic augering and sampling in a staggered triangular grid. Although these standards are generally accepted in Belgian and Dutch (commercial) archaeology, the instructions remain rudimentary on practical details. The basic goal of our study was to elaborate a protocol which allows maximum results with minimal effort. A similar study was recently published in a Dutch report on the reliability and applicability of auger survey in commercial archaeology (Tol *et al* 2004). However, the report only refers to examples in literature and no experiments were done. Results were all based on the comparison of different sites and theoretical (statistical) calculations. There is still no real consensus about the size of grid and meshes to be used to obtain the best results against the lowest cost.

APPLIED METHOD

Fieldwork always is conducted in several stages (table 1). Firstly, the covered palaeo-topography is reconstructed through gouge auger survey (2cm in diameter) in a 20×20m grid. Geomorphological exploration is needed to get insights into the area's covered topography and into the dynamics of the covering sediments. Different covered landscape features, such as gullies, ridges and so on are located and mapped.

Areas with archaeological potential are defined for the second stage: the detecting of archaeological sites. This second stage consists of systematic sampling of

TABLE 1
The fieldwork is conducted in several stages.

Fieldwork	Stage 1	Stage 2	Stage 3	Stage 4
goal	geomorphological study	detection	evaluation	confrontation
grid	20×20m	10×10m	5×5m	test pits
auger-type	gouge	hand auger	hand auger	–
auger-diameter	2cm	10cm	10cm	–

the subsoil with a 10cm diameter manual auger – the Edelman auger – according to a fixed, staggered grid of 10×10m. A bigger auger (the 'mega auger', with a 15cm or even 20cm diameter) might increase the chances of a positive hit because the sampled volume would be larger, but as the target layers of our survey are usually covered with a considerably thick alluvial sediment layer, using a bigger auger is probably not physically feasible.

Different samples are collected and wet sieved over 1mm meshes. When bore holes produce positive samples (positive hits), the auger grid is narrowed down locally. This is the third stage of the research procedure, which is aimed at an evaluation of the detected site. The final fieldwork stage is the control of the results through test pitting. Here the sample results are assessed with the actual situation.

STUDY AREAS

Seven test areas were chosen, both downstream and upstream the River Scheldt. Downstream auger survey was done at the vast Early Mesolithic sites of Verrebroek-Dok (fig 1b). These sites were situated on top of a large coversand dune. Partly excavated during the 1990s, some questions remained on the delimitation of the site (Crombé 1998).

Upstream, several sites were studied in different geomorphological contexts. The sites of Oudenaarde-Donk (fig 1a), Kalken-Molenmeers (fig 1d) and Schellebelle-Aard (fig 1e) are all situated on covered scroll bars. In Oudenaarde, an area close to the former excavation area dating from the 1980s (see above) was threatened by construction works (Ameels et al 2003). Situated in the same covered scroll bar environment, the potential for archaeology was estimated to be very high. The sites of Kalken and Schellebelle are situated within the floodplain of a large palaeomeander. The area has been well preserved, thanks to its wet conditions and its conversion into a nature reserve, but in the near future parts of it will be threatened by the construction of 'controlled inundation areas' and 'nature compensation areas'. Although well documented in geomorphological studies (eg Jacobs 1968, 1974; Verbruggen 1971), no archaeological research has been conducted here previously.

Gavere-Donkstraat (fig 1f) is a site located on a large sand ridge with only a thin alluvial covering. At the top of the ridge, still slightly visible in the present landscape, several flint artefacts have been collected, including a trapeze and some scrapers found during field walking. Half a kilometre away, where the river passes through a bottleneck between the Pleistocene

river banks, lies the Roman site of Asper-Jolleveld (Vermeulen 1986). Field walking and a small trench excavation at this location yielded several Neolithic artefacts (Vanmoerkerke 1986). At Ename and Eine (fig 1g, h), a Lateglacial channel filled in with peat was uncovered during clay extraction works (Ameels et al 2003). Palynological and geomorphological study situates the infilling of the channel between the Lateglacial and the Atlantic period. The rest of the area was surveyed to establish the further course of the channel and to detect eventual prehistoric sites at its banks. On the right bank of the palaeochannel (= Ename), geomorphological study soon demonstrated that the covered prehistoric surface is largely criss-crossed by (sub)recent gullies. The left bank (= Eine), on the other hand, seemed better preserved. It is characterized by a homogenous soil profile with an old, argillaceous surface immediately beneath the Holocene alluvial clay. Apparently, we have here an old surface without striking features on which to expect archaeological settlement. At the eastern border of the research area, however, a possible Lateglacial channel filled with peat was detected. Most probably this was part of the same channel as at Ename, as the two channel fragments are in line and are of similar composition, only to be separated by a recent meander.

RESULTS AND TESTS

GRID

Areas defined during the first stage of the fieldwork as potential locations for prehistoric settlement are further examined by sampling in a smaller grid using large augers. Usually a fixed staggered grid of 10×10m is chosen, although some deviations of this standard are possible. Results are considered positive if the auger samples contain archaeological indicators (such as lithic artefacts or burnt hazelnut shells). In this case, the grid is narrowed down to 5×5m around every positive auger point.

Table 2 reflects a virtual enlargement of the sample grid per site. First, the number of sample points is given, followed by the number of positive samples per grid. All sites were sampled with a 10cm Edelman auger (except for the site of Verrebroek-Dok where a 15cm auger was used); samples were wet sieved over 1mm meshes.

Part of the site of Verrebroek-Dok was sampled in a 5×5m grid (Crombé 1998). Due to its vast extent and the restricted time available, the limits of this site were definitely not reached, but several

TABLE 2
The virtual enlargement of the sample grid indicates an important decrease of positive samples.

GRID (1mm meshes)	Samples: total	5×5m		5×10m		10×10m		10×20m		20×20m		30×30m	
		min	max	min	max	min	max	min	max	min	max	min	max
Verrebroek	702	154	154	–	–	34	46	–	–	5	14	1	9
Oudenaarde	74	–	–	54	54	31	31	15	16	–	–	–	–
Kalken	78	–	–	–	–	6	6	–	–	1	2	0	2
Schellebelle	352	–	–	–	–	13	13	–	–	0	4	0	2
Ename	121	–	–	–	–	1	1	0	1	0	1	0	1
Eine	108	–	–	–	–	–	–	5	5	3	4	–	–
Gavere	342	–	–	–	–	27	27	–	–	5	8	2	7

individual artefact clusters could be mapped. Enlarging this sample grid to 10×10m, we more or less get the same picture, yet a less detailed one. In a 20×20m grid, the site is still detectable, but evaluation is no longer possible. Using a 30×30m grid is too risky: the site might be hit, but could just as well be missed.

It is clear that such large settlement complexes, as found on the coversand ridges in the *Scheldepolders*, are rather easily detected. The repeated occupation of these landscape features, resulting in a widespread and high artefact density, amplifies the chances of positive auger results considerably. Further upstream, in a scroll bar environment, the situation is different. In this dynamic landscape, settlements are usually smaller and possibly inhabited for shorter periods. Consequently, the artefact distribution and density is considerably lower, which makes these sites more difficult to detect.

Clear examples of this situation are the sites of Kalken-Molenmeers and Schellebelle-Aard. Even a narrow scroll bar like the one at Kalken, which is nowhere wider than 35m, yielded evidence of human occupation when augering in a 10×10m grid. When we alter the grid to 20×20m, the site is still hit but with a considerable loss of information. The use of a broader grid increases the risk of missing the site. At the somewhat larger ridge of Schellebelle, the auger survey is still going on, but the first results are already promising. Even here, in a 20×20m grid the site might be overlooked.

The (accessible) research area at Oudenaarde-Donk was very limited and therefore a sampling grid of 5×10m was used. Changing the grid from 5×10m into 10×10m did not really change the overall picture. A site was unmistakably detected on top of a large scroll bar, reaching down the slope into the depression, but the limits of the site could not be defined.

As (sub)recent channels criss-crossed the landscape intensely, only small and scattered areas of intact surfaces are left to investigate at the site of Ename-Castrum. It is clear that enlarging the grid in this situation is pointless. A striking contrast is the situation on the other side of the recent meander, at the site of Eine. Here the covered landscape is much better preserved. Due to limited research time, it was decided to sample the area in a 10×20m grid. This resulted in five positive hits, all containing several artefacts, but only two positive hits were situated close to each other. A smaller grid would possibly clarify this difficult situation of interpretation.

So far, not all collected samples from the site of Gavere-Donkstraat have been wet sieved and only preliminary results can be presented here. Even so, already 27 of the 342 bore holes contained archaeological finds, mostly flint artefacts (amongst which was one segment). Here, enlarging the grid dramatically diminished the chances for positive hits.

MESHES

All samples, as discussed above, were wet sieved over 1mm meshes. This clearly makes the detection of prehistoric sites possible. The remaining residue, however, includes very small objects, both archaeological and non-archaeological. Sorting out the artefacts is time-consuming and demands some experience, thus causing higher costs. Tol and Verhagen (2004) state that such small meshes can only be justified if they lead to an increase of the perceptibility by more than 50 per cent. If this is not the case, choosing a bigger auger or narrowing down the grid system should be more profitable.

To determine the eventual loss of information with the use of bigger meshes, all archaeological artefacts of the seven study areas were sieved again over 2, 3 and 4mm meshes while the initial grid system was retained. The results of this test are shown in table 3, with per site and per mesh size given first, then the number of positive samples, followed by the amount of artefacts.

The experiment shows that auger surveys will, most certainly, uncover high density sites such as Verrebroek-Dok, even if 4mm meshes are used. The vast extent and dense spread of artefacts ensures enough positive hits to find and to define these sites. For the site of Oudenaarde-Donk, which is rich in finds but probably smaller in extent, enlarging the meshes means a considerable loss of information. The survey would have revealed its existence anyway, even if 4mm meshes had been chosen. But for further evaluation of the site, such as delimitation and internal structure, the use of finer meshes is absolutely necessary. When plotted on a map, both 1mm and 2mm meshes give a fairly good idea of the site's dimension, showing a rather continuous spread of artefacts over the whole surface. The 3mm and 4mm fractions, however, seem to indicate separate artefact clusters. This interpretation is contradicted by the finer sieved survey samples and later excavation.

For the sites at Kalken and Schellebelle, the preliminary results demonstrate that, over 1mm, both sites were hit several times. Over 2mm, the positive results at Kalken-Molenmeers were reduced to two hits, whereas none were left when the chosen meshes were larger. For Schellebelle-Aard, the scarcely found artefacts lay spread out over the scroll bar surface. This became visible using 1mm or 2mm meshes. Larger meshes only seem to indicate some stray finds and further interpretation is impossible. Although it is too early to draw definite conclusions about these two sites, it seems clear that sieving over 3mm or 4mm meshes is, again, not to be recommended. Similar conclusions can be drawn for Gavere-Donkstraat.

In Eine, where artefact-rich samples were retrieved, using a 2mm and even a 3mm mesh did not cause a major loss of information. However, larger meshes considerably distort the picture.

CORRELATION BETWEEN SAMPLES AND EXCAVATION

In this stage of the project, only the site of Oudenaarde could be examined further after the survey campaign. Here we had the opportunity to compare our survey results with the excavation results from a trial trench. First the alluvial clay was mechanically removed. Subsequently the underlying organic clay, similar to the occupation layer at previous excavations of nearby Neolithic sites on the same scroll bar (Parent *et al* 1987), was shovelled. Next, the Pleistocene sandy matrix underneath was excavated in units of $50 \times 50 \times 5$cm and water screened over 1mm meshes.

The excavation results have not yet been studied completely. Therefore, we focused on the finds in the excavation units surrounding our bore holes. A total

TABLE 3

All archaeological finds were sieved again over different meshes. Results are given per mesh size; first the number of positive hits (samples), next the total amount of collected artefacts.

MESHES	Samples: total	1 mm		2mm		3mm		4mm	
		samples	artefacts	samples	artefacts	samples	artefacts	samples	artefacts
Verrebroek	702	154	693	149	437	128	268	100	169
Oudenaarde	74	54	1,507	22	36	11	15	6	8
Kalken	78	6	7	4	3	0	0	0	0
Schellebelle	352	13	22	7	9	3	3	1	1
Ename	121	1	1	1	1	1	1	1	1
Eine	108	5	49	5	11	4	7	2	3
Gavere	342	27	44	18	22	12	13	11	11

of 54 units were examined, yielding over 10,000 flint artefacts; one potsherd, some burnt bone fragments and charred hazelnut shells.

Some researchers try to estimate the expected amount of artefacts by simply multiplying the auger results. This implies a linear connection between the results from the auger survey and the excavation.

Comparing the survey results of Oudenaarde-Donk with the excavation results, however, this seems to be contradicted. Using a simple (Pearson) Correlation Test (table 4), the correlation between the amount of artefacts in samples and in their connected excavation units is calculated. The outcome is very low (0.002; p = 0.997). Therefore no linear connection exists between the amount of artefacts in samples and the excavation units from which they have been retrieved. This means that, based on auger survey, an artefact concentration can be defined but the quantity of artefacts cannot be predicted. The amount of artefacts found in a sample does not necessarily reflect the amount of artefacts in the soil. Most likely, this is due to the uneven spread of artefacts in the soil. Extrapolation of auger results therefore is risky and misleading. In the case of Oudenaarde-Donk, for example, it would have led to a serious overestimation of the site (table 5).

CONCLUSION

In our search for a reliable methodology to map the archaeological potential of the River Scheldt, the first results are promising. The systematic sampling in a fixed grid enables us to detect, delimit and evaluate buried archaeological sites in a variable landscape. However, choosing the appropriate sample grid and meshes for sieving the samples is of the utmost importance.

Extensive prehistoric sites with a dense artefact scatter situated on vast sand ridges, such as the Early Mesolithic sites of Verrebroek-Dok, are relatively easily detected. But the detection of smaller and less dense sites, situated on small ridges or in a less pronounced landscape, demands more intensive methods. By combining a tight sample grid and fine sieving meshes, chances of successful prospection are multiplied considerably. Otherwise these concentrations might easily be missed. Using a narrow grid and a fine mesh also provides insight into site structure and extent, needed for further evaluation of newly found sites.

TABLE 4
Pearson Correlation Test for the amount of artefacts in samples and excavation units at Oudenaarde-Donk (based on the data in table 5).

Correlations		Sample	Excavation
Sample	Pearson Correlation	1	0.002
	Sig. (2-tailed)	.	0.997
	N	8	8
Excavation	Pearson Correlation	0.002	1
	Sig. (2-tailed)	0.997	.
	N	8	8

TABLE 5
The amount of artefacts retrieved from the samples and the related excavation units (1mm meshes). Extrapolation of the auger results leads to a serious overestimation of the artefact density.

Bore hole	Sample	Excavation	Extrapolation
1/4	2	53	64
1/5	10	265	318
1/6	11	67	350
1/7	15	237	478
1/9	22	81.5	701
2/4	99	127.5	3,153
2/5	57	158	1,815
2/8	29	93	1,847
Total	245	1,082	8,726

ACKNOWLEDGEMENTS

Our thanks are due to the Special Research Fund of Ghent University (BOF, project nr 011/052/04) for the financial assistance of this project. The field work of this study was also supported by the Flemish Institute for the Archaeological Heritage (VIOE).

I am very grateful to my supervisor, Professor Philippe Crombé and my colleagues Joris Sergant and Gunther Noens for advice, critical comments and encouraging support. Also thanks to Professor Kris Erauw and Jos Deeben for advice on statistics.

REFERENCES

Ameels, V, Bastiaens, J, Bats, M, Crombé, P, Deforce, K, Haneca, K, Parent, J-P and Van Strydonck, M 2003 Recent Steentijdonderzoek in de regio Oudenaarde, Oost-Vlaanderen, België, *Notae Praehistoricae*, 23, 61–5.

Crombé, P 2006 'The Wetlands of sandy Flanders (NW-Belgium): potentials and prospects for Prehistoric Research Management', *in* Rensink, E & Peeters, H (eds) *Proceedings of the International Symposium 'Preserving the Early Past. Investigation, Selection and Preservation of Palaeolithic and Mesolithic Sites and Landscapes'*, Rijksdienst voor het Oudheidkundig Bodemonderzoek, Nederlandse Archeologische Rapporten. Amersfoort.

Crombé, P 1998 *The Mesolithic in Northwestern Belgium. Recent Excavations and Surveys*. British Archaeological Reports, International Series, 716. Oxford.

Crombé, P (ed) 2005 *The Last Hunter-gatherer-fishermen in Sandy-Flanders (NW Belgium). The Verrebroek and Doel Excavation Projects, Part 1: Palaeo-environment, Chronology and Features*. Archaeological Reports Ghent University, 3. Gent.

Crombé, P & Verbruggen, C 2002 'The Lateglacial and early Postglacial occupation of northern Belgium: the evidence from Sandy Flanders', *in* Eriksen, B V & Bratlund, B (eds) *Recent Studies in the Final Palaeolithic of the European Plain. Proceedings of a UISPP Symposium, Stockholm, 14–17 October 1999*. Jutland Archaeological Society Publications, 39, 165–80. Højbjerg.

Depredomme, L 1986 *Postglaciale landschapsgeschiedenis rond de site van Oudenaarde-Donk. Ghent*. Unpubl master thesis, Ghent University.

Groenewoudt, B J 1994 *Prospectie, waardering en selectie van archeologische vindplaatsen: een beleidsgerichte verkenning van middelen en mogelijkheden*. Rijksdienst voor het Oudheidkundig Bodemonderzoek, Nederlandse Archeologische Rapporten, 17. Amersfoort.

Howard, A J & Macklin, M G 1999 'A generic geomorphological approach to archaeological interpretation and prospection in British river valleys', *Antiquity*, 73, 281, 527–41.

Jacobs, P 1968 *Geologie en geomorfologie van de zuidrand van de Vlaamse Vallei tussen Destelbergen en Kalken*. Unpubl master thesis, Ghent.

Jacobs, P 1974 Kwartairgeologie van de streek tussen Destelbergen en Kalken (België, provincie Oost-Vlaanderen), *Mededelingen van de werkgroep voor Tertiair en Kwartair Geologie*, 11, 3–23.

Kiden, P 1986–7 'De bijdrage van de geomorfologie aan het interdisciplinair archeologisch onderzoek', *VOBOV-info*, 24/25, 6–8.

Kiden, P 1991 'The Lateglacial and Holocene evolution of the Middle and Lower river Scheldt, Belgium', *in* Sarkel, L, Gregory, K J & Thornes, J B (eds) *Temperate Palaeohydrology*, 283–99. Chichester.

Parent, J-P, Van Der Plaetsen, P & Vanmoerkerke, J 1986–7 'Prehistorische jagers en veetelers aan de Donk te Oudenaarde', *VOBOV-Info*, 24/25, 13–39.

Parent, J-P, Van Der Plaetsen, P & Vanmoerkerke, J 1987 'Neolithische site aan de Donk te Oudenaarde', *Archaeologia Belgica*, 3, 73–6.

Tol, A & Verhagen, P 2004 'Optimale en standaard boormethoden', *in* Tol, A, Verhagen, P, Borsboom, A & Verbruggen, M *Prospectief boren. Een studie naar de betrouwbaarheid en toepasbaarheid van booronderzoek in de prospectiearcheologie*. RAAP, RAAP-Rapport 1000, 63–81. Amsterdam.

Tol, A, Verhagen, P, Borsboom, A & Verbruggen, M 2004 *Prospectief boren. Een studie naar de betrouwbaarheid en toepasbaarheid van booronderzoek in de prospectiearcheologie*. RAAP, RAAP-Rapport 1000. Amsterdam.

Vanmoerkerke, J 1986 'A Neolithic site at Asper Jolleveld', *in* Vermeulen, F *The Roman settlement and cemetery at Asper (Gavere, East Flanders)*. Scholae Archaeologicae 5, 161–7. Ghent.

Verbruggen, C 1971 *Postglaciale landschapsgeschiedenis van Zandig Vlaanderen. Botanische, ecologische en morfologische aspecten op basis van palynologisch onderzoek*. Unpubl PhD thesis, Ghent.

Vermeulen, F 1986 *The Roman settlement and cemetery at Asper (Gavere, East Flanders)*. Scholae Archaeologicae 5. Ghent.

Wilkinson, K & Bond, C J 2001 'Interpreting archaeological site distribution in dynamic sedimentary environments', *in* Darvill, T & Gojda, M (eds) *One land, many landscapes. Papers from a session held at the European Association of Archaeologists. Fifth Annual Meeting in Bournemouth, 1999*. British Archaeological Reports International Series 987, 55–66.

Bronze Age craftsmanship in Ireland:
some unusual artefacts from County Meath

CAITRÍONA MOORE and INGELISE STUIJTS

INTRODUCTION

A cache of 131 similar wooden artefacts was found in Muckerstown, Co Meath. Whilst no other diagnostic material was found, dating of one of the artefacts puts the find in the Middle Bronze Age. Attention is given to the composition of the artefacts and the wood identification. Possible suggestions for their function feed back into traditional woodwork crafts and the underlying understanding of woodmanship and woodland management. The wood identification, although problematic, suggests that the objects were made of locally available material.

From February to May 2004, excavations were carried out by Caitríona Moore for Cultural Resource Development Services Ltd in Muckerstown, Co Meath (Ireland). The excavations were completed as part of the N2 Finglas–Ashbourne Road Scheme and were funded by the National Roads Authority. During the excavation, a number of intriguing wooden objects turned up in a large pit. These artefacts form the subject of this article.

Following the description of the site, the composition and likely manufacturing of the artefacts will be described. The identification of the components of the artefacts indicates which wood species were used in the fabrication process and the possible source of the material. It also informs on possible wear and tear, and on preservation conditions.

The function of the artefacts is not immediately clear, but a number of options taken from traditional woodland crafts will be explored.

SITE DESCRIPTION

The site (Site 13b), was excavated under excavation licence extension 03E1331 and was located in the townland of Muckerstown in Co Meath, just north of Co Dublin (fig 1).

The site was located in agricultural dryland and was discovered through pre-development test trenching of the development route. It consisted of a central semi-circular slot-trench within which were two postholes. Interpreted as structural, no diagnostic artefacts or material were recovered from the feature. External to this, in the south-western part of the site, were two very large pits, Cuts 069 and 147 (fig 2). These were almost identical in form, being teardrop shaped, and measuring on average, 10m long × 6m wide. They both began as very shallow cuts of approximately 0.1m deep, which gradually increased to an average of 2.5m.

Both pits were filled with a series of heavy waterlogged clays, rich in organic remains. Cut 069 produced a very high amount of well-preserved plant remains and a large quantity of worked wood. Cut 147 contained less plant material; however, 131 wooden objects were discovered deposited in its base. Given the scale and, in particular, the depth of the pits, it is likely that they were associated with the access to and/or the begetting of water. The gradual incline into both, especially that of Cut 147 which was very roughly cobbled, supports this suggestion; however, a definite function for the features remains uncertain. This uncertainty is caused in part by the distinct lack of diagnostic artefactual evidence from the site with only small amounts of pottery and stone finds being retrieved from late or disturbed contexts.

THE ARTEFACTS

The artefacts which form the basis of this article were all retrieved from Cut 147: they consist of 131 wooden objects, all of which lay in the basal 0.6m of the pit and were very irregularly deposited throughout thirteen separate contexts. A fragment of one of the artefacts has been radiocarbon dated to 1520–1310 cal BC (3148±67 BP, Wk 15499).

DESCRIPTION

Unparalleled in the archaeological record, each artefact consists of a bundle of c 20 twigs with

FIGURE 1
Site location: Muckerstown, Co Meath.

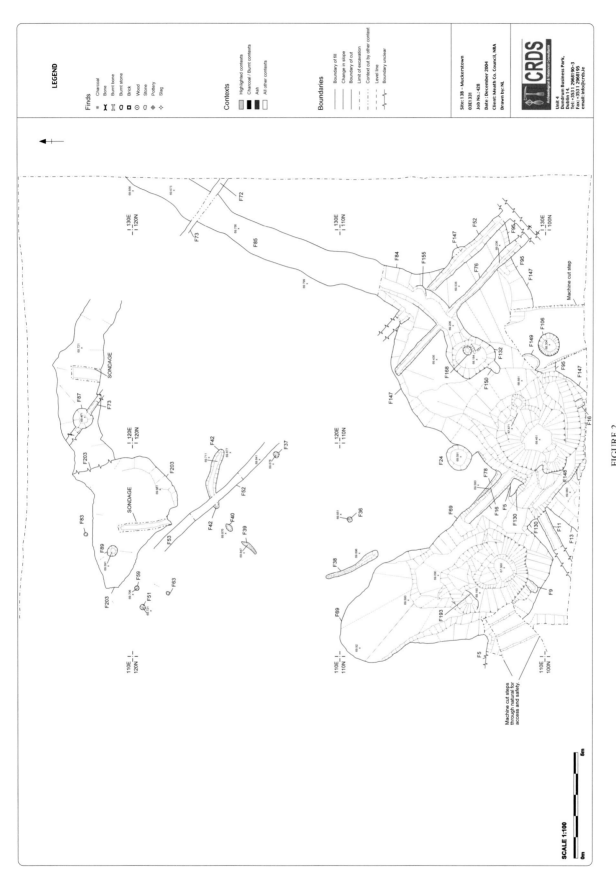

FIGURE 2
Site 13b: cut 069 and cut 147.

individual diameters of 0.2–0.4cm. The bundles are approximately 17cm long and 5cm wide and taper from one end to the other. The widest end is referred to as the splayed end, partially due to the fact that the tips of the twigs at this end display their natural shape and fan outwards. At the opposite end of the bundle the twigs are often worked with simple, flat, metal-cut, chisel point toolmarks and it should be noted that these are frequently all similarly aligned (fig 3). This narrow end of the bundle is referred to as the bound end (see below).

Incorporated within a large number of the bundles of twigs is a piece of brushwood, referred to as a brushwood spine (fig 4). These average 1cm in diameter and are frequently worked at one end, and occasionally at both, displaying chisel points at the narrow end of the bundle and pencil points or squared ends at the splayed end. As with the toolmarks on the ends of the twigs, these were all made using a small, flat metal tool. These central spines are almost as long as the twigs and so would have provided an overall rigidity to the objects (see below).

These bundles of twigs are held together by single ply withies which snake or spiral around the length of the bundle and are securely fixed at one end, that is, the narrow or bound end. Frequently, the withies are looped around this end up to three times and tied in a simple knot. In a large number of the artefacts, the withies can be clearly seen as incorporated within the bundle and emerging from the splayed end to spiral around the length of the artefact before being secured as described above.

Thus, it can be assumed with relative certainty that these objects were manufactured by gathering a small bundle of similar sized twigs and adding to them a single ply withy rope. This was then extracted from one end of the bundle, spiralled around the length and securely knotted at the opposite end. Given that in the artefacts in which the twigs display toolmarks, the toolmarks are frequently similarly aligned, it can be assumed that this trimming or cutting was the final action carried out. It cannot be ascertained when the brushwood spines were inserted or incorporated into the bundles, they may have been gathered in conjunction with the twigs and withy or have been inserted following the knotting. The working of many of the spines to a pencil point, however, could be seen as a mechanism to aid in their insertion into the already tied bundles.

WOOD IDENTIFMICATION RESULTS

Initially, only a few artefacts were identified, of which only one was analysed totally, until the basic construction pattern was established. It was then decided to identify the individual components of the remaining artefacts. This means, generally, six identifications per artefact, namely the withy (and ascertaining whether the withy continued inside the brushwood bundle), the central spine, at least four of the twigs inside the bundle, and any other wood fragments found associated with the artefacts. When some twigs were deviating visually in size, colour or other appearance, these were also identified.

Four artefacts consist of a withy only. One artefact is a loose spine (apple-type, *Pomoideae*).

FIGURE 3
Find 124: partial artefact made of willow brushwood and hazel withy, cut at bound end.

FIGURE 4
Find 102: complete artefact made of elder-type brushwood with hazel withy and spine.

The remaining objects are brushwood bundles of which almost half (57 objects or almost 42 per cent) comprise a central spine.

In most cases, both withies and central spine are made of hazel (*Corylus*). However, withies were also made of alder (*Alnus*, 6x), holly (*Ilex*, 1x) and ash (*Fraxinus*, 1x). For the central spine other wood species used include willow (*Salix*, 9x), elder-type (cf *Sambucus*, 5x), ash (5x), alder (5x) as well as the above mentioned apple-type (loose spine 1x).

The brushwood bundles can be divided roughly into three groups. The majority is made of the elder-type (91 artefacts). A separate group is formed of willow artefacts (10 artefacts). A third group includes brushwood with a mixture of species, including two artefacts made of alder and one of ash solely. A part of the third group contains elder-type brushwood mixed with alder and hazel. Loose wood includes rose (*Rosa*) and sloe (*Prunus spinosa*) that probably came in the brushwood by accident. It can therefore be concluded that, although the elder-type was the preferred wood species for the artefacts, there was no strict regime to make the bundles. The wood species can be found in scrub, hedges and in woodland margins and was readily available.

The willow bundles retain their bark and are made of the thin woody spray. The ash bundles are stiffer and the brushwood is slightly larger in diameter. The bundles made of the elder-type are thin, hollow and often flattened. A yellow/greenish layer of cells indicate the presence of the outer skin. There are no indications that the wood was used, based on the presence of the outermost cell layers, but also there are no abrasion marks or cuts visible, apart from the finishing cuts at the wider end.

The identification turned out to be problematic for approximately half of the artefacts, those made of the elder-type. This is due primarily to the fragility of the material. Another reason is the fact that the brushwood only in part consists of woody material. Whilst the brushwood bundles are woody at the bound end, they are herb-like at the splayed end. Therefore, all characteristics of the wood type in question are probably not yet fully developed.

The elder-type bundles are made of straight and smooth shoots with long internodes. The nodes were not well preserved. No leaves or spines have been observed. A yellow hue distinguishes these bundles from the others. The identification to elder-type is based primarily on the presence of simple perforation plates, absence of helical thickenings, heterogeneous rays with sheath cells and typical large, oval, ray-vessel pits. Macroscopically, the long internodes and hollow shoots are taken into consideration.

However, the transversal section does not present the characteristic view normally seen in elder. Macroscopically the pith in the brushwood is rather narrow, compared with the wide pith that is characteristically found in fresh material. Based on the latter two observations the identification is elder-type rather than elder.

FUNCTION OF ARTEFACTS/MODERN PARALLELS

Although there are some slight variations within the assemblage, such as one bundle which is tied with at least two, and possibly three, separate withies, overall it can be stated that the excavations at Muckerstown yielded a substantial cache of unique Bronze Age artefacts. As described above, it does not appear that these were difficult objects to manufacture; however, their uniformity, the numbers involved and their location at the base of a large water-filled pit suggest deliberation and intent on several levels. As stated previously, these objects have no known parallels in the archaeological record. However, research of later folk life traditions and tools has provided a number of, if not exactly identical, at least similarly constructed items.

Besoms or brooms

One such object is a besom or broom, which, although larger in scale, is traditionally made from a bundle of twigs tied at one end with a withy (Tabor 2004, 113). Into this end is inserted a handle that has the effect of further tightening the bundle (Seymour 2001, 33). Besoms and brooms are used for sweeping. Research at the National Museum of Ireland, Museum of Country Life at Turlough Park in Co Mayo found several examples of hand besoms and water sprinklers, smaller versions of that described above, which also had been trimmed at their bound end.

Traditionally, the best material for besoms in the historical past was broom (*Cytisus scoparius* L.). But most broom or besom heads are at present made from birch or heather (*Calluna vulgaris* Hull). The basic pattern of twig brooms is quite similar: a bundle of fine twigs approximately 90cm long, giving a finished broom of about 150cm (Tabor 2004, 114). The handle was made of a straight pole of about 4cm in diameter. Most besoms have two bonds or laps binding the head, and these are often cleft brushwood 0.25cm in diameter, of various wood species or a hazel withy of 0.6cm in diameter (Tabor 2004, 117).

Thatching wood

Thatching is one of the oldest of the building crafts. Vegetable matter used for thatching included a variety of materials such as reed, sedge, heather and bracken. Wheat and reed thatched roofs still form part of the vernacular architecture in England (Tabor 2004, 95). The thatch was usually made of bundles of vegetable material and a variety of small wood objects were required to fix the thatch.

In Spain (SW Asturia), there is a tradition to thatch byre-houses and cow-houses using bundles of broom (Menéndez 2004). The green broom is cut during the waning phase of the moon. When the weather situation is good – that means, a dry spell – part of the roof thatch of a building is re-thatched. Bundles of green broom are driven into the old beds of broom, with their leaves turned downwards. The top ridge is made by pairs of green broom with two or more timber poles laid over the ridge bundles. The bundles of broom are cut and set unaltered (Menéndez pers comm).

Menéndez (2004) suggests that green broom was used for thatch in Spain in areas where the economy relied on cattle rather than on cereal crops and where broom was locally available. The broom variety used in Spain is *Cytisus scoparius* L., the broom type with green needles and a grooved stem. The grooves would serve to drain water faster downwards.

A similar use of broom as thatch was found in Scotland and on the Isle of Man, where broom was used as roof thatch on the poor man's accommodation in the 1640s (Blundell 1648–56).

Firewood

Another suggestion for the function of these artefacts is that of their use as firewood. In traditional woodland crafts, firewood was a common use of left-overs, such as cordwood and brash. Firewood or wood fuel was not only used in the baker's kitchen and brewer's maltings, but also for a variety of industries such as drying of salt, firing of bricks, ties and pottery, the burning of lime (Edlin 1949, 157; Tabor 2004, 110). Bundles of sticks or twigs were also used as base for corn and hay stacks.

The most common fuel was a bundle of sticks or twigs bound together. It was made from the offal of the cut, those sticks with no craft use at all. Traditional words associated with firewood are faggot, bavin, pimp and kid.

The term 'faggot' first shows up in English around 1300, but the word probably derived from Old French. Originally, the word derived from the Greek word ó *phakelos* or the Latin word *facula* meaning torch. A faggot can be described as a bundle of sticks. A slender branch, twisted to form a withy, forms the usual band to hold the bundle together. A traditional faggot is 90cm long and 61cm in circumference (Tabor 2004, 110).

Smaller wood was made into bundles called bavins, with withies that formed two or three twists around a bundle. Bunce (=kids) was a term used for bundles of all the smallest wood and rubbish left after the brash had been faggoted.

A 'pimp' is a type of firelighter made on the borders of Sussex and Surrey. The making of pimps is usually done during summertime, using birch spray that has been cut during the winter months in a flat trough called a boy. A pimp is made of a small bundle 15cm long by 7.5cm across, to which is added two cleft sticks of hazel, and bound together with a withy. A bundle of 25 pimps are bound together to form a so-called kid (Edlin 1949, 158).

It seems the firewood makers were creative in their language, creating families out of their left-overs. All the above-mentioned firewood terminologies, especially the terms 'faggot' and 'pimp' nowadays are often associated with other meanings, including heretics and homosexuals. However, the latter association has its origin in the USA.

Brushwood bundles for drainage and defence

The term fascine is still used for bundles of brushwood to secure revetment for defence purposes in coastal or river situations. These fascines are basically bundles of long faggots, about 20 rods with a diameter of 2.5cm and a total length of 240–300cm, bound in three places to give a final diameter of about 26cm. Such bundles of brushwood were also used in ditches instead of pipes, to allow for drainage (Tabor 2004, 112). These ditches were called 'faggot-drains'.

Other comparable parallels

Further research of folk life traditions and artefacts has revealed several seasonal customs involving the twisting and fashioning of organic material such as rushes or straw into playthings or tokens used or bestowed at certain times of the year (Evans 1957, 208). Objects such as harvest knots and rush or straw hats and masks may have had both practical and ceremonial value (*ibid.*) and while the Muckerstown artefacts do not really emulate such items, the act or art of fashioning objects, however meaningful, from twisted plant or wood fibres is certainly echoed by these artefacts.

CONCLUSION

The brushwood artefacts from Muckerstown form a unique find in Ireland, with no immediate parallel. The manufacturing of the artefacts is reminiscent of a number of traditional woodland crafts using small round wood, some of which are described above. All woodland crafts – including the making of hurdles, an option that has not been discussed – have their basis in woodmanship and the knowledge of how to work with existing woodlands. In Ireland, however, there is no real woodcraft tradition that can be traced back for hundreds of years. The main reason for this is that history does not indicate the presence of large-scale managed forests before the Plantation period. Compared to, for example, Britain, knowledge of ancient woodlands and woodmanship is limited. Knowledge can, however, be gleaned from folk life traditions and medieval literature. However, the artefacts date to the Bronze Age, and therefore an immediate parallel does not need to be obvious.

Nevertheless, of the woodland crafts described above, some options seem more likely than others. Whilst the similarities between besoms and brooms and the objects excavated at Muckerstown are notable, several aspects of the latter prevent their definite interpretation as such. As stated above, the presence of a central spine, almost the same length as the entire artefact, means that those from Muckerstown would have been quite rigid. In addition there is no evidence of a bushy, brush-like end on any of the recovered artefacts. This is coupled with evidence from the wood identification programme which suggests that the twigs were without leaves and also were not damaged or utilized in any way. Nevertheless, the functional explanation of the artefacts as besoms or brooms with a sweeping function cannot be excluded.

Usage of the artefacts as thatch seems far-fetched. There is no need to make complicated individual artefacts, with or without support by a central spine, for a roofing function. On the other hand, whilst the intention of the artefacts might have been thatching material, the condition of the artefacts excludes that it was used as thatch before it was deposited into a pit.

A function of the artefacts as fascines seems unlikely based on the same argument as above, in that such a function would not require such an elaborate manufacturing procedure; a mere bundle of brushwood would suffice. The size of the bundles also seems rather too big, although, of course, the Bronze Age measurements do not need to coincide with present-day opinions and techniques.

The firewood option has been described in detail because there are many varieties on the same idea. Size matters in firewood bundles, and the present-day options of faggots, bavins, pimps, kids and bunces are discussed. According to Goodburn (pers comm), historically, a faggot was bound with two twists, and the smaller bavin with one twist of the withy. The Bronze Age artefacts from Muckerstown are thus very reminiscent of what, in traditional woodland crafts, is called a bavin.

This leads to a final suggestion that these artefacts may be ritual in nature. The votive deposition of objects in wet places is well documented throughout prehistoric times (O'Kelly 1989, 263). Given the Bronze Age date of the Muckerstown assemblage it can be reasonably suggested that these may be meaningful objects, perhaps representing an individual person or group of people, which were deliberately deposited in the base of the deep pit. Notwithstanding, it is possible they could have held both a practical and ritual significance.

ACKNOWLEDGEMENTS

Many thanks are due to Finola O'Carroll, Senior Project Archaeologist, for advice and support during excavation and post-excavation. Thanks to Mary Deevy and Maria FitzGerald, Project Archaeologists with the NRDO, Meath County Council and to the NRA for enabling the excavations. Special thanks are also due to Asta Vasiliskaite, Leigh Barker and Dave Harrison. Many thanks go to Damien Goodburn for the suggestion of faggots and bavins, and discussions on the matter.

REFERENCES

Blundell, W 1648–56 'Of the manksmen, the Inhabitants and Natives of the Isle of man in General', *in A history of the Isle of Man Vol. I Chapter VII*, 53.

Edlin, H L 1949 *Woodland Crafts in Britain*. London.

Evans, E E 1957 *Irish Folk Ways*. London.

Menéndez, C 2004 *Thatching with Green Broom in Spain*. Madrid.

O'Kelly, M J 1989 *Early Ireland*. Cambridge.

Seymour, J 2001 *The Forgotten Arts and Crafts*. London.

Tabor, R 2004 *Traditional Woodland Crafts*. London.

Wetland records of a coastal cultural landscape in north-west Scotland: application of the multiple scenario approach to landscape reconstruction

M JANE BUNTING, RICHARD MIDDLETON and CLAIRE L TWIDDLE

INTRODUCTION

Interpretation of pollen records in terms of the vegetation communities that they originated from is not straight-forward; the quantity of pollen grains produced by different plants varies, predominantly according to their reproductive biology and differences in grain morphology mean that the dispersal and deposition of pollen types also varies. The relationship between pollen and vegetation has been studied sporadically since the origin of pollen analysis as a discipline and algorithms have been developed to enable the calculation of past vegetation composition from a palaeosample (eg Parsons & Prentice 1983; Neilsen etc 2005; Sugita in prep). However, the vegetation data obtained is a single distance-weighted measurement, which is still some way from the spatially referenced maps of past vegetation ideally required by many end users.

In this paper we approach the problem from a different angle, using what we call a Multiple Scenario Approach or MSA. We simulate maps of many possible past landscape mosaics and then use the same model of pollen dispersal and deposition, which is used in the quantitative approach described above, to simulate the pollen deposited at a known point in those landscapes, a point from which we have obtained a palaeorecord. We then treat the simulated pollen assemblages from these many possible landscapes as if they were modern analogue samples and use analogue-matching statistics to identify which ones are most like the subfossil assemblages and thus which of the many landscape scenarios can be considered the best estimate of the past landscape which produced the palaeopollen signal.

This approach enables us to identify, with some confidence, the likely vegetation composition and the spatial distribution of the vegetation mosaic across the Coigach peninsula during the Middle and Late Holocene, an essential backdrop for better understanding of the archaeological record and of the cultural landscape created and occupied by previous human populations.

THE STUDY SITE

The sea-level isolation basin at Badentarbet, near Achiltibuie, Coigach peninsula, north-west Scotland (see fig 1) lies within an archaeologically rich landscape. The valley sides and the edges of the wetland have been ridged for cultivation in a discrete late historic field system within a head-dike, and the field system and settlement in the immediate area have been studied by Chrystall & McCullagh (2000). A comprehensive archaeological landscape survey of the whole peninsula has been carried out (RCAHMS 1997). In mountainous regions like northern Scotland, the low-lying land near the coast and along river valleys, with relatively fertile soils and the additional resources provided by the sea or river, is often a long-term locus of comparatively intense prehistoric and historic human activity, despite the relatively high degree of exposure to storms, salt spray and flood hazards. In order to reconstruct the vegetation history of the Badentarbet area, a 6.8m long core of sediments was collected from the basin for pollen analysis and radiocarbon dating (Bunting & Tipping 2004).

METHODS

Two time-slices were selected for investigation. They were chosen because they occur within periods of relative stability within the pollen diagram. The first time-slice chosen was 5500 BP, before the elm decline. This represents the landscape before the introduction of agriculture and a reconstruction should give an indication of the availability of terrestrial resources to hunter-gatherer populations in the area. The second time slice chosen was 3200 BP, after the elm and pine decline. At this point, the pollen diagram is interpreted as showing evidence of continuous (though small-scale) human activity, primarily pastoral, in the landscape.

The Multiple Scenario Approach (MSA) which we apply in this paper involves creating many possible landscape scenarios. Scenarios are created

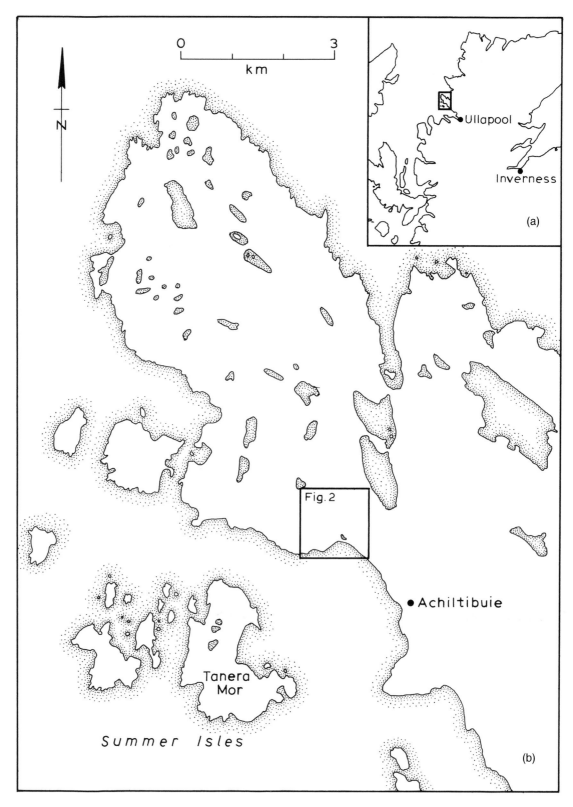

FIGURE 1
Map showing (a) the location of the study area in Scotland, (b) the landscape area used for modelling, and (c) detail of the area around the Badentarbet basin from which the pollen diagram was taken (see page 111).

by identifying the main plant taxa present in the region, and combining a knowledge of their ecology with the landscape's topography, geology and palaeogeography (eg Shennan *et al* 2000). The next stage is to simulate the pollen signal at the coring point in each. The resultant 'swarm' of possible pollen assemblages is then compared statistically with the actual palaeo-assemblage from the sedimentary

pollen record (Bunting & Tipping 2004) to identify which, if any, of the simulated scenarios produces a good fit of pollen signals.

CREATING LANDSCAPE SCENARIOS

An Ordnance Survey digital elevation model of a 20×15km region around the Badentarbet basin,

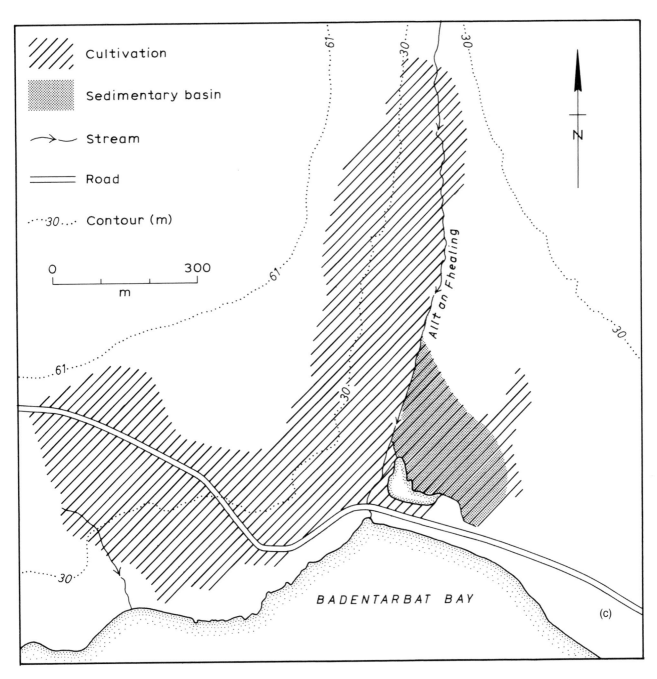

FIGURE 2

including the whole of the Coigach peninsula (see fig 1), was used as the basis for scenario generation. Relative sea-level (RSL) has fallen over the last few thousand years, so the palaeogeography at 5500 BP was simulated by 'flooding' all parts of the DEM below RSL at 5500 BP, as estimated from the Badentarbet sedimentary sequence (Shennan *et al* 2000), and removing the gravel bar from the mouth of the basin. Sea-level at 3200 BP was set at present-day levels.

Preparing for scenario creation involved three steps: firstly, identification of the main plant taxa present in the region at the time-slice, secondly, the making of assumptions about the main communities present and their composition, and, thirdly, identifying possible limits on their distribution imposed by landscape topography (eg altitude, slope angle, aspect). The main pollen taxa present were identified from the Badentarbet pollen record and from other pollen diagrams from the wider region (eg Pennington 1972). Simple communities were then identified. based on the known ecological preferences and behaviours of the main taxa and a limited number of topographic rules drawn up to control which parts of the landscape they could occupy. Some rules were evidence-based, for example, the altitudinal limits of *Pinus* were set at 600m, of *Betula* at 400m and of *Quercus* at 200m on the basis of published ecological data (Grime 1991). In less clear-cut situations, several alternative rules for the placement of one community were established to generate the widest possible range of scenarios (eg restricting bog to areas with 0° slope angle only or allowing it potentially to occur on slope angles up to 3° or 5°; restricting *Ulmus* to sunnier southerly slopes or allowing it to potentially occur on any aspect). All possible combinations of rules were used to generate scenarios.

The swarm of scenarios was generated using Landscape, an as-yet-unpublished software package. Landscape is a PC-based application which will interpret a rule-based script to distribute community patches within a landscape framework. The programme requires all rules to be specified with an accompanying level of probability and hence repeated runs of the same script will generate scenarios differing in detail, but still conforming to an underlying rule base. Since the rules for placement may be varied (see above), the proportions of each community can be set at several different levels (eg, the underlying rule could specify that 5 per cent, 10 per cent or 15 per cent of suitable land is occupied by *Quercus*) and multiple replicates made for each rule combination, large numbers of scenarios need to be created.

There are three major ways in which the pollen signal produced from a simulated landscape may be varied. The first is to change the composition of those communities which contain more than one taxon whilst keeping the distribution of those communities constant. The second is to change the proportion of the communities within the wider landscape, thus changing the background component of the pollen signal. The third is to change the position of communities within the local area around the basin being modelled, the spatial area within which changes in the detailed pattern of vegetation is registered most sensitively by the pollen signal (see, eg Sugita 1994). We chose to ignore the first and focus on the second (by using a range of possible levels for each community) and third (using the randomness of the placing of patches in the scenario creation stage). Scenario compositions and input parameters for the main taxa are shown in table 1.

SIMULATING POLLEN ASSEMBLAGES

Pollen assemblages at the Badentarbet coring location were simulated for each landscape scenario using the Prentice-Sugita pollen dispersal and deposition models (Prentice 1985; Sugita 1993, 1994). The model was enabled using Pollen, an unpublished variant on the PolFlow component of the HUMPOL software suite (Bunting & Middleton 2005). The input parameters required include the sedimentation velocity of pollen grains (which was calculated using the geometric estimate method; Gregory 1973, Sugita *et al* 1999) and estimates of Relative Pollen Productivity (RPP) for each plant taxon. Estimated RPP values were taken from Sugita *et al* (1999) and Broström *et al* (2004), based on work in south Sweden; these values have been used with apparent success in other simulation exercises in the British Isles (Caseldine & Fyfe in press; Fyfe in press).

IDENTIFYING THE BEST ANALOGUES

After computing simulated pollen loadings at the coring point in each scenario, the data are compared with the actual pollen signal using the same statistical approach as for modern analogue comparison studies (eg Overpeck *et al* 1985, Maher 1990). Measures of statistical distance, such as the squared chord distance, are calculated between the reference (palaeo) sample and all possible analogue samples to identify the closest match. The cut-off point, or distance beyond

TABLE 1

Properties of pollen taxa used in modelling pollen signals from landscape scenarios, community composition, and communities present in the scenarios created for 5500 BP and 3200 BP (see text for details of scenario creation process).

Taxon	Estimates relative pollen productivity	Fallspeed (cm s⁻¹)	Wet Alder woodland (WA)	Dry species – Poor woodland (DP)	Dry species – Rich woodland (DR)	Dry species – Rich woodland – Post elm decline (DRP)	Dry Pine woodland (DP)	Marsh within basin (M)	Heath (HE)	Grass-rich Heath (GH)	Pasture (PA)
Alnus *	4.2	0.021	85								
Salix *	1.3	0.022									
Corylus *	1.4	0.025		20	20	20					
Betula *	8.9	0.024	10	80		20					
Quercus *	7.6	0.035			20	60					
Ulmus *	0.8	0.032			60						
Pinus *	5.7	0.031					100				
Cyperaceae **	1	0.035	5					60	15		
Poaceae **	1	0.035						40	5	80	100
Calluna **	4.7	0.038							80	20	
present at 5500 BP?			Y	Y	Y	N	Y	N	Y	Y	N
present at 3200 BP?			Y	Y	N	Y	N	Y	Y	Y	Y

* RPP estimates taken from Sugita *et al* 1999
** RPP estimates taken from Broström *et al* 2004

which a match is not considered meaningful, varies somewhat; Overpeck *et al* (1985) use a squared chord distance of 0.15, whilst Maher (2000) recommends a distance of 0.20, which we chose as the cut-off for this study. Squared chord distances were calculated using the shareware software package ANALOG (Schweitzer 1994).

RESULTS

5500 BP

A total of 7,900 landscape scenarios were created and of these 204 produced squared chord distances below the 0.20 cut-off; the shortest distance was 0.150493. Thirteen scenarios had distances of less than 0.16 and their properties are summarized in table 2. The best-fit scenarios have a woodland cover of 93.5 per cent, suggesting an essentially tree-covered landscape with occasional clearings, which were simulated as heath. The pollen assemblage also contained over 90 per cent pollen from woodland trees. In these possible landscapes, patches of heath are occasionally present on flat hill tops and in some exposed coastal locations. Models of dominant woodland type across the British Isles at 5000 BP (eg Bennett 1989) show this part of Scotland dominated by birch-hazel woodland. The best-fit scenarios have vegetation with about 50 per cent birch-hazel but including a significant proportion of other broad-leaved trees (oak and elm together

cover 19 per cent) and of pine (21 per cent). The composition of the local area around the basin in these best-fit models does not differ much from the wider landscape.

3200 BP

For the 3200 BP time-slice 4,380 scenarios were created. Many of these scenarios (over 1,000) had squared-chord distances below 0.15 and eight had scores below 0.11. The landscape characteristics of these eight are summarized in table 3. The pollen sample from this time-slice contains 75 per cent pollen from the tree species making up woodland communities and 25 per cent from open community species. However, the best-fit landscapes have only 32 per cent woodland cover and almost 68 per cent open communities. Grass heath is the dominant community, occurring largely in flatter parts of the landscape, with some heath and small amounts of pasture. As at 5500 BP, the vegetation composition of the local area around the sampling point was broadly similar to that of the wider landscape.

DISCUSSION

This study demonstrates that it is possible to compare different scenarios of past landscapes using pollen dispersal and deposition models and to use a

TABLE 2
Summary of vegetation composition in best-fit scenarios (n = 13) at 5500 BP.

	Whole landscape	Concentric rings around sampling point		
		0–500m	501–1000m	1001–1500m
Water	57.0%	57.0%	23.2%	30.1%
Communities as a percentage of vegetated land				
Wet-alder?	1.6%	1.6%	10.4%	1.0%
Dry-poor?	51.5%	52.3%	40.8%	54.9%
Dry-rich?	19.3%	18.9%	23.3%	25.8%
Dry-pine?	21.0%	20.6%	19.5%	15.9%
Heath	6.6%	6.5%	6.0%	2.4%
Wooded	93.5%	93.5%	94.0%	97.6%
Open	6.6%	6.5%	6.0%	2.4%

TABLE 3
Summary of vegetation composition in best-fit scenarios (n = 8) at 3200 BP.

	Whole landscape	Concentric rings around sampling point		
		0–500m	501–1000m	1001–1500m
Water	55.8%	55.8%	14.75%	28.8%
Communities as a percentage of vegetated land				
Wet-alder?	1.7%	1.7%	12.3%	1.2%
Dry-poor?	21.2%	21.2%	15.6%	30.8%
Dry-rich, post	9.2%	9.2%	1.1%	8.6%
Heath	11.9%	11.9%	4.1%	2.2%
Grass-heath	54.6%	54.6%	60.0%	56.1%
Pasture	1.4%	1.4%	6.9%	1.2%
Wooded	32.1%	32.1%	29.0%	40.5%
Open	67.9%	67.9%	71.0%	59.5%

statistical tool to determine which is most likely to resemble the past landscape.

LIMITATIONS

The approach assumes that the model of pollen dispersal and deposition and its parameters are correct. The largest area of uncertainty in this assumption concerns the RPP estimates. The values used in this study were obtained from empirical investigation of the modern-day landscape mosaics of southern Sweden; no dataset collected using a comparable methodology in the UK or in other northern European areas is yet available to confirm the wider application of the results. A similar assumption of consistent RPP values in time and space is made implicitly in the use of modern-analogue matching approaches. Even if the results are found to be identical in different regions, there are still some concerns about applying them to past landscapes. Many plants grow today in conditions different from those they would have had in the past, for example, woodland occurs as discrete patches with a relatively high edge to area ratio, rather than as extensive tracts, and woodland management over centuries and millennia has shaped both woodland composition and, to some extent, architecture and tree growth form. Elm (*Ulmus*) is a particularly challenging taxon since it is probably still recovering from the 1980s outbreak of Dutch Elm Disease in north-west Europe.

Assumptions are also made about community composition, the relative importance of different environmental controls on vegetation distribution, about the size and shape of patches of different communities and about patch frequency within the landscape. We expect to achieve equifinality, producing multiple landscapes with distinctively different mosaics which produce pollen signals which are equidistant from the actual palaeo-signal. However, in this study we did not vary all four listed parameters, choosing instead to focus on varying the environmental controls and patch frequency only. Varying the other factors would have substantially increased the numbers of scenarios to be worked through but would also produce a more varied set of 'most similar' landscapes than those identified here.

It should be possible in future work to use large-lake records, which 'sense' landscapes as homogenous vegetation areas (Sugita 1994), to estimate the ratios of the taxa making up one of these broad communities (eg, we had a community 'Species-Rich Dry Woodland' which consisted of oak and elm) in the landscape as a whole. This would also use the RPP values discussed above and requires access to data from suitably large lakes, but might make the selection of a single fixed community composition more objective. In some circumstances, for example, where the landscape mosaic is believed to be well understood, varying community composition may be the first option to consider when creating landscape. For example, Caseldine & Fyfe (in press) used composition variation within a landscape-determined mosaic to assess the importance of elm in the Irish Midlands. In the simulations reported here, patch frequency for different communities was varied, but size was kept within the same parameters in all runs. In future work this should also be varied, even though it will increase the number of scenarios generated by at least another order of magnitude.

RECONSTRUCTION OF LANDSCAPE AT 5500 BP

This landscape reconstruction suggests that the woodland on the Coigach Peninsula at 5500 BP was more varied and also more extensive than earlier interpretations or general maps might suggest. Existing woodland cover would provide shelter for seedlings and saplings of trees, even in clearings and openings within the canopy, enabling regeneration despite the general exposure of the area. The reconstruction suggests that a more densely vegetated and hence perhaps less easily accessible landscape faced Late Mesolithic and Early Neolithic human populations than might have been inferred from the pollen record directly. If this were the case, the importance of the coastal fringe and of streams and lakes as access routes and as locations with better visibility might increase their significance and value. The diversity of woodland type suggests an accompanying diversity in understorey, habitat and resources for human use. The results suggest that we need to be very careful not to let our mental picture of mid-Holocene environments of north-west Scotland be dictated by the broad picture of the generalized maps but should be aware of the likelihood of local variation and greater diversity.

RECONSTRUCTION OF LANDSCAPE AT 3200 BP

This landscape reconstruction suggests that extensive woodland loss had already occurred by 3200 BP. The core recovered from the basin at this point suggests that sediment was accumulating in a shallow open water wetland, so the landscape scenario modelled the basin as having an alder-dominated fringe and a central open area with little vegetation. An equally likely scenario could have been created with a grass-dominated vegetation in the central open area or with a zone of reedbed inside the alder zone around the open area, which would have raised the proportion of grass pollen in the simulated pollen assemblage and thus been combined with a more wooded wider landscape. As mentioned above, equifinality is expected using this reconstruction method. In this study it is possible that we did not enable that to happen by restricting the variety in the local part of the landscape scenarios.

Therefore, the reconstruction does not demonstrate a high degree of openness in the landscape at 3200 BP but it suggests that it is possible. Given the limited indications of human activity in the pollen record, it is tempting to infer that this openness is at least in part the result of natural processes such as progressive soil change linked to the postulated change in climate towards wetter, cooler conditions in the Bronze Age. Alternatively, the site may be marginal to the area of human activity and therefore not picking up a strong signal. Extensive grassy heaths in the inland areas of the peninsula are present in the reconstruction, which might imply that pollen-signal-generating activity was concentrated in those areas rather than the coastal fringes. The alder belt postulated at the edge of the site would also reduce the strength of the signal from anthropogenic indicator taxa in the wider landscape reaching the sample point.

FURTHER WORK

This paper has demonstrated the possibilities for reconstructing landscape mosaics opened up by recent developments in software for modelling pollen dispersal and deposition, and that the example of Badentarbet raises many of the problems and challenges ahead for this method. Increasing the range of possible scenarios tested, exploring scenarios for additional time-slices and testing the predictions derived from the closest reconstructions against cores from another basin on the peninsula will all increase the robustness of the results from the Badentarbet site and contribute to the ongoing development of the method. Results reported here suggest that the outcomes may be surprising, that they will stimulate the development of theories about past human culture and environment, and that they will contribute to the development of well focused integrated archaeology and palaeoenvironmental research programmes.

ACKNOWLEDGEMENTS

We acknowledge helpful discussions with members of the PolLandCal (POLlen-LANDscape CALibration) network, particularly Chris Caseldine, Ralph Fyfe, Kari Hjelle and Anne Birgitte Neilsen. We also thank Keith Scurr and John Garner for producing the maps.

REFERENCES

Bennett, K D 1989 'A provisional map of forest types for the British Isles 5000 years ago', *J Quat Sci*, 4, 141–4.

Broström, A, Sugita, S & Gaillard, M-J 2004 'Pollen productivity estimates for the reconstruction of past vegetation cover in the cultural landscape of southern Sweden', *Holocene*, 14(3), 368–81.

Bunting, M J & Middleton, R 2005 'Modelling pollen dispersal and deposition using HUMPOL software: simulating wind roses and irregular lakes', *Rev Palaeobot Palynol*, 134, 185–96.

Bunting, M J & Tipping, R M 2004 'Complex hydroseral vegetation succession and 'dry land' pollen signals: a case study from north-west Scotland', *Holocene*, 14(1), 53–63.

Caseldine, C J & Fyfe, R M in press 'A modelling approach to locating and characterizing elm decline/landnam clearances', *Quat Sci Rev* (available on line).

Chrystall, F & McCullagh, R 2000 'The classification of field systems by shape and function', *in* Atkinson, J A, Banks, I & MacGregor, G (eds) *Townships to Farmsteads: Rural Settlement Studies in Scotland, England and Wales*. BAR British Series, 293, 117–29. Oxford.

Fyfe, R in press 'GIS and the application of a model of pollen deposition and dispersal: a new approach to testing landscape hypotheses using the POLLANDCAL models', *J Arch Sci* (available on line).

Gregory, P H 1973 *The Microbiology of the Atmosphere*. Aylesbury.

Grime, J P, Hodgson, J G & Hunt, R 1991 *Comparative Plant Ecology: A Functional Approach to Common British Species*. London.

Maher, L 2000 'Modpol.Exe: A Tool For Searching For Modern Analogs Of Pleistocene Pollen Data', *INQUA Sub-Commission on Data Handling Newsletter* 20.

Overpeck, J T, Webb, T III & Prentice, I C 1985 'Quantitative interpretation of fossil pollen spectra: Dissimilarity coefficients and the method of modern analogs for pollen data', *Quat Res*, 23, 87–108.

Pennington, W, Haworth, E Y, Bonny, A P & Lishman, J P 1972 'Lake sediments in northern Scotland', *Trans R Soc London B*, 264, 191–294.

Prentice, I C 1985 'Pollen representation, source area, and basin size: towards a unified theory of pollen analysis', *Quat Res*, 23, 76–86.

RCAHMS 1997 *Achiltibuie: The Archaeology of a Crofting Landscape*. Royal Commission on the Ancient and Historic Monuments of Scotland Broadsheet 3.

Schweitzer, P 1994 ANALOG: A program for estimating paleoclimate parameters using the method of modern analogs. US Geological Survey Open-File Report 94–645 (available on line from *http://geochange.er.usgs.gov/pub/tools/analog/doc/analog.html*).

Shennan, I, Lambeck, K, Horton, B, Innes, J, Lloyd, J, McArthur, J, Purcell, T & Rutherford, M 2000 'Late Devensian and Holocene records of relative sea-level changes in northwest Scotland and the implications for glacio-hydro-isostatic modelling', *Quat Sci Rev*, 19, 1103–35.

Sugita, S 1993 'A model of pollen source area for an entire lake surface', *Quat Res*, 39, 239–44.

Sugita, S 1994 'Pollen representation of vegetation in Quaternary sediments: theory and method in patchy vegetation', *J Ecol*, 82, 881–97.

Sugita, S, Gaillard, M-J & Broström, A 1999 'Landscape openness and pollen records: a simulation approach', *Holocene*, 9, 409–21.

Glimpsing the water

FIONA HAUGHEY

PERCEPTION

A river is one of the most common components in the physical landscape. This is not only for the number and consistency of appearance but also for the visual effect of movement and light reflected. For many, the word 'river' will produce a particular vision; from the Niagara with its thunderous falls and the huge basin of the Amazon with its tributaries, to just the chatter and rush of water over pebbles. Modern thinking of 'landscape' tends to distort our view of what it was like to inhabit in the past that physical landscape with all that it entailed. Rivers, for example, are often defined today as barriers (where they inhibit passage), boundaries (which divide one side or people from another), liminal spaces (that are at the extremities of being) and sites for sacred deposition (that involve setting apart items from the common or secular). They feature rarely in discussions of landscape, and in archaeological treatises, their stereotypical image is frequently re-rehearsed. Nowadays, rivers are placed primarily within the background, causing logistical difficulties where they traverse our paths. Often they are utilized as boundaries between modern political entities; the Tweed, for example, lies between Scotland and England, and the Severn between England and Wales. However, the rivers thus involved have become non-entities – just markers – belonging to neither side nor even being allowed to belong to themselves. Any earlier cultural meaning is swallowed up in the later imposition.

On a basic level, water is the most necessary of elements for living and subsistence. It is essential, whatever the diet. Rivers do not impinge greatly on the life of the average urban-dweller. The water that flows from the tap in the kitchen, particularly in the Western world, is often pumped from many miles away, so connection with its source is intangible. Yet these arteries, which run throughout the land, provide more than the basic commodity of water. They have values, which are being bypassed in our modern age of car, plane and supermarket. In the past they dictated not only the pace of life but also the way it was lived. With passing time they have become merely an adjunct to our existence rather than a necessity. They have become tantalizing glimpses in the landscape, not only physically but also experientially. This paper will begin to open a discussion on the way that rivers may have been perceived in the past and ways in which that meaning can be traced. It is in the nature of a discussion, rather than a conclusion, and should be viewed as work in progress.

CHANGING VIEWPOINTS

The word 'glimpse' conjures up images of snatched glances, things seen out of the corner of an eye, pictures and views seen intermittently while driving past masking trees and the like, and faint or momentary traces left of earlier states. Rivers may be termed 'glimpsed' entities both within our modern society and in the past. Nowadays, in cities, they are often something viewed only as they are passed over or hidden from view by flood barriers. It must be remembered that the accurate view of an entire river system is a fairly modern phenomenon, with the advent of aerial flight and satellites. In the country, they may be screened from the idle public gaze by trees and shrubs, or for those in a flatter landscape they may disappear completely from view until stumbled upon. With modern forms of transport, speed of movement is the prime requirement and glimpsing is all there may be time for as the vehicle flashes past features within the landscape. This is a pace much faster than in the past, when sailing boats and river vessels were the primary method of long-distance travel. In the past, tree cover, often dense in places, and the natural bends on the river would have restricted the vista – although this vista would have been one of constant change when travelling upon the water. The potentially available viewpoints would have also added variety. These include from any nearby heights, looking down; from adjacent wetlands, looking towards; from the riverbank, looking across, up- and downstream; from islands, looking around and within, and from the water, looking down into and up overhead. We have become so land-based in our assessment that we can only appreciate the view via a limited perspective.

Even now, with modern engineering and technological advances, it cannot truly be said that the wildness and waywardness of rivers have been tamed, especially when that river does not wish to be tamed. Flooding in many of the major English river systems, including the Thames and the Humber over the past few years, is illustrative of this lack of control. A look at ethnographic studies amongst hunter-gatherer communities on a number of river systems around the world suggests a dual approach. For Achuna and Tukano Indians in the Amazon basin, landing stages are not only the contact places with the rest of the world but also where they are intimately involved with the river and perform certain acts both sexual and ritual (Descola 1991). On the Alaskan river of the Koyukon, communities navigate their way by using not the usual north–south compass points but the direction of the rivers (Nelson 1986). In Australia, the Aboriginal tribes on the Murray use the river as a marker when burying their dead (Pardoe 1993).

Our Western view often chooses to ignore the intrinsic value of the rivers. For example, when examining the route of the Dorset cursus, Tilley chose to concentrate on potential land paths as the original markers of the monument rather than looking at the archaeological evidence for the three watercourses that are crossed during the cursus's passage across the landscape (Tilley 1994, 173ff). In his discussion of other landscapes, Tilley chooses to concentrate on land as the principal human focus rather than addressing the obvious waterways which, in at least one other case (the Black Mountains), dominate the location (Tilley 1994). The early report on the Iron Gates Mesolithic communities suggested that the reason for the building of the settlements in the gorge was purely for the seasonal deer, ignoring the catfish which swarm up the river (Srejović 1972). This way of examining land-based subsistence factors and ignoring riverine or lacustrine ones, is typical of many archaeological reports. Edmonds' *Ancestral Geographies of the Neolithic* singularly fails to grasp the nettle and discuss the relationship between humans and water (Edmonds 1999).

THE CHANGING 'VALUE' OF AND APPROACHES TO RIVERS

In the prehistoric past, the way people related to rivers changed through time. In the Mesolithic and Early Neolithic periods (hunter-gatherer and early farming communities), islands and sites adjacent to rivers seem to have been the locations of choice (eg, see Van de Noort *et al* 1997, 454ff). These sites were well within the floodplain and similar ones can be traced on many other major European rivers – such as the Elbe/Labe in the Czech Republic (Dreslerová 1995), on the Danube (Srejović 1972), the Seine (Mordant & Mordant 1988, 1992), and the Meuse (Wansleeben & Verhart 1990). Many of these sites have been buried under floodplain deposits or, where on islands still within the river, have suffered from erosion. Rivers formed markers in the landscape during the Neolithic period. They were probably shallower than at present, with all the physical constraints of agriculture and urban sprawl that have been placed upon them. Thus they may have presented very little in the way of obstacles to those wishing to ford them, anymore than a causewayed enclosure would have actually restricted physical access to its centre. Rivers do, however, seem to have been ulitized to create what might be termed significant territories, and this is most obvious in the Neolithic period in England. One such area is in West London, where the Thames, the Colne and other smaller rivers form a cordon round an area that has produced a wide range of monumental structures in the form of henges, cursus and enclosures (eg Cotton *et al* 1986, Robertson-Mackay 1987). Across the neck of land there are a number of smaller henges acting as a final 'barricade'. Similar significant territories can be seen in other locations, for example, further up the Thames near Dorchester (Whittle *et al* 1992) and in North Yorkshire between the rivers Swale and Ure (Harding 2000). At Marden, in Wiltshire, the river appears to intentionally form part of the actual enclosure (Wainwright 1971), which is similar to that at Noyen-sur-Seine (Mordant & Mordant 1988).

As agriculture became more established and human requirements altered, there was a shift away from the immediate river edge, although the salt marsh and marshlands were still seen as useful for grazing and the like. The human response to rivers changed too. In the Bronze Age, there is a return to the river but in a markedly different way. Now, substantial wooden structures can be found on the river's edge, but these are more in the nature of barriers or even protection against the river. They might be considered as a means of living close to the river with all its amenities, without the need for a physical contact with the water. The 'bridge' at Vauxhall on the River Thames is a structure comprising 26 oak timbers, up to 60cm in diameter, projecting out into the river, probably linking the mainland to a central gravel island now eroded or dredged (Haughey 1999, 19). It is situated between the two arms of the River Effra and is opposite the Tyburn delta. It is possible that at this time the tidal head on the Thames would have reached this point on the river, however, the water would still have been fordable so the expense in time and effort for constructing such a substantial structure must have been for something other than ease of access. Similarly, at Runnymede, further upstream in the non-tidal part of the river an extensive waterfront structure can be found (Needham 1991, 114ff). Those vessels used during this period, found thus far in Britain, did not need a deep draft as can be seen, for example, with the Dover boat (Clark 2004) and so the need for such extensive frontage akin to a quay on the water's edge is not clear. The closeness of the human/water relationship seems uneasy and the deposition of large amounts of objects and weaponry into watery contexts would indicate a placatory response (eg Burgess & Gerloff 1981; Pryor 1991). By the Iron Age rivers have definitely become barriers, utilized frequently as tribal boundaries, although settlement sites such as those on crannogs and in wetlands suggest a sense of 'overcoming' the earlier unease. Evidence of subsistence usage of rivers during this period is rare in Britain but one example can be found at Vauxhall in the form of a fishtrap (Haughey 1999, 19). Bridges such as those recorded at Dorney, Buckinghamshire, on a palaeochannel of the Thames, would indicate the need to cross the river barrier (Allen & Welsh 1997, 31–4).

LIFTING THE VEIL

So where can glimpses of this response to the river be seen? This paper will concentrate on examples from the Mesolithic and Neolithic periods, but must be seen as a work in progress, rather than a final conclusion. One way is possibly through the sound of the water movement. Kenneth Brophy argued that a cursus monument may be seen as a euphemism for rivers within a ritual or ceremonial setting, and of the two reasons that he put forward, one was practical ('You don't need to get your feet wet whilst walking the length

of a cursus') and one visual ('The white sheen of water is similar to newly stripped chalk or gravel') (Brophy 2000). He suggests that there is some sort of spatial relationship between rivers and cursus, and a number he notes actually cross water in their

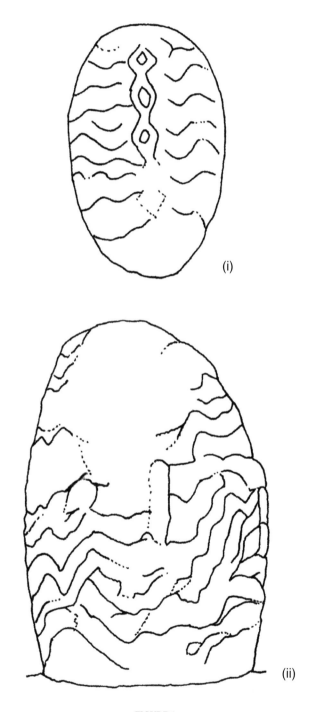

FIGURE 1
Lepenski Vir (no scale available): (i) back of sculpture from House 44; (ii) altar from House 54.

route while others lie within or are surrounded by wetlands, but, he really doesn't address the physical connection between the monuments and the water. Brophy and Tilley both noted that the Dorset cursus passed through three wet places on its route (Tilley 1994, 173ff; Brophy 2000, 64) and yet the reason for this is not considered by either. A simple realignment of the monument would have meant it could have avoided these, begging the question 'why?'. Could sound be one key to answering that conundrum? Any movement of water produces sound. Walking through water, for example, cannot be done quietly with ease – it is possible, but difficult. The resonance that is heard can be seen at a number of levels. On the three locations on the Dorset cursus for example, where water would have had to have been traversed, movement would have been very audible not only to those walking through the water but to others some distance away, perhaps on other parts of the monument. In two of those places it was also necessary to climb down a cliff to reach the water, so the wetlands would have also been visible as well as heard to those travelling along the monument prior to their being reached.

The use of sound in prehistoric societies has begun to be explored in a number of ways (eg Watson & Keating 2000) but this has tended to be humanly-manufactured sound, rather than that naturally achieved. In monumental circles, stones often can act as sound boards: on Orkney, for example, many of these are near water. Stone-built tombs and barrows all possess the facility to act as resonators of sound although most of the work undertaken on this particular aspect has been concerned with humanly generated sound radiating out from within the structure.

Rock art is one medium that can illustrate the importance of water and its sound. At Lepenski Vir, a Mesolithic settlement on the Danube, river stones were used to create the earliest known sculptures – many of them in forms which seem to relate more to fish and other aquatic species than humans – the goggle eyes, the pouting lips cannot be mistaken. Even allowing for the fact that these were pecked rather than carved, they do not suggest anything other than the huge Wels catfish which were found in these waters at the time (Srejović 1972, 80ff). Fig 1(i) and (ii) shows other sculptures, utilizing lines which could be mimicking the waters of the Danube (after Srejović 1972, plates 47, 35). Fig 1(ii) is described as 'a representation of turbulent torrents falling in cascade over the rocks' (Srejović 1972, plate 34).

At the tomb cemetery site on the bend of the river Boyne in Ireland, the main groups of tombs all lie near to the water (Stout 2002). The entrances of Knowth and Dowth face predominantly west or east, towards the arms of the river either side of the bend, with the central group at Newgrange nearest to the river and whose tombs face within the arc SE to SSW, all pointing at the curve of the Boyne itself.

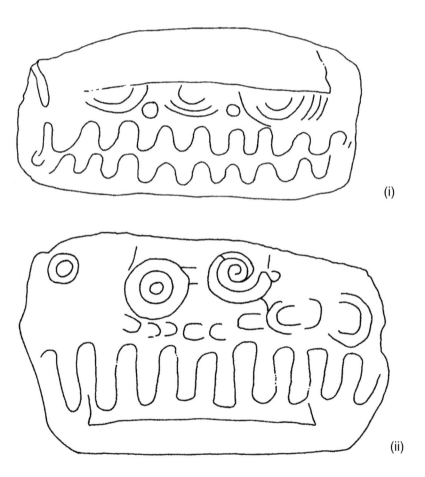

(i)

(ii)

FIGURE 2
Knowth kerbstone (no scale available): (i) K14–700; (ii) K93–190.

Zigzags and wavy-lines, circles and arcs are found here in profusion and feature at many other sites; not all are found in water-related regions but the contention here is that they do have a base in the movement and shape of water. Concentric circles can be seen as symbolizing the ripples when an object is dropped into water (fig 3). Rivers and wetlands are often perceived as places of ritual deposition. Dropping, throwing or even placing votive offerings in such a context would result in ripples being visible. A double zigzag could be indicative of a river; single or multiples for ripples. Fig 2 illustrates two kerbstones at Knowth (after Eogan 1986, plate 61) that combine a number of ciphers and which could almost be seen as 'plans' of the Boyne site, with the river and the three main tombs plus the satellite graves. The range of circles and arcs can be seen on a number of stones (after Eogan 1986, 158–9, 161, 162–3). While the more complex rock carving can be seen easily on kerbstones surrounding the tombs (such as fig 4(i) after Eogan 1986, plate III), the most ornate ones, particularly one at Newgrange (fig 4(ii) after O'Keilly 1982, 181), tend to be found deep inside the tombs. This latter one is on a roofstone. The decorated stones appear to indicate the points at which the sounds of the nearby water could still be heard – within the tombs as well as without.

Another example of the acoustic quality of water can be traced in Scotland. While not a river site, the Neolithic village of Skara Brae on Orkney is sited adjacent to a bay that has dynamic water movement especially in the winter months. Carvings comprising a number of zigzag and lozenge-shaped patterns have been found in a number of places in the complex during the later stages of its occupation, and it has been suggested that this patterning reflects the way the local rock fractures (Ritchie 1995, 34). Upon closer examination of the distribution of the carvings within the village, and given that the structures would have had roofs that would have muffled a large proportion of the exterior sound, it seems reasonable to suggest that these

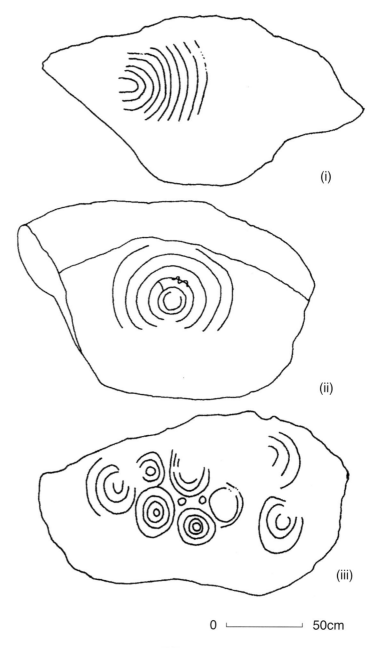

FIGURE 3
Knowth site 1: (i) K95; (ii) K69; (iii) K89.

decorations indicate the areas where sound might have travelled before being blocked perhaps by turns of the various passageways (Ritchie 1995, 35 fig 21).

DISCUSSION

The following discussion is more an airing of thoughts under construction than a final conclusion.

123

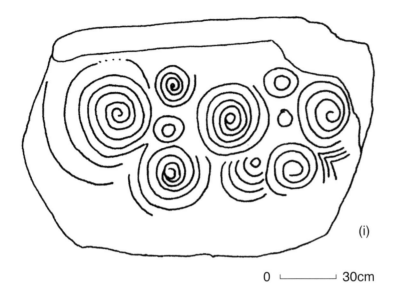

0 �⌐ 30cm

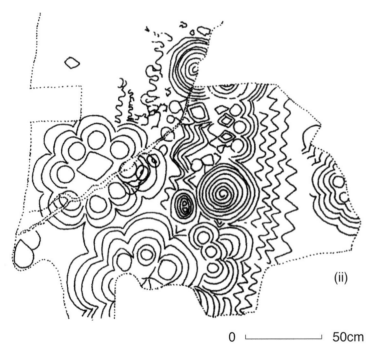

0 �⌐ 50cm

FIGURE 4
Knowth site 1: (i) K56; (ii) Newgrange, roofstone.

in that rivers may be considered self-excavating trenches, the erosion of which we cannot control. And when this is exacerbated with a tidal element, such as on the London Thames, then the archaeology must be considered to be under constant threat. They are also the poorer relative within the wetlands stable, so to speak, with the more accessible and predictable peat and marshlands being the areas of first choice. The connection between prehistoric communities and rivers is found at both the economic level and the experiential. Upon closer examination of settlement patterns and practices the fluctuating balance of these two aspects traces this relationship in discernible ways. The river was a central element in the lives of early prehistoric people and it is necessary to look in the floodplains under alluvium deposits in order to understand this. In this instance, a differing interpretation of the familiar Boyne rock art is suggested. Other routes might be the association between death, burial and rivers as well as varying subsistence levels.

Seeking to find ways to uncover different facets of the relationship between those living on and by the waterways and the rivers themselves requires a broad brush approach to what is already known from the archaeological record. So much of the interpretation that is expounded concerning sites within the floodplain tends to ignore the simple fact of where these sites are located. Drawings of specific features, such as cursus monuments, will only show the features but not the adjacent rivers (eg Brophy 2000) or, as in the case of Tilley's *Phenomenology*, only topographical features such as hills are considered (Tilley 1994). The main danger here is imposing modern opinions and interpretation on the river

Rivers, with their implied movement, are the one linking factor within the concept and gamut of wetlands. They flow through most of the other geomorphological settings such as lakes, marshland and peatlands, eventually ending within an estuarine setting. This movement itself is a cause for concern sites – assuming that what is perhaps valid in other wetland sites can automatically be applied across the board. The human responses to these sites may well have been entirely different and it behoves us to look for that difference without taking the easier 'All for one, one for all' approach.

REFERENCES

Allen, T & Welsh, K 1997 'Eton Rowing Lake, Dorney, Buckinghamshire, Second Interim Report', *South Midlands Archaeology*, 27, 25–34.

Brophy, K 2000 'Water Coincidence? Cursus monuments and rivers', *in* Ritchie A (ed.) 2000, 59–70.

Burgess, C & Gerloff, S 1981 'The dirks and rapiers of Great Britain and Ireland', *Prähistoriche bronzefunde* Abteilung IV, 7Band.

Clark, P (ed) *The Dover Bronze Boat*. London.

Cotton, J, Mills, J & Clegg, G 1986 *Archaeology in West London*. London.

Descola, P 1991 *The Spears of Twilight: Life and Death in the Amazon Jungle*. London.

Dreslerová, D 1995 'The prehistory of the middle Labe (Elbe) floodplain in the light of archaeological finds', *Památky archeologické*, 86, 105–45.

Edmonds, M 1999 *Ancestral Geographies of the Neolithic*. London.

Eogan, G 1986 *Knowth and the Passage Tombs of Ireland*. London.

Harding, J 2000 'Later Neolithic ceremonial centres, ritual and pilgrimage in the monument complex of Thornborough, North Yorkshire', *in* Ritchie, A (ed), 31–46.

Haughey, F 1999 'The archaeology of the Thames: prehistory within a dynamic landscape', *London Archaeologist*, 9, 16–21.

Mordant, C & Mordant, D 1988 'Les enceintes néolithiques do la haute-vallée de la Seine', *in* Burgess, C, Topping, P, Mordant, C & Maddison, M *Enclosures and Defences in the Neolithic of Western Europe*. BAR International Series, 403, 231–54. Oxford.

Mordant, D & Mordant, C 1992 'Noyen-sur-Seine: a mesolithic waterside settlement', *in* Coles, B (ed) *The Wetland revolution in prehistory*. The Prehistoric Society & WARP, 55–64. Exeter.

Needham, S 1971 *Runnymede Bridge, 1978*. London.

O'Keilly, M 1982 *Newgrange*. London.

Pardoe, C 1993 'Wamba yadu, a later Holocene cemetery of the central River Murray', *Archaeology in Oceania*, 28, 77–84.

Pryor, F 1991 *Flag Fen*. London.

Ritchie, A (ed) *Neolithic Orkney in its European Context*. Cambridge.

Robertson-Mackay, R 1987 'The Neolithic causewayed enclosure at Staines, Surrey: Excavations 1961–63', *Proceedings of the Prehistoric Society*, 53, 23–128.

Srejović, D 1972 *Europe's First Monumental Sculpture: New Discoveries at Lepenski Vir*. London.

Stout, G 2002 *Newgrange and the Bend of the Boyne*. Cork.

Tilley, C 1994 *A Phenomenology of Landscape*. Oxford.

Van de Noort, R, Dinnin, M, Lillie, M, Head, R, Fenwick, H & Chapman, H 1997 'Conclusions', *in* Van de Noort, R & Ellis, S *Wetland Heritage of the Humberhead Levels. An Archaeological Survey*, 453–62, Kingston upon Hull.

Wainwright, G 1971 'The excavation of a Later Neolithic enclosure at Marden, Wiltshire', *Antiquaries Journal*, 51, 177–239.

Wansleeben, M & Verhart, L 1990 'Meuse Valley project: the transition from the Mesolithic to the Neolithic in the Dutch Meuse Valley', *in* Vermeersch, P & van Peer, P (eds) *Contributions to the Mesolithic in Europe*, 389–402, Leuven.

Watson, A & Keating, D 2000 'The architecture of sound in Neolithic Orkney', *in* Ritchie, A (ed), 259–63.

Whittle, A, Atkinson, R, Chambers, R & Thomas, N 1992 'Excavations in the Neolithic and Bronze Age complex at Dorchester-on-Thames, Oxon 1947–52 and 1981', *Proceedings of the Prehistoric Society*, 58, 143–201.

Identifying anthropogenic deposits in alluvial settings on the Northwest Coast

KATHRYN BERNICK

An elementary but often overlooked observation is that perishable artefacts at alluvial wet sites do not necessarily represent *in situ* cultural deposition. A combination of flowing water, shifting stream channels, overbank deposits and buoyant materials require one to demonstrate that the objects came to be in their present locations through human agency. They may have been deliberately placed or accidentally dropped into stagnant water at the find site. But there are other possibilities. They may have floated in from upstream or they may have been redistributed at the site by floodwaters. Streams are dynamic. Cycles of scour and deposition affected the landscape for thousands of years and continue to do so today. Examples from two alluvial wet sites on the Northwest Coast illustrate the need for thorough understanding of depositional history.

The anthropological term 'Northwest Coast' refers to a culture area along the west coast of North America, extending from south-eastern Alaska through British Columbia, Washington and Oregon into northern California (fig 1). Human occupation in the region dates from early postglacial times. In the past 4,000 years, relatively large populations thrived on coastal and riverine resources. Their material culture was made in large part of organic materials, especially wood (Suttles 1990 and references therein; Matson & Coupland 1995; Ames & Maschner 1999).

The region features a narrow coastal plain between the Pacific Ocean on the west and rugged mountains on the east. The mountains are volcanic and some are active. Some are snow-clad year round. All of this area, including the plateau east of the Coast and Cascade Mountain Ranges, lies on the Pacific side of the continental divide (the Rocky Mountains). Large river systems, including the Fraser and Columbia, drain huge areas. Gradients are relatively steep and lateral movement is often restricted by bedrock. By the time they reach the coast, these rivers are laden with silt. In their lower reaches, where the valleys broaden, the large streams feature braided channels and expansive deltas.

Hydrologic characteristics of the Northwest Coast help to create anaerobic conditions with preserved perishable artefacts and ecofacts. Silt-laden streams that seasonally overflow their banks, freshet lakes, sloughs and a high water table characterize the region. Water levels in the Fraser, Columbia and other streams rise dramatically during the spring freshet as a result of melting snow packs in the mountains. They also rise for short durations in other seasons after heavy rainfall. Fluvial forces are credited with the discovery of many wet sites on the Northwest Coast;

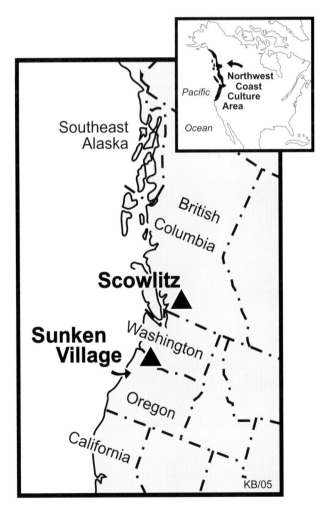

FIGURE 1
The Northwest Coast culture area.

they have also been agents of site formation. There are numerous locations where perishable artefacts came to light when they were washed out of river banks. Our focus on heritage preservation highlights recent site attrition and concerns for the future. We tend to forget that similar erosion occurred in antiquity and that the cycle includes deposition.

SCOWLITZ WET SITE INVESTIGATIONS

The Scowlitz wet site (DhRl 16W) is near the confluence of the Fraser and Harrison rivers in British Columbia, Canada. It has two parts: a river beach, or stream margin, which is under water part of the year; and an adjacent, flood-prone flat bank 15m wide and about 1.5m above the beach. A steep, forested slope with bedrock outcrops rises behind the flat. Basketry and other perishable artefacts eroding from the beach instigated exploratory investigations in the early 1990s. Excavations on the alluvial flat were not part of the original plan; they were undertaken when water levels in the river rose unexpectedly, precluding access to the beach. Information from the test pits in the flat exceeded expectations – the results taught me that the purpose of sediments is more than to hold up artefacts.

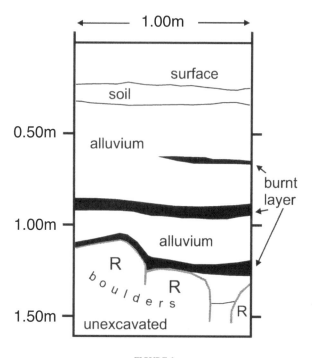

FIGURE 2
Strata in alluvial bank at Scowlitz wet site.

During initial reconnaissance, my terrestrially oriented colleagues focused their attention on carbonaceous layers visible in the eroding bank and became convinced that the stream-side flat had been a large-scale resource procurement area with hearths for smoking fish. Although unsupported by the subsequent investigations, that interpretation fits the regional cultural history (Mitchell 1971, 1990; Matson & Coupland 1995) as well as environmental parameters. There is a traditional salmon fishing location nearby, a village site with house pits just upstream on a small alluvial island, and remains of houses and burial mounds on a high terrace above the wet site (Lepofsky et al 2000). The flat and the perishable bearing beach deposits in front of it are in the middle of an archaeological complex that should include evidence of large-scale fishing – procurement, processing or consumption.

ALLUVIAL FLAT DEPOSITS

Excavations at the Scowlitz wet site revealed a typical alluvial sequence with coarse-grain sediments at the bottom, fine at the top. Fine laminations indicated alluvial deposition. The matrix consists of sandy mud with a large amount of clay and several discrete carbonaceous layers (fig 2). There is a shallow soil horizon at the present-day surface but no evidence of buried humic layers that would indicate former stable surfaces. The excavations on the flat extended below the water table without encountering the blue-grey clayey sediments that were associated with perishable artefacts on the beach. No postholes, defined hearths, or other cultural features were observed in the test pits on the flat or on the beach, nor are any visible in the bank face (Bernick 1994, 16–19).

The burnt layers, or carbonaceous sheets, range from 1cm to 10cm in thickness and extend over broad areas. One of these layers was traced in the bank face for a distance of 25m, dipping slightly downstream. Across the width of the flat, the layers seem to be nearly level – except the lowermost, which in places conforms to the contours of underlying boulders. The burnt layers consist of loosely arranged pieces of wood charcoal (up to 2.5cm in diameter), finely crushed burnt bone and small angular rocks (Bernick 1994, 20).

The alluvial flat appears to have been formed by episodic seasonal sedimentation and occasional flood-related transport of material of cultural origin. The thin, broad, relatively level layers of loosely packed, uncrushed pieces of charcoal almost certainly represent float material left behind by receding waters.

Interpretation as food-processing locations does not correspond to characteristics of the deposits.

Even so, the charcoal and burnt bone comprise remains from fires. If those fires were located on the flat at the site, then the burnt layers contain material dispersed by flood waters. However, rocks in the deposits, including those associated with the burnt layers, are colluvial in origin, their angular outlines the result of weathering, not exposure to fire. As the excavation report concludes (Bernick 1994), it is likely they broke off bedrock outcrops and rolled down the steep slope behind the site. Red and yellow staining on the rocks is consistent with outcrop-source weathering (Latas 1992).

The scope of the investigations did not extend to ascertaining the origin of the materials. Two complementary scenarios were developed by student volunteers. Doug Brown (1994) proposes that a confined meander loop of the Harrison River resulted in formation of the flat by sedimentation in a swamp behind a natural levee. John Maxwell (1994) conducted physical and chemical analyses of sediment samples and concluded that the burnt materials are the remains of anthropogenic refuse. He suggests that the refuse was discarded into a swamp behind the village and that undecayed buoyant material (such as charcoal) was deposited at the Scowlitz wet site locality during periodic incursions of the river into the swamp. These episodes would have flushed the basin and distributed lightweight matter to the edges of a natural settling pond. Essentially, a sewage lagoon.

RIVER BEACH DEPOSITS

The perishable cultural materials in the Scowlitz wet site beach component appear to have been deposited by fluvial action. Test pits in the beach showed that the perishables are contained in a coherent alluvial layer. Three radiocarbon assays provide age estimates for the inclusions (the artefacts) ranging from 600 to 1,200 years ago. If the artefacts had been discarded at this location while the sediments were being laid down, then the deposits would be the same age as the artefacts. However, a 600-year time span as indicated by the radiocarbon dates does not correspond to the usual pattern of rapid alluvial accumulation. For example, McLean (1990, 123) concludes that the entire depositional sequence required to form a channel bar island in the Fraser River typically takes place within 10–30 years. Moreover, the deposit appears to be relatively homogeneous, without the sequence of fine laminations one would expect from several centuries

of alluviation. It seems likely that the perishables were transported from another location, perhaps from more than one location, and that the deposit is younger than the artefacts.

The weak condition of the wood material and tumbled state of the basketry artefacts support the argument that they did not come to be in their present location through human agency. Recovered specimens were structurally weak and extensively infiltrated by rootlets – noticeably more so than similar artefacts from other riverbank sites, some of them much older (personal observation). Whereas at most wet sites in the region basketry is found lying flat, albeit broken and frayed, the Scowlitz baskets look as if they have been rolled and tossed by river current prior to coming to rest at the site (fig 3).

Whether the perishable artefacts at Scowlitz came from the same source as the carbonaceous refuse in the flat remains unexplored. There are no radiocarbon dates for the flat, and the pit-house village on the nearby island has not been investigated. There has not been a geoarchaeology study of the site. Nonetheless, the Scowlitz wet site provides insight for interpreting other archaeological sites in similar settings.

SUNKEN VILLAGE WET SITE

Recently, I conducted a research-oriented review of existing information about an archaeological wet site on the southern Northwest Coast (Bernick 2005). That site is called Sunken Village, a misnomer since it did not sink and is highly unlikely to be a village. Sunken Village (35MU4) is located on a large alluvial island at the confluence of the Columbia and Willamette Rivers, near Portland, Oregon.

Before dikes were constructed 65 years ago, the Columbia River's early summer annual freshet inundated the lowland areas of Sauvie Island on which the Sunken Village site is located. In some years the water covered the entire island except for the highest ridges. The island also was flooded for short periods following late-fall and winter storms. Both the Columbia and Willamette Rivers carry sediments, which are left behind when the waters recede. In addition, tidal fluctuations reach Sauvie Island (Spencer 1950, 65; Caniff 1981, 53–6).

Investigations at the Sunken Village site are limited to auger tests, mapping surface features on the beach, and documenting exposed sections of the cut-bank. These archaeological projects mainly sought to define site boundaries and identify cultural

FIGURE 3
Tumbled basket recovered from Scowlitz wet site (DhRl 16W:29).

deposits within a resource-management framework. They were conducted in 1977, 1987 and 2003 by various archaeologists. My knowledge of the site is based on their reports and field records (Pettigrew & Lebow 1987; Hibbs & Ellis 1988; AINW 2004) and an overview study by Maureen Newman (1991).

The Sunken Village (35MU4) archaeological site is located on a natural levee that parallels the stream and also on lower land on both sides of the levee. The levee is a 6m-high natural topographic feature that extends beyond the site area, along the stream. Prior to mid-twentieth-century alterations to the landscape, archaeological deposits were present

- on and buried within the levee for approximately 1,000m
- in low-lying fields between the levee and an inland swamp or shallow lake
- on and buried in the beach that lies between the levee and the stream
- under water in the streambed.

Major alterations involved dredging the stream channel and using the dredge spoils to raise the height of the natural levee, and ploughing and draining the fields east of the levee. These alterations were part of a national flood relief programme in the late 1930s. Although the site was well-known to local residents and artefact collectors, at the time there were no legal requirements or expectations for assessment or mitigation of impacts to cultural resources.

Artefacts recovered from the site by collectors include numerous prehistoric tools and art objects made of stone, bone, antler and wood – none with contextual information. Many had been in the streambed and were found in dredge spoils. Items recovered by archaeologists, from the surface and from auger holes, are modest. They include a few artefacts, mainly microdebitage and tiny wood chips, as well as pieces of wood and bark with no clear evidence of use or modification by humans and unmodified floral and faunal remains.

CHALLENGES OF INTERPRETING ALLUVIAL DEPOSITS

Sunken Village is larger and more complex than the Scowlitz wet site. Similarities include:

- a river-beach component intermittently covered by water
- perishable artefacts preserved in anaerobic deposits in the river beach
- a long, narrow alluvial landform adjacent to the stream
- 'burnt layers' visible in the cut-bank and extending for a considerable distance along the stream channel
- large pieces of charcoal and finely crushed calcined bone in the 'burnt layers'
- no postholes, defined hearths, or ash concentrations visible in the cut-bank
- association with a river system that seasonally swells with silt-laden water.

Reading the site inventory records and descriptions was a déjà vu experience. Previous investigators had assumed that the burnt layers represent large hearth areas and they identified matrix containing charcoal and crushed burnt bone as midden deposit. Those presumed hearths and 'occupation surfaces' were cited to support interpretation of the site as a significant village and a successful nomination as a National Historic Landmark (Newman 1991).

Profile views of the cut-bank at Sunken Village show thin dark layers that contain small pieces of charcoal as well as debitage, burnt bone fragments and fire-cracked rocks. These layers are buried within alluvium. The deepest are at the upstream end of the site. Charcoal samples yielded three radiocarbon age estimates within the past 700 years; the dates do not correlate fully with relative depths or strata designations. The archaeologists who conducted the Sunken Village profiling study do not consider the implications of an active floodplain setting. They interpret the stratigraphy to indicate intact cultural deposits in the 'dry' levee portion of the site. They conclude that human occupation of the levee surface occurred during the course of natural levee formation and that overbank sediments encased cultural materials (AINW 2004). This echoes the initial, disproved assumptions for Scowlitz.

Whether the perishable artefacts and ecofacts in the beach and streambed at Sunken Village represent washed-in materials, like at the Scowlitz wet site, or *in situ* deposition cannot be ascertained from available information. However, there are bough- or basketry-lined pit features in the Sunken Village beach that, without question, came to be in their present location solely through human agency. There once were about 200 in two rows parallel to the levee. About 40 were mapped but none has been excavated. They comprise a type of pit that has not been reported from any other site. Compelling ethnographic analogies suggest use for leaching acorns (DuBois 1935). Other suggested functions include food storage pits, fish traps and storage vessels for mussels. A radiocarbon age estimate for one of the features (Newman 1991, 80) indicates contemporaneity with burnt layers in the levee. Despite significant research potential and clear association with the location, the pit features have attracted remarkably little attention and none has been systematically excavated. Instead, there has been a management-driven focus on identifying site boundaries – using augers.

Subsurface deposits at Sunken Village were investigated with auger tests in 1987. Artefacts and ecofacts recovered by the augers were assumed to be in primary cultural deposits (Pettigrew & Lebow 1987). A review of the data indicates that, despite using an auger with a large, 25cm-diameter bit, this method of subsurface investigation was inadequate to characterize the deposits. Two examples illustrate the point.

One auger hole (Pettigrew & Lebow 1987, AH #1) revealed an anomalous 70cm-thick buried layer of surface-like sediment (labelled with a question mark in the report). The overlying sediments yielded artefacts and ecofacts, and on that basis were identified as intact cultural deposits. It seems likely to me that the auger passed through a silted-in hole, probably a pit feature. Field logs identify the location of that particular auger hole as being near pit features. The silted-in pit hypothesis explains the buried surface-like sediment, but it raises questions about the overlying matrix and its stratigraphic relationship to deposits elsewhere at the site.

Another auger test along the toe of the cut-bank produced cultural material to more than 2.5m below the surface (maximum reach of the auger) (Pettigrew & Lebow 1987, AH #8). The nearby cut-bank (AINW 2004, profile #3) shows what appears to be a filled-in freshet channel or crevasse, which strongly suggests that the deep, productive auger hole is located in the westward extension of the same relict channel. If that is the case, the deep culture-bearing deposits revealed by the auger represent a filled-in cross-channel. Contrary to assumptions, they would not be intact cultural deposits nor provide information about temporal and spatial patterns of site use.

Another potentially misleading aspect of auger tests at alluvial sites concerns the determining of cultural associations of vegetal inclusions. The auger test results for Sunken Village indicate excellent preservation of nearly all types of material and an exceptionally high density of organic items (Pettigrew & Lebow 1987), but they do not provide convincing evidence for the presence of a dense and diverse perishable artefact assemblage. Pettigrew & Lebow (1987) catalogue 884 objects as cultural items. However, only 6 per cent of these objects show unambiguous evidence of modification or use and most of those items are microdebitage (moreover, some of the wood chips may be products of the auger). Cultural attribution of the vast majority depends on association and depositional context. They may comprise cultural debris – or not. Small fragments of apparently unmodified twigs, wood, bark, charcoal, nuts, shells and animal bones do not in themselves indicate cultural activity. While they clearly inform paleoenvironmental reconstruction, it is not clear whether they represent the environment of the Sunken Village site, another nearby location, or a mix of locations upstream from the site.

On the other hand, basketry and other formed artefacts rescued from the streambed and beach at Sunken Village are indubitably cultural. They may have originated in an upland component of the site (the levee), but that remains speculative without depositional information. Alternatively, like the reconstructions for the Scowlitz wet site, the artefacts may have been introduced into the water at an upstream location. They may have washed out of another site or have been discarded into the water. Seaman (1946, 7–8) and Strong (1959, 24) relate that abandoned village sites nearby have collapsed into the river, including one upstream from Sunken Village. Farmers on the island have been throwing debris into the stream for the past 150 years and similar habits are likely to have prevailed in antiquity.

CONCLUSIONS

A geoarchaeology study designed to reconstruct depositional history is an essential component of any investigations at alluvial sites. Regardless of quantity, quality, variety and age, cultural material at sites in alluvial settings may not be in primary cultural deposits. In a regularly flooded alluvial environment, artefacts as well as ecofacts

– especially those of buoyant materials or thin lenticular shapes – could have been redistributed at the same site by water or floated into the site from afar. Archaeologists working in such environments risk misinterpreting their finds unless depositional context is firmly established.

Reflecting on the current state of wetland archaeology on the Northwest Coast, it seems that our collective promotional efforts have been fairly successful. Most practising archaeologists in the region are aware of the potential of wet-site finds. But this awareness is built on the allure of wondrous artefacts. Few are attuned to depositional process. It is an understatement to observe that on the Northwest Coast geoarchaeology is less appreciated than wetland archaeology.

ACKNOWLEDGEMENTS

The investigations I directed at Scowlitz in 1992 and 1993 operated under the auspices of the University of British Columbia (UBC) Laboratory of Archaeology, with funding by UBC and the British Columbia Heritage Trust. I wholeheartedly thank the volunteer field crew, Grant Beattie, Doug Brown, Joyce Johnson, Dean Jones, Heather Pratt, David Schneider and Ann Stevenson, as well as the many students who helped in the lab. The Canadian Conservation Institute treated the waterlogged perishable artefacts. I thank the US National Park Service, especially Kirstie Haertel, for the opportunity to review the history of investigations at the Sunken Village National Historic Landmark. Dr Ken Ames (Portland State University) facilitated access to Sunken Village collections. Charles Hodges (Northwest Archaeological Associates, Seattle) enthusiastically discussed details of geoarchaeology and loaned slides for my presentation at the conference in Edinburgh.

REFERENCES

Ames, K M & Maschner, D G 1999 *Peoples of the Northwest Coast: Their Archaeology and Prehistory*. London.

AINW (Archaeological Investigations Northwest) 2004 'Archaeological exploration at 35MU4, the Sunken Village site: a National Historic Landmark in Multnomah County, Oregon'. Draft. Report 1342. Archaeological Investigations Northwest Inc., Portland, OR. Submitted to Portland District, US Army Corps of Engineers, Portland, OR.

Bernick, K 1994 'Waterlogged deposits at the Scowlitz site: final report of 1992–3 archaeological investigations'. Permit 1992–117. On file, BC Archaeology Branch, Victoria, Canada.

Bernick, K 2005 'Research options for archaeological investigations at Sunken Village National Historic Landmark, 35MU4: a planning document'. Prepared for US National Park Service, Seattle, WA.

Brown, D 1994 'Geomorphological history of the Scowlitz wet site, DhRl 16W', *in* Bernick, K, 'Waterlogged deposits at the Scowlitz site: final report of 1992–3 archaeological investigations', 79–89. Permit 1992–117. On file, BC Archaeology Branch, Victoria, Canada.

Canniff, K 1981 *Sauvie Island: A Step Back in Time.* Portland, OR.

DuBois, C 1935 'Wintu ethnography', *University of California Publications in American Archaeology and Ethnology*, 36, 1–148.

Hibbs, C Jr & Ellis, D V 1988 'An inventory of cultural resources and an evaluation of the effects of the proposed north coast feeder gas pipeline located between Deer Island and Sauvie Island, Lower Columbia River Valley, in Oregon', report to Northwest Natural Gas Co, Portland, OR. Prepared by Charles Hibbs and Associates, Portland, OR.

Latas, T W 1992 'An analysis of fire-cracked rock: a sedimentological approach', *in* Stein, J K (ed), *Deciphering a Shell Midden,* 211–37. San Diego, CA.

Lepofsky, D, Blake, M, Brown, D, Morrison, S, Oakes, N & Lyons, N 2000 'The archaeology of the Scowlitz site, SW British Columbia', *Journal of Field Archaeology*, 27, 391–416.

Matson, R G & Coupland, G 1995 *The Prehistory of the Northwest Coast.* San Diego, CA.

Maxwell, J A 1994 'Sediment analysis of samples collected at the Scowlitz wet site (DhRl 16W), 1992–3', *in* Bernick, K, 'Waterlogged deposits at the Scowlitz site: final report of 1992–3 archaeological investigations', 67–77. Permit 1992–117. On file, BC Archaeology Branch, Victoria, Canada.

McLean, D G 1990 *The Relation between Channel Instability and Sediment Transport on Lower Fraser River.* PhD dissertation, University of British Columbia. Ann Arbor, MI.

Mitchell, D H 1971 *Archaeology of the Gulf of Georgia Area, a Natural Region and Its Culture Types.* Syesis, Vol 4, Suppl 1. Victoria, Canada.

Mitchell, D 1990 'Prehistory of the coasts of southern British Columbia and northern Washington', *in* Suttles, W (ed), *Handbook of North American Indians.* Vol 7, *Northwest Coast,* 340–58. Washington, DC.

Newman, M McN 1991 *Description and Management Plan for 35MU4, the Sunken Village Archaeological Site at Sauvie Island, Multnomah County, Oregon.* MA thesis, Dept of Anthropology, Portland State University, Portland, OR.

Pettigrew, R M & Clayton, G L 1987 'Archaeological investigations at the Sunken Village site (35MU4), Multnomah County, Oregon', prepared for Oregon Division of State Lands, Salem. Infotec Research Inc, Eugene, OR.

Seaman, N G 1946 *Indian Relics of the Pacific Northwest.* Portland, OR.

Spencer, O C 1950 *The Story of Sauvies Island.* Portland, OR.

Strong, E M 1959 *Stone Age on the Columbia River.* Portland, OR.

Suttles, W (ed) 1990 *Handbook of North American Indians.* Vol 7, *Northwest Coast.* Washington, DC.

Qwu?gwes – a Squaxin Island tribal heritage wet site, Puget Sound, USA

DALE R CROES, RHONDA FOSTER, LARRY ROSS, MELANIE DIEDRICH,
NEA HUBBARD, KATHERINE KELLY, MANDY McCULLOUGH,
TOM McCULLOUGH, KAREN MYERS, CASSANDRA SHARRON, BARBARA VARGO,
REBECCA WIGEN and LAUREN VALLEY

QWU?GWES LOCATION AND CULTURAL IDENTIFICATION

The Qwu?gwes wet site is located at the very head of Puget Sound in Washington State, USA (fig 1). Puget Sound has been referred to as an inland sea, but is better termed as a large glacially cut fjord that is approximately 145km long, running north to south, where the ocean salt water from the Pacific mixes with fresh water draining from the surrounding watersheds. Puget Sound was formed into the north–south fjord it is today by glaciers that advanced from the north at least four times, scouring and carving it for millions of years (Waitt & Thorson 1983). The Vashon Stade was the last major advance, reaching its maximum about 18,000 years ago, covering everything between the Olympic and the Cascade mountains and spreading as far south as our specific region of study. As the Vashon Stade retreated, its melting ice created a massive fresh water lake that released through the Black Lake spillway at the head of Eld Inlet, our site location, and down the Chehalis River drainage to the Pacific Ocean. Once the glaciers melted far enough north, the Straits of Juan de Fuca were open and salt water from the Pacific Ocean entered Puget Sound, making it the salt water 'inland sea' it is today (fig 1).

Our research area encompasses the southern reaches of the traditional territory of the Lushootseed-speaking Coast Salish People and language family, sometimes referred to as Puget [Sound] Salish (Suttles & Lane 1990, 485–502; Thompson & Kinkade 1990, 38; fig 1). Few systematic archaeological investigations have occurred in this region, especially in the southern section of Lushootseed traditional territory, so this paper should be considered a much needed synthesis of a well-preserved waterlogged site. Qwu?gwes forms the main reference point for our synthesized presentations, and this work is based on the original papers presented by the authors at the 11th International Wetland Archaeology Research Project (WARP) conference in Edinburgh (21–24 September 2005). This joint investigation of the Squaxin Island Tribe and South Puget Sound Community College has been ongoing for several years and provides both a scientific and cultural perspective of the many findings. Earlier publications stress the basis of this joint co-operative effort and the need for co-ordinated scientific and Native cultural understandings and explanations (Foster & Croes 2002, 2004).

BRIEF HISTORY OF WORK AND STRATEGY

The Qwu?gwes site, recently named such by the Squaxin Island Tribe, means a 'coming together, sharing', and cultural focus at the site falls within the Squaxin Island Tribe's Cultural Resources Department. The purpose for this excavation is to link a current living culture to a past culture. This is paramount for keeping the current culture alive, for identifying the lifeways of our ancestors, and to demonstrate the tribe's cultural resource management (CRM).

The main focus of this project is not the excavation, in fact less than 25 cubic metres of the site (1.6 per cent of total site area) have been recorded in the past seven summer seasons of investigation.

Joint testing of the Qwu?gwes Site at Mud Bay by South Puget Sound Community College and Squaxin Island Tribe began during the summer of 1999 and, after recording the site (now designated 45TN240), excavations through a field school programme continued throughout the summers of 2000 to 2005, with the results recorded by annual reports to the Washington Department of Archaeology and Historic Preservation. Our 1999 test and the 2000–2005 excavations have determined the site to be:

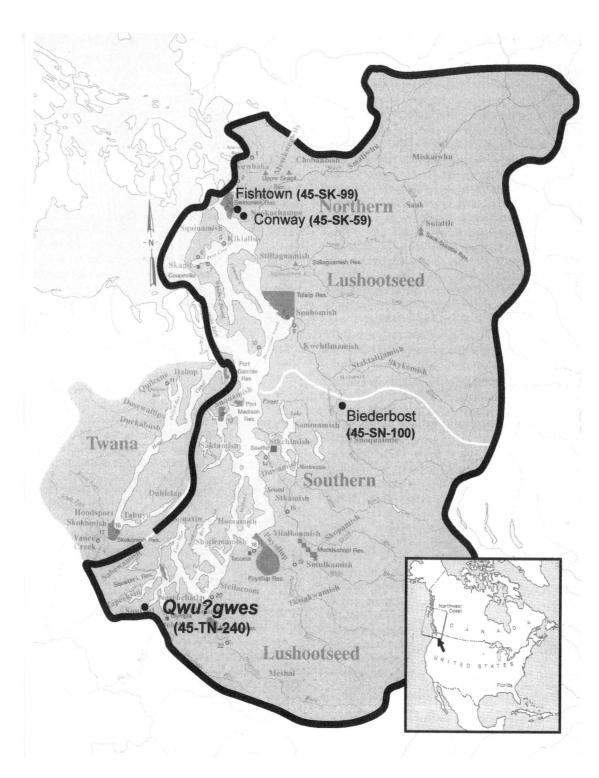

FIGURE 1

Location of the Qwu?gwes wet site in southern Puget Sound and southern Coast Salish Lushootseed language speakers. Other sites are wet sites that have basketry that interrelates in style to the examples recovered from Qwu?gwes (see Croes, Kelly & Collard 2005 for statistical comparisons) (Base map adapted from Suttles, W (ed) 1990 *Handbook of the North American Indians. Vol 7: The Northwest Coast.* Smithsonian Institution, Washington DC).

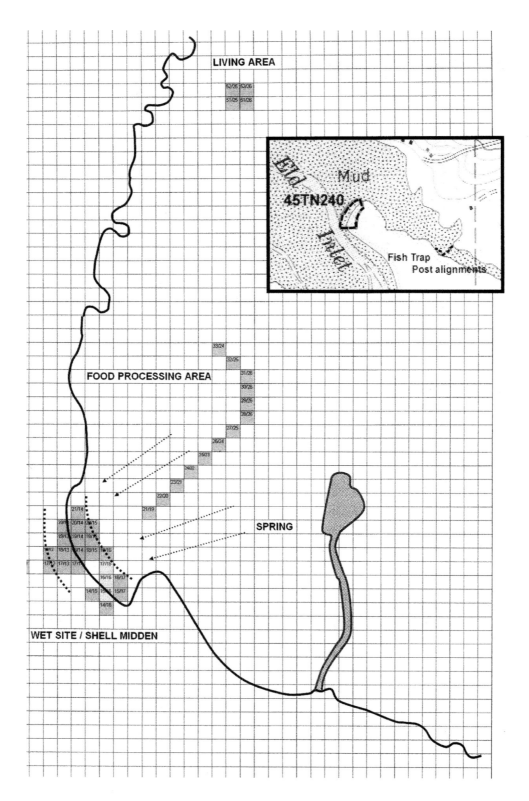

FIGURE 2

Qwu?gwes excavation areas and spring. Shaded areas represent reconstruction of ancient channel. The three squares containing the cedar bark net in the wet site area are a lighter shade. Inset: USGS map shows site location at end of a small peninsula and where the fish traps have been recorded (see Croes & Foster 2004).

- A 91-metre long shell midden, resource-processing location, and possible village site, exposed on a beach front, with 1,600 cubic metres of undisturbed site area remaining (fig 2).

- A site with abundant faunal and floral remains representing the rich food resources used at the site (see below).

- A location containing a large array of stone, bone and shell artefacts typical in style of the last 1,000 years. Additionally, tens of thousands of Thermally Altered Rocks (TAR) have been recovered and analysed. This gives us an idea of the amount of shellfish steaming taking place at the major camp, and in other areas of the site.

- A site containing a buried waterlogged portion in the inter-tidal area with excellent preservation of wood and fibre artefacts, including a large section of cedar bark string net and baskets recovered and dating to approximately 500–700 years old (C^{14} dating). The sensitive basketry and cordage styles show close similarities to Lushootseed and Coast Salish style basketry from ancient sites dating back to as early as 3,000 years ago, demonstrating the time depth and vast extent of these traditions (Croes 1977, 1992; Croes, Kelly & Collard 2005).

The 34 1×1m units excavated so far clearly revealed examples of: (1) possible household living areas where cooking took place; (2), lower-lying food-processing areas with surrounding drying racks where shellfish, fish and possibly berries were steamed on pavements of rocks and dried for storage; and (3) an inter-tidal waterlogged discard shell-midden area on the beach, near the site's fresh water spring (fig 2). We now better understand the 3-dimensional stratigraphic relationships throughout the site and have begun an extensive mapping programme.

We will elaborate and synthesize two main areas of analysis, equally important in our 50/50 sharing of the Qwu?gwes research: (a) the

scientific analyses by student and faculty researchers; and (b) the cultural analysis by the Squaxin Island tribal representatives of their Cultural Resources Department. Working together we can provide a far better overview.

SCIENTIFIC ANALYSIS

STRATIGRAPHIC CONTEXT

The Qwu?gwes heritage site sits on the end of a small peninsula that is underlain by alluvial lake deposits called Bellingham fine silty clay loam, deposited from glacial melt-waters of fresh-water Lake Russell (fig 2). It is very deep, poorly drained soil, formed in alluvium and lacustrine sediments. Slopes are 0–3 per cent. The native vegetation is mainly hardwoods and conifers along the peninsula margins and open prairie in the higher grounds. These alluvium deposits are overlain by a mantle of silty, sandy, gravelly and glacially derived deposits as well as culturally formed shell midden at the site. An aquifer spring provides the ground waters through these overlying deposits and moves easily through the lower half of the inter-tidal offshore cultural midden deposits (see current surface spring and direction of flow, fig 2). This contrasts with peat-bog wet sites in most other parts of the world, where relatively stagnant waters create

FIGURE 3
Example of inter-tidal shell midden area with concentrated vegetal mat below water-table. Note preservation of sticks and wood in these areas of aquifer about 50cm below the surface.

the waterlogging and build up the organic deposition. In the aquifer wet site, the deposits, such as the shell midden, are culturally deposited in areas that form aqueducts for moving ground waters, thereby remaining water-saturated.

Much of our geoarchaeological attention in the wet inter-tidal shell midden area of the site has focused on finding the boundaries and layout of a vegetation-filled channel seen in the profile (fig 3), containing concentrations of wood and fibre artefacts. This ancient channel probably once flowed openly from the spring through this part of the site, in a manner similar to the current open channel flowing from the artesian spring to the inter-tidal (fig 2). In the northernmost squares of the wet site, the vegetal layer of the channel is thicker and more pronounced. This same vegetal layer or channel configuration in the shell midden is where nets (fig 2), basketry and other delicate wood and fibre artefacts are found. Woodchips, split wood and basketry debris of various sizes and varieties are also found throughout this layer. As we have developed the 3-dimensional view of the site, a more detailed view of the overall shape and stratigraphy of this dense vegetal mat channel is taking shape. In many of the excavated squares there is a layer of broken blue mussel shells and charcoal directly above this layer, showing as a dark, almost purple, layer. At the bottom of the thick vegetal mat there is often a dense thin layer of disarticulated salmon bones present.

The spatial correlation of the artefacts and macroflora to the substrata involved detailed mapping of the sidewalls of the excavated squares within the dig site. For the wet site, 29 detailed stratigraphic profiles were created using photographs taken of the walls each year at the end of the season. In addition to the existing data of surface elevations, more detailed elevations of the area directly concerned with the wet site were required. The South Puget Sound Community College survey/CADD class recorded close-interval elevations of the wet site area so that the standardized stratigraphic drawings could be placed into a 3-dimensional view of the layering, and in particular the vegetal mat layers representing the ancient channel (fig 4, also see figs 2 and 3). The standardized and detailed sidewall stratigraphic maps were scanned and put into this programme, giving a visual 3-dimensional view of the layers of interest. At this point, we have detailed views of three directions, the north-east face (fig 4), the south face and the west face. This is sufficient to provide spatial correlation to the wood and fibre (and other) artefacts and a better picture of where the cultural material may be found in the future. In 2005, a panoramic view of the wet site was taken with a digital camera, pieced together and drawn to get a better idea of the overall shape of the vegetal mat channel area (fig 4; Diedrich 2005).

Additionally, the food-processing area stratigraphy, just above the wet site area (fig 2), has been compiled into a 3-dimensional map to show how these shellfish-steaming oven areas relate to the inter-tidal shell midden and wet site squares (fig 5).

FOOD RESOURCES – VERTEBRATE, INVERTEBRATE AND PLANT

Wet sites such as Qwu?gwes not only preserve wood and fibre artefacts, but also the vertebrate bone and invertebrate shellfish; however, the bone and shell are preserved differently to those in the non-waterlogged areas of the site. Vertebrate remains are far less degraded, possibly better preserving the platy bones such as in fish skulls. This may mean that these bones may be underrepresented in non-waterlogged areas of the site. The shellfish at Qwu?gwes are also much better preserved in the waterlogged levels, with whole mussel shells only preserved below the capillary fringe or water-table. Also, the periosticum valve hinges of butter clams are still attached and only found below the water-table. Plant foods, no doubt an important component of the diet, are, as expected, only preserved in the waterlogged deposits. The vertebrate fauna from Qwu?gwes and another wet site, Little Qualicum River, will be analysed and compared later in this paper for both dry and wet segments of the sites.

VERTEBRATE FAUNA

A substantial vertebrate faunal assemblage has been recovered from Qwu?gwes, but it is unevenly distributed among the taxa and the site areas. Of the 18,229 elements present, 77 per cent are fish (almost exclusively salmon), 21.5 per cent are mammal (mostly mule deer, elk and fur-bearing animals hunted for their pelts), only 1.3 per cent are bird (mostly waterfowl), and the remaining <1 per cent are snake and frog (Wigen 2003, 2006). The well-preserved wet site portion of the site has contributed 76 per cent of the bone assemblage, followed by the food preparation area with 12.7 per cent and the living area with 11.3 per cent. Some of the difference in sample sizes between these areas is directly related to variation in the volume of material excavated. The living area has the smallest volume, with only four

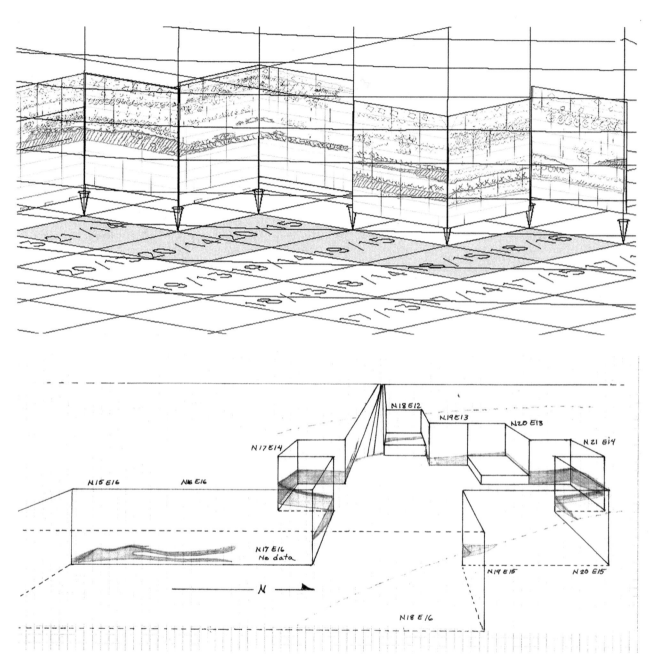

FIGURE 4
Composite of stratigraphic drawings through north-east face of wet site stratigraphy (above; 3-dimensional created by Professor Michael Martin, Computer Aided Design Department, South Puget Sound Community College). Drawing compiled from panoramic views from photographs indicating the vegetal mat concentrations and directions of ancient channel (below and fig 2).

excavation units, followed by the food-processing area with 13 units, and the wet site has the largest volume excavated with 23 units. Calculating the density of the bone per cubic metre (NISP/m³) shows that the living area actually has the highest densities of mammal and bird bone, followed by the food-

140

preparation area, while the wet site area has the highest density of fish bone.

Salmon (*Oncorhynchus* sp.) dominates the vertebrate assemblage. More than 18,200 vertebrate fauna elements have been analysed and reported through 2004, with salmon contributing 49 per cent of the total bone assemblage, and an unusually high, by Northwest Coast site standards, 95.4 per cent of the identified fish (Wigen 2003, 2006). In the inter-tidal wet site (fig 2), salmon contribute about 57 per cent of the fish assemblage, or 98 per cent of the NISP. The salmon elements include all parts of the body, indicating whole salmon skeletons were present. The proportions of the salmon elements are similar to those found in a whole fish. In complete salmon skeletons, about 68 per cent of the elements are head and 32 per cent are vertebrae and tail. In the wet units, the proportions are 69 per cent head bones and 31 per cent vertebrae. The wide variety of elements, some of which are quite thin and presumably fragile, also indicates the exceptional preservation in the lower half of the inter-tidal wet site area.

Salmon are also the dominant fish in the non-wet living and food-preparation areas (fig 2), contributing 30–40 per cent of all the elements recovered. Within the fish assemblage they contribute 75–86 per cent of the NISP, not too dissimilar from the wet site quantities. However, their element distribution is quite different, with only 28 and 21 per cent being from the head. In these areas, the bulk of the bones are vertebrae, possibly reflecting differential preservation or taphonomic processes.

Combined together, the fauna shows a very narrow range of fish caught, with a very strong focus on salmon. Many of these were probably caught using the preserved wooden fish trap on the creek, just on the other side of the point from the site, as reported in Foster and Croes (2005; see location in inset, fig 2).

The opportunity to compare contemporaneous wet and dry deposits is relatively rare, but shows how wet site preservation may affect the faunal analyses. This type of wet and dry area comparison was also possible at the Little Qualicum River site on Vancouver Island (Bernick 1983; Bernick & Wigen 1990). At this site, a small dry midden is associated with contemporaneous wet deposits in the river in front of the dry midden. Both areas were excavated, but the mammal bones show some differences. All harbour seal bones were found in the wet units. The fish assemblages from the two sections of the site show strong differences. In the wet units, salmon dominates, 96 per cent of the NISP, with herring and dogfish the next most common, but in substantially smaller proportions. In the dry units,

herring dominates with salmon and dogfish following in lesser quantities, but not as dramatically different as in the wet units. In addition, salmon cranial elements dominated the assemblage from the wet units, while in the dry units there were many more vertebrae and a higher quantity of broken, unidentifiable fish bones. The authors point out that the interpretation of the season of occupation and function of the site would be quite different if the wet component had not been excavated. This has implications for the interpretation of many sites on the Northwest Coast of North America and elsewhere, since wet components are usually not present.

Clearly, there are some similarities and differences between Qwu?gwes and Little Qualicum River. For one similarity, more salmon cranial bones were found in the wet components in both sites. Unfortunately, the data from the Little Qualicum site are not presented in a fashion that allows one to judge whether salmon cranial bones, such as teeth, were also present in the dry units. Thus it is difficult to know whether the differences at Little Qualicum represent a different disposal pattern between the wet and dry portion, or mainly a difference in preservation – as appears to be the case at Qwu?gwes. At Qwu?gwes, the type of fish present is very similar in both the wet and dry components. This is definitely not the case at Little Qualicum, where herring dominates the dry units and salmon dominates the wet units. Both sites show a higher proportion of mammal bones in the dry components. However, the mammal assemblage is quite similar in composition in the wet and dry areas of Qwu?gwes, unlike the Little Qualicum site, where there are some major differences. In summary, while there are some differences between the wet and dry units at Qwu?gwes, they are not so dramatic as at the Little Qualicum site and may be related mainly to preservation differences. At Qwu?gwes, the final interpretation of site function would be the same whichever part of the site was excavated.

INVERTEBRATE FAUNA

Although only 1–2 per cent of the Qwu?gwes site has been excavated, over 210,000 intact shell valves representing five major shellfish species have already been collected for analysis. As reflected in the stratigraphic photograph above, Qwu?gwes is one of the densest shell middens known on the Northwest Coast of North America (fig 3).

Of the eight taxa gathered from Qwu?gwes, five species significantly dominate the counts at both the wet and dry areas: Olympia oysters (*Ostrea lurida* 72

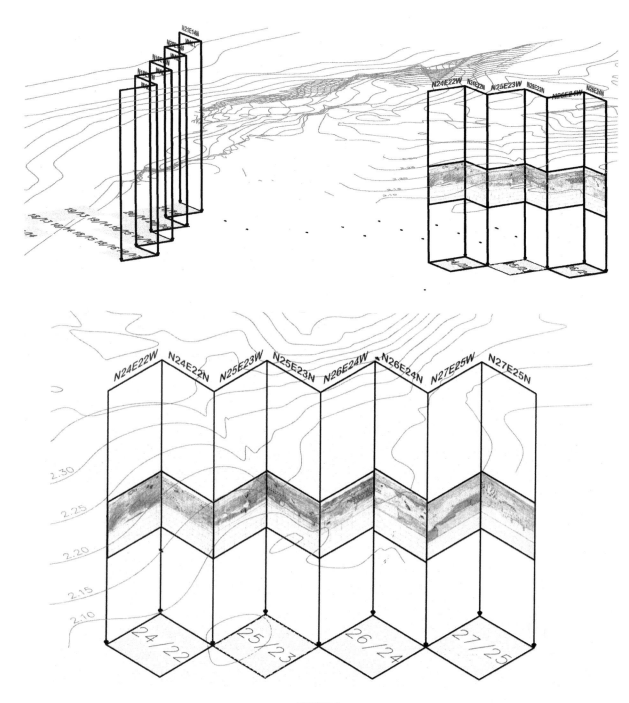

FIGURE 5
Three-dimensional perspective of the food-processing area stratigraphy in orientation (higher ground) to inter-tidal shell midden wet site (above) and a closer view of steaming oven area stratigraphy (3-dimensional created by Professor Michael Martin, Computer Aided Design Department, South Puget Sound Community College).

per cent), butter clams (*Saxidomus giganteus* 22 per cent), bay mussels (*Mytilus edulis* 4 per cent), native littlenecks (*Protothaca staminea* 1 per cent) and horse clams (*Tresus capax* 1 per cent). These species represent 94 per cent of the total bivalve and univalve

collection from the Qwu?gwes site (Hubbard, Foster & Myers 2005).

The Squaxin Island Tribe's traditional territory appears to coincide with the highest densities for the range of the Olympia oyster, the native oyster species

(Armstrong, Dinnel *et al* 1993). The Qwu?gwes ancient shellfish record also reflects their abundance through time, with over 70 per cent of the counts representing Olympia oysters throughout the site.

The vast majority of the shellfish are concentrated in the inter-tidal shell midden area, with the highest percentage of butter clams represented – 25 per cent, versus 4 per cent in the living area and 9 per cent in the food-processing area. In the food-processing area, oysters are again dominant (83 per cent by

count) and contribute much more in relevant meat weight.

Butter clams are the main meat-weight contributors, especially as seen in the waterlogged inter-tidal shell-midden (fig 6). Again, that probably reflects the emphasis on processing large quantities of this more dryable shellfish for later (winter) consumption and trade. Horse clams are the highest calculated meat-weight in the food-processing area, which may also reflect the use of these large clam shells as tools –

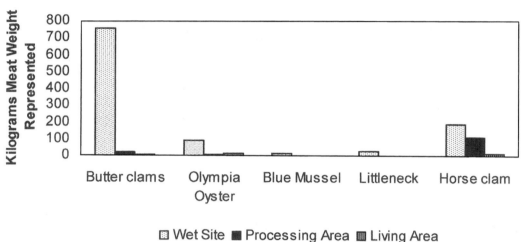

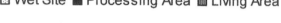

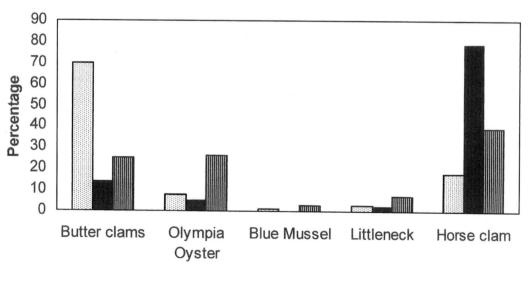

FIGURE 6
Shellfish meat-weight estimates by species and area in kilograms (above) and as percentage ratios (below).

ladles or bowls. The horse clam shells are often found stuck into the ground vertically (Hubbard, Foster & Myers 2005).

Age-at-harvest studies, via the analysis of the external growth lines, are often regarded as a somewhat controversial method (Houghton 1973; Claassen 1998, 155). The age-at-harvest studies on the butter clam assemblages were initially regarded with the same discretion (Hurst 2003). However, when the results of the age-at-harvest study reflected similar patterns of clam selectivity as inferred by the growth analysis study, the age-at-harvest results were reconsidered as possibly being more accurate than previously thought (Hurst 2003).

Of the 146 individual clams assessed for age-at-harvest, an overwhelming 71.23 per cent of the sample was representative of the development of 7–9 growth lines within the lifetime of the clams. This age range was predominate throughout the entire sampled population, as the other clams displaying more or less annuli were dramatically less prevalent than the clams in the 7–9 range (fig 7). This suggests that the clams were at least 7–9 years of age before harvest, as the annuli are believed to be representative of one full year of growth. Butter clams may survive up to 20 years in Puget Sound, though generally are thought to live to 15 years old at least (Harbo 1997, 164). Since our data appear to be tightly ranged between 7–9 years of age at harvest, and not much younger or older, this no doubt reflects ancient management of the butter clam beds for at least this 700-year time range.

MACROFLORA

Although many species of macroflora have been identified at the site, they are not in great concentrations, as seen, for example, in berry seeds at wet sites of Ozette and Hoko River (Croes 1995, 68–70; 2005, 67–70). This suggests that Qwu?gwes was probably not the main site for plant food processing, being more a major station for shellfish and salmon capture and processing. This section will primarily focus on the preliminary analysis of hazel nutshell, but, even in this case, the numbers found are limited.

A dense vegetation layer has been unearthed at a 50cm depth, in some areas of the wet site portion of the dig, revealing distribution and possibly cultural use of ancient native plants. In some parts of the site this layer is thicker and deeper, extending from 60cm down to 75cm (see figs 2–5, above). To date, more than 700 entries of macrofloral remains, from the excavation seasons of 1999 to 2004, have been tentatively identified, documented and entered into a spreadsheet database (Diedrich 2005).

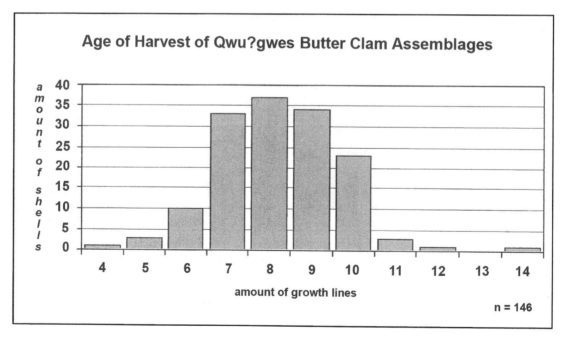

FIGURE 7
Overall growth line frequencies from the Qwu?gwes butter clam assemblages. Shells attaining 7–9 annuli before death represent 71.23 per cent of the entire sampled population.

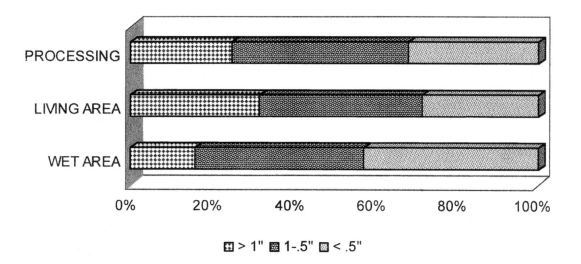

FIGURE 8
Ratio of TAR size divisions between major site areas (see fig 2) based on 31,347 TAR counts.

Of particular interest, regarding cultural use of plants, are what appear to be handfuls of hazelnut shells (*Corylus cornuta* Marsh), that may have been thrown into the waterlogged midden area. The major amounts of the hazelnut shells, along with other wood and fibre cultural materials, have been found in the dense vegetal mat in the reconstructed ancient channel-way (see figs 2–4 above). As previously mentioned, these are not in quantities that would be associated with extensive food processing, in contrast to the evidence of large amounts of clam steaming and salmon processing at the site (Diedrich 2005).

THERMALLY ALTERED ROCK (TAR)

Following shellfish, the second most common category of cultural remains from Qwu?gwes are thermally altered rocks (TAR), undoubtedly the main by-product of steam baking the huge quantities of butter clams and Olympia oysters being processed at the site. In fact, the food-processing area is so characterized because of the remnants of pavements of such rocks in the steaming ovens themselves (fig 5). Today, some Squaxin Island tribal members maintain these shallow pit ovens, and set up large stone ovens to steam bake clams for major celebrations, serving hundreds of people. Working as a team with the tribe, we have been better able to understand the main use of these fist-sized basalt cobbles by ancestors at Qwu?gwes, as a major shellfish processing station (Sharron 2005).

Most of the fist-sized cobbles from Qwu?gwes are basalt, a volcanically derived, mafic rock, that holds heat well. We have observed experimentally how these cobbles are affected by high temperatures in controlled laboratory conditions (Strong & Croes 2001). Groups of cobbles were heated inside a pre-heated electric furnace at 100 degree Celsius incremented temperatures for three-hour periods. Real alteration to the mafic stones did not occur until reaching temperatures of 600 degrees Celcius or higher, indicating that, like today's ovens, ancient Squaxin built up heat in their cobbles to over 600 degrees Celsius (see full results in Strong & Croes 2000; Sharron 2005).

At the Qwu?gwes site over 31,000 TAR examples have been excavated, weighed and screened into size groups (small <0.5", medium 0.5"–1", and large >1") by the 5cm arbitrary levels excavated at the site (producing about 352kg of TAR, fig 8). There is some variation in size groups from different areas of excavation, with larger sized examples more common in the living area followed by the food-processing area, and smaller sized examples in the waterlogged shell midden area. Possibly, the smaller, normally sharper pieces of broken TAR were removed from the living and food-processing area for comfort and safety and then thrown into the midden with shucked clam shells and other debris, while the larger, still usable TAR remained in these areas for use (Sharron 2005).

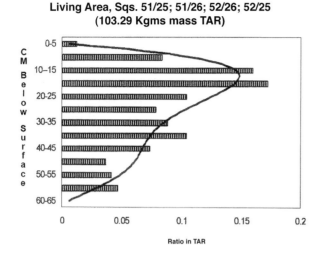

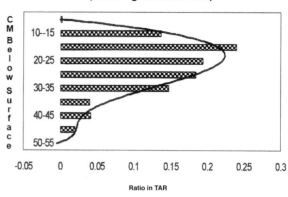

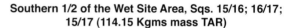

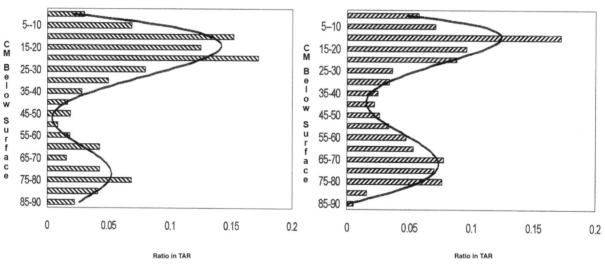

FIGURE 9
Distribution of TAR by weight and 5cm levels in the living area, food-processing area and wet site area
(Northern and Southern squares).

In distribution from top to bottom in the different site areas and squares, most of the TAR concentrated in the upper 25cm (or 5 levels, fig 9). The living area squares and food-processing areas slowly taper down in mass, normally reflecting the most recent hearth and steaming oven levels towards the top (fig 5). The wet site shell midden squares have a different pattern, in both northern and southern areas of the midden. The TAR is very concentrated on the top areas, possibly from erosional concentrations of TAR on the beach since abandonment of the site about 150 years ago, then tapers down rapidly into the lowest frequencies in the site (about 45–50cm depth) and then increase again in the waterlogged levels of the shell midden to a high of about 70–75cm, before they taper down again. Therefore a very bi-modal distribution exists in both areas of the wet site, increasing especially where the waterlogging begins (fig 9). Possibly these TAR were deposited in the low 'channel' areas as a place to fill. Obviously, preservation has little to do with it, since we are dealing with stone, but certainly a concentration occurs in these lower waterlogged wet site deposits not seen in the other areas of the site investigated (Sharron 2005).

ARTEFACT ANALYSIS

Though the emphasis is on the wood and fibre artefacts found at Qwu?gwes for this wet site synthesis, the site contains a typical Central Northwest Coast Late Period component of stone, bone-antler and shell (SB-AS) artefacts (Kelly 2005; Vargo 2005). The waterlogged sections contain a larger quantity of cultural wood and fibre artefacts and debris, including basketry, nets, cordage, fish traps and wooden artefacts as well as large quantities of wood and fibre artefact manufacturing debris. To best place Qwu?gwes into the cultural, historical context of the Central Northwest Coast, we have conducted widespread cluster analyses of degrees of similarity between all these artefacts and those commonly found in northern Puget Sound, Gulf of Georgia, Strait of Juan de Fuca and the West Coast of Washington and Vancouver Island, BC (Croes, Kelly & Collard 2005; Kelly 2005; Croes et al 2006).

The contrasting results between stone, bone-antler and shell artefacts and those of basketry demonstrate a distinct difference between diffusion of ideas (ethnogenesis) and the guarding of ideas (branching or phylogenesis) in ethnic styles and identity, especially through sensitive basketry artefacts (Croes, Kelly & Collard 2005; Croes 2005; Kelly 2005). For example, the SB-AS types from Qwu?gwes statistically link with those found at the waterlogged and contemporary site of Ozette Village; however, it becomes quite clear from the basketry artefacts that they have very different cultural traditions. In fact, because of the styles and late time periods of these sites, they clearly represent Makah (Ozette) and Squaxin Island Tribe (Qwu?gwes) in cultural tradition – language families that are guessed to be separated by over 6,500 years through lexicostatistical techniques (Swadish 1953, 1954, 362), which are certainly controversial in true validity, but suggestive of considerable separations as well. Therefore, ethnic identity appears to be 'guarded' more through basketry traditions (phylogenesis) than stone, bone-antler, shell artefact traditions that are more closely associated with widely spread and shared procurement and manufacturing related artefacts (ethnogenesis). These regional trends in basketry styles appear to be preserved for at least 3,000 years from wet sites in the Makah/Wakashan areas and those in the Puget Sound/Gulf of Georgia Salishan regions (Croes, Kelly & Collard 2005).

A recent study we conducted on Puget Sound projectile point types revealed a sequence from the earliest known occupations of North America, with nine scattered surface finds of Clovis points throughout the region, through Qwu?gwes late period styles (Croes et al 2006). In comparison to better established projectile point type sequences, slightly north of our region, in the Gulf of Georgia/Fraser/San Juan Islands regions, we found that Puget Sound styles follow the same exact sequencing seen through time (Matson & Coupland 1995; Ames & Maschner 1999). Of course, since this also is the strongest and best known region of wet site basketry style continuity for 3,000 years, proposed to reflect a Coast Salish cultural continuity for at least this time stretch, the projectile points would be expected to follow a similar sequencing throughout the region, and they did (Croes et al 2006).

We will touch on the main analyses of wet site materials from Qwu?gwes with regional comparisons below, reviewing results of analyses of netting, basketry, woodworking and the fish traps.

QWU?GWES NET ANALYSIS

During the initial auger testing at Mud Bay in the summer of 1999, we pulled up an auger drive cut that contained a section of twisted cedar bough withe, and immediately realized that the site contained a waterlogged area with preserved wood and fibre cultural remains – in other words, a wet site, in our Northwest Coast vernacular (Croes 1976). We decided to do a careful 1 × 1m test pit, at 5cm level intervals, in two areas of the inter-tidal shell midden deposit. In the southern square (N15/E16, see map, fig 2), we reached the waterlogged deposits at about 50cm, and came directly down on a large pile of cedar bark string net. In fact, in the whole wet site excavations, only three of the 1 × 1m squares have contained the contiguous large quantity of net, suggesting that all of the net is from one section or pile of fragmented net (see map, fig 2; and examples illustrated in Foster & Croes 2002, 2004).

Examination of the net in these three excavation squares revealed that the two-strand string net was made of the twisted inner bark of Western Red Cedar (*Thuja plicata*) with an average web approximately 5cm between knots or 25sq cm each (McCullough, McCullough & Valley 2005). We have counted over 1,600 square knots visible in the recovered portions of the net – since it was a pile, no doubt many knots remain obscured within the preserved clumps. Square knots are non-slip knots often used when making nets without a netting needle (Ashley 1944, 64–5). If the minimum number of knots needed to represent the existence of one web is at least two knots, since obviously webs would share knots, then the net involves a minimum of 800 webs × 25sq cm, equalling a minimum area of 20,000sq cm or at least 2sq metres of recovered net (McCullough, McCullough & Valley 2005). The two-strand twisted strings average 0.3–0.4cm diameter, which would fall into the string gauge diameter as established at the Ozette Village wet site (Croes 1980, 18–25).

Nets are found in many Northwest Coast wet sites, dating back as early as 5,000 years ago, and reflect a wide variety of materials used, filament or two-strand twisted strings, web sizes and proposed uses (see table 1, Croes & Foster 2004). Often a site with two-strand twisted string nets emphasizes either Z- or S-laid string, considered a cultural prescription. However, the Qwu?gwes strings appear to have about a 50/50 emphasis on lay, with 54 per cent having an S-lay and 46 per cent a Z-lay (N = 448 strings observed; McCullough, McCullough & Valley 2005).

WOODWORKING

Wet site excavations at Qwu?gwes have unearthed a large quantity of woodchips, as well as jadite adze bits (N = 3), splitting wedges of wood (N = 1) and elk antler (N = 4). To better understand the amount and kind of woodworking taking place, woodchip samples were selected from a series of squares and levels to measure length, thickness, angle-in and angle-out points, profile and feathering. Each of these characteristics shows how different tools and woodworking technologies were used at the site. To gain a better understanding of ancient woodworking chips, we worked closely with Squaxin master woodcarver, Andrea Wilbur-Sigo (McCullough, McCullough & Valley 2005).

The Qwu?gwes woodchips are mostly western red cedar, though a fair amount of large hardwood

FIGURE 10
Example of checker work cedar bark basketry with overlay bear-grass decoration. This piece is folded, so two sides are preserved.

woodchips are also seen at the site (species unidentified at this time). A woodchip is any piece of wood that had obviously been cut from a piece of wood, as distinguished from any piece that could have been split or broken off. Woodchips can be distinguished by the difference between the point where the blade entered the wood and the exit point. Slicing pieces of wood along the surface plane of the wood produces feathering at the point of entrance. Another important attribute of woodchips is their plane view shape. When the adze bit cuts into the wood, it enters the wood at a certain angle. As the blade cleaves the wood from the wood surface, it tends to do so with less of an angle, leaving us with an inverted triangle. When the cutting edge of an adze bit enters the wood it compresses the wood along the cutting edge. Three other attributes, which are quite important in interpreting the woodchips, are angle-in, angle-out, and the profile (see Gleeson 1980).

Most of the Qwu?gwes woodchips have a flat-shaped plane view, as opposed to the inverted triangular profile of the other chips. According to Andrea Wilbur-Sigo, the woodchips seem to come from shaving, planing, light adzing, or finer detailed woodworking. Chips created from 'moving wood', or roughly cutting, would tend to be larger, with a sharper entrance angle. A number of these chips were flat, possibly resulting from cutting into the wood at a certain angle to achieve the 'final finishing process' (McCullough, McCullough & Valley 2005).

While there were woodchips found in different levels, they were mostly concentrated in the vegetal mat channel of the waterlogged squares (fig 2). In these waterlogged levels, the woodchips reflect the intensity of the woodworking activity during these times, levels and years.

BASKETRY

So far, three main types of basketry have been found at the Qwu?gwes site: (1) cedar bark checker weave matting, sometimes with bear-grass overlay decoration (fig 10); (2) open-twined small to large 'pack' baskets of cedar splints (n = 4) and (3) fine twill weave bark basketry (see Foster & Croes 2004 and Croes, Kelly & Collard 2005 for full descriptions and analyses).

With the growing basketry data base, we have conducted several basketry attribute (mode) presence/absence comparative analyses with other ancient basketry collections from Northwest Coast wet sites, to begin to see what degrees of similarity may be demonstrated from this new southern Puget Sound wet site. Statistically, in terms of degrees of similarity, Qwu?qwes clustered closely with two other recent (within last 1,000 years) Lushootseed language area wet sites, Fishtown and Conway, and then with an early one, Biederbost, dating to 2,000 years ago (see fig 1; Croes & Foster 2004, Croes, Kelly & Collard 2005). Fishtown and Conway wet sites are about 200km north of Qwu?gwes on the Skagit River Delta.

The basketry construction debris that has been preliminarily measured consists of cedar bark strips, cedar bough/root splints and cherry bark strips. The distributional patterns, through time and space of the basketry construction debris, and the measurements, have aided us in understanding the magnitude of basketry construction taking place at the site. Variations in width and thickness have been documented and so aids in understanding the kinds of basketry being made (Smith 2004).

The examples of basketry waste materials include strips and edge clippings that were discarded during manufacturing or repairs of baskets, hats, mats, blankets and other useful products that were made from cedar bark and splints of roots or limbs (boughs). The Hoko River archaeological site, located 150 miles north-west of Qwu?gwes on the opposite corner of the Olympic Peninsula, is the only other wet site that has fully analysed basketry waste detritus. The large quantities of materials at Qwu?gwes indicate that basketry manufacturing had occurred at this site. The levels of production are comparable to that found at Hoko River archaeological site (Smith 2004).

Basketry waste element materials emphases were different between Qwu?gwes and Hoko River, with a major emphasis on splint bough/root material at Qwu?gwes and a heavier emphasis on cedar bark at Hoko River, probably reflecting the kinds of basketry emphasized at the two wet sites (fig 10).

In comparing preliminary measurements, the average width of cedar bark basketry waste strips at Qwu?gwes is 0.7cm (SD = 0.31cm, N = 139) and the Hoko River examples were about the same, with a mean width of 0.7cm (SD = 0.5cm, N = 927). Similarly, the Qwu?gwes splint bough/root elements, with a mean width of 0.42cm (SD = 0.91cm, N = 450) were about the same as Hoko River examples, with a mean width of 0.7cm (SD = 0.5cm, N = 542). Preliminary measurements of Qwu?gwes cedar bark strip thickness (Mean = 0.18cm, SD = 0.29cm, N = 139) indicate that they are approximately twice as thick as those from Hoko River (Mean = 0.10cm, SD = 0.06cm, N = 927). The mean thickness of Qwu?gwes cedar splint bough/roots average 0.12cm

(SD = 0.11cm, N = 450), very similar to splints at Hoko River, with a mean of 0.11cm (SD = 0.06cm, N = 542). At Qwu?gwes, the length of cedar bark strips average 5.4cm (SD = 2.5cm, N = 139) compared with Hoko River where the mean length was 9.1cm (SD = 6.6cm, N = 927). Only 8 per cent of the cedar bark at Hoko was over 15cm in length, with 1 per cent at Qwu?gwes. This leaves 99 per cent of the materials recovered falling in the category of being too small to be considered useable for making whole baskets, indicating that these pieces were most likely remnants that were trimmed off during the final steps of production (Smith 2004).

CULTURAL ANALYSIS

For the Squaxin Island Tribe, the Qwu?gwes site at Mud Bay is much more than just an archaeological excavation. Qwu?gwes (the modern name recently given by the tribe to this major harvesting and processing site) is a link to the tribe's cultural history that has continued at that location for hundreds of years. Scientific methodology and study provide a means of identifying and analysing this ancient culture, but by themselves do not provide the complete picture. Comprehensive Cultural Resource Management (CRM) that incorporates the Squaxin Island Tribe's cultural component into the work at Mud Bay, using oral history, current technologies and practices, and traditional beliefs has helped provide a more complete picture of that ancient culture to understand how the tribe's ancestors lived their lives. This cultural component is rarely included in typical archaeological work.

CRM is the identification, preservation and protection of all the various types of cultural resources that are of value to the community, from the past (ancient and historical), present day and the future. Archaeological sites and artefacts are only one type of cultural resource, and excavation only one source of information. At Mud Bay we use and embrace the science of archaeology, but also look to see how all types of cultural resources were and are part of the site and of the lives of the descendants of our ancestors who inhabited the site; how the cultural information can be used to help to interpret their lifestyles; how these cultural resources can be preserved and protected; and supporting all activities of the tribe that are traditional to keep the culture alive. It is also about teaching those who will be the future archaeologists and CRM professionals how to work with native peoples in a personal way, and to get an understanding of the cultures they will be working with that goes beyond the science alone. Squaxin Island members and members of other tribes

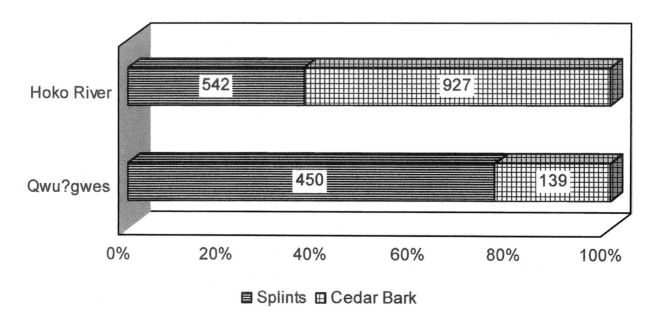

FIGURE 11
Ratios of cedar bark to splint root/bough basketry materials found at Qwu?gwes and Hoko River wet sites.

who come to Mud Bay learn about the preservation and protection of their heritage, experience the links to the past, have the opportunity to teach others about their heritage, and are trained to become certified Cultural Resource Technicians so that the tribes can manage their own cultural sites and resources. It is important for the tribe to manage its own cultural resources, as this strengthens the connection between our ancient past and ancestors, and helps us to continue our culture for future generations. The following examples illustrate how much clearer and more complete an understanding is possible when the cultural component is balanced with the science.

In one area of the site a large number of bones were discovered. Scientific analysis could identify the species, but the cultural knowledge of the tribe correctly interpreted that the particular species found would not have been eaten, but would have been used only for spiritual and ceremonial uses.

Tribal members from the tribe's shellfish programme, who grow and harvest many of the species found in the site's shell midden, provide information about where and under what conditions the various species grow, the differences between modern and ancient shell types, sizes and shapes, and when to harvest those species.

Traditional tribal knowledge has been invaluable in interpreting the basketry, cordage, fish trap and gill net fragments discovered at the site. Tribal weavers identified materials used, described how artefacts were made and their uses, understood their designs, and pointed out the similarities and differences from current weaving methods and materials. The weavers also taught students how to make the cordage.

The cedar bark gill net recovered at the site measured as a 13cm stretch mesh. Tribal members who fish today recognized how the net was made, that this size of net was for smaller salmon species, described the fishing techniques and uses of a gill net and a fish trap, and knew when to use one or the other. A cedar bark gill net gives a fisher person flexibility and mobility to cover large areas in search of schools of salmon. At a young age, a child is taught how to study a school of salmon, the best approach when surrounding a school, and to only catch what can be processed in a short period of time.

Hazelnut shells have been found, but the significance of these shells would not be understood without the tribe's traditional knowledge of the importance of this food in the ancient diet. The nuts were mixed with berries and fat to make a valuable winter food, the husks were used for medicine, which may explain why few husks have been found at the site, and most of the nuts would have been brought to the site from the drier hilltops of the neighbouring hills.

Cherry bark is found extensively at the site. Tribal members knew that cherry bark is very supple when wet, but shrinks and becomes stiff and strong, making it excellent material for reinforcing the edges of baskets and tying cork lines to the gill nets. It would be easy to assume that the cherry bark all came from the immediate area of Mud Bay. However, many tribal families knew the ancient cherry bark gathering place, which is not at Mud Bay.

The beach at Mud Bay is littered with TAR, the remains of boiling stones that have split apart. Tribal members pointed out that rocks were spread on the beach for newly growing oysters to attach to, which demonstrates active management of shellfish resources by the ancient peoples.

As the examples have illustrated, including the cultural component from the tribe provides a wealth of knowledge and skills that are needed to manage more effectively cultural resources, and these are beyond anything that is learned in a typical university or college anthropology programme.

SUMMARY, FUTURE GOALS AND CONCLUSIONS

It is hoped that the value of a 50/50 sharing of the research at the Qwu?gwes wet site between archaeological scientists and indigenous cultural experts is understood.

Our synthesis is preliminary and we expect to continue to expand the training and joint research to assure the protection and proper presentation of our wet site work at Qwu?gwes – as this Lushootseed name implies.

ACKNOWLEDGEMENTS

We would all like to personally thank the 11th International Wetland Archaeology Research Project (WARP) Conference Chair, Dr Alison Sheridan, for helping our whole group travel to Edinburgh, providing housing for three of our students (and several receptions for our group at her home), while conducting a brilliant – the best yet – WARP Conference. The entire National Museum of Scotland faculty and personnel made sure the best conference facilities and support were always available to us and all conference attendees. John and Bryony

Coles, WARP leaders, attended our session, asking excellent questions, while our students gave confident responses. The authors would also like to thank Karen and Ralph Munro, property owners, Qwu?gwes Site, for supporting the Squaxin Island Tribe and South Puget Sound Community College in opening their property for several summer field school seasons of training and investigations, so this research could be conducted and presented. South Puget Sound Community College provides dedicated laboratory space for the preservation, stabilization and analysis of the cultural materials reported here. The Squaxin Island Tribe Cultural Resources Department and Museum Library and Research Center provide interpretation and public exhibition of the Qwu?gwes materials. Numerous project researchers, Squaxin Island Tribe community members, field personnel and students have contributed to data recovery, analysis and reporting. Jean and Ray Auel have generously supported Qwu?gwes excavations through the years. Though this research owes its existence to these individuals, programmes, facilities and previous and current researchers, the summary and conclusions remain the responsibility of the authors.

REFERENCES

Ames, K M & Maschner, H D G 1999 *Peoples of the Northwest Coast, Their Archaeology and Prehistory.* London.

Armstrong, D A, Dinnel, P A *et al* 1993 *Washington Shellfish Resources.* Seattle.

Bernick, K 1983 'A site catchment analysis of the Little Qualicum River site, DiSc 1: a wet site on the East Coast of Vancouver Island, BC', *National Museum of Man Mercury Series*, 118, Ottawa.

Bernick, K & Wigen, R 1990 'Seasonality of the Little Qualicum River West site', *Northwest Anthropological Research Notes* 24(2), 153–9.

Claassen, C 1998 *Shells.* Cambridge.

Croes, D R 1976 (ed) 'The excavation of water-saturated archaeological sites (wet sites) on the Northwest Coast of North America', *National Museum of Man Mercury Series,* 50.

Croes, D R 1977 *Basketry from the Ozette Village Archaeological Site: A Technological, Functional and Comparative Study.* PhD dissertation, Washington State University. University Microfilms 77–25, 762, Ann Arbor, MI.

Croes, D R 1992 'An evolving revolution in wet site research on the Northwest Coast of North America', *in* Coles, B (ed) *The Wetland Revolution in Prehistory, WARP Occasional Paper*, 6, 99–111. Exeter.

Croes, D R 1995 *The Hoko River Archaeological Site Complex, the Wet/dry Site (45CA213), 3,000–2,600 BP.* Pullman, WA.

Croes, D R 2005 *The Hoko River Archaeological Site Complex, The Rockshelter (45CA21), 1,000–100 BP.* Pullman, WA.

Croes, D R, Kelly, K & Collard, M 2005 'Cultural historical context of Qwu?gwes (Puget Sound, USA): a preliminary investigation, *Journal of Wetland Archaeology,* 5, 137–49.

Croes, D R, Williams, S, Ross, L, Dennler, C & Vargo, B 2006 (submitted manuscript) 'Projectile points from Puget Sound and the Cascade Foothills', *in* Carlson, R (ed) *Projectile Point Sequences in Northwestern North America.* Burnaby, BC.

Diedrich, M 2005 *Nuts, Seeds, and Raw Materials, Macrofloral Analysis at the Ancient Qwu?gwes Wet Site, Southern Puget Sound, USA.* Paper presented at the 11th Wetland Archaeology Research Project (WARP) Conference, Edinburgh.

Foster, R & Croes, D 2002 'Tribal-archaeological co-operative agreement: a holistic cultural resource management approach', *Journal of Wetland Archaeology,* 2, 25–38.

Foster, R & Croes, D 2004 'Joint tribal/college wet site investigations: a critical need for Native American expertise', *Journal of Wetland Archaeology,* 4, 127–39.

Foster, R & Ross, L 2005 *Tribal Cultural Resource Management Review of Ancient Qwu?gwes Wet Site.* Paper presented at the 11th Wetland Archaeology Research Project (WARP) Conference, Edinburgh.

Gleeson, P 1980 'Ozette woodworking technology', PhD dissertation, Washington State University.

Harbo, R M 1997 *Shells and Shellfish of the Pacific Northwest.* Madeira Park, BC.

Houghton, J P 1973 *The Inter-tidal Ecology of Kiket Island, Washington, with Emphasis on Age and Growth of Protothaca staminea and Saxidomus giganteus.* PhD dissertation, University of Washington, Seattle, WA.

Hubbard, N, Foster, S & Myers, K 2005 *Shellfish Analysis from Qwu?gwes, a Wet Site on Southern Puget Sound, USA.* Paper presented at the 11th Wetland Archaeology Research Project (WARP) Conference, Edinburgh.

Hurst, J L 2003 *The Analysis of Shell Growth and Age at Harvest of the Butter Clam (Saxidomus giganteus Deshayes): An Insight to the Implementation of Management Practices at the Qwu?gwes Archaeological Site (45TN240) in Olympia, WA, USA.* MA thesis, University of Exeter, England.

Kelly, K M 2005 *Analysis of the Stone, Bone-Antler and Shell Artefacts from the Qwe?gwes Site (45TN240), South Puget Sound, Washington, USA.* Paper presented at the 11th Wetland Archaeology Research Project (WARP) Conference, Edinburgh.

Matson, R G & Coupland, G 1995 *The Prehistory of the Northwest Coast.* San Diego, CA.

McCullough, M, McCullough, T & Valley, L 2005 *Woodworking and Net-making Technologies at the Ancient Qwu?gwes Wet Site, Southern Puget Sound, USA.* Paper presented at the 11th Wetland Archaeology Research Project (WARP) Conference, Edinburgh.

Sharron, C V 2005 *TAR – Thermally Altered Rock from the Ancient Qwu?gwes Wet Site, Southern Puget Sound, USA.* Paper presented at the 11th Wetland Archaeology Research Project (WARP) Conference, Edinburgh.

Smith, S 2004 *Qwu?gwes Basketry Debris: Measurements, Comparisons and Analysis.* Paper on file, Qwu?gwes Cultural Site Project, Department of Anthropology, South Puget Sound Community College, Olympia, Washington.

Strong, J M & Croes, D R 2001 'Heat capacity and fragmentation pattern determinations of potential cooking stones: a case study at the Qwu?gwes archaeological Site (45-TN-240), Olympia, Washington', *Northwest Anthropological Research Notes*, 35(1), 41–54.

Suttles, W & Lane, B 1990 'Southern Coast Salish', *in* Suttles, W (ed) *Handbook of North American Indians, Vol 7: Northwest Coast*, 485–502. Washington, DC.

Swadesh, M 1953 'Mosan I: a problem of remote common origin', *International Journal of American Linguistics*, 19, 26–44. New York.

Swadesh, M 1954 'Time depths of American linguistic groupings', *American Anthropologist*, 56, 3:361–77. Menasha.

Thompson, L C & Kinkade, M D 1990 'Languages', *in* Suttles, W (ed) *Handbook of North American Indians, Vol 7: Northwest Coast*, 30–51. Washington, DC.

Vargo, B A 2005 *Raw Material Variation in the Qwe?gwes Stone Tool Assemblage.* Paper presented at the 11th Wetland Archaeology Research Project (WARP) Conference, Edinburgh.

Waitt, R B Jr & Thorson, R M 1983 'The Cordilleran ice sheet in Washington, Idaho, and Montana', *in* Wright Jr, H E & Porter, S C *Late-Quaternary Environments of the United States, Volume 1: The Late Pleistocene*, 53–70.

Wigen, R 2003 *Qwu?gwes Faunal Report, 2002 Excavations.* Report submitted to the Qwu?gwes Archaeological Project, on file, Office of Archaeology and Historic Preservation, Olympia, WA.

Wigen, R 2006 *Qwu?gwes Faunal Report, Through 2004 Excavations.* Report submitted to the Qwu?gwes Archaeological Project, on file, Office of Archaeology and Historic Preservation, Olympia, WA.

Part III
THE PEATLAND SESSION

Peat, pine stumps and people: interactions behind climate, vegetation change and human activity in wetland archaeology at Loch Farlary, northern Scotland

RICHARD TIPPING, PATRICK ASHMORE, ALTHEA DAVIES, ANDREW HAGGART, ANDREW MOIR, ANTHONY NEWTON, ROBERT SANDS, THEO SKINNER and EILEEN TISDALL

INTRODUCTION

In 1993, a peat-cutter, Bruce Field, working on the blanket peat bank he rented from the Sutherland Estate by Loch Farlary, above Golspie in Sutherland (fig 1), reported to Scottish Natural Heritage and Historic Scotland several pieces of pine wood bearing axe marks. Their depth in the peat suggested the cut marks to be prehistoric. This paper summarizes the work undertaken to understand the age and archaeological significance of this find (see also Tipping *et al* 2003 in press). The pine trees were initially thought to be part of a population that flourished briefly across northern Scotland in the middle of the Holocene period from *c* 4800 cal BP (Huntley, Daniell & Allen 1997). The subsequent collapse across northernmost Scotland of this population, the pine decline, at around 4200–4000 cal BP is unexplained: climate change has been widely assumed (Dubois & Ferguson 1985; Bridge, Haggart & Lowe 1990; Gear & Huntley 1991) but anthropogenic activity has not been disproved (Birks 1975; Bennett 1995). It was hypothesized that the Farlary find would allow for the first time the direct link between human woodland clearance and the Early Bronze Age pine decline.

MATERIALS AND METHODS

To test this hypothesis, the following techniques were applied. The buried topography and peat stratigraphy in a 25.0 × 12.0m area round Mr Field's bank were recorded on a 1.0m grid by Eijelkamp peat probes (fig 2), surveyed to OD. These also permitted concealed wood to be discovered and plotted. Wood within a metre's depth of the ground surface, that most threatened by disturbance, was excavated by hand

(literally), identified to species and origin (trunk, root) and each piece inspected for cut marks: 20 pieces of wood (*c* 70 per cent of the total) were retrieved (fig 2). Nine of these had axe marks. Blade size and curvature were reconstructed on the three pieces with complete blade marks (Sands 1997) and compared with corpuses of known tools and comparable marks (Harbison 1969; Manning & Saunders 1972; Schmidt & Burgess 1981; O'Sullivan 1991; Coombs 1992). Cut marked pieces were conserved after freeze-drying in polyethylene glycol and are housed in the NMS collection. Dendrochronological techniques were applied to six complete slices of pine trunks sampled by chain-saw to assess the ages of individual trees and correlate their growth patterns. The outermost tree rings of a number of wood pieces, including all those cut, were AMS radiocarbon dated (table 1). Thin slices of peat in different stratigraphic settings were also dated by radiocarbon and by tephrochronology (table 1). High-resolution pollen and pine stomatal counts, microscopic charcoal and palaeohydrological analyses using colorimetry were applied to sediments at point Y25, within 5m of the blanket peat containing wood remains, to provide a continuous local record of vegetation, land use, hydrological and climatic change (Tipping *et al* 2003 in press).

RESULTS AND INTERPRETATIONS

Beneath the present peat surface, there are two granite bedrock surfaces. A shallow (2m deep) surface between points A13 and P21 lies above the edge of a much deeper (7m deep) basin beneath point R21 (fig 2), a former arm of Loch Farlary (fig 1). Both surfaces are buried by peat, a thin blanket over the shallow surface, a much thicker fen peat in the deep basin. Wood remains are preserved with a very high density

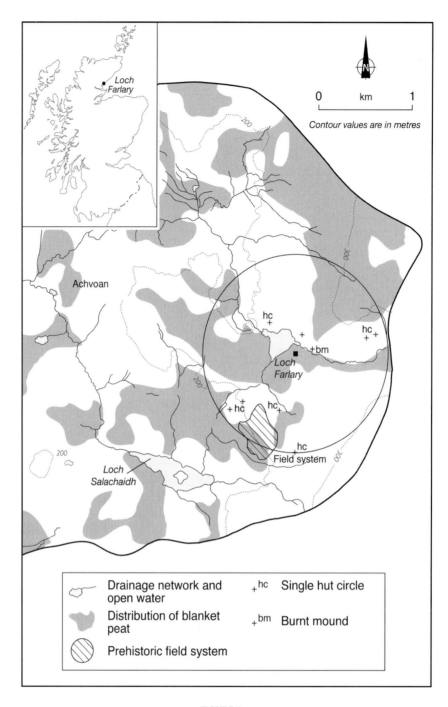

FIGURE 1

The location of Loch Farlary in Scotland, and the catchment of the loch, showing contours at 100m intervals, the current extent of blanket peat, the distribution of later prehistoric archaeological monuments and the findspot south-west of Loch Farlary. The circle around the findspot represents the probable recruitment area for most pollen grains recorded at point Y25.

in a single layer *c* 1m thick in the upper layers of the blanket peat and in two layers in the basin.

Loch Farlary last occupied the deep basin in the earliest Holocene, before 8500 cal BP. After this, the sediment stratigraphy and palaeoecological analyses at point Y25 record the development of a fen. Radiocarbon dates on the basal blanket peat on shallow bedrock at points A13 and L19 (fig 2) show that peat was established across the grid between 9000 and 8500 cal BP. Temporal correlation with palaeohydrological data at point Y25 show that this was promoted by very wet ground conditions and a markedly wet climate (Tipping *et al* 2003 in press). Pollen analyses at point Y25 show that open deciduous woodland of birch, willow, hazel, rowan and juniper grew on blanket peat and adjacent mineral soil. This woodland survived a major climate shift to pronounced aridity at 8200 cal BP. Pollen analyses suggest that the very dry peat was invaded by colonizing pine trees first at 7600–7500 cal BP. Repeated, short-lived phases of dry and wet mire surfaces and changes in fire frequency/intensity are thought to have cumulatively destabilized and fragmented the pine woodland by 6400 cal BP, leading over 400 years to pine trees probably being rare around Loch Farlary (Tipping *et al* 2003 in press).

Late Neolithic farming communities briefly disturbed this deciduous woodland, over 150–200 cal years from *c* 5100 cal BP, for pasture and cereal cultivation. During this disturbance phase, or in the subsequent woodland regeneration, pine trees were re-established on the dry peat. Pine re-colonization may have been facilitated by human disturbance of the woodland, inadvertently reducing competitive stresses between deciduous trees and pine. Pine re-colonized the blanket peat in significant numbers, as suggested by the radiocarbon dated macrofossil record (table 1; fig 2). All but one of the 11 wood pieces cut by axes grew between 5200 and 4350 cal BP (table 1). The exception is Stump 2 (fig 3), a massive 3m bole and root system established by radiocarbon dating (table 1) to have formed part of the pine population that had colonized the peat before 6000 cal BP. Of the 20 wood pieces retrieved by excavation, 11 are of horizontally trending root, one is a

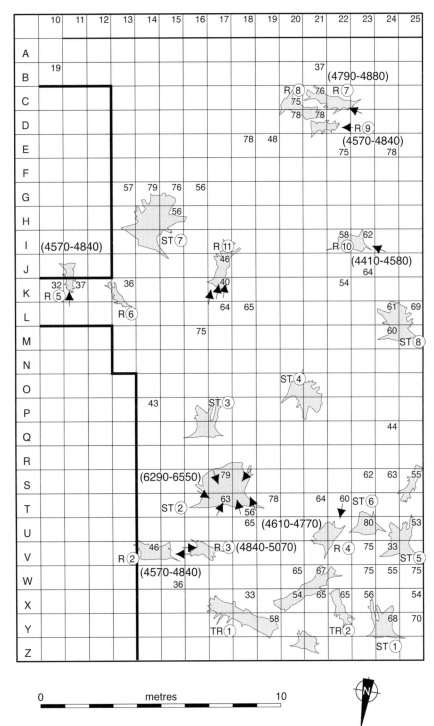

FIGURE 2

Plan of the grid (squares A10–Z25) showing the locations and depths (numbers within grid squares) of all wood pieces <80cm below the present peat surface hit during depth-probing and the outlines, positions, approximate sizes and shapes of excavated wood pieces, labelled Roots (R), Stumps (ST) and Trunks (TR). The positions of cut marks on roots and Stump 2 are indicated by arrows, and the calibrated age ranges of ^{14}C dated wood pieces are given.

159

TABLE 1
Details of all radiocarbon assays and calibrations.

(a) Calibrated radiocarbon assays for the sediment stratigraphy at Point Y25

Location	Depth (cm)	Lab. code	^{14}C age BP ($\pm 1.0\sigma$)	$\delta^{13}C$	Cal. age range BP (2.0σ)
Y25	50.0–55.0	Beta-167560	2660 ± 60	−26.2	2869–2715
Y25	100.0–105.0	Beta-167561	4220 ± 50	−27.1	4862–4573
Y25	150.0–155.0	Beta-167562	5570 ± 70	−24.7	6493–6205
Y25	217.0–222.0	Beta-83361	7500 ± 170	nd	8600–7963
Y25	290.0–295.0	Beta-83360	8410 ± 140	nd	9676–9029
Y25	342.0–347.0	Beta-83359	9090 ± 90	nd	10485–9923
Y25	389.0–394.0	Beta-83358	10570 ± 100	nd	12944–12098

nd = not determined

(b) Calibrated radiocarbon assays for basal and mid-depth peats at points A13 and L19

Location	Depth (cm)	Lab. code	^{14}C age BP ($\pm 1.0\sigma$)	$\delta^{13}C$	Cal. age range BP (2.0σ + probability)
A13	151.0–150.0	AA-52518	7995 ± 45	−28.1	9020–8700 (93.2%)
L19	211.0–210.0	AA-52519	7860 ± 45	−27.7	8790–8520 (82.3%)
A13	120.0–119.0	AA-52520	6605 ± 40	−28.7	7570–7420 (95.4%)

(c) calibrated radiocarbon assays for wood excavated within the grid and sampled by SNH

Location	Lab. code ($\pm 1.0\sigma$)	^{14}C age BP	$\delta^{13}C$	Cal. age range BP (2.0σ) & % probability
V14–15 (R2)	AA-53143	4185 ± 40	−23.6	4840–4570 (95.4%)
V16 (R3)	AA-53144	4395 ± 50	−24.4	5280–5170 (11.9%)
				5130–5100 (1.7%)
				5070–4840 (81.8%)
U/V21–22 (R4)	AA-53145	4195 ± 40	−25.5	4840–4780 (20.6%)
				4770–4610 (70.5%)
				4600–4570 (4.3%)
S/T16–18 (S2)	AA-53146	5630 ± 55	−24.4	6550–6290 (95.4%)
K11 (R5)	AA-53147	4175 ± 40	−25.1	4840–4570 (95.4%)
C20–21 (R8)	AA-53148	4260 ± 45	−25.2	4970–4930 (3.0%)
				4880–4790 (56.3%)
				4770–4620 (36.1%)
D21–22 (R9)	AA-53149	4175 ± 40	−25.2	4840–4570 (95.4%)
I22–23 (R10)	AA-53150	4020 ± 40	−25.1	4790–4760 (1.2%)
				4620–4590 (1.5%)
				4580–4410 (92.7%)
East of Z10	GU-3964	4140 ± 50	−26.2	4830–4450 (95.4%)

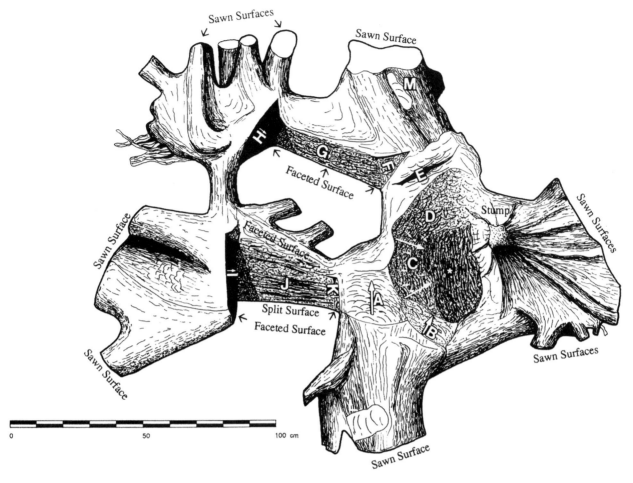

FIGURE 3
Drawing of Stump 2 by Robert Sands showing the locations of cutting activity (A–M).

horizontal trunk, and eight are the bases of vertical stumps (fig 2). Trunks are probably rare because they would be decayed above and on the peat surface. Pine trees colonized all parts of the peat in the grid from *c* 5200 cal BP. Despite the nutrient-poor, acid substrate provided by the granite bedrock, dendrochronological analyses showed that the six trunks sampled grew to mean ages exceeding 200 years.

A gradual decline in the local population of pines is recognized from pollen analyses at point Y25, from *c* 4000 cal BP until *c* 3250 cal BP, seemingly not through climate deterioration (cf Gear & Huntley 1991) because changes in mire surface wetness were insignificant, but possibly because of subdued but sustained grazing pressures.

The tool marks on the eleven 4,350–5,200-year-old pines were made by metal axes. This is clear from the cuts themselves, with their crisp inter-facet ridges and sharply defined facet terminations, and

by their being much longer and wider than any of O'Sullivan's corpus of marks (1991) made by Neolithic axes on wood in Ireland. All but one of the wood pieces cut were roots, cut with downward chopping actions from above: the exception is Stump 2 (fig 3). Two types of axe were used. A smaller axe with a facet width of 57mm, facet length of 52mm and curvature index of 14 per cent (Sands 1997) was used on Root 10 (fig 2). The axe is thought to be of Middle to Late Bronze Age date. Larger dish-faceted axes were used on Root 2 and repeatedly on Stump 2 (fig 2). These axes had facet widths between 83 and 87mm, facet lengths of between 67 and 68mm and curvature indices of 9–11 per cent (n = 2), and were probably used after the beginning of the Iron Age, although an Early Bronze Age date cannot be eliminated. No piece of wood was cut by more than one type of axe. If the wood was cut at different times, which seems most likely, the following

161

sequence can be suggested: already dead roots in a dense layer were cut in the Middle to Late Bronze Age, after which peat continued to grow, until after the beginning of the Iron Age, when more dead roots from the same layer were cut.

The earliest cutting of wood may have coincided with increased agricultural activity, suggested from palynological evidence after 3500 cal BP, increasingly intensive after 3250 cal BP. Grazing pressures, purposeful vegetation burning and possible local cultivation of barley led to the loss of all but a few deciduous trees by 3000 cal BP. With climatic deterioration and increasingly wet soils demonstrated from the palaeohydrological analyses after 2800 cal BP, cereal cultivation around Loch Farlary may have ceased (Tipping *et al* in press).

DISCUSSION

The hypothesis that the cut marks on pine wood around Loch Farlary represent the felling of a population of pine trees coincident with the timing of the regionally synchronous Early Bronze Age decline in pine woodland in northern Scotland is rejected. The explanation developed to account for this so-far unique findspot in Scotland is much more complicated than the initial hypothesis supposed.

The population of pine trees around Loch Farlary was not part of the population recorded further west that rapidly but briefly expanded its range *c* 4500 cal years ago (Huntley *et al* 1997). Pine trees colonized peat surfaces around Loch Farlary on two occasions, the first at *c* 7600 cal BP until *c* 5900 cal BP, and then at *c* 5200 cal BP until *c* 3200 cal BP. It is almost exclusively this second population of trees, established around 5200 cal BP and mostly dying between 4800 and 4600 cal BP, that is represented by the rare trunks, common stumps and abundant roots within the uppermost layers of blanket peat. Only one tree, Stump 2, was excavated that grew in the first phase of pine growth. It died at around 6200 cal BP, but this stump was so large that its upper roots and bole probably remained above the peat for a long time, now found at the same shallow depth (115cm) as much younger trees.

This very old stump, and the roots of several trees of this second population of trees, were cut by metal axes after the Early Bronze Age. Two types of metal axe, probably of different ages, were used. The trees that were cut were all much older than the age range of the earliest possible axe type. Nearly all pieces of wood cut were roots, and these were chopped

through in repeated, downward strokes. Although trees can be killed by the cutting of roots, this is less effective than the cutting of trunks. This, and the independently developed chronologies of tree growth and axe manufacture, make it most likely that already dead wood, either on the peat surface or covered by growing peat, was being cut. Indeed, given the rapidity with which wood on a peat surface decays, the tree trunks originally growing from the roots need not have survived when the roots were cut.

The purpose of cutting the wood remains speculative. We have found it most useful to distinguish between the cutting of roots and the cutting of the monstrous Stump 2, illustrated in fig 3. The cutting of roots may have been to use the dead wood, either in building or as fuel, or to get rid of the wood in obtaining peat for fuel. The first use, as a building material, is thought least likely, at least in the Bronze Age. The later prehistoric archaeological landscape in the uplands around Loch Farlary is very rich (fig 1: D Cowley pers comm), with abundant and extensive field systems, a number of hut circles and burnt mounds of probable Bronze and Iron Age date (eg McCullagh & Tipping 1998 at nearby Lairg). However, living pine trees were available around Loch Farlary until *c* 3300 cal BP, though were probably increasingly rare after *c* 4000 cal BP, and deciduous trees were also available for use until the end of the Bronze Age. The roots that were cut and left behind in the peat are spindly, no thicker than a forearm, and unlikely to be load-bearing. Resin-rich dead pine was a common taper, and the roots may have been cut to provide these.

However, our preferred explanation relates what happened in later prehistory with the late twentieth-century process of discovery of the cut marked wood by Mr Field. Cutting low into the stratigraphy of his peat bank, reaching the layer of mid-Holocene pine roots, had led Mr Field to remove wood thousands of years old because it impeded peat extraction and resulted in poor quality bricks. Without saws, the wood is best removed from the vertical banks by repeated downward chopping as they are reached by the peat spade. Because of their lateral extent and preservation within the peat, roots are far more commonly encountered than stumps, and so roots have to be cut through more commonly. The purpose of cutting is not to use the wood, but to get rid of it. The same thing may have happened in prehistory, when the same dense layer of pine wood in the peat was similarly encountered, perhaps repeatedly, accounting for the observation that no root was cut by more than one type of axe. An almost cyclic pattern of peat-cutting, wood removal, peat regrowth and subsequent cutting, and rediscovery of the same problematic wood layer, can be envisaged, which gives this later prehistoric activity a timeless quality, the acting-out of routines, commonplace and yet fundamental to life in the Highlands.

To extend this comparison, it can be asked why Mr Field does not simply move his peat bank, because in other banks at Farlary, peat thickness is such that this wood layer has not yet been reached. However, Mr Field is not free to move. The peat is not his, and other cutters work adjacent banks. In later prehistory, the same layer of wood within the peat appears to have been hacked at and hoiked out on at least two occasions. Why couldn't people then simply move from this part of the bog? Might it have been that land tenure in the comparatively densely populated uplands was as involved then as it is now?

Commonplace interpretation seems to fail when the cutting of Stump 2 (fig 3) is considered. Stump 2 provided a profoundly different problem for people working the peat. So large is it that, once encountered, the simplest option might have been to steer clear of it. But quite clearly people did not do this: instead, their working of this massive bole and root system might be described as obsessive.

Stump 2 grew at *c* 6400 cal BP. This is around 1,500–2,000 years before other trees that were cut. Because the tree grew so large, and the probable rate of growth was rapid in comparison to peat accumulation rates, the bole and root system of Stump 2 may have quickly emerged above its contemporaneous peat surface. Stump 2 also seems to have stood above the peat surface long after the tree died, despite this growth increasing the likelihood of wood decay. This reconstruction suggests that Stump 2 was visible on the bog for a long time.

Stump 2 is the most massive single pine stump recovered from peat in this or, apparently, in other investigations (Dubois & Ferguson 1985; Gear 1989; Bridge *et al* 1990; Daniell 1997). It is also distinctive in being the only stump known to have been cut at Farlary. This was more intricately cut into than any other piece of wood. Its manner of working is entirely different to other pieces, with many discrete patches of bole and root worked, again by chopping actions but more tangentially, perhaps induced by the futility of chopping at right angles to the tree. The purpose of cutting was probably not to remove the tree from the peat: if it was, it clearly failed. Short wedge-shaped chips, rather than long slivers, were produced in their hundreds by the cutting, but many of these were left in the ground, and because of this it is unlikely that chopping was intended to generate chips or tapers.

The apparently frenetic character of the repeated cuts into the tree suggests that cutting served no utilitarian purpose. It is not fanciful to argue that Stump 2 was highly visible to later prehistoric people moving across the peat, standing proud of the peat surface. The tree, or what was left of it, was already old, and known to be old, and people began to cut into its core with an intensity that was different to that committed to other trees. Stump 2 was cut into by one type of axe, the flat-faceted axes that are probably of either Early Bronze Age or Iron Age date. It is frustrating not to know more precisely the temporal context of the cutting because one explanation for this astonishing activity might link the use of a new tool, a metal axe within the earliest Bronze Age, to the cutting of an old stump, and relate this action to ideas about dominion over nature (Bradley 1993). Nevertheless, our interpretation has to move beyond the prosaic in explaining our observations. This stump became symbolic to these people, both commonplace and yet different, that could be worked on energetically and probably repeatedly, to make enduring impressions of an axe on a tree.

REFERENCES

Bennett, K D 1995 'Postglacial dynamics of pine (*Pinus sylvestris* L.) and pinewoods in Scotland', *in* Aldhous, J R (ed) *Our Pinewood Heritage*. Farnham, 23–39.

Birks, H H 1975 'Studies in the vegetational history of Scotland. IV. Pine stumps in Scottish blanket peats', *Philosophical Transactions of the Royal Society of London* B270, 181–226.

Bradley, R 1993. *Altering the Earth*. Edinburgh.

Bridge, M C, Haggart, B A & Lowe, J J 1990 'The history and palaeoclimatic significance of subfossil remains of *Pinus sylvestris* in blanket peats from Scotland', *Journal of Ecology* 78, 77–99.

Coombs, D 1992 'Flag Fen platform and Fengate Power Station post alignment – the metal work', *Antiquity* 66, 504–17.

Daniell, J R G 1997 *The late-Holocene Palaeoecology of Scots pine (*Pinus sylvestris* L.) in north-west Scotland*. Unpubl PhD thesis, University of Durham.

Dubois, A D & Ferguson, D K 1985 'The climatic history of pine in the Cairngorms based on radiocarbon dates and stable isotope analysis, with an account of events leading up to its colonization', *Review of Palaeobotany and Palynology* 46, 55–80.

Gear, A J & Huntley, B 1991 'Rapid changes in the range limits of Scots Pine 4,000 years ago', *Science* 251, 544–7.

Harbison, P 1969 *The Axes of the Early Bronze Age in Ireland*. Munich.

Huntley, B, Daniell, R G & Allen, J R M 1997 'Scottish vegetation history: the Highlands', *Botanical Journal of Scotland* 49, 163–75.

Manning, W H & Saunders, C 1972 'A socketed iron axe from Maids Moreton, Buckinghamshire, with a note on the type', *The Antiquaries Journal* 52, 276–92.

McCullagh, R P J & Tipping, R 1998 *The Lairg Project 1988–1996: the Evolution of an Archaeological Landscape in Northern Scotland*. Edinburgh.

O'Sullivan, A 1991 *Prehistoric Woodworking Techniques: The Evidence from Excavated Trackways in the Raised Bogs of Co Longford*. Unpubl MA thesis, University College, Dublin.

Sands, R 1997 *Prehistoric Woodworking. The Analysis and Interpretation of Bronze and Iron Age Toolmarks*. London.

Schmidt, P K & Burgess, C B 1981 *The Axes of Scotland and Northern England*. Munich.

Tipping, R, Ashmore, P, Davies, A, Haggart, A, Moir, A, Newton, A, Sands, R, Skinner, T & Tisdall, E 2003 *The Chronology, Significance and Environmental Context of Later Prehistoric Axe Marks on* in situ *Pine Trees at Farlary, near Golspie, Sutherland*. Archived report to Historic Scotland. Edinburgh.

Tipping, R, Ashmore, P, Davies, A, Haggart, A, Moir, A, Newton, A, Sands, R, Skinner, T & Tisdall, E in press 'Prehistoric *Pinus* woodland dynamics in an upland landscape in northern Scotland', *Vegetation History & Archaeobotany*.

Living with peat in the flow country:
prehistoric farming communities and blanket peat spread at Oliclett, Caithness, northern Scotland

RICHARD TIPPING, EILEEN TISDALL, ALTHEA DAVIES, CLARE WILSON and SUZANNE YENDELL

INTRODUCTION

The Caithness Plain in north-east Scotland is a gently rolling, lowland, coastal landscape on the edge of the largest expanse of blanket peat in the British Isles: the 'flow country' (fig 1). It has most often been assumed that prehistoric farming communities retreated in the face of the remorseless spread of blanket peat across such a landscape (Piggott 1972; Barber 1998), but it has also been argued that farmers were not so helpless, because, with effort, blanket peat can be kept at bay by repeated cultivation (Carter 1998). This model has not been closely tested before: Carter's ideas emerged from work at Lairg, Sutherland, and little was understood from that study of the chronology of blanket peat growth (McCullagh & Tipping 1998). Excavation of Mesolithic artefact scatters at Oliclett in Caithness (Pannett 2002), from beneath a hillside almost entirely buried by blanket and marsh peat, allowed the rates of peat spread across a single hillside to be understood in great spatial and temporal detail. This paper presents the ^{14}C dating evidence for peat growth and spread at Oliclett, and evaluates what this analysis might mean for how we perceive the responses of prehistoric people to environmental stress.

Oliclett (ND 302452; fig 1) is an east-facing and gentle (20m/km) slope, north of the archaeologically rich landscape at Yarrows. Fig 2a shows the bedrock contours of a grid outlined in fig 1, SE of Oliclate Farm. Locations are given in the text and in table 1 with reference to the grid superimposed on fig 2. Upper slopes, west of 200m E, are gentle. Between 200 and 260m E the slope steepens appreciably, above a very low gradient surface extending east beyond 450m E. Small and slow-flowing water courses run on slopes above 100m OD, between a series of very low till mounds. Below 100m OD, across the low gradient surface, an extensive marsh has developed at

the head of the Burn of Swartigill (figs 1, 2). On one of these (located at c 250m E/190m N: fig 2), later Mesolithic flint scatters were excavated by Amelia Pannett (2002), and on another (c 350m E/160m N), ard marks were recorded. No other archaeological monuments are known on the slope, in contrast to the abundant remains in the later prehistoric ritual and domestic landscape around Yarrows (fig 1), but the continuous peat cover inhibits discovery.

METHODS

Within the area outlined in fig 1 and plotted in fig 2, detailed sediment stratigraphies were recorded from test pits and excavated trenches, and hundreds of boreholes cored by hand-operated, 2.5cm diameter, Eijelkamp peat sampler, surveyed by EDM to OD. Boreholes at c 10m intervals ran along five major transects on the hillside from the high ground to the valley floor. A highly resolved chronological framework for peat development was generated from 36 AMS ^{14}C assays. These were sampled either with closed-chamber Russian corer or with a closed-chamber piston corer, from which the fine particulate fraction of thin peat slices was assayed, after removal of coarse, potentially intrusive, plant fragments. Humic acid and humin fractions were dated on six samples (Tipping et al 2003a) because organic fractions can differ in ^{14}C age (Shore, Bartley & Harkness 1975). No significant differences between fractions were found in five samples. Differences in one sample remain unexplained, but all assays reported in table 1 were obtained on humin fractions and are considered to provide correct ages. Although hard water error from calcareous glacial till is possible (Hall & Whittington 1989), analyses in Tipping et al (2003a) suggest that this error persists only in peat developed on unweathered sediment.

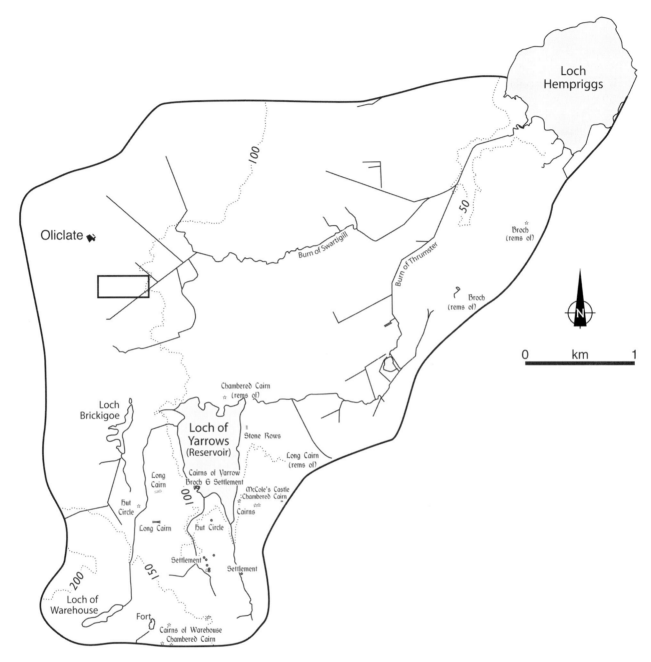

FIGURE 1

The location in Scotland of the fluvial catchment of Loch Hempriggs on the coastal Caithness Plain, showing the study area at Oliclett (Oliclate Farm) in the north-west, the hill slope analysed in fig 2 in the box, and the main archaeological monuments recorded by the RCAHMS in the catchment.

Thirteen assays define the onset of peat growth across the grid in fig 2 (table 1). Assays in the text are referred to by their original sample number (OLIC-). At the deepest and oldest peat, on high ground (260m E/145m N: fig 2), pollen analyses and the analysis of peat humification were made, with age controls for the sequence from 12 AMS ^{14}C assays: these data are not presented here. Pollen analyses from a peat sequence on the valley floor at *c* 400m E/200m N (fig 2) were made on a sequence dated by three AMS ^{14}C assays: selected data on cereal type pollen grains are presented for the later prehistoric period in fig 3, plotted against calibrated age BP.

RESULTS AND INTERPRETATIONS

The results of the ^{14}C dating programme on blanket peat development are presented as a series of maps (fig 2) which interpolate across slopes the chronological data from key points. Peat inception occurred earliest on the upper slopes at 270m E/145m N (fig 2a), where at *c* 8450 cal BP (OLIC-1b: table 1) a very shallow basin began to retain water from, perhaps, a small spring-fed flush. Rising groundwater levels may have led to peat inception. Peat then began to accumulate *c* 7100 cal BP (OLIC-18: table 1) within a gully separating two low mounds at 260m E/170m N (fig 2b). Peat may then have spread northward over the next 1,000 cal years at a rate of 1m per 40–50 cal years, dated at 265m E/180m N (fig 2c) by assay OLIC-15 (table 1) to *c* 6100 cal BP. By this time, the peat cover represented more than the lateral growth of a spring-fed flush, and a blanket of peat was developing across the upper slopes (fig 2c), 50–60cm thick where it had grown earliest.

Peat spread towards the low till mound on which a concentration of later Mesolithic stone tools were excavated, at 250m E/190m N (Pannett 2002). Basal peat at this point, however, is dated to 1550–1300 cal BP (OLIC-2b: table 1) and, 3.65m downslope, to 660–540 cal BP (OLIC-3b: table 1). The last blanket peat to grow on this mound developed much later than peat 30m away, and diachronously. Blanket peat formation was either delayed for thousands of years on this mound or the present peat has grown following removal of a former cover. The latter interpretation is preferred because there is no topographic barrier to

peat spread on this mound, and it is thought that peat-cutting or paring removed peat on this mound.

The next dating controls indicate that the lowest parts of the hillside, over 200m east of and 10m lower (450m E/150m N: fig 2d), began to be covered by a marsh, initially infilling a wide, incised river valley, around 4900 cal BP (OLIC-6b: table 1). Then at *c* 4300 cal BP (fig 2e) peat began to accumulate 1.5m higher, on the left bank of this channel, at 400m E/150m N (OLIC-16: table 1). Wood remains in basal peat on this surface suggest that a wood was swamped by peat. To the north, at *c* 400m E/220m N, another river valley began to fill with peat at *c* 3750 cal BP (OLIC-8: table 1), and 65m away and 1.4m above this channel, at 335m E/220m N, peat also began to form at *c* 3700 cal BP (OLIC-9: table 1). Twenty metres further west and higher still at 99.5m OD, peat also began to accumulate at *c* 3700 cal BP (OLIC-10: table 1). These data suggest that the entire valley floor was being swamped by marsh peat very rapidly, shortly before and just after 4000 cal BP (fig 2e). Later peat-forming events are recorded in most detail on the lower slope along transect A–B (fig 2b). Above the accumulating marsh peat of the valley floor and below the blanket peat of the upper slope there is a succession of colluvial deposits. Dating controls suggest these to have been deposited episodically, and three events are defined:

EVENT 1: IMMEDIATELY PRIOR TO *c* 3500 CAL BP

Between 400m E/150m N and 360m E/150m N, a prominent grey-white colluvial silt is traced beneath

TABLE 1
Details of ^{14}C assays obtained on humin fractions of basal peats at Oliclett.

Number (OLIC-)	Location	Lab. no. (GU-)	Depth (cm)	^{14}C age BP ± 2σ	δ^{13}C PDB (‰)	Calibrated age BP (2σ)	Probability (%)
1b	260m E/150m N	-9911	237–238	7660 ± 55	−28.5	8560–8360	93.0
18	260m E/180m N	-10442	149–150	6170 ± 60	−28.0	7250–6890	95.4
15	265m E/190m N	-10439	75–76	5275 ± 55	−28.3	6200–5920	95.4
2b	260m E/200m N	-9912	40–41	1535 ± 65	−30.2	1550–1300	95.4
3b	264m E/200m N	-9913	20–21	620 ± 40	−30.1	660–540	95.4
6b	450m E/150m N	-9916	223–224	4255 ± 60	−28.5	4970–4780	48.7
16	400m E/150m N	-10440	170–171	3880 ± 70	−29.7	4450–4140	88.7
8	400m E/220m N	-10432	137–138	3480 ± 55	−28.8	3890–3630	95.4
9	335m E/220m N	-10433	87–89	3420 ± 45	−29.4	3830–3550	95.4
10	315m E/220m N	-10434	44–45	3420 ± 50	−28.7	3830–3480	93.6
5b	400m E/150m N	-9915	48–49	3265 ± 55	−30.1	3640–3370	95.4
14	375m E/150m N	-10438	25–26	2910 ± 45	−29.1	3170–2920	88.5
13	250m E/190m N	-10437	21–22	2140 ± 50	−28.7	2210–1990	72.9

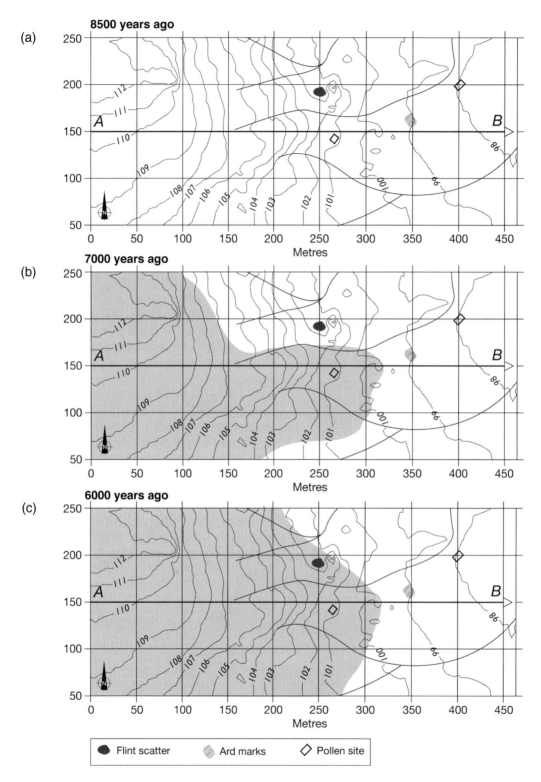

FIGURE 2

Bedrock contour map of the hill slope at Oliclett (a) and the proposed model of peat inception and spread across the hill slopes and over the valley floor between (a) 8500, (b) 7000, (c) 6000 years ago, and Fig 2 between (d) 5000, 4000 and 2000 years ago (cal BP). Blanket peat is dark-shaded; marsh peat is pale-shaded. Also indicated are the locations of the Mesolithic flint scatter and probable prehistoric ard marks on low glacial mounds, and the locations of the two pollen sites.

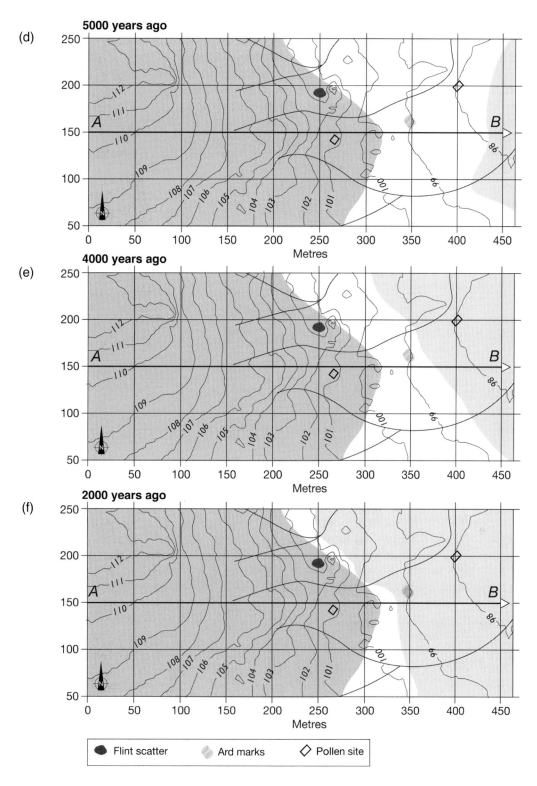

FIGURE 2 (continued)

the peat. The band lies on till, is water-sorted and in some boreholes is stratified, and contains abundant charred herb and wood fragments. The base of the overlying peat is dated at 400m E/150m N to 3640–3370 cal BP (OLIC-5b: table 1). Westward, the till surface steepens in a break of slope at 97.5m OD which is thought to have constrained, for a time, the westerly spread of the marsh. Northward, in other valleys, colluvial sediments derived from till mounds bordering them were covered by peat at 3830–3550 cal BP (OLIC-10: table 1), 3830–3480 cal BP (OLIC-9: table 1) and at 3890–3630 cal BP (OLIC-8: table 1).

EVENT 2: IMMEDIATELY PRIOR TO c 3050 CAL BP

At 350m E/150m N a second colluvial deposit, a 7cm thick, poorly sorted, grey-white gravelly sand with no charred plant fragments, is overlain conformably by peat, the base ^{14}C dated to c 3050 cal BP (OLIC-14: table 1).

EVENT 3: AT c 2100 CAL BP

At the base of the steep middle slopes of the transect, over a length of c 60m, is a third colluvial deposit. This unit was intensively analysed in an excavation trench at 340m E/150m N. It is a weakly stratified silty clay, deposited with low energies compared to colluvial events 1 and 2 (above) and was probably water-sorted. Thin-sections show the unit to have comprised many individual mm-thick units, representing successive depositional events that probably took several years or decades to accumulate. The colluvial unit contains some large charred wood as well as microscopic fragments, some of which are abraded and probably transported, but it is entirely minerogenic. The colluvial units also contain worked flints, including microliths, but at very low concentrations compared to the assemblages directly upslope at 250m E/190m N (Pannett 2002), and athough largely unabraded, the assemblage is regarded as derived during soil erosion from these steeper slopes. An hiatus in sediment deposition led to the weathering and leaching of colluvial sediments and in situ peat formation, dated by ^{14}C assay to 2210–1990 cal BP (OLIC-13: table 1). Sediment deposition then recommenced for a few more years or decades, but probably ceased at a time indistinguishable in age from assay OLIC-13.

Two pollen sequences were analysed at Oliclett. One is from the deep peat at 260m E/145m N and describes the development of plant communities on the upper slopes. This analysis contains little evidence

for prehistoric human activity, bar the modification of *Calluna* heath by low-intensity grazing pressures (Tipping *et al* 2003a). A second sequence was analysed on the valley floor at 400m E/200m N (fig 3), in a peat which developed at c 3700 cal BP (OLIC-9: table 1), close to, and receiving colluvial sediment from, surrounding low mounds. This shows evidence for cereal cultivation from peat inception to c 2500 cal BP, most intensely in the Mid-Late Bronze Age.

DISCUSSION

Peat inception on the upper slopes at Oliclett was in the early Holocene period, in accord with other data from the region (Lewis 1906; Durno 1958; Robinson 1987; Charman 1992; Bunting 1994; Huntley 1995). Specific climatic or anthropogenic triggers to peat inception have not been found at Oliclett, and it is probably not necessary to define particular events as driving peat development in this landscape. Once established, peat may have simply spread from *foci*, providing slope and groundwater conditions were right.

Peat then spread laterally, or developed from multiple *foci* which coalesced (Edwards & Hirons 1982) across the upper slope, infilling shallow gullies and climbing up low till mounds. The peat on the upper slope at Oliclett thickened appreciably with time, with rapid growth rates in a constantly wet environment (Tipping *et al* 2003a). However, fig 2a implies that this thick blanket of peat did not then spread down the steeper, middle slopes of the hillside. There is an absence of ^{14}C dating evidence for early Holocene peat colonization downslope. Thin-section analyses at the base of this slope (340m E/150m N) show that colluvial sediment eroded prior to c 2100 cal BP contained no peat inclusions. This may be because peat that did spread in the early-mid Holocene period was then lost during later prehistory. Our interpretation of some young ^{14}C assays on the upper slope is that peat-cutting or paring occurred before the early historic period (above).

Upper slopes appear from borehole records (Tipping *et al* 2003) to have been totally unaffected by later prehistoric colluviation. Because blanket peat had spread and was 1–1.5m deep by 4000 cal BP over much of the upper slope, the slope had become geomorphologically inert. The steeper middle slopes were highly active sediment sources in later prehistory, though these are argued to have begun to be covered in blanket peat before 6000 cal BP (above). If correct, it is unclear why this peat was subsequently lost, whether by natural erosion or anthropogenic cutting of peat or organic turf, but it is likely that the middle slopes were reclaimed from blanket peat in the later prehistoric period.

Peat then covered lower parts of the hillside at Oliclett, not by downslope spread but, at least in part, by upslope inundation from marshes that began to occupy river valleys and adjacent surfaces after c 5000 cal BP. The interpretation here relates peat spread to periods of episodic colluviation, with lower slopes on transect A–B impacted by a series of discrete sediment erosion events between 3800 and 2100 cal BP. The material eroded was glacial till and this was not covered by peat when eroded. Colluvial sediments are entirely minerogenic save for rare *in situ* peats. Sediments are stratified at macro- and microscopic scales and their transport was facilitated by flowing water. Each event was composed of many individual pulses generated, probably, during storms, in comparatively high energy flows in which small gravels were transported with silts and sands. Each event was therefore sustained for at least several decades. Hiatuses during events appear to have been rare but *in situ* peat could form (eg event 3), suggesting that erosional pulses were clustered in time and could be separated by several years. The lengths of slope impacted by sediment re-deposition were considerable in each event, over several tens of metres if sediment-stratigraphic correlations are correct. The burning of vegetation on this slope, sometimes of substantial wood remains, was a feature of two events, although this evidence does not allow us to suggest fire was concentrated in these events.

The earliest event, immediately prior to c 3500 cal BP, occurred in soils on till on the lowest part of the slope, on mineral soils above the laterally expanding marsh, across which eroding sediment was flushed. Soil disturbance, erosion and re-deposition may have retarded marsh expansion. The pollen analyses from this part of the hillside show that till surfaces were cultivated (fig 3). Peat was then quickly established at c 3500 cal BP across these colluvial surfaces. Colluvial event 2, immediately prior to c 3050 cal BP, originated higher on the lower slope, above where peat had, by then, covered the surface and on a mineral substrate which peat had not yet covered. Cereal cultivation persisted in this phase. Blanket peat developed very quickly after soil instability. Sediments in event 3 at c 2100 cal BP were derived from lower and middle slopes. Cereal cultivation may not have been part of the agricultural economy by then. Peat rapidly grew during pauses in sediment accumulation and immediately after soil erosion.

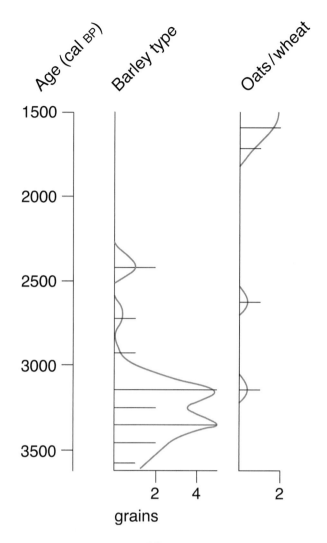

FIGURE 3

Numbers of pollen grains of cereal type recorded from a ^{14}C dated sediment sequence on the valley floor at Oliclett, plotted against age cal BP.

Several mechanisms are feasible for altering slope hydrology and initiating peat spread. Climate change may have led to increased precipitation or to lowered temperature, which also impacted adversely on evapotranspiration rates. Soil disturbance through increased erosion, perhaps a response to climate change or through ploughing, may have increased surface and through flow of water. Vegetation disturbance may have increased runoff through reducing tree cover and increasing evapotranspiration ratios from less efficient grassland and heath water 'pumps', either anthropogenically through conversion to agricultural land or as a natural response to soil or climatic deterioration. We cannot differentiate between mechanisms on current evidence. A number of factors alone or in combination, climatic and anthropogenic, may have led to the same geomorphic and sedimentological responses. A climatic explanation is tentatively preferred to account for the very rapid development of peat at *c* 3800 cal BP at different altitudes and different substrates on valley floors. There is evidence in northern Scotland for abrupt climatic deterioration commencing at 4200–4000 cal BP (Birks 1975; Gear & Huntley 1991; Barber *et al* 1994; Huntley, Allen & Daniell 1997), which included a probable shift to increased precipitation, although recent interpretations have found it more difficult to define this event in as clear a way as originally argued (Anderson 1995; Tisdall 2000). There is no peat-stratigraphic evidence for increased mire surface wetness at this time at Oliclett (Tisdall unpublished).

Soil disturbance and erosion were also common at this time at Oliclett, but continued through the later prehistoric period. This trend is opposite to that of increased slope stability expected from extensive peat establishment, and so is supportive of the idea that additional disturbing factors, such as anthropogenic activity, drove landscape change. A correlation with palynological evidence for cereal cultivation can be made. We relate increased mineral sediment supply on valley floors to ard cultivation on till mounds at Oliclett (above), although these soils are as yet undated. On lower till slopes above the marsh, with climatic and anthropogenic pressures inevitably leading from 4000 cal BP to blanket peat, colluvial events are interpreted as having retarded peat development. The relation between soil disturbance and peat growth is thus spatially and causally very complex because peat growth in the lowest parts of the landscape, on the valley floors, may have been encouraged by increased runoff from soil disturbance which was retarding peat growth on higher surfaces.

The spatial patterning suggested along transect A–B supports the idea that soil disturbance was anthropogenic, driven through a need to maintain agriculture. The focus of soil erosion on transect A–B moved upslope through time with a consistency thought hard to explain by natural processes. Areas of soil erosion were increasingly confined to parts of the slope that had not yet been lost to peat growth. However, by *c* 2100 cal BP the lower slopes had been given up to peat.

We would see the retardation of peat on lower slopes as the product of sustained cultivation. The sediment-stratigraphic evidence from transect A–B is for three colluvial events, each of uncertain duration, but seemingly widely separated in time over some 1,400 cal years. The record from other transects may extend the earliest phase to 3700–3600 cal BP and the latest phase to *c* 1700 cal BP, but colluvial events are in total few. Ploughing need not, of course, have inevitably led to soil losses, and colluvial events may represent phases when short-term climatic impacts forced cultivated soils over erosional thresholds. There is no archaeological evidence for later prehistoric monuments or field systems in the Oliclett sub-catchment, although hut circles and associated clearance cairns and agglomerative field walls are found at Yarrows (fig 1). The evidence for anthropogenic activity is entirely palaeoecological, but increasingly we have to accept that in areas empty of archaeology, this evidence provides great insight (Whittington & Edwards 1994; Davies & Tipping 2004; Carter, Dalland & Long 2005). Fields may, perhaps, have been unwalled open patches within the expanding peat, undetectable archaeologically.

Land use below the blanket peat of the upper slopes appears to have changed or intensified early in the Bronze Age, from *c* 3700 cal BP, inducing some soil erosion, or changing land use simply coincided with short-term climatic deterioration (Mercer & Tipping 1994). For the previous several hundred years, terrestrial soils over very large areas had been buried by marsh peat. The land available for agriculture was being squeezed between blanket peat on the upper slopes and spreading marsh. At *c* 3800 cal BP there was a rapid and simultaneous loss of soils to peat on valley floors and probably also on the lowest slopes above these. This is associated, however, with evidence for colluviation on these lowest slopes as farmers ploughed increasingly peaty soils, both to maintain cultivation and keep peat at bay. Over the next *c* 2,000 years the locations of these probably small, not necessarily walled, fields shifted, constrained more and more to higher parts of the lower slopes as peat growth could not be resisted. Perhaps intermittently, farmers went to the extraordinary length of moving ploughs across the wide and wet valley floors to plough the till mounds that still stood as low islands within the marsh.

The loss of land to peat was clearly a very gradual process in this part of Caithness, over more than 2,500 cal years from the first loss of valley floors to marsh. No comparanda for this detailed record are available in the region or elsewhere in northern Scotland. Land abandonment towards the end of the Bronze Age at *c* 3000 cal BP was argued for, on archaeological grounds, at the Achany Glen and in the Strath of Kildonan (McCullagh & Tipping 1998;

McIntyre 1998), but the regional extent of this event in upland Scotland has been recently challenged from palaeoecological evidence by Tipping (2002) and Davies, Tisdall & Tipping (2004). At Oliclett there is no geomorphological or peat-stratigraphic evidence for a reduction in activity in the early first millennium BC, although the pollen record in fig 3 indicates that crop-growing was not a significant component of agricultural practices after c 3000 cal BP. Local abandonment may have occurred between 2100 and 1400 cal BP, perhaps as farmers finally lost the battle with the peat.

REFERENCES

Barber, J 1998 *The Archaeological Investigation of a Prehistoric Landscape: Excavations on Arran 1978–1981*. Edinburgh.

Barber, K E, Chambers, F M & Maddy, D 1994 'Sensitive high-resolution records of Holocene palaeoclimate from ombrotrophic bogs', *in* Funnell, B M & Kay, R L F (eds) *Palaeoclimate of the Last Glacial/Interglacial Cycle*, 57–60. London.

Birks, H H 1975 'Studies in the vegetational history of Scotland. IV. Pine stumps in Scottish blanket peats', *Philosophical Transactions of the Royal Society of London* B270, 181–226.

Bunting, M J 1994 'Vegetation history from Orkney, Scotland: pollen records from two small basins in West Mainland', *New Phytologist* 128, 771–92.

Carter, S 1998 'Palaeopedology', *in* McCullagh, R & Tipping, R (eds) *The Lairg Project 1988–1996. The Evolution of an Archaeological Landscape in Northern Scotland*, 150–60. Edinburgh.

Carter, S, Dalland, M & Long, D 2005. *Early Land-use and Landscape Development in Arisaig*. Scottish Archaeology Internet Report 15 (*www.sair.org.uk*).

Charman, D J 1992 'Blanket mire formation at the Cross Lochs, Sutherland, northern Scotland', *Boreas* 21, 53–72.

Davies, A L & Tipping, R 2004 'Sensing small-scale human activity in the palaeoecological record: fine spatial resolution pollen analyses from West Glen Affric, northern Scotland', *The Holocene* 14, 233–45.

Davies, A L, Tisdall, E & Tipping, R 2004 'Holocene climatic variability and human settlement in the Scottish Highlands: fragility and robustness', *in* Housley, R A & Coles, G M (eds) *Atlantic Connections & Adaptations*, 2–11. Oxford.

Durno, S E 1958 'Pollen analyses of peat deposits in eastern Scotland and Caithness', *Scottish Geographical Magazine* 74, 127–35.

Edwards, K J & Hirons, K R 1982 'Date of blanket peat initiation and rates of spread – a problem in research design', *Quaternary Newsletter* 36, 32–7.

Gear, A J & Huntley, B 1991 'Rapid changes in the range limits of Scots Pine 4,000 years ago', *Science* 251, 544–7.

Hall, A M & Whittington, G 1989 'Late Devensian glaciation of southern Caithness', *Scottish Journal of Geology* 25, 307–24.

Huntley, B, Daniell, R G & Allen, J R M 1997 'Scottish vegetation history: the Highlands', *Botanical Journal of Scotland* 49, 163–75.

Huntley, J P 1995 'Pollen analytical investigations', *in* Morris, C D, Batey, C E & Rackham, D J (eds) *Freswick Links, Caithness: Excavation and Survey of a Norse Settlement*. Inverness.

Lewis, F J 1906 'The plant remains in the Scottish peat mosses. Part II: the Scottish Highlands', *Transactions of the Royal Society of Edinburgh* 45, 335–60.

McCullagh, R & Tipping, R 1998. *The Lairg Project 1988–1996: The Evolution of an Archaeological Landscape in Northern Scotland*. Edinburgh.

McIntyre, A 1998 'Survey and excavation on Kilearnan Hill, Sutherland, 1982–3', *Proceedings of the Society of Antiquaries of Scotland* 128, 167–201.

Mercer, R & Tipping, R 1994 'The prehistory of soil erosion in the Northern and Eastern Cheviot Hills, Anglo-Scottish Borders', *in* Foster, S & Smout, T C (eds) *The History of Soils and Field Systems*, 1–24. Aberdeen.

Pannett, A 2002 *Excavation of a Mesolithic site at Oliclett, Caithness*. Cardiff.

Piggott, S 1972 'A note on climatic deterioration in the first millennium BC in Britain', *Scottish Archaeological Forum* 3, 63–70.

Robinson, D E 1987 'Investigations into the Aukhorn peat mounds, Keiss, Caithness: pollen, plant macrofossil and charcoal analyses', *New Phytologist* 106, 185–200.

Shore, J S, Bartley, D D & Harkness, D D 1995 'Problems encountered with the ¹⁴C dating of peat', *Quaternary Science Reviews* 14, 373–83.

Tipping, R 2002 'Climatic variability and "marginal" settlement in upland British landscapes: a re-evaluation', *Landscapes* 3, 10–28.

Tipping, R, Davies, A, Tisdall, E, Wilson, C & Pannett, A 2003a *Holocene Landscape Development at Oliclett, near Wick, Caithness*. Archive report. Historic Scotland.

Tipping, R, Tisdall, E & Davies, A 2003b 'Peat development in West Glen Affric', *in* Tipping, R (ed) *The Quaternary of Glen Affric & Kintail*, 49–54. London.

Whittington, G & Edwards, K J 1994 'Palynology as a predictive tool in archaeology', *Proceedings of the Society of Antiquaries of Scotland* 124, 55–65.

A Middle Bronze Age occupation site at Ballyarnet Lake, County Derry: the site and its wider context

JOHN Ó NÉILL and GILL PLUNKETT

INTRODUCTION

Ballyarnet Lake, Co Derry, comprises a small, infilling lake basin located 4km to the north-west of Derry City, at the south-eastern end of Inishowen Peninsula, at a height of just under 30m OD (fig 1). The basin is enclosed to the north-west and south-east by rising ground, and the lake is fed and drained by a small stream that runs east down to Lough Foyle. The lake itself consists of two areas of open water today covering less than 3ha as a result of drainage, surrounded by extensive fens and areas of wet woodland. Now bounded by farmlands, a golf course and residential developments, the lake and its fens have been designated a public park by the local council.

Human activity around the lake can be traced back to the Neolithic, when a possible platform or trackway, associated with pottery, crude flints and a portion of a porcellanite axe, was constructed in the south-western margins of the fens (Hurl 1996).

Nearby, a collection of Neolithic artefacts was also identified during the cutting of a drainage channel (NISMR LDY 14A:022). Approximately 0.5km to the north-east of the lake, a further scatter of finds associated with burnt soil was also recorded. More extensive Neolithic occupation was recently uncovered at Thornhill, just over 1km to the east of Ballyarnet, where at least five timber buildings were constructed during several phases of activity (Logue 2003). During the Bronze Age, continued activity around Ballyarnet is attested by two burnt mounds along the western fringe of the lake basin, and a third located 1km to the north-west. A Food Vessel cist burial (Brannon et al 1988) was excavated to the south-east of the lake and is one of several in the southern Inishowen region. Later prehistoric sites include the bivallate hilltop enclosure at An Grianán Ailligh, 9km west of Ballyarnet. Reportedly the seat of the northern Uí Néill in the first millennium AD, the enclosure may have its origin in the Later Bronze Age or Iron Age. Continuing activity into

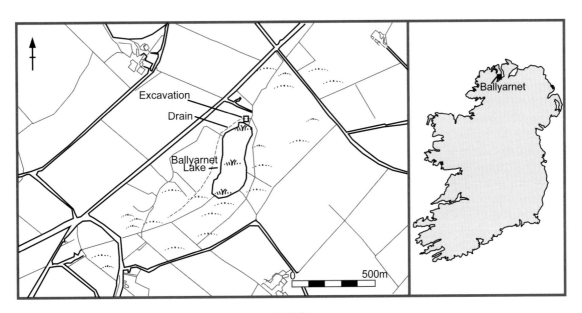

FIGURE 1
Location of Ballyarnet Lake and the excavated site.

175

the historic period is demonstrated by a range of site types, including ringforts, souterrains and various ecclesiastical sites in the region.

In 2001, a local amateur archaeologist noted that a drainage operation through the north-eastern fen peats had exposed a cultural horizon containing quantities of clay, stone, burnt stone, charcoal and worked wood. The discovery prompted two seasons of excavations, in 2002 and 2004, that revealed an extensive timber platform enclosed by a palisade, dating to the Middle Bronze Age. The site is one of a small number of wetland sites where occupation dating to this period has been identified in Ireland. The dominant cultural assemblage, which includes Cordoned Urn pottery and faience, suggests that the occupants were relatively wealthy, in comparison to the evidence known from contemporary settlements. This paper describes the activity revealed at Ballyarnet and considers the site in its wider context.

MIDDLE BRONZE AGE ACTIVITY AT BALLYARNET

Fig 2 outlines the trenches investigated during the 2002 (trenches 1–4) and 2004 (trenches 1–6) excavation seasons. Trenches 1 and 2 from 2002 were incorporated into a larger trench in 2004; trenches 3 and 4 were extended and the area that appeared to be immediately under threat was excavated.

The site consists of a timber platform composed of a single shallow layer of irregularly deposited brushwood and roundwoods, placed directly onto fen peat and retained by a wooden palisade. Recent land drainage and reclamation in the immediate vicinity of the site prohibited an estimation of the full extent of the site, but it appears to have enclosed an area exceeding 20m in diameter (fig 3). Finds from the platform structure included worked flint, pottery, a single piece of slag and a possible anvil stone. Investigation of a short section of the palisade revealed closely set oak and alder posts that typically measured up to 0.30m in diameter. The oak posts contained too few annual rings to provide a dendrochronological date but a radiocarbon determination from the outer rings of one post returned a date of 1742–1524 cal BC (3344±39 BP, UB-4893). This places the site within the Irish Middle Bronze Age (conventionally *c* 1700–1200 BC, eg Cooney & Grogan 1994), although there is little in the artefactual assemblage to distinguish the material culture greatly from that of the preceding Early Bronze Age. This illustrates, on the one hand, a certain level of cultural continuity from the former period, and on

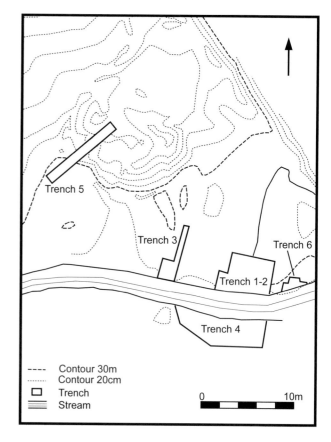

FIGURE 2
Plan showing excavated trenches at Ballyarnet. The mound to the north (investigated in trench 5) is modern.

the other, the rather capricious nature of an Early to Middle Bronze Age distinction that is based almost entirely on developments in metal-working (cf Cooney & Grogan 1994; Ramsay 1995).

To the south of the modern drainage ditch that truncates the site, a substantial spread of fire-reddened clay appears to be the remains of a central hearth (fig 4). Traces of this spread were also identified to the north of the drainage ditch, indicating an original extent of more than 5m in diameter. Alternating horizons of fire-reddened clay and charcoal suggest that the hearth had been re-surfaced on at least four different occasions. Finds from this feature included a flint scraper, a flint flake, a single sherd of pottery and some small, unidentifiable fragments of burnt bone. A semi-circular setting of posts, apparently truncated by the drainage ditch, surrounded the hearth and points towards the former existence of a circular wooden structure some 5m in diameter.

A second phase of activity is represented by a rough stone surface, 0.15m deep, laid across the hearth

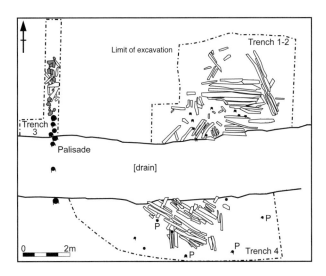

FIGURE 3
Overall plan of excavated areas, showing the palisade, the
area removed by the drain, the horizontal timbers and uprights
(marked with 'P').

recently disturbed during the cutting of the modern drainage ditch, however, and upcast material appears to have been spread across the ground surface either side of the drain. Finds from these disturbed deposits were similar to those recovered from the archaeological contexts.

BALLYARNET IN ITS WIDER CONTEXT

Broadly contemporary with the Ballyarnet occupation, lakeside settlements at Moynagh Lough, Co Meath (radiocarbon-dated to 1880–1660 cal BC; Bradley 1991) and Cullyhanna, Co Armagh (dendro-dated to 1526 BC; Hodges 1958; Hillam 1976) provide close parallels for the site, and finds from Moynagh Lough also included a large quantity of Cordoned Urn ware, as well as scrapers, amber, bronzes, bone objects and a variety of stone tools (Bradley 1997). All three sites are characterized by relatively superficial deposits of brushwood enclosed by a palisade. A further comparable structure, also yielding a notable assemblage of Cordoned Urn pottery at Meadowlands, Co Down, seems to have been located beside sloblands (mudflats) in the Quoile estuary,

and beyond the limits of the primary structure, and originally incorporating some flagstones. This stone deposit seems to have covered an area measuring 4.50 × 3.60m. Finds from this horizon include sherds of a number of Cordoned Urn vessels, including at least one miniature example, and worked flint and stone tools. In turn, this surface was overlain by a deposit of heat-shattered stone and charcoal, covering a minimum surface area of 8 × 5m. A further quantity of Cordoned Urn pottery was recovered from this layer, including at least one additional miniature vessel. Other finds included various chipped stone tools, two tanged projectile points, hammerstones and a perforated stone net or loom weight. A fragment of a quoit-shaped faience bead was also recovered.

The artefactual assemblage from the site is consistent with a single cultural phase. Finds include more than 500 sherds of pottery (mostly of Cordoned Urn type (*sensu* Kavanagh 1976; Waddell 1995) and representing at least 21 Cordoned Urn and two undecorated vessels), two tanged projectile points, an anvil stone, a perforated stone, a polished stone axe and a fragment of faience bead. Apparent metalworking residues were recovered from the site during excavation, mainly from overlying material, although one piece was recovered from a context associated with the Bronze Age occupation. This material has since been identified as clinker (Tim Young pers comm), and appears to be intrusive.

The occupation deposits were subsequently sealed by a sequence of peat formation. These peats were

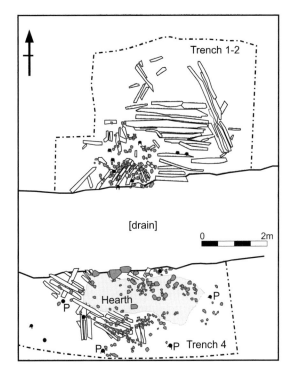

FIGURE 4
Plan of upper excavated level, showing hearth, upright
posts (P) and deposit of stones.

and has produced dates ranging from *c* 1870–1412 cal BC for these levels (Pollock & Waterman 1964). This small group of sites thus seems to represent one distinct aspect of Middle Bronze Age settlement, although the site type – roundhouse surrounded by palisaded enclosure – is by no means limited to wetland contexts. At Ballybrowney Lower, Co Cork, for example, one of three broadly contemporary, large enclosures measuring 19×21.5m, surrounded a sub-oval house structure 6×4m, and has been radiocarbon-dated to 1940–1520 cal BC (National Roads Authority 2005).

Indeed, a comparison of vernacular architecture in Ireland in the Bronze Age, suggests that a number of settlement forms can be identified, ranging from circular to rectilinear structures, isolated houses to large aggregated settlements – including both open and enclosed settlements (Doody 2000). As yet, regional distinctions have not become apparent. In addition to the aforementioned sites, evidence broadly contemporary with Ballyarnet has also been identified at Ballyveelish, Co Tipperary (Doody 1987), Killoran, Site 8, Co Tipperary (Cross May *et al* 2005), Castleupton, Co Antrim (Gahan 1997), Fota Island, Co Cork (O'Connell & Rutter 1992) and Coney Island in Lough Neagh (Addyman 1965). The structural record from these sites varies with a rectangular construction represented at Coney Island, oval structures at Fota Island and Ballyveelish, and circular structures at Castleupton and Killoran, both with an internal ring of roof supports. Limited artefactual assemblages were recovered from these sites, in comparison to Ballyarnet, although some Food Vessel pottery was recovered from Coney Island.

Cordoned Urn pottery, traditionally viewed as a predominantly funerary ware, appears to be a recurrent feature at some of the wetland sites and is increasingly known from settlements. Radiocarbon determinations for secure contexts in which this pottery is found (Williams 1986; Bradley 1991; Hedges *et al* 1993) consistently produce dates within a range of *c* 1800–1500 cal BC, to which can now be added that of Ballyarnet. The pottery belongs to an Irish-Scottish tradition, and in Ireland is known mainly from the north-east, although finds extend as far south as counties Limerick and Waterford (Waddell 1998). The largest assemblage so far recorded from a domestic context is that from Meadowlands, Co Down (Pollack & Waterman 1964), where some 21 individual pots seem to be represented. Decorative motifs on the Ballyarnet assemblage are all typical of the range of motifs recorded on Irish and Scottish Cordoned Urns, although a higher incidence of incised decoration and a lower incidence of cord-impressions distinguish it somewhat from typical funerary examples (eg Kavanagh 1976; Waddell 1995). The association of faience with Cordoned Urn pottery has also been noted elsewhere, but until now, only in burial contexts. Relative to the contemporary settlement record, as currently understood, Ballyarnet can be considered as artefactually rich, and, by implication, its occupants may have been accorded considerable status and prestige.

The exploitation of wetlands in Ireland can be traced back to Mesolithic sites located on the shores of former lakes such as Lough Boora, Co Offaly (Ryan 1980, 1984), and Lough Derravaragh, Co Westmeath (Mitchell 1972). Although possibly an artefact of our current state of knowledge, the occurrence of wetland sites, including bog trackways, seems to become more frequent from the Middle Bronze Age, with an apparent concentration of wetland activity emerging from the sixteenth century BC, including a significant number of dendro-datable sites (ie sites incorporating large oak timbers) coming to light soon after *c* 1600 BC and continuing until at least the fourteenth century BC (Plunkett & McDermott in press; cf Cross May *et al* 2005). At Derryville Bog, Co Tipperary, an increase in wetland sites from this time represents a change in the use of the landscape, including casual activity on the bog as well as the establishment of trackways aimed at facilitating travel across the bog (Cross *et al* 2001). Evidence to date therefore hints at a general expansion of settlement into wetland areas around the time of the Ballyarnet occupation. In this respect, activity at Ballyarnet can be viewed as part of a widespread cultural phenomenon, possibly entailing a wider use of the landscape and its resources.

The use of Irish wetlands for settlement and other activities has been interpreted from a range of perspectives. Some have regarded wetland sites as distinct within a settlement hierarchy (eg Grogan *et al* 1996) and certainly, during the Late Bronze Age and Early Medieval periods, a number of lake settlements appear to have held elite status (eg Ballinderry 2, Co Offaly – Hencken 1942; Lagore, Co Meath – Hencken 1950). Others suggest that the use of wetlands may have had more symbolic connotations, and point to an increase in the incidence of votive deposits in wet places from the Middle Bronze Age (Bradley 1984; Cooney & Grogan 1994). Examining one landscape unit at Lough Gara, Co Sligo, Fredengren (2002) suggests that votive deposition in specific watery contexts marks peripheries between settlement concentrations in the Early to Middle Bronze Age. This pattern does not change until lakeside occupation sites begin to be constructed in the Late Bronze Age, by which time, Fredengren suggests, the sites serve as places in which votive offerings can be prepared for deposition. In this sense, lakeside occupation sites are seen not merely as part of a widespread settlement continuum, but rather as special areas with a well-established cosmological significance.

A recent consideration of societal responses to changing climatic conditions in Ireland throughout the post-glacial period has suggested that lake settlement construction, including that in the Middle Bronze Age, should be regarded as symptomatic of socio-economic disruption brought on by increased wetness (Turney *et al* 2006). Implicit in this interpretation is that such sites were defensive in their nature and were occupied in order to protect limited resources. This conclusion does not take into consideration the fact that, in many cases, these already wet settings would have become yet more inhospitable to occupation in the event of environmental deterioration, notwithstanding the potential economic value of these rich, biodiverse locations. Indeed, in contrast, Baillie (1999, 38) suggests that the occupation of both Irish and German wetlands in the mid-second millennium BC is most likely the outcome of a change to drier conditions, during which the fall of water levels would have rendered new lands available for occupation. Generalized statements about the environmental significance of wetland sites as a whole should therefore be treated with caution, bearing in mind that a multitude of circumstances – environmental, economic, social, political or cultural – may have prompted the occupation of lake margins at any one time.

In the past, wetland sites have all too easily been regarded as 'marginal', sometimes believed to have been occupied only out of necessity, for example, due to population pressure (eg Baillie 1993). At their most basic, such conjectures assume that the construction of habitable dry areas within wetlands reflect the unavailability of more 'prime' drylands, and, indeed, historical evidence from eighteenth-century Ireland provides a good model for marginal land exploitation during periods of large population growth (Bell 1998). However, in the case of Ballyarnet, parallels in the existing architectural and settlement record suggest that it is not a form unique, or indeed suited, to the colonization of wet lake margins. Where architectural parallels exist for Ballyarnet, they are present in both wet and dry landscapes, indicating that the site is part of a broader settlement culture. The proposed high status of the occupants of the site,

as suggested by the artefactual assemblage, on the other hand, seems to be shared by other (but not all) broadly contemporary settlements which also happen to be preserved due to the wet contexts in which they were located. In these respects, it seems untenable to suggest that the occupants of Ballyarnet and similar sites were 'pushed' to the margins for reasons of land pressure, and settlement by the lake edges should instead be considered within socio-cultural terms. Indeed, the facility to extend ownership to newly available lands, such as dried-out lake margins, may be indicative of the status of the occupants.

CONCLUSIONS

Recent excavations at Ballyarnet Lake, Co Derry, have uncovered an occupation site dating to the Middle Bronze Age. In its structural form, the site can be seen as part of a wider form of settlement during this period, not only as one of an increasing number of wetland sites at this time, but also within the broader architectural landscape. Whether settlements of this type, with rich artefactual assemblages such as Ballyarnet and its close parallels at Meadowlands and Moynagh Lough, should be seen as representative of a time-limited period of materialistic lifestyles, or whether they reflect a hierarchical aspect of the settlement record is not yet clear. Certainly, the identification of contemporary settlements with extremely limited artefactual assemblages would support the latter theory. How significant these sites are within the overall settlement record for the Bronze Age will only become clear when all of the recently collected evidence has been collated.

A preliminary corpus of 78 Irish Bronze Age houses was published by Doody in 2000, but the current number of such structures in Ireland has now reached more than 200 following the significant increase in archaeological excavations throughout Ireland in the last few years. While a satisfactory synthesis of these data has yet to appear, it would seem, initially, that settlements with as rich an artefactual assemblage as that at Ballyarnet are relatively rare. Similarly, the existing evidence suggests that individual sites do not appear to have been used for repeated occupation since examples with one house directly overlain by another are almost unknown. On the other hand, instances of multiple structures are now commonplace, although there is often little evidence to suggest a constructional chronology. However, it is also clear that the abandonment of lake settlements, such as Ballyarnet, cannot be immediately interpreted as a reflection of a deterioration of ground conditions, since a similar explanation does not have to be evoked to explain the limited occupation of most other sites. In this regard, an on-going programme of palaeoenvironmental research at Ballyarnet is expected to provide a better sense of the dynamics that underscore the initial selection of the site of occupation and the background to its demise.

ACKNOWLEDGEMENTS

Thanks to Dr Bruce Bradley (University of Exeter), Dr Colm Donnelly (QUB), Ronan McHugh (QUB), Clare McGranaghan (QUB), Dr Brian Williams (EHS(NI)), Declan Hurl (EHS(NI)), Dr Alison Sheridan (NMS), Ian Leitch, Dr Tim Young, Naomi Carver (QUB), Ann Oldroyd, Pat Quigley, Derry City Council and the excavation team for their various assistance during the course of the excavation and post-excavation stages. Data Structure Reports from the investigations by the Centre for Archaeological Fieldwork, Queen's University Belfast, are available to view on the internet at *www.qub.ac.uk/caf/CAFDSR05.pdf* and *www.qub.ac.uk/caf/CAFDSR38.pdf*.

REFERENCES

Addyman, P V 1965 'Coney Island, Lough Neagh: prehistoric settlement, Anglo-Norman castle and Elizabethan native fortress', *Ulster Journal of Archaeology*, 28, 78–101.

Baillie, M G L 1993 'Dark Ages and dendrochronology', *Emania*, 11, 5–12.

Baillie, M G L 1999 *Exodus to Arthur*. London.

Bell, J 1998 'The spread of cultivation into marginal land in Ireland during the 18th and early 19th centuries', *in* Mills, C M & Coles, G (eds) *Life on the Edge: Human Settlement and Marginality* (Oxbow Monograph 100), 39–43. Oxford.

Bradley, R 1984 *The Social Foundations of Prehistoric Britain*. London.

Bradley, J 1991 'Excavations at Moynagh Lough, Co Meath', *Journal of the Royal Society of Antiquaries of Ireland*, 121, 5–26.

Bradley, J 1997 'Archaeological excavations at Moynagh Lough, Co Meath 1995–96', *Ríocht na Midhe*, 9(3), 50–60.

Brannon, N F, Williams, B B & Wilkinson, J L 1988 'A Bronze Age cist burial in Shantallow townland, County Londonderry', *Ulster Journal of Archaeology*, 51, 134–6.

Cooney, G & Grogan, E 1994 *Irish Prehistory: a Social Perspective*. Dublin.

Cross, S, Murray, C, Ó Néill, J & Stevens, P 2001 'Derryville Bog: a vernacular landscape in the Irish Midlands', *in* Raftery, B & Hickey, J (eds) *Recent Developments in Wetland Research* (Seandálaíocht Monograph 3 and WARP Occasional Paper 14), 87–97. Dublin.

Cross May, S, Murray, C, Ó Néill, J & Stevens, P 2005 'Catalogue of dryland sites', *in* Gowen, M, Ó Néill, J & Phillips, M (eds) *The Lisheen Mine Archaeological Project, 1996–98*, 283–310. Bray.

Doody, M 1987 'Ballyveelish, County Tipperary', *in* Cleary, R M, Hurley, M F & Twohig, E A (eds) *Archaeological Excavations on the Cork–Dublin Gas Pipeline (1981–82)*, 8–35. Cork.

Doody, M 2000 'Bronze Age houses in Ireland', *in* Desmond, A, Johnson, G, McCarthy, M, Sheehan, J & Shee Twohig, E (eds) *New Agendas in Irish Prehistory*, 135–59. Bray.

Fredengren, C 2002 *Crannogs*. Bray.

Gahan, A 1997 'Castle Upton, Templepatrick, Co Antrim', *in* Bennett, I (ed) *Excavations 1997: A summary account of archaeological excavations in Ireland*, No. 6. Bray.

Grogan, E, Condit, T, O'Carroll, F, O'Sullivan, A & Daly, A 1996 'Tracing the late Prehistoric landscape in north Munster', *Discovery Programme Reports*, 4, 26–46.

Hedges, R E M, Housley, R A, Ramsey, C B & van Klinken, G J 1993 'Radiocarbon dates from the Oxford AMS system: Archaeometry datelist 17', *Archaeometry*, 35, 305–26.

Hencken, H O'N 1942 'Ballinderry Crannog No 2', *Proceedings of the Royal Irish Academy*, 47C, 1–76.

Hencken, H O'N 1950 'Lagore Crannog: an Irish Royal residence of the 7th to 10th centuries AD', *Proceedings of the Royal Irish Academy*, 53C, 1–247.

Hillam, J 1976 'The dating of Cullyhanna hunting lodge', *Irish Archaeological Research Forum*, 3, 17–20.

Hodges, H W 1958 'A hunting camp at Cullyhanna Lough near Newton Hamilton, Co Armagh', *Ulster Journal of Archaeology*, 21, 7–13.

Hurl, D 1996 'Ballyarnet Lake, Shantallow', *Database of Irish Excavation Reports* (*www.excavations.ie/Pages/HomePage.php*).

Kavanagh, R M 1976 'Collared and Cordoned cinerary urns in Ireland', *Proceedings of the Royal Irish Academy*, 76C, 293–403.

Logue, P 2003 'Excavations at Thornhill, Co Londonderry', *in* Armit, I, Murphy, E, Nelis E & Simpson, D (eds) *Neolithic Settlement in Ireland and Western Britain*, 149–55. Oxford.

Mitchell, G F 1972 'Some Ultimate Larnian sites at Lake Derravaragh, Co Westmeath', *Journal of the Royal Society of Antiquaries of Ireland*, 102, 160–72.

National Roads Authority 2005 *N8 Rathcormac–Fermoy Road Scheme, County Cork*. Dublin.

O'Connell, P & Rutter, A E 1992 'Fota Island, Carrigtwohil, Co Cork', *in* Bennett, I (ed) *Excavations 1992: A summary account of archaeological excavations in Ireland*, No. 20. Bray.

Plunkett, G & McDermott, C in press 'Exploring the role of environment in wetland archaeological contexts', *in* Murphy, E & Whitehouse, N J (eds) *Environmental Archaeology in Ireland*. Oxford.

Pollock, A J & Waterman, D M 1964 'A Bronze Age habitation site at Downpatrick', *Ulster Journal of Archaeology*, 27, 31–58.

Ramsay, G 1995 'Middle Bronze Age metalwork: are artefact studies dead and buried?', *in* Waddell, J & Shee Twohig, E (eds) *Ireland in the Bronze Age*, 49–62. Dublin.

Ryan, M 1980 'An early Irish Mesolithic site in the Irish midlands', *Antiquity* 54, 46–7.

Ryan, M 1984 'Archaeological excavations at Lough Boora, Boughal townland, Co Offaly, 1977', *Proceedings of the 7th International Peat Congress Dublin 1984*, 407–13.

Turney, C S M, Baillie, M, Palmer, J & Brown, D 2006 'Holocene climatic change and past Irish societal response', *Journal of Archaeological Science*, 33, 34–8.

Waddell, J 1995 'The Cordoned Urn tradition', *in* Kinnes, I & Varndell, G (eds) *Unbaked Urns of Rudely Shape*, Oxbow Monograph No 55, 113–22. London.

Waddell, J 1998 *The Prehistoric Archaeology of Ireland*. Galway.

Williams, B B 1986 'Excavations at Altanagh, County Tyrone', *Ulster Journal of Archaeology*, 49, 33–88.

Anthropomorphic wooden figures: recent Irish discoveries

MICHAEL STANLEY

INTRODUCTION

The main focus of this paper is to outline recent discoveries of possible anthropomorphic artefacts made by the Irish Archaeological Wetland Unit (IAWU) during surveys of Bord na Móna's (BnM) Derrygreenagh bogs in east Co Offaly in 2002 and 2003. In particular, the paper details the most representational of the possible anthropomorphic objects, which was recovered from Kilbeg townland, Ballykean Bog, in 2003. Prior to 2001, only three anthropomorphic wooden figures were known from Ireland, all of which are prehistoric in date. These came from Lagore, Co Meath, Ralaghan, Co Cavan, and Corlea, Co Longford. In 2001, a fourth artefact interpreted as an anthropomorphic figure was discovered by chance at Broughal, Co Offaly. A further seven artefacts that might be interpreted as anthropomorphic in nature were recovered from the Derrygreenagh bogs between 2002 and 2003. The interpretation of these artefacts is problematic; however, if the latest discoveries are accepted as true anthropomorphic figures, this brings the total number of Irish figures to 11.

PAST DISCOVERIES

Before detailing those figures that have been preserved down to the present day, it is important to cite two 'paper figures' discovered in the Bog of Cullen, Co Tipperary, in the late eighteenth century. Pownall documented the two fragmentary figures discovered during peat-cutting. The first figure consisted of a 'fragment which was said to be part of an image … of black wood entirely covered and plated with thin gold'. The second figure consisted of 'another fragment of the same kind of wood … of an human form … of sufficient size to make a gate-post, to which use it was applied' (Pownall 1775, 357). Such discoveries serve to emphasize the role of chance preservation and the fact that many anthropomorphic figures of organic material must once have existed.

The oldest surviving figure was discovered by Hencken (1950) in 1934, during the excavation of an early medieval crannog at Lagore, Co Meath. This figure, carved from oak, is explicitly anthropomorphic and is 0.47m in height. It has a clearly identifiable head, shoulders and legs, and may also have a phallus, which has led to the artefact being interpreted as a male figure. Radiocarbon dating returned an Early Bronze Age date of 2135–1944 cal BC (3650±70 BP, OxA-1720; Coles 1990); however, the figure was recovered from disturbed contexts and its exact provenance is unknown.

A second Bronze Age figure was discovered by turf cutters at Ralaghan, Co Cavan. Dr Adolf Mahr published the Ralaghan find in 1930 (Mahr 1930) but the date of this discovery is unknown. This figure consists of finely carved yew and is 1.14m in height; it represents the most explicitly anthropomorphic figure discovered in Ireland to date. Its head has clearly depicted facial features and the body is well carved. Although armless, the figure has distinct legs. There is a circular slot positioned centrally in the pelvic area, which may have been intended to hold a separate phallus but may also represent female genitalia. As such, the intended sex of this figure is indeterminate. The Ralaghan figure has been radiocarbon-dated to 1096–906 cal BC (2830±70 BP, OxA-1719; Coles 1990).

The third figure in the series, that from Corlea, Co Longford, is the least representational. Its identification as an anthropomorphic figure is subjective to some extent, although this can be said for a number of figures identified across north-west Europe (Raftery 1996, 285; van der Sanden & Capelle 2001). The Corlea figure consists of a 5m tall ash roundwood cut to a wedge point at one end, the other end has been deliberately modified to form a neck and bulbous head. Two branch stumps were retained on the head, giving the appearance of a nose and an eye. A third stump below the neck has been described as having a 'distinctly phallic appearance' (Raftery 1996, 286). This artefact was incorporated within the substructure of Iron Age trackway Corlea 1, which was dendro-dated to 148 BC.

RECENT DISCOVERIES: THE BROUGHAL FIGURE

The fourth Irish anthropomorphic figure was discovered in 2001 by Dr Harald Rosmanitz (Archeological Spessart-Project, Lohr) while on a European Pathways to the Cultural Landscape field trip to Broughal Bog, Co Offaly, conducted by Dr Eoin Grogan of the Discovery Programme. This object was found *ex situ* on the surface of a BnM bog and may have been associated with an adjacent trackway. It consists of a split oak trunk (0.64m long, 0.11m wide and 0.06m in thickness) with a distinct head and an undifferentiated body giving a general anthropomorphic appearance. Two sharp cuts form the shoulders and the head is straight-edged with a central projection, which has been interpreted as representing hair (possibly a topknot). An iron axe was used to carve the object and it is closely paralleled with the Corlea figure (Dr E Grogan pers comm). In the absence of scientific dating, the present evidence suggests an Iron Age date for the Broughal figure.

THE BALLYKILLEEN FIGURES

In 2002, the IAWU conducted a survey of a number of BnM's Derrygreenagh bogs in east Co Offaly, which included Cloncreen Bog where 117 new sites were identified (for location of Cloncreen Bog see fig 4 in McDermott, this volume). These surveys were undertaken on behalf of *Dúchas* The Heritage Service (which subsequently became part of the Department of the Environment, Heritage and Local Government (DEHLG)). During the course of the Cloncreen survey, four wooden artefacts were identified in the north-east corner of the bog in Ballykilleen townland where the bulk of the sites were recorded. Partial exposure of two of the artefacts revealed varying numbers of incised V-shaped notches along their length. A third artefact had similar notches and had been carved to create the impression of a neck and bulbous head. The fourth find was similarly carved but was devoid of notches.

Three of the objects were associated with trackways and one was associated with a sparse deposit of archaeological wood. Two of the artefacts were recovered during the survey as they were fully exposed on the field surface and were in very fragmentary condition. The two partially exposed objects were secured *in situ*, to be recovered by Archaeological Development Services Ltd (ADS) on behalf of BnM the following year. On excavation, ADS interpreted

both these artefacts as anthropomorphic figures, and two further figures were discovered during these excavations (Corcoran 2003).

These latter discoveries have prompted the author to reassess the two artefacts recovered by the IAWU in 2002 and it is suggested that these finds might also be viewed as being anthropomorphic in nature. The first find was initially described as a notched roundwood (Find No. 02E0941:5a–c) and was recovered from the surface of a short trackway (IAWU site code OF-BKL 0034) composed of densely laid brushwood and twigs. The roundwood artefact had been broken into three pieces and was heavily milled on one side (fig 1). Its surviving length is 0.43m and the maximum diameter is 0.09m. The artefact has been partially dressed along its length and is broken at one end. At a point 0.09m from the opposite end, there is a broken V-shaped notch; this carving has served to give the appearance of a neck and head similar to the other Ballykilleen figures (see below). The intact end is worked to a tapering chisel point, cut to a curved, bunted terminal. Abrasion, possibly indicative of wear, was noted on the head, neck and main body. The artefact has been identified as alder and material from the trackway has been radiocarbon-dated to 1770–1497 cal BC (3349 ± 57 BP, Wk-11730).

The second recovered artefact was also initially described as a notched roundwood (02E0941:4a–c) and was recovered from within a short brushwood trackway (OF-BKL 0039), which also incorporated an enigmatic wooden artefact (02E0941:13a–n) consisting of a naturally hollow, slightly twisted trunk or root bole with four carved grooves, each spanning its entire external circumference. The notched roundwood artefact was broken into four fragments, only three of which are extant, as a central portion (*c* 46cm long) had been destroyed by milling (fig 1). It is estimated to have been *c* 1.3m long originally and the surviving fragments vary from 0.11–0.18m in width. The entire length is dressed and one end is cut to a wedge point, while the other end is cut at a 65° angle; however, milling has destroyed one side so that the original end shape is indeterminate. Two roughly V-shaped notches are cut into the broken end, one of which spans the entire circumference to create the impression of a neck and bulbous head. There are also two separate, subrectangular sockets, positioned either side of this notch. A wedge-shaped cut, evident on the broken end of 02E0941:4b, may be the remains of a third notch, therefore, it is quite possible that further notches were incised along its length. This artefact has also been identified as alder

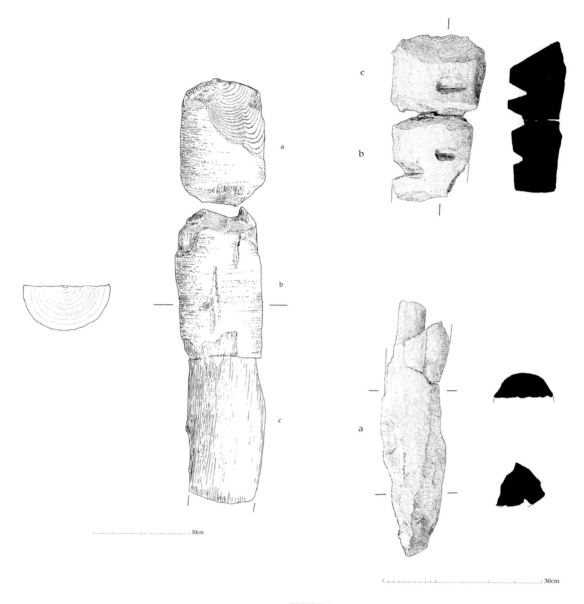

FIGURE 1

Possible anthropomorphic wooden figures from Ballykilleen townland, Cloncreen Bog, Co Offaly. Find 02E0941:5a–c is positioned to the left and find 02E0941:4a–c is to the right. Drawings by Simon Dick. (Source: after IAWU.)

and the trackway has been radiocarbon-dated to 1734–1455 cal BC (3066 ± 53 BP, Wk-11728).

The first of the unrecovered notched roundwoods was set at a 45° angle beneath the main body of a possible trackway composed of brushwood and roundwoods (OF-BKL 0020). This partially exposed artefact was initially identified by the IAWU as a dressed roundwood with up to seven V-shaped notches. The second of the unrecovered artefacts was located approximately 50m to the west and was associated with a sparse deposit of archaeological wood (OF-BKL 0030). Milling activity had revealed one side of the object, which had an exposed length of 2.09m. One end of the object had been destroyed by milling, the other end had been squared. Up to seven V-shaped notches were visible at the time of the survey.

In 2003, ADS undertook a number of excavations in Cloncreen Bog. Part of this excavation campaign entailed the recovery of the two artefacts described above; however, two further artefacts of similar form were also discovered during the course of these excavations. Once fully exposed, these four notched artefacts were interpreted as anthropomorphic figures, manufactured to a common design consisting of a neck, a bulbous head and a roughly worked point. Each object had been subject to complete surface dressing and three of the figures had 10 or 11 V-shaped notches carved along one or two sides. Three V-shaped notches were visible on the fourth figure; however, this artefact had not been fully excavated when the discoveries were first reported (Corcoran 2003). The four artefacts measured 2.1m × 0.25m; 1.8m × 0.3m; 1.2 × 0.2m and 2.2m × 0.16m. Three of them were discovered within 10m of each other, and appeared to be associated with one or two wooden structures interpreted as platforms. The fourth figure was discovered c 50m south-west of these but did not appear to be associated with a structure.

A fuller description of the excavation results is pending, therefore no independent dating evidence or wood species identifications are available as yet. The excavators believed that the four objects were possibly carved from alder; however, this appears to be based on field identification only. It was observed that none of the objects displayed any evidence of weathering and it has been suggested that the figures would have been set upright to act as markers across the bog and were deliberately deposited beneath wooden structures in the case of three of the figures (*ibid.*).

THE KILBEG FIGURE

In 2003, the DEHLG commissioned the IAWU to undertake a survey of Ballykean Bog, which is located c 7km south-west of Cloncreen Bog. Forty-three previously undocumented sites were identified, the bulk of which were located in the south-eastern corner, in Kilbeg townland, where the bog narrows (fig 2). Two plank trackways, one 643m long and the other 918m long, were recorded in this area and were dendro-dated to 1425 ± 9 BC and 1454 ± 9 BC, respectively. During the course of the survey, an isolated notched figure, broken into three pieces, was identified face downwards on the bog surface between the two trackways (McDermott *et al* 2003, 23). Though closely comparable to the Ballykilleen figures, the anthropomorphic features of the Kilbeg figure are arguably more convincing.

The Kilbeg figure consists of a curved roundwood (2.31m in length with a maximum diameter of 0.16m), which is heavily damaged on one side. It is worked to a point at one end, beyond which is a short unworked portion, retaining bark (fig 3). One end of the bark section is cut perpendicular to the long axis as if to represent a waist. Approximately half the circumference of the remainder of the object has been surface dressed but for a small area of bark at the junction of the neck and the main body. The opposing side is unworked but has been stripped of bark. At the opposite end, the wood has been carved to form a narrow, well-defined neck. Originally attached to the neck was a bulbous head, which has fractured from the main body and is broken in two. The junction of the neck and head consists of a straight edge cut perpendicular to the long axis. Eleven narrow notches, each set c 0.03m apart, are cut across its width between the bark section and the neck. These notches have one edge cut perpendicular to the long axis, while the other edge is cut at a 60° angle. The notches are crudely carved and on average measure 0.11m × 0.02m and are 0.01m in depth. (It is tempting to view the notches as representing ribs.) A centrally placed, lozenge-shaped incision between the notches and the bark section has been interpreted as representing a navel. This incision was created by two simple blows from opposing directions and appears to be quite deliberate as it is out of character with the surrounding surface dressing. Despite the possible depiction of a number of anatomical features, the figure is of indeterminate sex.

The wood has been identified as alder and is in very good condition, exhibiting no root or insect damage indicative of prolonged exposure. This suggests that the figure may have been deliberately deposited soon after its creation. It would appear, however, that the object may have been exposed in an upright position for an unknown period of time as the pointed end is the least degraded portion of the figure, the head and the upper five notches being the least well preserved. A sample from the Kilbeg figure has been radiocarbon-dated to 1739–1530 cal BC (3356 ± 37 BP, UB-6565 (AMS)), establishing close links with the two dated alder figures from Ballykilleen.

COMPARABLE FIGURES

Anthropomorphic wooden figures from various periods are known from throughout north-west Europe, the Kilbeg figure forming part of the more abstract end of the spectrum within this tradition. Many Continental figures exhibit carved necks and bulbous heads, but notches are less frequent. The closest parallel from mainland Europe is a female figure from Rebild, Denmark. This figure, which is 1.05m in length, has a carved neck and a bulbous head

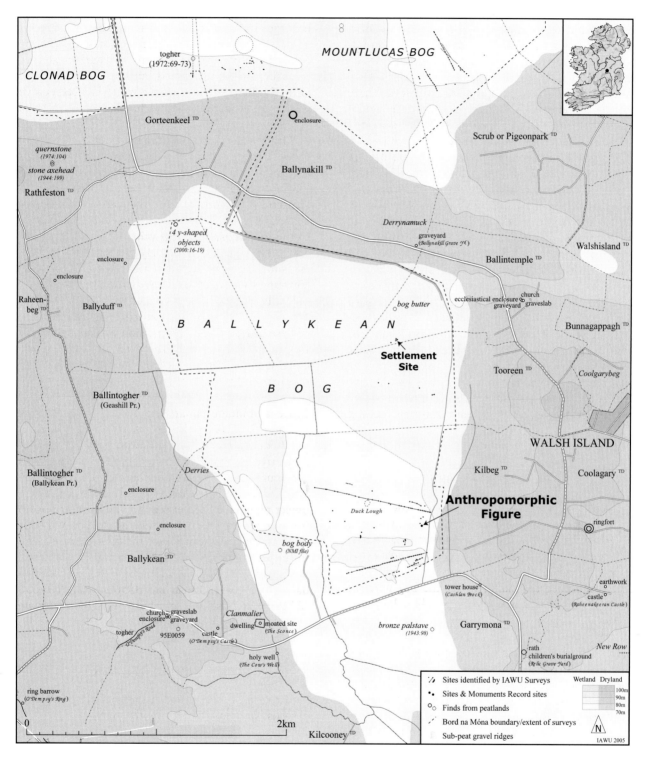

FIGURE 2
Map indicating the findspot of the anthropomorphic wooden figure recovered from Kilbeg townland, Ballykean Bog, Co Offaly.
(Source: IAWU.)

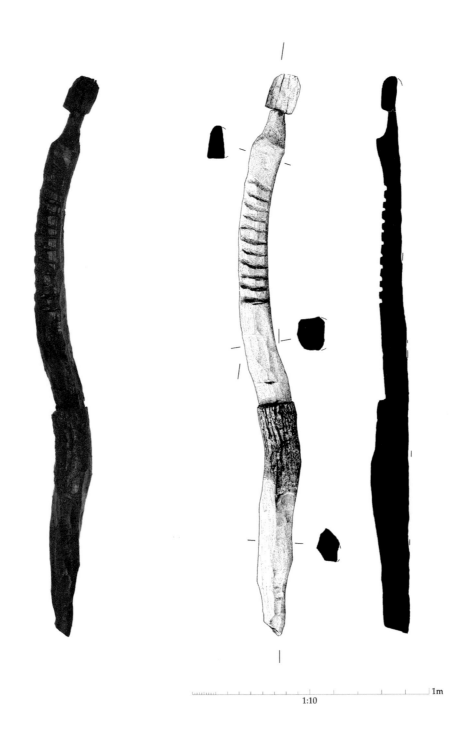

FIGURE 3
Anthropomorphic wooden figure from Kilbeg townland, Ballykean Bog, Co Offaly. The head alignment has been reconstructed in both images. Photograph by Rob Sands and drawing by Simon Dick. (Source: after IAWU.)

TABLE 1
Radiocarbon dates.

Lab code	Sample material	Yrs BP	$\delta^{13}C$(‰)	Calibrated dates* 1 sigma	2 sigma
UB-6565 (AMS)	Fragment of wood (*Alnus*) from Kilbeg figure	3356±37	−29.6±0.2	1731–1608 BC	1739–1530 BC
Wk-11728	Piece of brushwood (*Corylus*) from trackway associated with Ballykilleen figure 02E0941:4a–c	3306±53	−28.3±0.2	1661–1516 BC	1734–1455 BC
Wk-11730	Piece of brushwood (*Betula*) from trackway associated with Ballykilleen figure 02E0941:5a–c	3349±57	−27.3±0.2	1727–1535 BC	1770–1497 BC

* Dates calibrated in OxCal 3.10 (Bronk Ramsey 1995; 2001), using the IntCal04 calibration dataset (Reimer *et al* 2004).

that bears a striking resemblance to the Kilbeg figure (Glob 1965). The Rebild figure also has five straight-edged notches carved towards its base (van der Sanden & Capelle 2001, 19); however, palynological analysis of the findspot suggests a date of *c* AD 400 (Danish Roman Iron Age) for the Rebild figure.

Clearly, the closest Irish parallels for the Kilbeg figure are found amongst the Ballykilleen figures, particularly the five examples with pointed ends, well-defined necks, bulbous heads and incised V-shaped notches. It appears likely that all of the Ballykilleen finds were carved from alder and are of Bronze Age date. Material associated with two of the figures has produced radiocarbon dates closely matching that of the Kilbeg figure. Furthermore, ten of the sites in the north-east corner of Cloncreen Bog have produced dates spanning the Bronze Age, seven of which are dated to the first half of the 2nd millennium BC.

CONCLUSION

Although not explicitly anthropomorphic, the figures from Ballykilleen and Kilbeg form part of a wider European tradition of similarly abstract artefacts and may represent a discrete regional group within the Irish corpus of wooden idols. In addition to their broadly similar design, the seven figures are all likely to be alderwood and of similar date. The Ballykilleen figures were closely clustered together (the furthest distance between any two being approximately 170m) and the Kilbeg figure was located only 7km from them. The seven figures also share similar settings, being located at narrow sections of the bog, more amenable to safe passage.

Anthropomorphic wooden figures have generally been interpreted as cult figures – representations of various deities in human form. These idols would have been revered and may have been permanently on display at cult centres prior to their final deposition. Alternatively, they may have functioned as portable items, which were only exhibited at certain times of the year. When not in use, they could have been deposited in bogs for safekeeping and preservation. However, examples of figures found in close association with wooden structures have been documented previously (eg Corlea, Co Longford and Wittemoor, Germany), and it is into this category that at least seven of the new Irish figures probably belong. All but one of the Ballykilleen figures were associated with structures (interpreted as either trackways or platforms), and this may also be the case for the Broughal figure. Although the Kilbeg figure was an isolated find, it is quite possible that it was deposited beneath a trackway or platform, all evidence for which has since been destroyed.

Given their setting and associated structures, there is a case for interpreting some of the figures as protective markers, ensuring the safety of people traversing or accessing the bog on trackways or while accessing and using platforms. If set upright, the figures would have been helpful visual aids, demarcating safe areas from dangerous ones. They may also have been imbued with symbolic meaning and perceived supernatural powers. The figures may have communicated another symbolic message, that of territorial authority, signifying ownership of particular routeways or tribal territories, and giving physical expression to a distinct cultural identity guaranteed by the presence of supernatural guardians (or effigies thereof).

Nonetheless, most of the Ballykilleen figures (and perhaps the Kilbeg figure also) appear to have been deliberately deposited beneath/within structures. Perhaps they were deposited in this manner so as to confer supernatural protection upon the sites and those who used them. These figures may have been revered in other contexts prior to becoming offerings of this sort or perhaps they were created specifically for the purpose. The unweathered condition of most of the figures certainly indicates that they were not subject to prolonged exposure.

An alternative interpretation is that some of these wooden idols were ritually deposited as sacrificial human effigies in lieu of actual human sacrifices. The Late Bronze Age alder figure from Ballachulish, Scotland, may have been such an offering. An account of its discovery suggests that it was deposited face down in a pit at the base of a bog and held in place by stakes and wickerwork (Coles & Coles 1996, 75–6). Evidence from bog bodies indicates that certain individuals were ritually slain, deposited in bogs and were sometimes held in place by brushwood, stakes and so on. In this regard, it may be significant that the Kilbeg figure was similarly deposited in a prone position. The choice of alderwood may also be important. When cut, alder is orange-red in colour, giving the impression of bleeding like a human. Perhaps the alders' blood red colour was symbolic of the blood of human sacrifices. This characteristic has given alder much notoriety in folklore and, perhaps significantly in the present context, 'the red man' is among the common folk names for alder.

ACKNOWLEDGEMENTS

Special thanks to my former IAWU colleagues Caitríona Moore, Cara Murray and Nathalie Rynne, and to Conor McDermott in particular, who provided the illustrations. Many thanks to Sarah Gearty for additional help with the illustrations. Thanks also to Magz Bray and Deirdre Walsh who assisted in the Ballykean Bog survey and to Dr Ingelise Stuijts for the wood species identifications. I would like to express my appreciation to the Royal Irish Academy National Committee for Archaeology for providing the funding to date the Kilbeg figure, and to the Radiocarbon Dating Laboratory, Queen's University, Belfast, for ensuring that the date was available for the conference. Final thanks to Dr Gillian Plunkett for re-calibrating the radiocarbon dates at very short notice.

REFERENCES

Bronk Ramsey, C 1995 'Radiocarbon calibration and analysis of stratigraphy: the OxCal program', *Radiocarbon*, 37(2), 425–30.

Bronk Ramsey, C 2001 'Development of the radiocarbon calibration program', *Radiocarbon*, 43(2A), 355–63.

Coles, B 1990 'Anthropomorphic wooden figures from Britain and Ireland', *Proc of Prehist Soc*, 56, 315–33.

Coles, J & Coles, B 1996 *Enlarging the Past: The Contribution of Wetland Archaeology*. Society of Antiquaries of Scotland Monograph Series 11 and Wetland Archaeology Research Project Occasional Paper 10. Edinburgh.

Corcoran, E 2003 'Bog enigmas', *Archaeology Ireland*, 17(3), 12–13.

Glob, P V 1965 *The Bog People: Iron-Age man preserved*. St Albans.

Hencken, H O'N 1950 'Lagore crannog: an Irish Royal residence of the 7th to 10th centuries AD', *Proc Roy Irish Acad*, 53C, 1–247.

Mahr, A 1930 'A wooden idol from Ireland', *Antiquity*, 4, 487.

McDermott, C, Moore, C, Murray, C & Stanley, M 2003 'Bog standard?', *Archaeology Ireland*, 17(4), 20–3.

Pownall, T 1775 'An account of some Irish antiquities', *Archaeologia*, 3, 335–70.

Raftery, B 1996 *Trackway excavations in the Mountdillon Bogs, Co Longford, 1985–1991*. Transactions of the Irish Archaeological Wetland Unit 3. Dublin.

Reimer, P J, Baillie, M G L, Bard, E *et al* 2004 'IntCal04 Terrestrial Radiocarbon Age Calibration, 0–26 Cal Kyr BP', *Radiocarbon*, 46(3), 1029–58.

van der Sanden, W & Capelle, T 2001 *Immortal Images: Ancient Anthropomorphic Wood Carvings from Northern and Northwest Europe*. Silkeborg.

Monuments at risk in Somerset's peatlands

RICHARD BRUNNING

THE THREAT

The lowland peatlands of Somerset are famous for their waterlogged prehistoric sites. The area is thought to contain roughly a quarter of the surviving known prehistoric waterlogged sites in England and has more scheduled examples of such sites than the whole of the rest of England combined (Brunning 2003). Many of the Somerset sites were discovered during, or just before, their destruction by peat extraction, but another threat, that of peat wastage, is operating on a wider landscape scale (Brunning 2001).

Peat wastage is a result of the desiccation, oxidation and decay of peat soils caused by a lowering of the water table. In arable regimes, wastage rates have been measured between 10mm and 39mm per year (Richardson & Smith 1977; Hutchinson 1980; French & Pryor 1993; Hall *et al* 1995). Permanent grassland predominates on the Somerset moors but, even in these conditions, wastage by oxidation may be as high as the 1–2cm per year suggested for western Europe (Armstrong 1996, 8). Ground anchors in wet grassland regimes in Somerset have shown loss of between 4cm and 7.1cm over a decade (Brunning 2001, 12). In the central Brue valley, peat-cutting has been going on since Roman times and between 4 and 6m of peat has probably been lost (Brunning 2001, 14).

The project was established in response to this threat. Of the 116 waterlogged sites discovered on the Somerset moors, 54 were thought to survive wholly or partially *in situ* but, in almost all cases, recent information on their condition was lacking. The Somerset Levels Project assessed the condition of some of the monuments they discovered (eg Coles & Orme 1981; Coles *et al* 1996), but hydrological monitoring was only undertaken over part of the Sweet Track in Shapwick Heath. Only three subsequent detailed *in situ* assessments of waterlogged sites have been carried out in Somerset (Cheetham 1998; Brunning *et al* 2000; Cox *et al* undated) and only a handful more from the whole of England (Coles 2001).

FIGURE 1

New categories of decay had to be developed for the project to enable repeatable assessments of the condition of pollen and plant remains. Here are shown four levels of erosion of the fruit of *Sparganium erectum* (branched bur-reed). Photo: Julie Jones.

191

FIGURE 2
The Neolithic Abbot's Way. The water-table remained below the track throughout the year resulting in the timbers being in a very poor state of preservation. The shallow depth of burial is likely to preclude preservation *in situ*.

THE MONUMENTS AT RISK IN SOMERSET'S PEATLANDS (MARISP) PROJECT

The MARISP project was established with funding from English Heritage, Somerset County Council and the Environment Agency, to obtain information from a significant number of the waterlogged archaeological sites on the peat moors that were thought to still survive *in situ*. There were five specific main aims of the MARISP project:

1. To obtain information on the present condition of the chosen sites.
2. To provide baseline condition data from which subsequent changes could be measured by future assessments.
3. To assess the hydrological setting of the monuments and provide predictions for the future survival of waterlogged remains.
4. To suggest what changes might be required to achieve such preservation *in situ*.
5. To maximize the research potential of the keyhole excavations.

A total of 14 sites were investigated. Five of these waterlogged structures could not be located by coring or excavation, because they were destroyed, were buried beneath modern roads or did not extend into the areas investigated. The remaining nine sites that were excavated and assessed included a Saxon causeway between Street and Glastonbury (Morland 1881; 1922), the Chilton, Abbot's Way, Bell & Tinney's prehistoric wooden trackways (Coles & Hibbert 1968; Coles *et al* 1975; Coles 1980; Coles & Orme 1980; Dymond 1980; Norman 1980), the Iron Age 'lake villages' at Meare (Bulleid & Gray 1948; Gray & Bulleid 1953; Gray 1966; Coles *et al* 1986; Coles 1987) and Glastonbury (Bulleid & Gray 1911, 1917; Coles & Minnitt 1985), the Bronze Age wooden platform at Sharpham Park (Somerset Historic Environment Record 15525) and the Late Bronze Age ritual timber alignment at Harter's Hill (Brunning 1998).

Each location was investigated by one or two trenches, of a size that would allow the removal of representative samples to assess site condition. The stratigraphy was described, the archaeological structures recorded as normal, and samples were taken of worked wood, pollen, plant macrofossils and beetles. The palaeoenvironmental samples were taken for two reasons, because they represented an important part of the archaeological resource in their own right and because they might be more responsive to recent drainage and desiccation than the wooden remains. New methods of assessing the preservation of pollen and plant macrofossils had to be specifically developed for the project in order to produce baseline condition data that would allow meaningful measurements of change in future reassessments.

The hydrological regime of each monument was analysed using a series of piezometers and redox probes. On each site a transect was established, leading away from the monument to the nearest ditch edge and a series of three piezometer stations were installed, with piezometers at three different depths at each station.

At the station nearest the monument, redox probes were installed at three different depths with three duplicates at each depth (per station). The depths of the probes were positioned to be at, above and below the monument. Water levels and redox were monitored every four weeks over 12 months. Water samples were taken from the piezometers nearest to the sites and from the adjoining field ditches. Water chemistry tests included pH, ammonia, nitrate, potassium, chloride, electrical conductivity and phosphorous as outlined in Brunning *et al* (2000).

RESULTS

The results were both interesting and depressing. Two Bronze Age wooden trackways, the Viper's and Nidon's tracks (Godwin 1960; Coles 1972), had been completely destroyed in an area of arable farming. At every other site the wooden remains were moderately or heavily degraded, with much evidence of ancient bacterial and fungal decay. The wood cells had lost their hemicellulose and significant amounts of their cellulose component. The lignin component was generally unaffected and represents a less attractive food source to present day micro-organisms. Possibly as a result, no evidence

of active microbial decay was noted in any of the samples using a scanning electron microscope.

Preservation of beetle remains ranged from good to very poor, with mediocre to poor preservation in many layers. There has probably been significant post-depositional (possibly recent) decay of insects, in addition to the random pattern of decay predictable in a gradually accumulated natural deposit (Kenward & Hall 2004). The remains were in a fragile state and are likely to degenerate further unless anoxia is restored. There was not a simple correlation between preservation and depth or between beetle preservation and water table variations.

Pollen and plant macrofossil preservation varied significantly from site to site and within sites. One

FIGURE 3
The house platform foundations (bottom), walkway (middle) and collapsed palisade (top) of Glastonbury Lake Village that had previously been exposed by excavations in 1897.

FIGURE 4
Glastonbury Lake Village was the best preserved of all the sites in the study. The visual condition of the wooden remains was very good just below the 1897 backfill. (Scale 20cm)

major influence was the nature of the environment before the remains entered an anoxic regime. There was also evidence that pollen deterioration in the upper peat samples was less marked under a sealing mineral layer than in situations where the peat was exposed at the surface. At the Bell Track, for example, pollen was poorly preserved and the peat was exposed at the ground surface, while at the nearby Abbot's Way, pollen was well preserved even though the peat was buried by just 0.24m of clay.

There was not always a significant correlation between the observed conditions of the three sets of palaeoenvironmental data. At the Meare Lake Village, for example, pollen preservation was moderate to good while plant macrofossils and beetles were poorly preserved. Overall, there was a better correlation between the recorded condition of plant macrofossils and beetles and the contemporary hydrology than was the case with pollen remains.

The monitoring of the burial regime showed that redox measurements closely followed the fluctuations of the water table. Water quality did not appear to be a problem at any site but low water levels were. At Meare Lake Village and the Abbot's Way the water table stayed below the remains throughout the year, producing oxidizing conditions at the former and oxidizing to slightly reduced conditions at the latter. The wood that survived at both sites was in an appalling state of preservation.

At the other seven sites monitored, the water table dropped below the level of the organic remains between spring and autumn, for periods varying from three to eight months. This produced oxidizing to slightly reduced burial conditions at these times. In all but one case there were no recent factors that should have significantly altered the local hydrology, so this pattern of seasonal desiccation has almost certainly been ongoing for decades. As the organic remains have been shown to be in a 'fragile' condition their continuing survival is perhaps remarkable. These results emphasize that the simplistic correlation between organic preservation and anoxic conditions is more complicated, governed by a range of factors that are not yet fully understood.

Overall, the project has shown that two sites have been destroyed, two other sites are so desiccated that their waterlogged components are virtually destroyed and that the remaining sites are threatened to varying degrees by seasonal desiccation. Every site studied is probably now degrading at a much faster rate than at any time since they entered an anoxic burial environment. Each year more archaeological information will be lost.

The potential to improve the burial environment varies significantly from one site to another. Of the nine sites monitored, two are in such a poor condition that improving the burial condition may be a wasted effort. A further two sites are so close to the surface that sustainable management *in situ* is probably not a realistic option. Improved hydrological management of the other five sites may be possible, if the landowners are willing to accept changes.

Three of the sites studied in the project had been subject to previous investigations in the same areas. At Meare Lake Village there had been two previous excavations in the area of one of the MARISP trenches, but the extremely bad preservation encountered was probably due to the very low present day water table. The other two sites showed surprisingly good preservation. The Bell Track had been excavated in 1968, but produced some of the best preserved timbers, despite being very close to the ground surface. One trench at Glastonbury Lake Village was located in an area excavated and backfilled in 1897, after the wood had been exposed for many months. Despite this, the timbers had survived the intervening period and the monument was in the best condition of any of the sites investigated.

CONCLUSION

The MARISP project has challenged some of our preconceptions about waterlogged archaeological preservation. Although some sites have been destroyed or degraded to the point of being 'dry' sites, at many other locations waterlogged organic remains still survive after decades of seasonal desiccation. Although it is now possible to assess and quantify the condition of a site and monitor meaningful parameters concerning the burial environment, it is still very hard to relate the two together.

A lot of useful archaeological information must have been lost from the sites studied over the last

FIGURE 5
To preserve the waterlogged sites *in situ* a more traditional farming regime with a high summer water-table is required, as shown here on Chilton Moor SSSI.

FIGURE 6
Assessment trench across the pile alignment at Harter's Hill – built in 1076 BC with additions until at least 1046 BC – showing wood survival at the highest and most vulnerable part of the monument.

30 to 40 years. For half the sites in the study it is probably too late to ensure their preservation. For the other half, short to medium term preservation is a possibility through improving summer irrigation.

A parallel project has been dating the top of the surviving peat on different moors (Brown *et al* 2003). The combined results of the two projects show that the palaeoenvironmental remains and waterlogged archaeological sites in Somerset's peatlands have been suffering greatly over recent decades and that each year more is being destroyed. The wet grassland

SSSIs (Sites of Special Scientific Interest) on the moors are also mainly in 'unfavourable' condition but the government target to get them into favourable condition by 2010 is proving a great driver for change. No such target exists for archaeology and, unlike natural environments, once an archaeological site is gone it can never be restored and it has disappeared forever.

The challenge today is not just to protect *in situ* the most important sites but also to seek the sustainable management of the Somerset lowland peat moors as a whole landscape. The overlap of interest with nature conservation aspirations will probably continue to prove to be very useful in this regard and the new Environmental Stewardship scheme may become an effective source of funding. For some important archaeological sites it is already too late and others will prove impossible to protect in a sustainable burial environment. Limited rescue excavation may have to be carried out to preserve by record what cannot be protected *in situ*.

Current predictions on climate change (UKCIP 2002) suggest that summers may become drier and warmer, increasing the risk to waterlogged archaeology at the most vulnerable time of the year. Over the longer term, the more pessimistic forecasts for sea level rise would see large parts of the moors at risk from flooding. The future is uncertain for Somerset's waterlogged archaeology. The MARISP Project shows that waiting to see what happens next is not a viable option.

ACKNOWLEDGEMENTS

The detailed work was undertaken by a number of specialists including David Hogan (hydrology), Mark Jones (wood), Heather Tinsley (pollen), Julie Jones (plant remains), Harry Kenward (beetles), Paul Davis (snails) and the excavation team of James Brigers, Lorrain Higbee, Keith Faxon, Jan Grove and Steve Membery. Thanks are also due to Gareth Watkins, the English Heritage Project Manager.

REFERENCES

Armstrong, A 1996 *The conservation of peat soils on the Somerset Levels and Moors.* Mansfield.

Brown, A G, Dinnin, M & Toogood, T 2003 *Peat Wastage in the Somerset Levels. A study based on field evidence.* Exeter.

Brunning, R 1998 'Two Bronze Age wooden structures in the Somerset Moors', *Archaeology in the Severn Estuary* 9, 5–8. SELRC.

Brunning, R 2001 *Archaeology and peat wastage on the Somerset moors.* Taunton.

Brunning, R 2003 *A review of waterlogged prehistoric wood in England.* Taunton.

Brunning, R, Hogan, D, Jones, J, Jones, M, Maltby, E, Robinson, M & Straker, V 2000 'Saving the Sweet Track. The *in situ* preservation of a Neolithic wooden trackway, Somerset, UK', *Conservation and Management of Archaeological Sites*, 4, 3–20.

Bulleid, A & Gray, H St G 1911 *The Glastonbury Lake Village Volume 1.* Glastonbury.

Bulleid, A & Gray, H St G 1917 *The Glastonbury Lake Village Volume 2.* Glastonbury.

Bulleid, A & Gray, H St G 1948 *The Meare Lake Village Volume 1.* Glastonbury.

Cheetham, J L 1998 *Characterisation of burial environments exhibiting well preserved wet archaeological wood: An investigation at Greylake, Somerset.* Unpubl MSc dissertation. University of Hull, Hull.

Coles, B J 2001 'Britain and Ireland', *in* Coles, B J & Olivier, A 'The Heritage Management of Wetlands in Europe'. WARP Occasional Paper 16, Exeter.

Coles, J M 1972 'Later Bronze Age activity in the Somerset Levels', *Antiquaries Jnl*, 52, 269–75.

Coles, J M 1980 'The Abbot's Way 1979', *Somerset Levels Papers* 6, 46–9.

Coles, J M 1987 'Meare Village East, the excavations of A Bulleid and H St George Gray 1932–1956', *Somerset Levels Papers* 13.

Coles, J M & Hibbert, F A 1968 'Prehistoric roads and tracks in Somerset, England: 1 Neolithic', *Proc Prehist Soc*, 34, 238–58.

Coles, J M & Minnitt, S 1995 *Industrious and fairly civilised: The Glastonbury Lake Village.* Exeter.

Coles, J M & Orme, B J 1980 'Tinney's Ground, 1979', *Somerset Levels Papers* 6, 61–8.

Coles, J M, Orme, B J, Hibbert, F A & Jones, R A 1975 'Tinney's Ground, 1974', *Somerset Levels Papers* 1, 41–53.

Coles, J M & Orme, B J 1981 'The Sweet Track 1980', *Somerset Levels Papers* 7, 6–12.

Coles, J M, Rouillard, S E & Backway, C 1986 'The 1984 excavations at Meare', *Somerset Levels Papers* 12, 30–57.

Cox, M, Earwood, C, Jones, J, Pointing, S, Robinson, M, Straker, V & West, S undated *The Abbot's Way: Assessment of trackway condition 1992.* Unpubl MS. Somerset Historic Environment Record.

Dymond, C W 1880 'The Abbot's Way', *Proc Somerset Archaeology and Nat Hist Soc*, 26, 106–13.

French, C A I & Pryor, F M M 1993 'The South-West Fen Dyke Survey Project, 1982–86', *East Anglian Archaeology 59*.

Godwin, H 1960 'Prehistoric wooden trackways of the Somerset Levels: their construction, age and relation to climate change', *Proc Prehistoric Soc*, 26, 1–36.

Gray, H St G & Bulleid, A 1953 *The Meare Lake Village Volume 2.* Glastonbury.

Gray, H St G 1966 *The Meare Lake Village Volume 3.* Glastonbury.

Kenward, H & Hall, A 2004 'Actively decaying or just poorly preserved? Can we tell when plant and invertebrate remains in urban archaeological deposits decayed?', 4–10 *in* Nixon, T (ed) *Preserving Archaeological Remains In Situ? Proceedings of the 2nd [PARIS] Conference 12–14 September 2001.* London.

Hall, D, Wells, C & Huckerby, E 1995 *The Wetlands of Greater Manchester.* North West Wetland Survey 1. Lancaster.

Hutchinson, J N 1980 'The record of peat wastage in the East Anglian Fenlands at Holme Post, 1848–1978 AD', *Journal of Ecology*, 68, 229–49.

Morland, J 1881 'On an ancient road between Glastonbury and Street', *Proc Somerset Archaeology and Nat Hist Soc*, 27, pt ii, 43–50.

Morland, J 1922 'The Roman road, Pons Perilis, and Beckery Mill: A Regional Survey', *Proc Somerset Archaeology and Nat Hist Soc*, 68, pt ii, 68–86.

Norman, C 1980 'Timber structures in the peat to the south of Chedzoy: Moor Drove', *Proc Somerset Archaeology and Nat Hist Soc*, 124, 159–63.

Richardson, S J & Smith, J 1977 'Peat wastage in the East Anglian Fens', *Journal of Soil Science*, 28, 485–9.

UKCIP 2002 *Climate Change Scenarios for the United Kingdom: The UKCIP02 Briefing Report.* UK Climate Impacts Programme, 2002.

The trials and tribulations of upland peat: results of investigations into the archaeological potential of the higher peatlands

JAMIE QUARTERMAINE, JO COOK, DENISE DRUCE and ELIZABETH HUCKERBY

INTRODUCTION

This paper outlines the aims and results of the Upland Peat Project, a survey commissioned by English Heritage. The project, which was management oriented, was an experimental study intended to research the nature of the peatland threats, and to trial techniques that will predict the location and extent of archaeological remains. The project was concentrated on the extensive uplands of north-west England (fig 1), but with the intention of developing a cost-effective strategy that could serve to identify threatened upland, peat-covered archaeology across the rest of the country.

AIMS

The principal aims of the project were:

- to investigate the threats, past, present and future, to the peat and how these may result in damage to the archaeological resource;

- to establish to what extent these peats may obscure archaeological remains;

- to combine these separate sources of data, to establish whether it is feasible, or indeed possible, to create models that highlight areas of upland peat where there is a potential for significant archaeological remains, and where these may be threatened either at present or in the future.

THREATS PAST AND PRESENT

A recent study – *Monuments at Risk in the English Wetlands* (Van de Noort *et al* 2001) – has shown that as much as 20 per cent of the upland peats have been subject to severe damage by erosion over the last 50 years. This erosion results from a combination of different agencies rather than one specific one, which include forestry, land improvement, visitor pressure, peat-cutting, grazing levels, upland drainage, both natural and man-made, and burning.

The damage caused by burning is perhaps the most severe and was particularly notable at Anglezarke Moor in South Lancashire, where periodic burning, either accidentally or by arson, has resulted in huge peat-free scars extending across the landscape, which have exposed a significant archaeological resource (Howard-Davis 1996). Probably the most dramatic example of fire damage to an archaeological landscape occurred at Fylingdales on the North York Moors; there, a policy of nature conservation had led to a reduction in sheep stocking and this, combined with a deliberate policy of not managing the heather moorland, allowed the rampant growth of heather. Thus, when there was an accidental roadside fire, this rapidly got out of control and destroyed 2–3km² of moorland (Vyner 2005). Whilst this was a heather moor with a thin organic soil, rather than a peatland landscape, the impact was considerable and exposed the underlying extensive and rich archaeology. The fire damage was exacerbated when the extant organic soils dried out and blew away.

Climatic factors also damage the delicate peatland ecosystem. Prolonged periods of drought increase dramatically the risk of serious fires in upland peat/moorland environments, the exceptionally dry winter and spring of 2003 leading, for instance, to a spate of fires in the Pennines around Manchester. Even in Cumbria, where fires are largely unknown in the recent past, two quite severe fires occurred in Ennerdale and Borrowdale at about the same time. In contrast, extremes of rainfall can bring peat slides, when the hydrology of the peat reaches a critical mass, causing blocks of peat to become unstable and slip. In the southern Pennines, for example, Tallis (1987) has identified areas of peat slides, which were probably associated with a reported cloudburst in 1777. If climate change does indeed result in more extreme climatic events, as seems to be likely, then peat slides may become more commonplace.

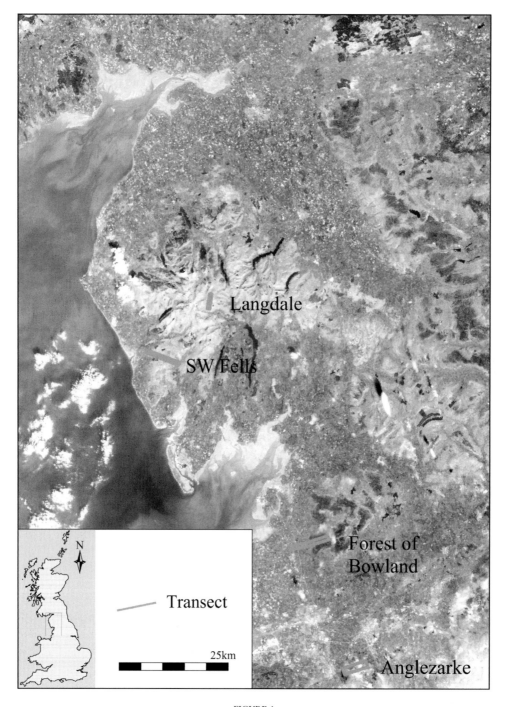

FIGURE 1
Location of the transects in the north-west.

Farming can damage, since sheep tracks can become the catalyst for the formation of drainage channels. Again, on Anglezarke, there were suggestions that sheep tracks adjacent to a major drainage gully damaged the surface vegetation and were instrumental in causing large blocks of peat to separate from the main body. Sheep will also shelter under the peat hags left by peat-cutting or drainage channels and, by rubbing against them, will increase their extent. Cattle can also cause considerable damage to the vegetation cover but do not typically graze the higher peat-covered lands.

PLATE 1
Area of footpath erosion at Harrison Coombe, Langdale.

The development of peats can be adversely impacted on by atmospheric pollution. The bog mosses (*Sphagnum* spp), which are one of the most important plants in the formation of peat, are extremely sensitive to high levels of SO_2 and NO_2, which inhibit their growth (Mackay & Tallis 1996; Caporn 1998). With the reduction in industry and coal-fired power stations, however, this problem is lessening.

A further source of erosion is that caused by the ever-increasing recreational use of the uplands, resulting in channels forming, which then allow water to drain from the peat (plate 1). The increased run-off exacerbates the erosion of the channel sides, as well as drying out the peat, upsetting the hydrology. The

permeability of the surface can be reduced, making it difficult to re-wet (Anderson *et al* 1998), which would therefore allow any fires to spread more rapidly. The Countryside and Rights of Way Act (2000) has enabled visitor access onto areas that previously did not have any significant visitor pressure, potentially damaging delicate surface vegetations and allowing other agencies to increase the damage.

More extensive damage can, and is, being caused by the increasing recreational use of 4×4 vehicles and motorbikes; legislation is clearly needed as a vehicle driving over the peat can destroy several thousands of years of history in minutes.

Peat-cutting in the uplands, although still taking place today in the Peak District, is no longer the

PLATE 2
Artificial drainage feeding into Black Brook, Anglezarke.

problem that it was, but it has, in the past, severely depleted the resource and allowed other causes of erosion to become considerably more damaging. Significant threats have also, in the past, come from both forestry and artificial drainage, and their long-term impacts are still very evident, although both threats are less of a problem for the future. There are now considerable environmental pressures to discourage new plantations on the unimproved moorland, and the impact is consequently much reduced. Some of the worst damage on the moors was initiated by deliberate drainage in the 1960s and 1970s (Backshall *et al* 2001) (plate 2), which has been exacerbated by natural drainage erosion that expands the existing area of scarring; however, grants are no longer available and their impact is dramatically reduced.

In summary, although each threat to the upland peat may not individually have an enormous impact,

when combined with others they can result in major damage. For example, an undamaged moorland is typically not affected by drainage erosion, but disturbance of the surface by other erosion forces can enable drainage erosion.

TRANSECT SURVEYS

In addition to consultation and bibliographic research, the project surveyed four transects in north-west England, which were intended to test the assumptions about factors, such as topography and altitude, that affect the formation and erosion of peat. These also investigated archaeological potential beneath the peat in very different topographical circumstances. Two of these transects were in Cumbria and two in Lancashire, and each had individual problems or questions that were being asked of it (fig 1). The field survey also served to test a suite of techniques that could record the extent of peats and identify buried archaeological remains.

The westernmost study area was on the south-west Fells in Cumbria, selected for its abundant archaeology, high potential for buried remains and limited peat cover. Adjacent is an enormous cairnfield, comprising elements of a Bronze Age settlement/field system, and also a superimposed Romano-British settlement/field system (Quartermaine & Leech forthcoming) (fig 2).

Langdale, in the central Lake District, was selected because of its very high visitor numbers and therefore the potential for considerable visitor-related erosion, and also because it has a nationally important archaeological resource: the Neolithic axe factories.

The Forest of Bowland transect in Lancashire was selected as a control area because it was perceived that, as a long-standing grouse moor, it would be relatively undisturbed. In the event, this was not the case, since it proved to be an area with severe peat erosion (plate 3). The desk-based study identified two

major fires in the area in about 1943 and 1946. Both had followed a reduction in the management of the grouse moors because of a decrease in the number of gamekeepers during the Second World War and, in the latter case, the fire followed an exceptional drought (Mackay & Tallis 1996).

Anglezarke Moor is an area with a high level of erosion caused by fires; indeed, there was a major fire at the outset of the present project. It also has considerable visitor pressure reflecting its proximity to major conurbations that include Bolton, Wigan and Chorley.

EXPERIMENTAL METHODOLOGY

In order to protect and conserve buried archaeological remains, there is a need to know where they are, which is difficult when they are under 3m of peat. One element of the programme was therefore to experiment with means of identifying the buried archaeology. This included probing, using thin steel

FIGURE 2
1988 survey of Barnscar.

PLATE 3
Peat scars in Forest of Bowland.

rods to find stone features, ground penetrating radar (GPR), resistivity, small-scale test pits to look for evidence of lithics, and looking in peat scars where the erosion has already exposed the underlying mineral soil. Much of this experimental work was undertaken where the peat was relatively shallow and there was plenty of archaeology at Barnscar (fig 2).

Peat scars

The most rapid and economical method of below-ground investigation was to look in peat scars for artefacts and structural elements; however, this was limited by the distribution of these scars. Undamaged moorland, or where the scars are relatively shallow, cannot be investigated by this technique. It was successful, however, in discovering both cairns and lithic sites from Langdale (fig 3) and Anglezarke.

Probing

This was developed in Ireland and used extensively to locate field boundaries and cairns at Ceide fields in Co Mayo (Caulfield 1988; O'Connell & Molloy 2001). Long steel probes are used to measure peat depth, to identify mineral soil or stone elements and to define their edges. The method was tested at Barnscar where it was applied on an approximate 1m grid across a wide area and more intensively when features were revealed; this was a relatively fast but somewhat subjective technique. A more detailed approach was to mount a survey prism on top of the probe and to take readings with a total station for every position on a 0.4m grid. The data were then processed to create a contour model of the underlying peat/mineral soil interface (fig 4) and cairns and other elements were clearly highlighted and definitively recorded.

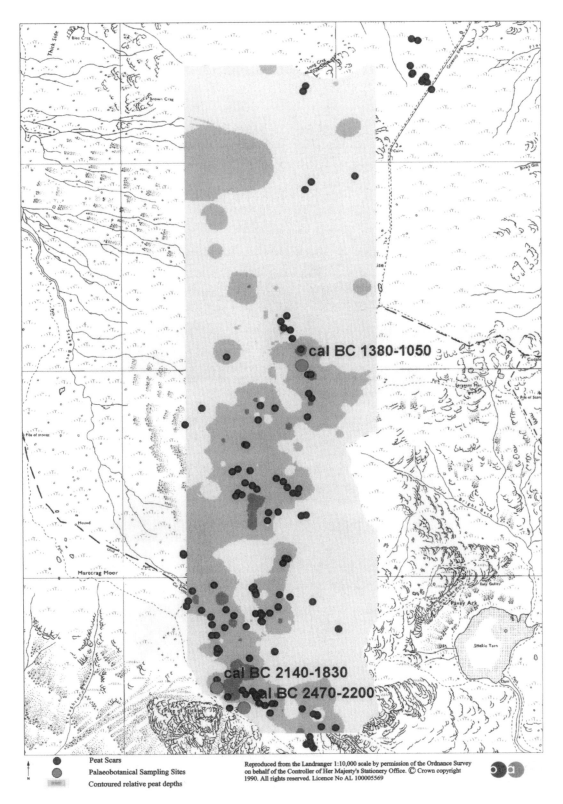

FIGURE 3
Locations of peat scar superimposed onto peat depth on the Langdale transect.

Geophysical survey

Geophysical survey was undertaken in the same area so that the results could be compared. Resistivity measures the conductivity of the soil, which is greatest through areas of wet peat, but is lower where there are stone elements. It was considered that this would identify stone, and this proved to be correct, as it very effectively found cairns and stone banks.

The other geophysical technique was GPR, which produced very similar results to the resistivity, but in addition also provided a depth component to the results (fig 4) (Utsi 2005).

Small test pits (0.2m×0.2m) were also dug in an area to the east of The Knott, on a raised bench above Barnscar. This had only limited success and was extremely time-consuming, although significantly it did reveal a small axe made of volcanic tuff, adjacent to a high level cairnfield (SD 1453 9519), which may suggest Neolithic activity at the site. However, the results did not justify the effort and damaged the surface vegetation, allowing erosional agencies to become active, thus threatening the peat.

Conclusion

Both the resistivity and GPR surveys were effective within shallow peats, although GPR would also be effective within deeper peats. Both techniques are relatively expensive and unable to identify artefact sites. Test pitting can identify artefacts, but was time-consuming and unproductive. The examination of peat scars in areas of scarring was undoubtedly economic and productive. It is therefore suggested

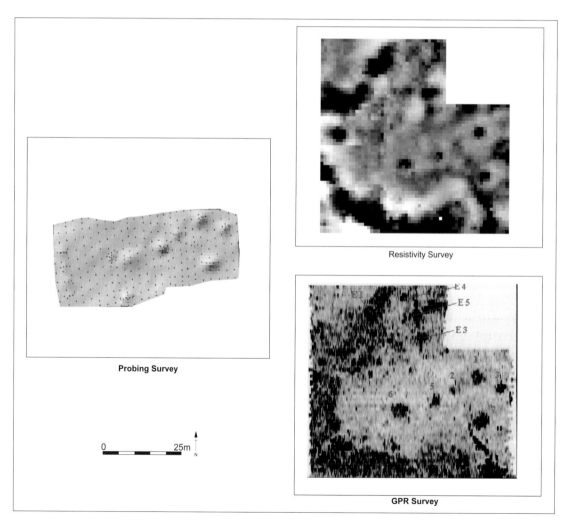

FIGURE 4
Probing, resistivity and GPR surveys of the same part of the Barnscar cairnfield, south-west Fells.

that, for efficiency and productivity on shallow peats, a combination of peat scar examination, where appropriate, in conjunction with the probing of undisturbed peat, that would look for structural components. However, probing is impractical in peats deeper than 1.5m, and here the use of GPR would be more appropriate.

PALAEOECOLOGICAL METHODOLOGIES AND RESULTS

The major aims of the palaeoecological studies were to determine the extent and depths of the peat, the dating of the inception of peat growth, the levels of recent and historic disturbance to the peat deposits, and the amount of peat loss. The data capture entailed a combination of probed measurement of peat depth across the extent of each transect, gouge auger cores to record the stratigraphy of the peat and the retrieval of monolith or core samples for more detailed analysis, and dating from three sample sites in each transect.

A combination of radiocarbon dating, pollen analysis and diatom analysis of the surface peat was used in an attempt to establish how much of the surface of the peat had been lost. Radiocarbon dating was also used to date peat inception at each sampling site except at Anglezarke, where detailed palaeoenvironmental work existed (Bain 1991); it was accompanied by pollen analysis at the interface of the basal peat with the underlying soil/mor humus. This proved invaluable in determining the nature of the vegetation, both prior to and during the early development of the peat, in order to identify any human activity and/or the processes of change. In the south-west Fells and Langdale, the pollen evidence suggests that peat development occurred following a long period of human modification of the landscape. Significantly, the date of peat inception/spread gave a *terminus ante quem* for any archaeological remains underlying the peat, as anthropogenic activity may have been curtailed by peat development, unless abandonment of the land encouraged peat formation.

The somewhat limited data has demonstrated that the date of peat inception varies widely across the north-west and even within transects. Peat in the Forest of Bowland started forming in a depression on a higher plateau in the Mesolithic period (5720–5550 cal BC (6720±35 BP; SUERC-4505) and appears to have gradually spread down the slope towards the coastal plain at Nicky Nook; peat started to develop

at 760–380 cal BC (2350±40 BP; SUERC-4504), which appears to be synchronous with a phase of very wet conditions in the stratigraphy of the raised mire at Fenton Cottage, in the Wyre District west of Bowland Forest (Middleton *et al* 1995; Wells *et al* 1997). Eileen Tisdall (Tisdall *et al* 2005) has discussed the possibility that prehistoric agriculture inhibited the spread of peat, and this may be pertinent at Nicky Nook, which lies in a narrow corridor between the blanket peat of the Pennine Hills and the large raised mires of the Wyre District of North Lancashire, where there is a nearby cairnfield that is devoid of peat.

At Anglezarke, peat inception on the higher plateau was dated to 3800–3650 cal BC (4945±35 BP; SUERC-4512 (GU-6066)), which is coincident with a rapid expansion of peat in the Forest of Bowland. Peat expansion at Anglezarke at around 2220–1940 cal BC (3685±35 BP; SUERC-4515 (GU-6070)) appears to conform to a general increase in peat growth towards the end of the third millennium BC. This may be attributed to a regional increase in precipitation at around 2000 cal BC, which was visible at Fenton Cottage in the Wyre District of Lancashire, as a flooding horizon (Middleton *et al* 1995, Wells *et al* 1997) (fig 5).

On Langdale, the highest point of the transect, which was on the slopes of High Raise and remote from the axe factories, had the latest inception date of 1380–1050 cal BC (2980±35 BP; SUERC-4517 (GU-6074)), whereas that from peat overlying an axe factory site (Site 123), behind the Pike of Stickle, gave an inception date of 2470–2200 cal BC (3865±35 BP; SUERC-4521 (GU-6076)), similar to Anglezarke. On present evidence, this post-dated axe production. In contrast, a charred *Empetrum nigrum* seed, found in the mor humus in which the debitage of this site was recorded, was dated to 5968–5732 cal BC (6965±30 BP; KIA23485) (Oxford Archaeology North 2004), indicating Mesolithic activity, although this does not necessarily date the axe factory debitage. There are several possible explanations for this early date: the mor humus may have accumulated over a long period of time or the debitage, when deposited, may have become incorporated into much older deposits.

The radiocarbon dates have demonstrated that peat initiation is complex and, in some instances, coincided with anthropogenic changes to the landscape. Given that most of the archaeological remains have been recovered from the peat/mineral soil interface, the peat inception dates typically provide a *terminus ante quem* for any identified archaeological sites.

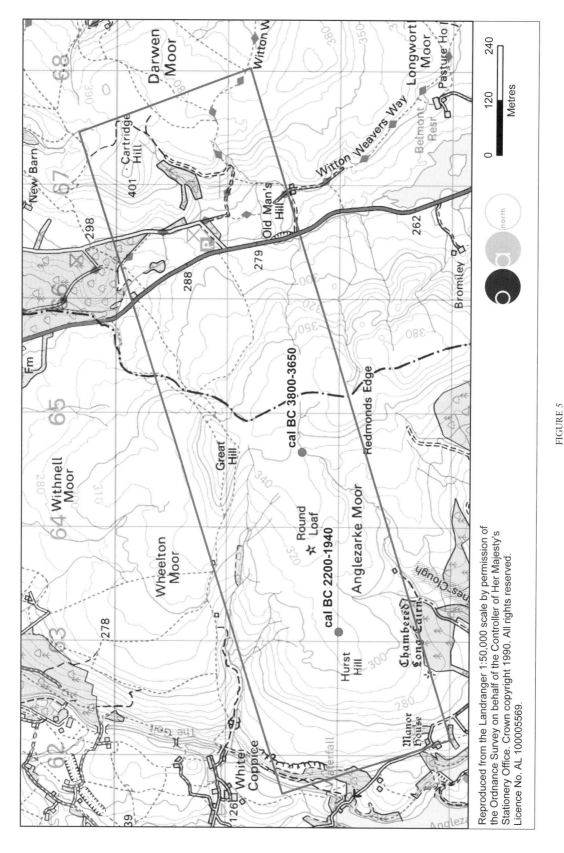

FIGURE 5
Location of Anglezarke peat inception dates.

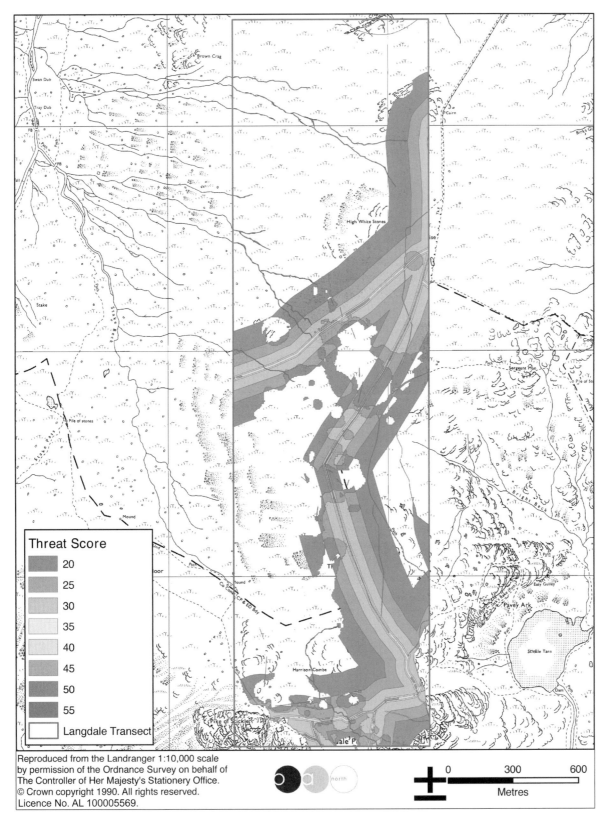

FIGURE 6
Map of predicted threats in Langdale transect.

209

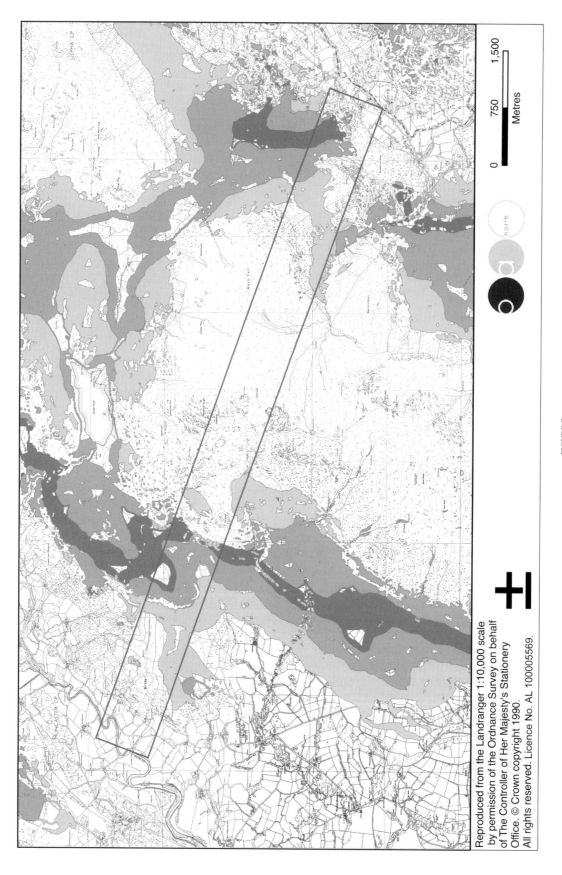

FIGURE 7
South-west Fells transect, showing zones of predicted archaeological poetential.

MODELLING

The ultimate aim of the programme has been to create a GIS-based model to predict where the greatest level of threat is likely to be, and also to model where the most likely areas of archaeological potential are. While this can never be definitive, the intention was to provide an informed estimate of the conditions in which there could be an increased probability of an archaeological resource that is threatened, and to determine if it was possible to produce a workable model that would be applicable for all uplands in England.

The first stage was to determine the extent of the peat, which was achieved by a combination of mapping soils, fieldwork and vertical and oblique photography. Previous studies (eg Anderson & Tallis 1981, 74–83; Anderson *et al* 1998, 42–8) have produced figures for marginal retreat or surface lowering of the peat that could be used to calculate rates of erosion over time. Areas of threat, such as footpaths, rivers, extant erosion and vegetation damage were mapped. These rates of erosion for each threat were then used to calculate the amount of peat loss over 5, 10 and 20 years. Varying widths of buffer zones were then defined around existing threats, indicating that the level of threat would decrease with distance away from the area in question.

Topographical features were also taken into account, as studies have indicated that the threat of erosion increases with altitude, particularly above 400m (Tallis 1998, 106), and with the degree of slope (Coleman 1981, 129). Using features such as rivers and breaks of slope as break lines, it was possible to produce a digital elevation model of the topology of each of the transects, that was as close a match to reality as was possible. Cell-based modelling techniques were then used to highlight areas of high altitude and steep slope. Similarly, a raster contour map of the depth of peat across the transect was created from the probing survey data using a statistical interpolation technique (fig 3).

Buffer zones of each threat were created, and converted into cell-based grids (rasters); the threat value at each point was then numerically assigned to each cell. By overlaying these raster grids on top of each other, combined with cell-based representations of the topographic characteristics and peat depth, a cumulative threat map, highlighting areas of peat under the greatest combined threat, was produced (fig 6). While this was an essentially crude approximation, independently it does highlight areas where peat erosion has been observed.

A second model attempted to highlight those areas where archaeology is more likely to be present. This was based on the detailed surveys of archaeology on the south-west Fells, and used the standard Kolmgorov-Smirnov technique (Kvamme 1990) for randomly distributed datasets, to investigate any correlation between the location of prehistoric settlement sites and a range of environmental or topographic parameters. It was important, however, not to overstep the bounds of the original survey, as this risked skewing the data. Initial results suggest that this technique will be able to highlight areas of archaeological potential in similar types of landscapes (fig 7).

In conclusion, the two models created show great potential. Combined, they provide a tool for assessing the likely archaeological resource of a particular type of landscape, and highlighting areas likely to be under threat from a prescribed set of factors, which can be expanded if data on other threats are available.

CONCLUSION

The study has shown the immense magnitude of the threats to the upland peats, as well as the fragility and vulnerability of the upland peat ecosystem and the archaeological record associated with it. The end product of the study, in the form of the models and report, will institute management recommendations for planning authorities. With the establishment of clear guidelines, it is intended that it will be possible to establish workable models for other upland peat areas that will enable local authorities to manage their upland resource more effectively. It will inform Department of Farming and Rural Affairs (DEFRA) when Environment Stewardship Schemes are being considered, and it will help land agents and the national agencies to take steps to preserve the peatlands. The need for such a management approach is essential because, although the upland peats are damaged and degrading, it is still possible to prevent the widespread destruction that has already happened in the lowlands.

REFERENCES

Anderson, P & Tallis, J H 1981 'The nature and extent of soil and peat erosion in the Peak District', *in* Phillips, N J, Yalden, D & Tallis, J H (eds) *Peak District Moorland Erosion Study, Phase 1 Report*, Bakewell, 52–64.

Anderson, P, Tallis, J H & Yalden, D W (eds) 1998 *Restoring moorland: Peak District Moorland Management Project Phase III*, Bakewell.

Backshall, J, Manley, J & Rebane, M 2001 *Upland Management Handbook*, English Nature, Peterborough.

Bain, M G 1991 *Palaeoecological Studies in the Rivington Anglezarke Uplands, Lancashire*. Unpubl PhD thesis, Univ Salford.

Caporn, S 1998 'Air pollution and its effects on vegetation', *in* Anderson, P, Tallis, J H & Yalden, D W, 80–9.

Caulfield, S 1988 *Ceide Fields and Belderrig guide*, Killala.

Coleman, R 1981 'Footpath Erosion in the English Lake District', *Applied Geography*, 1, 121–31.

Howard-Davis, C 1996 'Seeing the sites: survey and excavation on the Anglezarke Uplands, Lancashire', *Proc Prehist Soc*, 61, 133–66.

Kvamme, K L 1990 'One sample tests in regional archaeological analysis: new possibilities through computer technology', *American Antiq*, 55, 367–81.

Mackay, A W & Tallis, J H 1996 'Summit-type mire erosion in the Forest of Bowland, Lancashire, UK: predisposing factors and implications for conservation', *Biological Conservation*, 76, 31–44.

Middleton, R, Wells, C E & Huckerby, E 1995 *The wetlands of North Lancashire*, Lancaster Imprints, 4, Lancaster.

O'Connell, M & Molloy, K 2001 'Farming and woodland dynamics in Ireland during the Neolithic', *Proc Royal Irish Acad*, 101B 1–2, 99–128.

Oxford Archaeology North 2004 *Site 123, Harrison Coombe, Great Langdale*. Unpubl rep.

Quartermaine, J A & Leech, R H forthcoming *Archaeological Landscapes of the Cumbrian Uplands: Results of the Lake District National Park Survey*.

Tallis, J H 1987 'Fire and flood at Holme Moss: erosion processes in an upland blanket mire', *J Ecol*, 75, 1099–129.

Tallis, J H 1998 'Growth and degradation of British and Irish blanket mires', *Environmental Rev*, 6, 81–122.

Tisdall, E, Tipping, R & Davies, A 2005 *Living with Peat in Caithness; Prehistoric Farming Communities and Blanket Peat Spread*. WARP Wetland Conference, Edinburgh.

Utsi, E 2005 *Ground Penetrating Radar Survey of Two Areas on Birkby Fell, Cumbria*. Unpubl rep.

Van de Noort, R, Fletcher, W, Thomas, G, Carstairs, I & Patrick, D 2001 *Monuments at Risk in England's Wetlands (draft V.2)*. Unpubl rep.

Vyner, B, 2005 *Stony Marl, Howdale, Stoupe Brow Moors, Mossey Moor, Fylingdales, North Yorkshire: Report on Walk-over Survey of the Fire Sites*. Unpubl rep.

Wells, C, Huckerby, E & Hall, V 1997 'Mid- and late-Holocene vegetation history and tephra studies at Fenton Cottage, Lancashire, UK', *Vegetation History and Archaeobotany*, 6(3), 153–66.

Wetlands viewed through the antennas of a ground penetrating radar

ERICA UTSI

INTRODUCTION

Although the use of ground penetrating radar (GPR) in archaeological investigations is increasing, it is less routinely applied than other non-intrusive methods. This is regrettable since, if properly applied and not over-interpreted, GPR is an extremely useful geophysical technique, of special relevance to the wetlands since it is the primary non-destructive investigative technique suited to use in this environment.

TWO-DIMENSIONAL AND THREE-DIMENSIONAL DATA

Traditional GPR output consists of a plot of the depth of returned signals against the distance travelled by the radar (fig 1). Physically this is equivalent to an archaeological section but differs in that returned signals from targets do not necessarily reflect the outline of their physical shape. Two-dimensional output is extremely useful for identifying changes in stratigraphy and the outlines of features such as ditches or, in the case of fig 1, spurs of rock intruding into the peat. Within the wetlands, this means peat depths, sub-peat stratigraphy and anomalous material located within peat deposits are all susceptible to investigation by GPR. For these investigations to be successful the peat does not have to be shallow nor does it require to be particularly dry: good GPR traces of over 10m depth have been recorded in fully waterlogged conditions (Utsi 2001).

Where a series of parallel survey transects is completed, a three-dimensional data block can be constructed from which horizontal time slices can be extracted. Time slices are a powerful potential tool for understanding buried archaeology since the horizontal patterning of the GPR data may provide clues as to their nature and purpose (fig 2). One advantage of a wetland environment for GPR is the prevalence of flat surfaces below ground, removing the need for re-contouring of the data to take account of changing landscapes. This is not, however, true of the sub-peat strata.

CRITICAL FACTORS FOR GPR IN A WETLAND ENVIRONMENT

GPRs measure time in nanoseconds for the simple reason that the transmission speed of the electro-magnetic pulses they emit is not a constant and varies with each material they enter. Although this is true of all environments, it is more critical in a wetland environment since water slows the transmission speed to as little as a third of its speed in dry deposits. Potentially, this could limit the depth of GPR investigation relative to a dryland site, in practice, it means that a lower frequency antenna with greater potential for depth penetration should be used (Utsi 2006).

Water also increases signal attenuation or loss. Since signal attenuation is directly proportional to antenna frequency, lower frequency radars are more suited to wetlands.

For all radar applications, no single radar can be used to explore all depths and there has to be a compromise between depth and target resolution. Higher frequency radars have the capability to resolve smaller targets but can only be used for shallow penetration. Lower frequencies give greater depth capability but have coarser resolution capability. Although this is true of dryland sites, it becomes more critical in the wetlands because of the limitations placed on depth penetration by the effect of the water content on transmission speed.

Wetlands also present two additional essentially physical problems. In order to ensure good transmission into the soil, the ideal ground surface for a radar is flat and even. This is rarely the case in wetland environments, with the notable exception of fresh water itself. This also favours lower frequencies since shorter wavelengths are more easily reflected at the ground surface, decreasing the signal to noise ratio. Site access can often also be a problem (cf Utsi 2001).

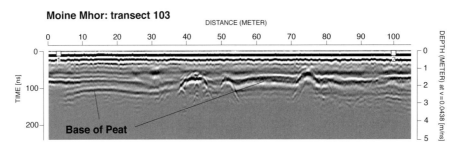

FIGURE 1
2-dimensional profile from Moine Mhor survey.

WETLAND GPR STRATEGIES

Although it is not possible to compensate for all of these factors, the best compromise for wetland investigation is to use low frequency radars, typically with a central frequency of 400MHz or less. One implication of this is that fine target resolution is an unrealistic expectation in a wetland environment.

Another implication is that the volume of water present matters both for the frequency of antenna used and for calibrating depth. It is not possible to evaluate water content from the conditions prevailing at the site surface and an explicit measurement of transmission speed needs to be made (Utsi 2006).

In recent years, GPR has been consistently used both for environmental and archaeological investigations. Environmental use includes landscape profiling, in particular where water flow management is critical, monitoring of peat stocks and monitoring of sub-water stratigraphy. Examples include the mapping of complicated peat and sub-peat stratigraphy at Bowness Common, Cumbria; an investigation into peat depths at Crowle Moor; water reservoir monitoring and the commercial use of GPR for determining peat stocks and for ensuring adherence to environmental guidelines for the preservation of protected wetland sites (Utsi 2001; Szynkiewicz 2004; Utsi 2006).

Stratigraphic information is not only of use in environmental studies: archaeological investigations also benefit from being placed in their environmental context (Conyers & Goodman 1997; Burdukiewicz et al 2002). The successful site detection and mapping at North Ballachulish Moss and Birkby Fell in Cumbria are very good examples of this (Clarke et al 1999; Utsi 2004; fig 2). Other GPR investigations include sites in Scotland where Historic Scotland has recognized the potential of GPR and been active in funding peatland surveys such as Mòine Mhór; Auchenkilns; and Parks of Garden (Utsi 2006). Research work on prehistoric sites in the Kopanica valley in Poland has included GPR investigations of the surrounding environment (Burdukiewicz et al 2003).

Where time and resources permit, the completion of an area survey is of greater benefit than a number of isolated 2-dimensional profiles. An area survey uses a series of closely spaced parallel transects to build a 3-dimensional data block from which horizontal maps, known as time slices, can be extracted. Horizontal patterning observed in a series of time slices is often more revealing than 2-dimensional GPR output. However, it is not always possible to distinguish between geological and archaeological remains, even by this method. Auchenkilns 1 was a good example of this lack of distinction. For this site,

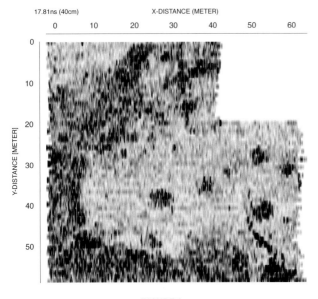

FIGURE 2
Time slice from Birkby Fell.

GPR was used as an initial investigative tool in order to place trial excavation trenches. The time slices revealed a rectangular feature, subsequently proved to be of geological origin. Nevertheless, the radar could be said to have delivered what was required of it, that is, the rapid identification of anomalous material at the base of the peat (Utsi 2006). Unlike resistivity plots, GPR time slices can reveal changes in patterning at a range of depths. However, good definition in the time slices is highly dependent on the spacing between adjacent transects as well as the resolution capability (effectively the frequency) of the radar. The transect spacing for the Ballachulish survey was set at a time when the 3-dimensional interpretation package was not widely in use and was determined primarily by the time and manpower available to cover the survey area. The definition of the time slices could be improved considerably if the transect spacing were to be reduced (Utsi 2004). The superior definition of the time slices from Birkby Fell, an upland site with shallow peat deposits covering features including Bronze Age barrows, is evident from fig 2. This survey was able to make use of a higher frequency antenna, 250MHz as opposed to 50MHz, and transect spacing of 0.5m in place of the 2m used at North Ballachulish.

There needs to be an awareness that, although transect spacing is often determined by the resources available for the survey, this will not necessarily yield optimal results (cf Dennis 2004). For good 3-dimensional definition in the wetlands, the relationship between transect spacing, frequency of antenna and depth of archaeological targets can be defined as $T_S = 2\sqrt{[(d + \lambda/4)^2 - d^2]}$ where T_S is the transect spacing; d is the expected depth of targets and λ is the central wavelength emitted by the radar. Fig 3 shows the results of applying this formula to waterlogged peat: the calculation changes for dry sites since the wavelengths emitted change in the absence of water.

From this table, it can be seen that using a 50MHz antenna on North Ballachulish Moss, with archaeological remains at a depth of 1m to 2m, the transect spacing should ideally have been reduced from 2m. On Birkby Fell, a 250MHz antenna pair was used and the remains were within 1m of the

ground surface. The 50cm transect spacing was the maximum acceptable for good definition.

The other important implication to draw from this diagram is that whereas a 5m transect spacing may be acceptable for an initial assessment across a peat moss, this is not adequate for demonstrating the presence or absence of archaeological remains: the distance between transects is simply too wide.

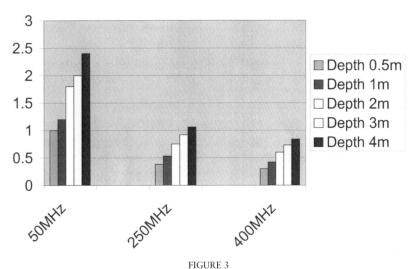

FIGURE 3
Maximum transect spacing as a function of antenna frequency (MHz) and target depth.

WHY DOES GPR NOT ALWAYS WORK?

There are three primary reasons why GPR surveys may not work: these apply equally to wetland and dry sites:

- High levels of attenuation;
- Inability to distinguish the target; and
- Equipment problems.

In certain environments, notably wet clay or salt water, the electromagnetic pulses pass into solution as a weak electric current and the radar receives no return signal. Although it is possible to enhance weak signal returns, lost signal is irretrievable. Such environments are said to be signal attenuating or lossy. Fig 4 illustrates total attenuation. The apparent target in the centre of the profile is merely the extra interface between a large puddle and the underlying ground surface. It also illustrates the slowing effect that water has on radio waves. Waterlogged deposits which contain high levels of clay, or which have a layer of clay above them, will not be suitable to investigation by GPR. Small amounts of clay may

215

reduce the signal without prejudicing the results of a GPR survey, as was the case in the Bowness example referred to above (Utsi 2001).

Target differentiation is also potentially a problem: the radar recognizes changes in materials on the basis of their electromagnetic content. Over time, wood immersed in peat takes on many of the characteristics of its host environment, particularly its water content, and deteriorates to a state of fragility while still buried (Coles & Orme 1980). Is it therefore reasonable to expect to detect wooden artefacts in a wetland environment?

Early GPR surveys in Denmark identified wooden trackways, for example at Speghøje Mose and Sjellebro (Jørgensen 1977; Bruch & Jørgensen 1984). In the latter case, the trackway included quantities of large stones, which may well be the primary reflectors in the GPR data. Speghøje Mose, however, remains one of the few examples of a wooden artefact detected by GPR in peat. In recent years it has proved possible for GPR to detect both the remains of bog oak, layers of woody peat or even wood chippings (Utsi 2001; Utsi 2006). However, other instances of successful detection of wooden artefacts are rare. In some cases this is because the survey design has not permitted sufficiently close sampling or surface conditions have made it necessary to use a lower frequency radar than was needed to resolve a relatively insubstantial target: not all trackways are large, solid features.

In 2001, an attempt was made to survey a short section of three trackways in the Somerset Levels: the Sweet Track, the Abbot's Way track and the track at Harter's Hill, using a 400MHz Groundvue 1. The survey parameters used were intended to provide reasonable imaging: the radar pulses were emitted every 5cm and transect spacing was 0.5m. It was expected that the remains at Harter's Hill, being the most substantial and best preserved of the three, would be the easiest target. The results, however, were not particularly successful.

The shallow remains of the Abbot's Way track were traceable in both 2-dimensional data and horizontal time slice but it was not possible to establish whether the remains being detected were the trackway itself or the re-buried material from previous partial excavation.

Expectation of detecting the Sweet Track had been low, in view of the age and condition of this track. Although it was not possible to produce a recognisable image of the track remains, the depth at which a maximum level of signal responses occurred, 35ns (c 78cm), was identified by three experienced, independent GPR data analysts.

Harter's Hill proved to be a great disappointment. Anomalous signals were clearly identified and indications of changing stratigraphy were revealed, particularly in the immediate vicinity of the former island. Identifying the patterning with what was known of the archaeological remains was not straightforward and the task was not completed. A profile from the Harter's Hill survey is shown at fig 5. Comparison with fig 4 makes it easy to see that the problem is not one of total attenuation. Although the data are relatively faint, there are real signal returns. Can we therefore conclude that the problem lies in wood being indistinguishable from the peat that surrounds it?

The final category of problem with GPR surveying may loosely be defined as equipment-related. GPRs are transmitting devices. As such, they retain the potential capacity to interfere, or be interfered with, by other transmitting equipment. Since they are typically very low powered, there exists a greater potential for higher powered transmitting devices, notably laptops and mobile phones, to interfere with GPR data. The extent to which this will happen depends on the number of potential reflectors above ground but, more than that, on the degree to which the antennas have been screened. Unscreened antennas not only radiate as much as a quarter of their power into free space (in contact with a dry surface) but also fail to protect against external sources of interference. Although the resulting noise can be removed during processing of the survey data, the contrast inherent in the data is also reduced, thus potentially contributing to a lack of target definition. This may not matter where the distinctions between a target and its surrounding environment are clear, typically stone walls in a soil matrix. Where lesser differences in material composition exist, or in a signal attenuating environment, this may make a critical difference to target detection. Typical signal attenuating environments are waterlogged clays and any soil in which water and salt are present together.

There can be problems even where antennas are screened and no external independent transmission

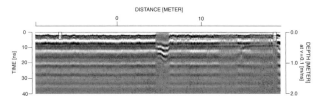

FIGURE 4
Total attenuation (with thanks to the late Jerry Hamer).

source is present. In the case of the Somerset Levels, discussed above, the radar used for the survey had been fitted with temporary metal reinforcement plates at both sides (since removed). Although the antennas were well screened, returns from the surface were reflected back from the metal into the ground. Removal of this noise from the survey data effectively weakened the contrast inherent in the data to the point where it was not easy to distinguish the archaeological remains from their surrounding peat. It may be that the removal of this noise, coupled with a signal attenuating environment, was responsible for the lack of clarity in results.

The potential still exists to make a much better definition of the circumstances under which water-logged wood can be detected by GPR. In order to define the limiting parameters, it would be useful to carry out further experimental work with a GPR over known wooden remains, preferably in advance of excavation, so that the results of both procedures can be compared. Such a project needs to take account also of the degree of attenuation inherent in the ground conditions. In the three sites investigated by GPR within the Somerset Levels, the upper levels of the peat are known to contain some clay. As demonstrated at Bowness Common, this will diminish the data through signal attenuation but, depending on the volume of clay present, may not prevent a successful survey being completed (Utsi 2001). Another important factor is that these peats have formed above marine clays. In principle, this means that it should be possible to survey the peat layers above, a fact confirmed by the presence of real signal returns in the data (fig 5). The degree to which the signals have been additionally attenuated, by a combination of salt and clay seeping into the peat layers, is not known and this may also have been a contributory factor to the unsatisfactory results. Conductivity can and should be measured since this can be used to distinguish the peats suitable for GPR survey from those which induce severe signal attenuation.

There are two main advantages of undertaking such a study. The first is the prospect of being able to monitor the condition of known remains rapidly and regularly. As a by-product, calibration of transmission speed not only allows the radar depths to be expressed in metres with reasonable accuracy, it also provides a measure of the relative water content of the buried deposits. Secondly there is the potential for rapid and efficient

evaluation of the archaeological potential of unknown areas, particularly in advance of development. It will never be possible to replace excavation with GPR, but it may be possible to concentrate the resources on areas of greatest potential.

FUTURE GPR IN WETLAND ENVIRONMENTS

Anyone doubting the usefulness of GPR in the wetlands has only to compare the results achievable with other geophysical methods. As a bare minimum, GPR is capable of detecting and mapping the base of the peat and, in the absence of waterlogged clay, the sub-peat stratigraphy. In most cases, it will also have the capability to map any internal stratification and anomalies such as archaeological remains. Time slices give the opportunity to view the changes in plan at different depths: see, for example, Utsi (2004).

Careful consideration needs to be given at the planning stage to the use of resources, balancing what is available against what may be achieved. Although the traditional 2-dimensional output is valuable, particularly in determining stratigraphy, 3-dimensional output is of greater archaeological potential. This implies consideration of closer transect spacing, at least in part of the investigation area.

As far as the detection of wood is concerned, a small research project leading to the derivation of good guidelines in terms of antenna frequency, target size, target age and survey strategy is long overdue. This issue has particular importance given the potential of GPR as a rapid assessment tool.

Although much of this paper has referred to peat, the principles discussed also apply to fresh water. The potential for using GPR on fresh-water sites such as crannogs is yet to be explored.

Some of the most successful archaeological explorations on dry sites rely on using more than one frequency of radar: the development of multi-frequency GPR applications on wetland sites is a distinct, and hopefully not too distant, possibility.

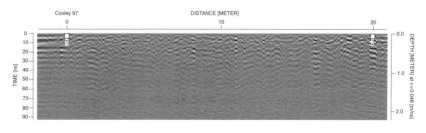

FIGURE 5
Sample 2-dimensional data from Harter's Hill.

ACKNOWLEDGEMENTS

The author would like to thank Historic Scotland, the Scottish Executive Trunk Road Design and Construction Division, AOC Scotland, English Nature, English Heritage, North Lincolnshire Council and the University of Portsmouth for funding and/or grant assistance to the various surveys; also Scottish Natural Heritage for assistance with resources and permission to work in the Moine Mhor area.

Thanks also to AOC (Scotland) Ltd, CFA Ltd, English Nature, the Macauley Land Use Research Institute, North Lincolnshire Council and Oxford Archaeology North for commissioning the GPR surveys; Patrick Ashmore, Ciara Clarke, Clare Ellis, Sarah Govan, Frank Mawby, Lawrence Shackman, Amir Alani, Karl Taylor, Bruce Glendinning and Iain Stewart for permission to use the data; and all of the many collaborators who helped during the (usually wet) fieldwork.

REFERENCES

Bruch, H & Jørgensen, M S 1984 'Speghøje Mose 1981', *Archaeology and Geophysical Prospections*. Working papers, The National Museum of Denmark 14, 85–7.

Burdukiewicz, J M & Szynkiewicz, A 2002 'Badania Archeologiczne I Paleogeograficzne Stanowiska Łęgoń, Pow. Wschowa', *in Śląskie Sprawozdania Archeologiczne*, Vol 44, 57–78 (English summary, 77– 8).

Burdukiewicz, J M, Szynkiewicz, A & Malkiewicz, M 2003 'Dalsze Badania Osadnictwa Schyłkowapalealitycznego na tle Warunków Paleoekologicznych w Łęgoniu, Pow. Wschowa', *in Śląskie Sprawozdania Archeologiczne*, Vol 45, 17–34 (English summary, 33–4).

Clarke, C M, Utsi, E & Utsi, V 1999 'Ground Penetrating Radar Investigations at North Ballachulish Moss, Highland, Scotland', *Archaeological Prospection, 6*, 107–21.

Coles, J M & Orme, B J 1980 'Prehistory of the Somerset Levels', Somerset Levels Project.

Conyers, L B & Goodman, D 1997 'Ground-Penetrating Radar: An Introduction for Archaeologists', Altamira Press, 195, London.

Dennis, T J 2004 'Imaging geophysical data – taking the viewer into account', *Archaeological Prospection, 11*, 35–48.

Jørgensen, M S 1997 'Looking into the landscape', *Aarhus Geoscience, 7*, 157–66.

Szynkiewicz, A 2004 'Ground-penetrating radar (GPR) monitoring of water reservoir', *in Proceedings of the 32nd International Geological Congress*. Florence, Italy.

Utsi, E 2001 'The investigation of a peat moss using ground-probing radar', *in Proceedings of the Workshop: 'Remote Sensing by Low-Frequency Radars'*. Naples, Italy.

Utsi, E 2004 'Ground-penetrating radar time-slices from North Ballachulish Moss', *Archaeological Prospection, 11*, 65–75.

Utsi, E 2006 'Sinking into Old Ground', *in* Jones, R & Sharpe, L (eds) *Going over Old Ground: Perspectives on Archaeological Geophysical and Geochemical Survey in Scotland*, BAR Report, 174–84.

Part IV

LACUSTRINE SETTLEMENT

Lacustrine settlement

JON HENDERSON and ROBERT SANDS

Lake-dwellings are a common and fascinating component of the archaeological record of some parts of Britain, Ireland and Europe. The proliferation of such sites within Scotland made this conference an ideal forum to discuss a number of issues surrounding the examination of sites of this type. The bulk of the papers presented in this section relate to work focusing on Scottish crannogs or lake-dwellings but there was also representation from Ireland, England and Poland.

Recent years have seen a flurry of activity surrounding the study of lake-dwellings in Scotland. This increased activity was well represented at the conference, including Crone's detailed re-examination of a previous excavation at Loch Glashan, Dixon's new dating evidence from Perthshire sites and Henderson and Cavers' discussions of new survey work and excavation. Hale provided a welcome overview and explanation of the gaps in the south-eastern record, while Harding re-emphasized the importance of aerial reconnaissance in crannog research. Issues surrounding the long-term preservation of lake-dwellings were addressed in two papers: Lillie *et al* described methods of monitoring *in situ* preservation on crannog sites in south-west Scotland while Henderson considered how the monitoring results recovered so far relate to the recent survey work carried out in the region.

The work in Scotland was complemented by research elsewhere. Fletcher and Van de Noort once again demonstrated the importance of antiquarian studies to modern archaeological work, while Pydyn provided a timely overview on the current state of research on lake and lakeside sites in Poland. Research in Ireland by O'Sullivan and Sands provided useful parallels with the Scottish work and once again reaffirmed the rich data sets that can be derived from lake settlement.

An underlying theme of the session addressed our understanding of the taphonomic processes that occur as lake-dwellings get used, reused and ultimately fall into disuse. While lake-dwellings may be argued to express certain common human reactions to living by and on water bodies, we need not assume any common cultural, symbolic or functional reasons for construction, although clearly such connections do exist for certain regional and chronological subsets of the overall type. Consequently, in many ways it can be argued that it is the depositional environment and the consequent taphonomic processes that form the most coherent link between many of the sites that were discussed during the conference. Two papers in particular, one by Crone and one by Cavers, provided thought-provoking discussion that specifically addressed the challenges represented by lake-settlement taphonomy. These papers provided an ideal opportunity to revisit and develop some issues that were raised in a previous WARP conference (Crone, Henderson & Sands 2001).

The papers in this session were thought-provoking and well presented. However, perhaps the best testimony to the overall success of the session was the long and lively discussion that it provoked amongst all participants.

REFERENCE

Crone, A, Henderson, J & Sands, R 2001 'Scottish Crannogs: construction, collapse and conflation: problems of interpretation', *in* Raftery, B & Hickey J (eds) *Recent Developments in Wetland Research*, 55–68. Seandálaíocht: Mon. 2, Dept Archaeol, UCD and WARP Occasional Paper 14. Department of Archaeology, University College Dublin, Dublin.

'From indirections find directions out'; taphonomic problems at Loch Glashan crannog, Argyll

ANNE CRONE

INTRODUCTION

The title of this paper is a quote from Hamlet (Act 2 Scene 1). Polonius is instructing his servant how to find out what his son Laertes is up to; by asking indirect questions about Laertes's imagined behaviour he hopes to elicit information about his real behaviour. In the same way, archaeologists cannot directly interrogate the past but must strive to understand it from its decayed and often much altered remains.

As with all archaeological sites, it is increasingly being recognized that crannog deposits will have been affected and shaped by non-anthropic events or actions – and that an understanding of these processes must be brought to bear on our interpretations of the deposits themselves (Crone *et al* 2001). This has been brought home forcefully during the writing up of the excavations at Loch Glashan crannog.

This crannog, in Argyll on the west coast of Scotland, was excavated in 1960 by Jack Scott. However, it was not until his retirement that Jack began the process of writing up the site and, sadly, he died before post-excavation analysis was completed. The work was subsequently completed by Ewan Campbell and this writer, and, in trying to make sense of the surviving evidence, the question of the taphonomy of the deposits came to the fore.

The crannog survived as a mound of material, from the landward periphery of which a rich artefact assemblage was recovered. This paper focuses on two strands of the evidence from Loch Glashan which are integral to our understanding and interpretation of the site, the taphonomy of the mound deposits and the taphonomy of the artefact assemblage. As befits a conference contribution, this paper is necessarily short; the reader is therefore directed to the recently published monograph (Crone & Campbell 2005) for a fuller account of the investigation of the crannog.

THE EVIDENCE

The crannog was first exposed when the waters of Loch Glashan were reduced so that a dam could be built across the outlet of the loch. The crannog appeared as a low, stone-covered mound, still partially submerged. Fragments of Continental E ware pottery (including a virtually complete vessel), whetstones, some 21 quern fragments and iron slag were found lying on top of the crannog, amongst the stones.

Jack Scott recorded what appeared, at first sight, to be a quite simple, single phase structure. The stratigraphy of the site was very straightforward (fig 1). A mound of organic debris consisting primarily of brushwood, with some larger timbers and occasional stones was laid on top of lacustrine silts. The brushwood mound appeared to be homogenous throughout; certainly, no distinctive layers were recorded. Probing confirmed that there were no stone or heavy timber foundations underpinning the crannog infrastructure. Furthermore, it was observed that the crannog quaked when walked upon, again implying that there was no solid foundation. The brushwood mound was covered with a layer of large horizontal timbers, over and between which lay a layer of sand and gravel. Finally, a layer of large stones covered the site.

A swathe of wooden piles driven into the brushwood layer was recorded on the landward side of the crannog (fig 1). The northern perimeter of the crannog remained underwater during the excavation but a few piles were visible in the water and it is assumed that the piling encircled the crannog, forming a palisade of sorts. Although not clearly seen in section, the piling marks the transition from scattered to more densely packed horizontal timbers and demarcates the extent of the sand and gravel layer. There are few piles in the interior of the crannog and thus the piling seems to define the crannog core.

Loch Glashan crannog thus appears to be another example of the *packwerk* method of construction, in

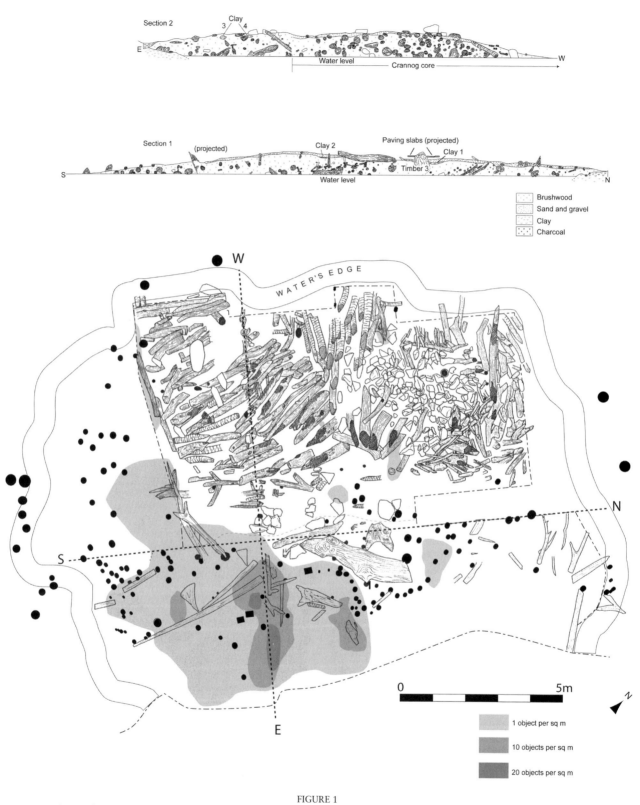

FIGURE 1
Plan and sections of the crannog showing the features mentioned in the text and the distribution of the artefacts.

which material, in this case primarily brushwood, is dumped onto the lochbed until a mound is formed above the level of the water, contained and pinned down by encircling piles (Davies 1942; Crone 2000, 105).

What was most remarkable about the excavation at Loch Glashan was the wealth of artefacts retrieved there. Apart from the inorganic artefacts found on top of the crannog when it was first discovered, the bulk of the artefact assemblage was found in a very discrete area on the landward side of the crannog, amongst and outwith the halo of piling and all within the brushwood layer (fig 1). The inorganic finds from this deposit included a copper alloy penannular brooch with amber studs at the terminals, a segmented silver-in-glass bead, an iron axehead and more sherds of E ware pottery, as well as more prosaic items of stone such as spindle whorls and a pot lid. However, the bulk of the assemblage consisted of organic material, primarily wood and leather, and constitutes the largest such assemblage for this period in Scotland. The range of wooden artefacts included a variety of containers such as large troughs and bowls, a range of spatulae and other more enigmatic tools, a paddle and rowlocks for a boat, pegs and wooden gaming pieces. The bulk of the leather assemblage consisted of waste material such as offcuts and scraps but also included fragments of shoes, and most significant of all, the components of a worn leather satchel, the design of which suggests that it was intended to carry a book.

INTERPRETATION

Jack Scott interpreted the evidence that he had found as a domestic settlement, the layers overlying the brushwood mound being the remnants of the original occupation surface (RCAHMS 1988, 205–8). In the southern half of the crannog, the horizontal timbers form a distinct rectangular area, or 'platform', and Jack saw this as the sub-floor of a rectangular building. The sand and gravel layer formed the floor of the structure, patches of clay were interpreted as the remains of hearths, and a number of forked timbers were interpreted as the corner posts of the structure. The artefact-rich deposits outside the piling were interpreted as the midden of this settlement and the presence of the E ware pottery and of the brooch placed the occupation in the latter half of the first millennium AD.

TAPHONOMY OF THE MOUND DEPOSITS

However, there are a number of observed features which cannot be accommodated within this interpretation and which therefore cast doubt on its integrity. Principal amongst these is the layer of stones over the crannog and the concentration of so many inorganic artefacts within this layer. Many Scottish crannogs, particularly those in Highland lochs, are characterized by a similarly stony carapace and this has prompted suggestions that the stones represent later refurbishment (Dixon 1984). However, the ubiquity of the stone 'capping' suggests, to this author at least, that it is the result of more natural post-depositional processes rather than a deliberately laid deposit. One could envisage a process in which, after abandonment of the crannog, the organic component of the *packwerk* mound and superstructure (turves, brushwood, wood etc) decay away while the inorganic component (stones, mineral soil etc) settles down, eventually forming a continuous layer which then affords protection to the surviving organic deposits below (fig 2). Thus, the stony layer represents a conflation deposit, that is, all that is left after the organic matrix in which they were originally embedded has decayed away. At Loch Glashan the inorganic artefacts found within the stony layer are thus the residue of a much larger artefact assemblage, the organic element of which has also decayed away.

If we accept this conflation model, it implies that the depth of mound material was greater than that which has survived, something that is also intimated by the evidence of the water levels (Crone & Campbell 2005, 5, fig 2). The surviving surface of the crannog lay at least 1.2m below the original water level – and possibly as much as 2.2m – so a further 1.2 to 2.2m of deposits would have been needed to bring the surviving surface to a habitable level above the water. Settlement in the mound would undoubtedly have caused some lowering of the occupation surface but at Buiston crannog, for example, this surface was refurbished to maintain its level above the water (Crone 2000) and there is no reason to suppose that this would not have happened at Loch Glashan. Even allowing for some settlement over time, the evidence of the water levels suggests that the excavated features would originally have lain beneath 1m to 2m of deposits, thus casting doubt on their interpretation as the occupation surface.

There are a number of other observations that also militate against the original interpretation. The sand and gravel deposits interpreted as a floor surface over the timber sub-floor are not limited to

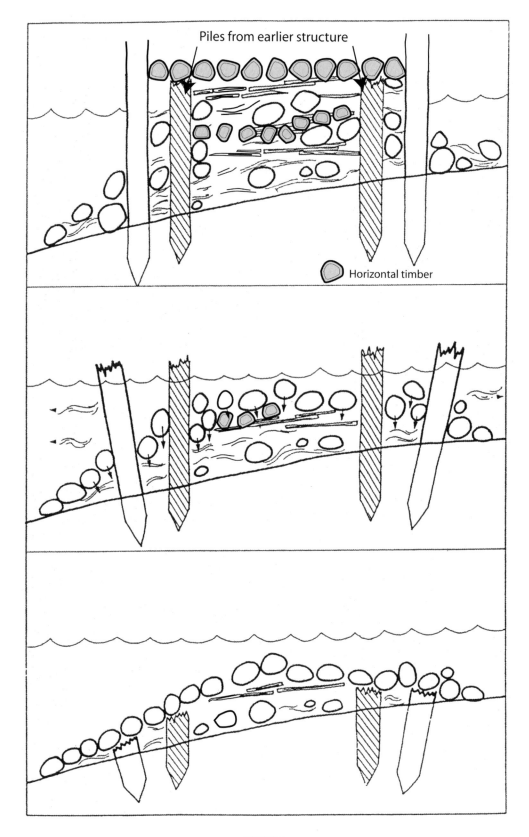

FIGURE 2
Schematic section through a crannog showing the process of deflation.

the boundaries of the rectangular timber 'platform' but cover the entire surface of the crannog within the halo of piling (fig 1). In the conflation model, this horizon could represent the accumulation of the smaller mineral component of the *packwerk* mound, possibly brought onto the mound either as deliberate dumps of beach deposits or as inclusions in turves. The clay patches are also not convincing as hearths, in that they are located too close to the piling palisade to have functioned as such. Furthermore, the recording of clay lenses within the brushwood mound, just outside the palisade, suggests that these lenses were simply another inorganic component of the *packwerk* mound. Similarly, the 'platform' of horizontal timbers could be just one element in a patchwork of log layers which were laid down to build up the core of the mound. This conjecture finds support in the presence of another patch of parallel-laid logs lying adjacent to the northern edge of the rectangular 'platform' which were partially submerged (fig 1).

This interpretation, that the surviving features on the upper surface of the crannog are components of the build-up of the mound rather than structural features, is proposed here as that which most closely fits the available evidence at Loch Glashan.

TAPHONOMY OF THE ARTEFACT ASSEMBLAGE

The second strand of evidence, the taphonomy of the artefact assemblage, provides additional support for this interpretation. As stated earlier, the bulk of the artefact assemblage was found in a concentration within the brushwood deposits on the landward side of the crannog and, as such, was thought to represent the midden of the settlement. However, new radiocarbon dates for some of the objects, together with more detailed analysis of items within the assemblage, suggests a more complex depositional history.

Fig 3 summarizes the dating evidence for the crannog. Those artefacts to which some chronological significance can be ascribed are illustrated. The date range traditionally assigned to E ware pottery on the basis of stratigraphic evidence, the late sixth–seventh centuries AD, has been confirmed at Loch Glashan through the dating of carbonized residues on the vessels, indicating that the pots were actually in use at this time. A seventh-century date is also ascribed to a sub-triangular crucible. However, the profile of one of the vessels, Vessel 5, suggests that it might be a later form, possibly eighth to ninth century in date.

The penannular brooch and the glass bead are also likely to be eighth to ninth century in date, while the wooden gaming counters, if they are accepted as copies of Norse counters, must have been manufactured sometime in the ninth to eleventh centuries.

The only structural timbers that had been retained were radiocarbon-dated together with three of the wooden artefacts. Timber 1 and Vessel 15 appear to be roughly contemporary with the E ware, while Timber 2 and the other wooden artefacts indicate activity in the second to fourth centuries AD, significantly earlier than expected.

In summary, we have radiocarbon and artefactual evidence, albeit some of it ambiguous, for activity on the crannog from the second to fourth centuries AD to the eighth to ninth centuries AD. There is also evidence for possible fourteenth-century activity which resides solely in the quern assemblage. All but one of the 21 quern fragments and grinding stones were found on the very top of the crannog, amidst the stone 'capping', so they were clearly late in the chronology of the site. Furthermore, some of them display characteristics which suggest that they are typologically late in the development of quern technology; they may have been dumped on the crannog when the neighbouring island was occupied during the medieval period.

Whether activity on the crannog was continuous or intermittent is moot; there are inconsistencies and conflicts in the available evidence that cannot now be resolved and consequently three versions of the chronology have been presented in the monograph. What is clear is that, with such a long history of activity on the crannog, the very nature of the deposit in which the bulk of the artefacts were found is called into question. There is no evidence in the recorded stratigraphy to indicate that this deposit, the brushwood layer, represents anything other than a single depositional event, yet it contained artefacts that had been manufactured possibly as much as five to seven centuries apart. This throws the interpretation of the brushwood layer as a midden into doubt.

Firstly, it seems inconceivable that the occupants would have thrown their rubbish in exactly the same spot over so many centuries. Secondly, the artefacts are all on the landward side where the water is at its shallowest and more sheltered, and through which the occupants would have had to make their way to the shore. Does it not seem more likely that they would have thrown their debris into the loch on the other side where it would have sunk into deeper water or have been dispersed by wave action?

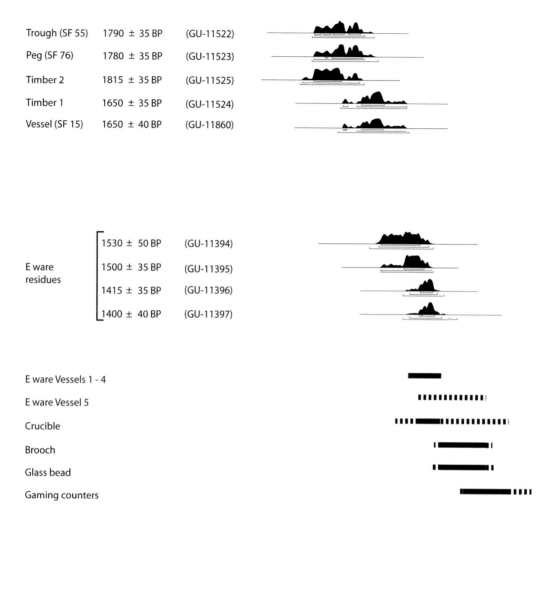

Trough (SF 55)	1790 ± 35 BP	(GU-11522)
Peg (SF 76)	1780 ± 35 BP	(GU-11523)
Timber 2	1815 ± 35 BP	(GU-11525)
Timber 1	1650 ± 35 BP	(GU-11524)
Vessel (SF 15)	1650 ± 40 BP	(GU-11860)

E ware residues	1530 ± 50 BP	(GU-11394)
	1500 ± 35 BP	(GU-11395)
	1415 ± 35 BP	(GU-11396)
	1400 ± 40 BP	(GU-11397)

E ware Vessels 1 - 4

E ware Vessel 5

Crucible

Brooch

Glass bead

Gaming counters

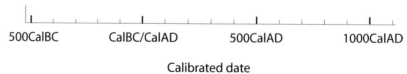

500CalBC   CalBC/CalAD   500CalAD   1000CalAD

Calibrated date

FIGURE 3
Graph showing the calibrated ranges of the radiocarbon dates and the date ranges of the chronologically diagnostic artefacts.

We have proposed an alternative mechanism to explain the location of the artefacts on the landward side of the crannog which is consistent with the theory of conflation deposits. If the crannog was periodically abandoned, wave and wind action would have eventually swept or washed settlement debris over to the landward side of the crannog. Some may have ended up in the water, while other material might have become buried within the mound as it was refurbished with every re-occupation, only eroding out on that side of the crannog as the organic mound deflated after final abandonment.

A similar set of circumstances must have prevailed at Llangorse crannog in Wales. Here, virtually the entire artefact assemblage, which contained a rich variety of metalwork and metalworking waste, was found on the lake bed in a spread lying south and west of the crannog: nothing was found on the crannog itself (Redknap & Lane 1994). It is thought that the final distribution of the artefacts was due to erosion and the scouring of the crannog deposits, which were possibly middens on the periphery of the site, by water and wave action.

At Loch Glashan this depositional model would more readily explain the mixing of material from multiple phases, the prevailing wind concentrating the material washed off the mound onto the lee side of the crannog. There is some circumstantial evidence to support this hypothesis. Many of the artefacts do not look like broken, discarded objects; most of the troughs and bowls were still functional, and, in some cases, were just too large to have been lost by accident. Furthermore, it would surely have been more efficient to burn discarded wooden artefacts than to throw them over the side of the crannog. Abandonment is a more likely explanation for their condition and survival. There are woodworm tracks on the face of one wooden artefact suggesting that it had lain abandoned on the crannog surface for some time before final burial, while one of the troughs had clearly decayed before it settled in the loch silts.

The condition and findspots of the E ware pottery also support this hypothesis; the sherds were all quite large, indicating that they had not been moved about much after deposition and many of them were also found along the edge of the crannog, as though they had been swept into a rubbish heap, as at Llangorse.

DISCUSSION

The interpretation of a site that was excavated nearly half a century ago, before modern standards of excavation recording and the systematic collection of environmental samples were applied, has been fraught with problems, not least because, in the intervening half century, the site archive had become dispersed and is now incomplete. It is therefore possible that the interpretation of the remains at Loch Glashan put forward in this paper is flawed. There remain inconsistencies in the evidence even within the proposed depositional model. For instance, one might

have expected the superstructure of the habitation on the crannog to have decayed and the remains swept off in the same way as the artefacts, yet there were no timbers which could be construed as structural in the brushwood layer. It could be that there were no structures on the crannog or that the structures were built entirely of small withies which broke up and became indistinguishable from the natural debris in the loch itself.

Whatever might have happened to the superstructure of the crannog, the bases of the piling inserted into the loch bed will not have been subjected to the same processes of decay and erosion and we might thus expect the extant remains, particularly on the sheltered side of the crannog, to reflect the real history of construction on the crannog. Yet, at Loch Glashan, we have an apparently simple defensive perimeter with none of the complexity one might expect from a structure which has been occupied, even if only intermittently, for between five and seven centuries. Buiston crannog was only occupied for 70 to 80 years yet its defensive perimeter was frequently refurbished, resulting in a veritable forest of piling around the crannog (Crone 2000, fig 132). The comparison with Loch Glashan is stark, the latter encircled by a thin swathe of piles, which displays only slight evidence for two possible phases of construction. This contrast, between meagre structural evidence and a rich, disassociated artefact assemblage which appears to have been deposited over many centuries, is one that cannot be fully accommodated even with the depositional model proposed above.

Nevertheless, our interpretation that Loch Glashan represents a severely deflated site, much of the associated structural evidence having been eroded and dispersed by over a millennium of wind and wave activity, is the one that we feel best accommodates the available evidence. Even if we accept the initial interpretation of the features on the surface of the crannog as the remnants of occupation structures, this does not undermine the argument that succeeding deposits over these structures have been lost.

If this interpretation of Loch Glashan is correct, it has implications for the presumed integrity of other crannogs in similar environments. It seems likely that occupation deposits may not survive in situ or will have been severely compromised, particularly on crannogs in the high energy regimes of the Highland lochs. The crannog at Oakbank, Loch Tay, will provide a testbed for these suppositions, but it is not yet clear from the published accounts whether in situ occupation deposits have survived (Dixon 2004).

At Buiston, the survival of *in situ* occupation deposits was due to the fortuitous (for the archaeologists not the occupants!) collapse of the crannog mound around the north-west perimeter, causing the house floor to subside below the present water-table (Crone 2000, 26–7). This was enhanced by the nature of the loch in which the crannog was built, a small post-glacial depression which had gradually filled up with organic-rich lacustrine muds creating an anaerobic environment around the crannog. It is probably impossible to model the conditions under which we might encounter a similar structural collapse, but the smaller, sediment-filled lochs of south-west Scotland would seem to hold out the best chances of survival. These are not the conditions that prevail in the Highland lochs and there the challenge must be to identify the characteristics of those sites which may not have suffered comprehensive deflation.

Wetland archaeologists always 'talk up' the watery environment for its ability to preserve organic remains but they do not often consider the downside of this environment, its active, erosional qualities. The depositional environment is not a passive wrapper (*sensu* Marshall McLuhan) yet there is still very little consideration of the post-depositional history of crannogs and what this might mean in terms of the surviving remains. For instance, Fredengren has examined the history of the crannog at Sroove, in Lough Gara, Ireland through to the present day (2002, 223–41), interpreting the remains entirely in terms of human activity, without considering the impact of the natural environment on the structure. 'Low-cairn' crannogs such as Sroove will surely have taken a seasonal hammering in a shallow lough which is 'stirred up in bad weather' (*ibid.*, 65), breaking up and dispersing the structures and artefacts left on the crannog.

If we take the observed stratification on crannogs as direct and clear evidence of the structures and processes that formed them we will be misled. It is imperative that we understand fully the post-depositional processes that have formed the remains we now observe. Thus, 'from indirections', by separating the works of God and nature from the works of man, we may hope to come closer to finding 'directions out'.

REFERENCES

Crone, B A 2000 *The history of a Scottish lowland crannog: excavations at Buiston, Ayrshire 1989–90*. STAR Monog Ser 4, Edinburgh.

Crone, B A, Henderson, J C & Sands, R 2001 'Scottish crannogs: construction, collapse and conflation. Problems of interpretation', *in* Raftery, B & Hickey, J (eds) *Recent Developments in Wetland Research*, 55–68. Seandálaíocht: Mon 2, Dept Archaeol, UCD and WARP Occ Paper 14. Dublin.

Crone, A & Campbell, E 2005 *A Crannog of the 1st Millennium* AD; *Excavations by Jack Scott at Loch Glashan, Argyll, 1960*. Edinburgh.

Davies, O 1942 'Contributions to the study of crannogs in South Ulster', *Ulster J Archaeol* 5, 14–30.

Dixon, T N 1984 *Scottish crannogs: Underwater excavation of artificial islands with special reference to Oakbank Crannog, Loch Tay*. Unpubl PhD thesis, University of Edinburgh.

Dixon, N 2004 *The crannogs of Scotland. An underwater archaeology*. Stroud.

Fredengren, C 2002 Crannogs. *A study of people's interaction with lakes, with particular reference to Lough Gara in the north-west of Ireland*. Dublin.

McLuhan, M & Fiore, Q 1967 *The Medium is the Massage: An Inventory of Effects*. New York.

RCAHMS 1988 *Argyll. An inventory of the ancient monuments. Vol 6. Mid-Argyll and Cowal. Prehistoric and early historic monuments*. Edinburgh.

Redknap, M & Lane, A 1994 'The early medieval crannog at Llangorse, Powys: an interim statement on the 1989–93 seasons', *Int J Nautical Archaeol* 23.3, 189–205.

Recognizing complexity and realizing the potential of Scottish crannogs

JON C HENDERSON

INTRODUCTION

The Scottish lake-dwelling resource is extremely rich and as a result should be recognized as being of major international significance. Unfortunately, the importance and potential of this resource has yet to be fully appreciated outside the Scottish archaeological community. So much so, that in a recent overview of European lake-dwellings (Menotti 2004), Scotland's 370 known crannogs were covered in a single paragraph. With occupational evidence ranging from the Neolithic right up until the seventeenth century AD, living on crannogs or artificial islets located in inland water bodies was a major part of Scottish life for millennia. Crannogs are also one of the most prolific archaeological site types in the country as the existence of some 353 referenced sites in the National Monuments Record for Scotland attests. The ability of waterlogged and submerged crannogs to preserve organic cultural material that is usually totally lacking from dryland sites further enhances their archaeological potential and value. Despite this extraordinary pedigree, crannogs have, like wetland archaeology in general, failed to have had the impact on wider archaeological narratives that they should, and the often quoted 'potential' of these sites remains largely unexploited.

The obsession with discovering more sites and obtaining more dates – an approach akin to stamp collecting – with no accompanying stratigraphical information or consideration of how crannog mounds were formed has been one of the problems of recent crannog research. It certainly accounts for one of the reasons why crannogs have remained largely absent from general, usually period-based, archaeological narratives – to terrestrial archaeologists crannogs appear too typologically and chronologically un-specific (Henderson 1998, 234). The complexity of crannog deposits has long been recognized. It's hard not to sympathize with Munro, writing in 1882, when he states of one excavation that he 'failed to adduce a satisfactory theory for the details recorded' (259), while Morrison, in 1985, stated 'a crannog mound is something like a wet *tel*, with all the problems of sorting out rebuilding phases, and recognizing later constructional elements that come down from above, to pierce through earlier deposits and structures' (93). Understanding the dynamics of construction, use, collapse and decay of crannog mounds is crucial to their interpretation but despite recent attempts at model building (Crone *et al* 2001) we still lack baseline excavated data on the taphonomic processes that form the matrix of crannog deposits.

This paper discusses the results from two small-scale crannog excavations recently carried out by the Underwater Archaeology Research Centre (UARC) and offers some insights into what the remains at these particular sites represent. The paper ends with some consideration of the way crannog studies might develop to be more fully integrated into mainstream archaeology.

LOCH ARTHUR CRANNOG, NEW ABBEY, DUMFRIES AND GALLOWAY

The crannog in Loch Arthur appears above water as a tree-covered island, some 30m in diameter, which is connected to the shore by a muddy reed bed. Small scale exploratory terrestrial excavations were carried out on the surface of the island in 1966–7 revealing the footings of drystone/clay packed walls that the excavator interpreted as the stone undercroft of a wooden framed building (Williams 1971, 123). Despite a complete absence of finds, Williams offered a fifteenth to sixteenth century AD date for the crannog, based on two bronze tripod cooking pots which had been recovered from the loch in the nineteenth century. Thus Loch Arthur entered the general literature as an example of a late medieval crannog. However, in 1989, a vertical birch pile off the northern side of the site was sampled for radiocarbon dating and provided evidence of Iron Age activity at the site (GU-2463, 2260±50 BP, calibrating at 400–200 BC; GU-2644, 2240±60 BP, calibrating at 410–160 BC).

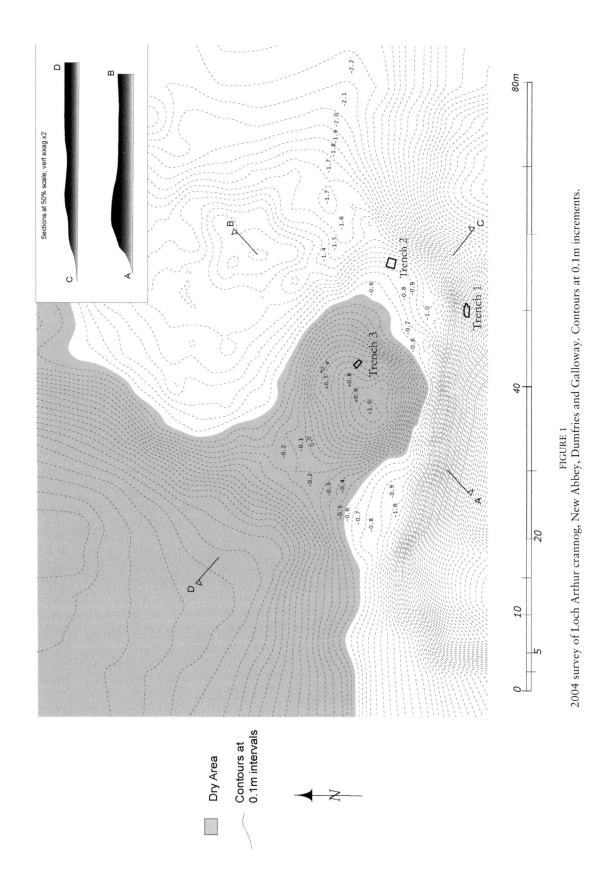

FIGURE 1

2004 survey of Loch Arthur crannog, New Abbey, Dumfries and Galloway. Contours at 0.1m increments.

Loch Arthur was examined as part of the current South-West Crannog Survey (Henderson *et al* 2003, 89–90; Henderson 2004 and this volume). Diving on the site revealed that the majority of the structure of this crannog lies underwater as the island visible from the shore appeared to sit on a much larger, fully submerged structure. Detailed survey of the site demonstrated that the dry island sits on a long promontory, some 81m long and 46m wide, running north-west/south-east from the shore, which may be, if not entirely, then at least partly artificial. These two features could be distinguished by their composition, the upper mound (the island) being built primarily of large boulders within a well-developed soil, and the lower submerged structure of timber (alder and oak), organic deposits and stones (fig 1). Evidence of artificial construction (horizontal alder timbers and organic deposits) could only be seen on the southern and eastern sides of the promontory where active erosion is occurring, presumably due to wave fetch. The western and northern sides of the promontory are completely obscured by soft silts, making it difficult to say with certainty that the whole promontory is artificial. The upper surface of the submerged structure lies only 0.3m below the water level while the base of the artificial levels occurs at a depth of 3.5m, after which no other timbers can be traced in the soft loch silts. Oak and birch vertical piles can be found in the silt along the northern edge of the promontory, providing more evidence for artificial construction, but these cannot be directly linked to the main structure of the mound.

Nothing could be traced of a stone causeway to the upper island, observed in 1874 (Gillespie 1874, 23) but apparently obscured by 1968 (Williams 1971, 123). It seems most likely that this causeway lies underneath mud and reeds in a deposit that has built up between the closest point of the island to the shore and the shore itself. Indeed, it is this build-up which makes it possible to walk to the island today, something that was certainly not possible *c* 1860 based on the evidence of the First Edition Ordnance Survey map of Loch Arthur, where the crannog can clearly be seen to be an island. The build-up of silt along the western and northern margins of the site may be the result of the re-deposition of silt, carried by wave fetch and currents (see also the discussion on Dorman's Island in Henderson this volume). With this in mind, it is possible that the promontory revealed in the digital terrain survey may not be entirely artificial but rather a large oval artificial island which is now connected to the shore due to the build-up of silt.

Small-scale excavations were carried out in 2003 to both stabilize and sample eroding submerged deposits and to attempt to clarify the dating and structure of the site. Examination of the submerged exposed sections (trenches 1 and 2) suggested that the lower mound was constructed through the deposition of layers of alder timbers, laid horizontally and weighed down with comminuted plant material, brushwood and stones. Both exposed sections were located to the south-east of the upper island; one on the southern edge of the submerged promontory in 2.5m to 3.5m of water (trench 1) and the other on the flatter top of the submerged mound in 0.75m to 1m of water (trench 2).

Over 50 alder timbers were exposed and recorded in trench 1 (see fig 2). These timbers were arranged in horizontal layers, radially into the centre of the mound. Each layer of timbers was laid at approximately 30–60 degrees to the layer below; in a matrix of twigs and comminuted organic material containing hazel nuts and woodchips as well as many fire cracked stones (most likely used in cooking and dumped onto the site from occupation above). Trench 2 revealed a very similar structure in existence on the top of the submerged mound. Over 30 alder timbers were uncovered within a matrix of comminuted plant matter as well as broken-down twigs, woodchips and fire cracked stones. All of these timbers were laid in parallel, horizontal layers, with each layer laid at approximately 30–60 degrees (in plan) to the layer above and below (see fig 3). Several of the large timbers had mortise joints cut through them, though there was no evidence of any tenon or other structural purpose of these joints (similar to the joints in two timbers recently uncovered at Oakbank crannog in Loch Tay, Perthshire; Dixon this volume). It is possible, given the rough nature of the mortise joints, which are rather weak and lack any tenon or obvious structural purpose in their current position, that these holes were cut into the ends of timbers simply for the purpose of dragging them on to the site. Rather surprisingly, undisturbed natural loch bed marl was encountered in trench 2 at a depth of just 1.1m from the top of the trench, suggesting that the artificial structure may have capped an existing natural feature. Anthropogenic deposits on the southern and eastern margins of the site, however, are considerably thicker, occurring at depths down to 3.5m (as seen in trench 1), suggesting that the sides of the site may have been built up into the water. Whatever the case, at 46m across, the submerged artificial structure is quite substantial.

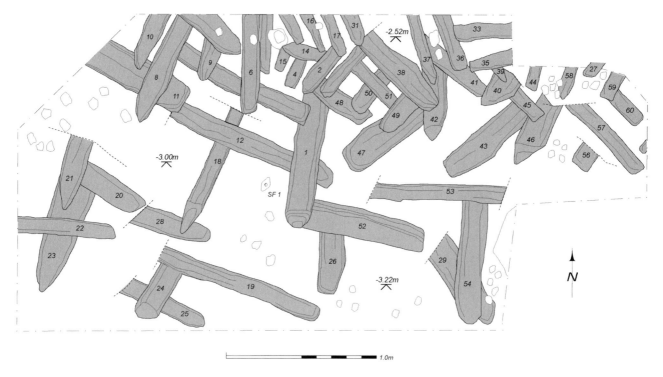

FIGURE 2
Loch Arthur crannog, trench 1 plan.

The deposits revealed in the exposed sections suggest that only foundational constructional material is present underwater. No artefacts or *in situ* occupational material were uncovered in trenches 1 or 2. Consequently, it seems likely, from the evidence of trench 2, that if any occupational deposits existed on top of the submerged mound they have since been eroded away, leaving only foundation deposits. There were no vertical piles in the sections examined and such piles could only be traced off-site, in the surrounding silts (particularly along the northern margins). Thus the possibility of external structures such as breakwaters, boat nausts or a walkway exists, but as far as the main structure of the mound is concerned it must be considered to be of *packwerk* construction.

A small 2m by 1m trench (trench 3) was opened on the dry area of the crannog, to determine the relationship between the upper dry island and the submerged mound. The structure of the island was seen to be entirely artificial. Beneath a 0.8m thick layer of rounded boulders, horizontal alder timbers were encountered which had been laid in horizontal lines resembling the foundations for a floor. These two contexts were separated from each other by a thin (0.12–0.14m) grey layer of re-deposited loch silts,

indicating a period of inundation and abandonment between the two constructional phases. Significantly, a sherd of medieval green glazed pottery was recovered, sitting within the matrix of the upper boulder layer. The sherd provided the first definitive evidence for medieval activity on the site. On comparison with other Galloway wares, the fabric, form and well-fired nature of the sherd suggested a fifteenth-century AD date (Laing pers comm).

Timber samples were taken for radiocarbon dating, from contexts in all three trenches, to provide the basis for a secure chronological framework for the site. These are presented in table 1, alongside the two dates obtained in 1989.

The dates taken at various levels throughout the submerged mound suggest that it was probably constructed in one event, sometime between 400 and 200 BC; the limitations of the radiocarbon calibration curve for this period prevent closer dating. The date of 2240 ± 35 BP (GU-12173) obtained from a timber located at the base of trench 1 (Timber 19, fig 2) is identical to that obtained from the top of the timber mound, sampled in trench 3, which provided a date of 2215 ± 35 BP (GU-12175). Significantly, the date from trench 3 came from a constructional layer of alder timbers which underlay the upper stone

TABLE 1
Radiocarbon dates from Loch Arthur (GU-2643 and GU-2644 from the 1989 work; GU-12173, GU-12174 and GU-12175 from the current South-West Crannog Survey work).

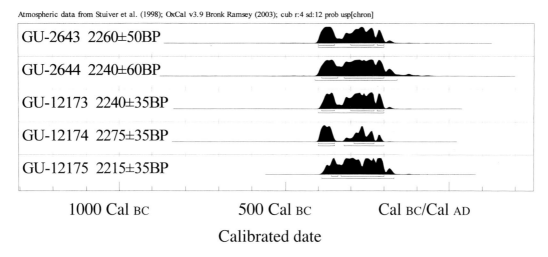

Atmospheric data from Stuiver et al. (1998); OxCal v3.9 Bronk Ramsey (2003); cub r:4 sd:12 prob usp[chron]

GU-2643 2260±50BP

GU-2644 2240±60BP

GU-12173 2240±35BP

GU-12174 2275±35BP

GU-12175 2215±35BP

1000 Cal BC   500 Cal BC   Cal BC/Cal AD

Calibrated date

Sample code	Trench	Timber no.	Species	Age BP	±	Cal range 2σ
GU-2643	N/A	N/A	*Betula* sp.	2260	50	400–200 BC
GU-2644	N/A	N/A	*Betula* sp.	2240	60	410–160 BC
GU-12173	1	19	*Alnus glutinosa*	2240	35	400–200 BC
GU-12174	2	201	*Alnus glutinosa*	2275	35	400–200 BC
GU-12175	3	*c* 3003	*Alnus glutinosa*	2215	35	390–170 BC

mound, and was separated from it by a deposit of grey, inorganic loch silts. The medieval green glazed sherd, recovered from within the boulder matrix of the upper stone mound, suggests that it was built sometime in or after the fifteenth century AD, on a pre-existing artificial mound that was built in one event during the pre-Roman Iron Age, while the silt layer that separates the two contexts is concurrent with a period of abandonment in between these two phases of use. The dates recovered in 1989 come from a birch pile located during the 2003 survey, just off the northern margins of the site, and may indicate that there was an external pile driven element to the Iron Age use of the site.

EDERLINE BOATHOUSE CRANNOG, LOCH AWE, ARGYLL AND BUTE

The crannog at Ederline Boathouse in Loch Awe was examined by McArdle and McArdle (1973) as part of the first complete underwater crannog survey of any loch in Scotland, and was further described by Morrison (1982). The site itself is located at the south-western end of Loch Awe and is visible above water in the summer months, as a low grass-covered stony mound, approximately 4m in diameter. This dry area represents only a small fraction of the true extent of the site, as the main mound is submerged and measures 37m by 27m and rises over 2.5m from base to top. Ederline is unusual in that it is one of a minority of crannogs which utilize a natural bedrock outcrop as a foundation; at Ederline this consists of an elongated reef running south-west to north-east for approximately 80m in 3m to 4m of water. The crannog appears as a massive boulder mound overlying this reef at its south-western end (see fig 4).

There are numerous structural timbers (horizontals and piles) protruding from the site, principally on the surface of the crannog, in less than 1m of water. At the time of the survey by McArdle

FIGURE 3
Loch Arthur crannog, trench 2 plan.

and McArdle in 1972, the water level of Loch Awe was extremely low due to a dry summer, allowing the inspection of the flat surface of the site above water. A large number of oak structural timbers were recorded at this time, as well as two saddle querns and a rotary quern, all of which were left *in situ* on the site (McArdle & McArdle 1973, 9). In the early 1980s, the site was revisited and one of the oak vertical piles from the surface of the site was sampled and provided a radiocarbon determination of 370 BC ± 45 (UB-2415), calibrating at 400–190 BC (Morrison 1982; Dixon pers comm).

In 2004, a two-week trial underwater excavation was carried out and a trench measuring 3m by 5m was opened on the northern side of the site, in approximately 3m of water, and excavated to loch bed level (Cavers & Henderson 2005). The aim of the work was, firstly, to assess whether pristine organic

layers existed underneath the boulder capping of the site which could form the focus for a more extensive excavation project, and, secondly, to contribute stratified data to the discussion of the construction and taphonomy of crannog sites in Scotland. The trial trench was positioned at the side of the site to provide a section through the deposits and to attempt to locate the basal remains of the crannog structure. Timbers located at the base of crannog mounds are usually selected for radiocarbon dating as it is assumed they must relate to the earliest phases of occupation at the site.

Organic deposits were encountered underneath a layer of boulder capping (ranging from 0.5m to 1m in thickness) and were typical of those recorded on other crannog excavations carried out underwater (eg at Oakbank crannog, Dixon 1981; and at Loch Arthur above), consisting of moderately compacted, extremely well-preserved, ecofactual material including bracken, hazelnuts, twigs and worked timbers. Approximately 0.4m of organic deposit was excavated (see fig 5). The uppermost layer, context 103, contained large amounts of charcoal and animal bone alongside numerous pieces of worked wood, ranging from large timbers to worked points and woodchips. Several timbers were superficially charred and much of the bone was burnt, clearly having been close to fire prior to their deposition on the site. Two sherds of E ware pottery – a continental ware of western French origin, found

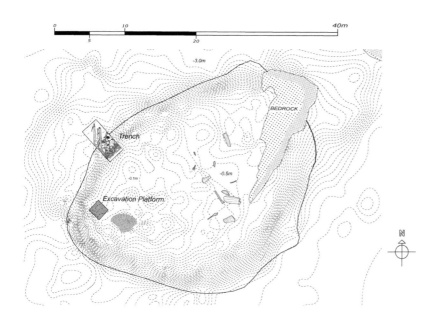

FIGURE 4
2005 survey of Ederline crannog, Loch Awe, Argyll and Bute. Contours at 0.1m increments.

on coastal sites of late sixth to early seventh century AD date in western Britain (Thomas 1990) – were also recovered from this deposit (SF 1 on section; Campbell 2005). The second organic deposit, 105 – separated from the upper layer by a layer of white grey inorganic silt (context 104) – was very similar to context 103, consisting of the same organic matrix and artefactual material (worked timbers, bone, charcoal and woodchips).

The timbers encountered in the trench were predominantly alder and were all horizontals; no piles were encountered within the excavated area (see fig 6). With the exception of two large horizontals, which may represent collapsed palisade revetment posts (timbers 10 and 12), the extent of each of

these timbers was established during the excavation, and it was clear that these were not *in situ* structural timbers. Timber 9 was the only major timber that displayed any evidence of having been structural as it featured a circular mortise-hole, approximately 0.15m in diameter, cut through the timber at one end (Cavers & Henderson 2005, figs 8 and 9). Timber 9 was clearly not *in situ*, however, as it lay at the very base of the organic deposits, and, more importantly, was broken at the opposite end to the mortise. This break had clearly occurred in antiquity, since the wood had eroded and discoloured around the broken area. Although a lot of burnt material (bone, charcoal and timber) was recovered from the trench, no discrete area of burning was identified. None of the burnt timbers were demonstrably structural, so that the burnt material most likely represents dumped fire-waste.

The deposits excavated in 2004 raise a number of questions about the taphonomy of the surviving mound. The Early Iron Age date obtained from an oak timber protruding from the surface of the mound and the Early Historic sherds recovered from basal material sealed by the boulder capping on the side of the site suggests at first glance an inverted stratigraphy. The presence of broken, disarticulated structural timbers and re-deposited hearth material, ceramics and bone in the deposits on the side of the site suggest they are most likely discard from activity taking place on the upper parts of the site or equally may have been eroded from the top of the site and re-deposited. The same processes of erosion most likely exposed the earlier timber sampled on the top of the mound. It remains a possibility that any Early Historic occupation has been completely eroded from the surface of the mound exposing earlier occupation and now only survives along the basal margins of the site in the form of deliberate discard relating to the later occupation of the site or material deposited naturally as part of the erosive process. What the evidence from Ederline clearly demonstrates is that deposits taken from the basal layers of crannogs cannot be assumed to relate to the earliest activity on the site and in turn those surviving on the surface of the mound may not necessarily relate to its latest use.

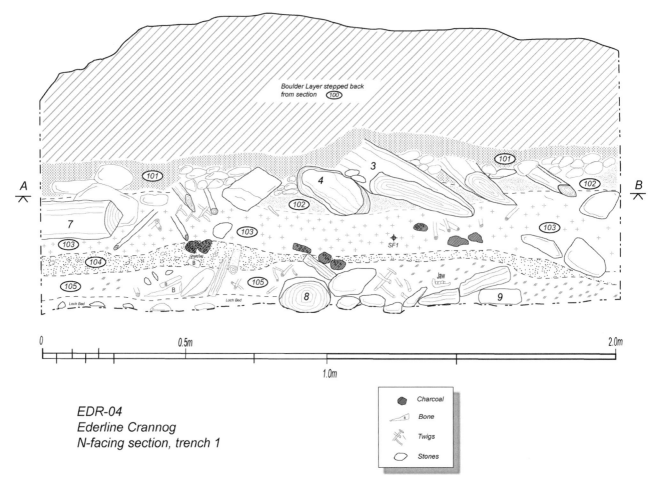

EDR-04
Ederline Crannog
N-facing section, trench 1

Charcoal
Bone
Twigs
Stones

FIGURE 5
Ederline crannog, north-facing section plan.

THE TEMPORALITY OF CRANNOGS

Both Loch Arthur and Ederline are *packwerk* mounds (at least in their final phases) that have been subject to multi-period occupation. The radiocarbon dates from Loch Arthur suggest that the main *packwerk* mound was constructed in one event, at some point during the fourth to third centuries BC. After a period of abandonment, represented by the deposition of natural loch silts, a boulder capping was placed on the original *packwerk* mound, sometime in or after the fifteenth century AD. An oak pile from Ederline provided a comparable fourth to third century BC date, while the deposits excavated in 2004 produced sealed deposits containing sherds dating to the late sixth or early seventh century AD. Whether or not occupation was continuous at Ederline will only be determined through further excavation but it is possible that an original

packwerk mound was re-used in much the same way as envisaged at Loch Arthur.

To date, no crannog that has been subject to any level of excavation has provided evidence of single phase occupation. In light of this, it is interesting to note that, while the vast majority of timbers sampled and submitted for radiocarbon dating have provided dates in the latter half of the first millennium BC and first half of the first millennium AD (Henderson 1998), the artefacts recovered from crannogs tend to date towards the second half of the first millennium AD and later. We are almost totally reliant on radiocarbon evidence for evidence of pre-Roman Iron Age occupation. It is possible that the re-use of crannog mounds was a widespread practice in Scotland and that this later activity could mask or even destroy evidence of earlier occupation on the upper parts of the mounds. The evidence from Milton Loch crannog – where timbers

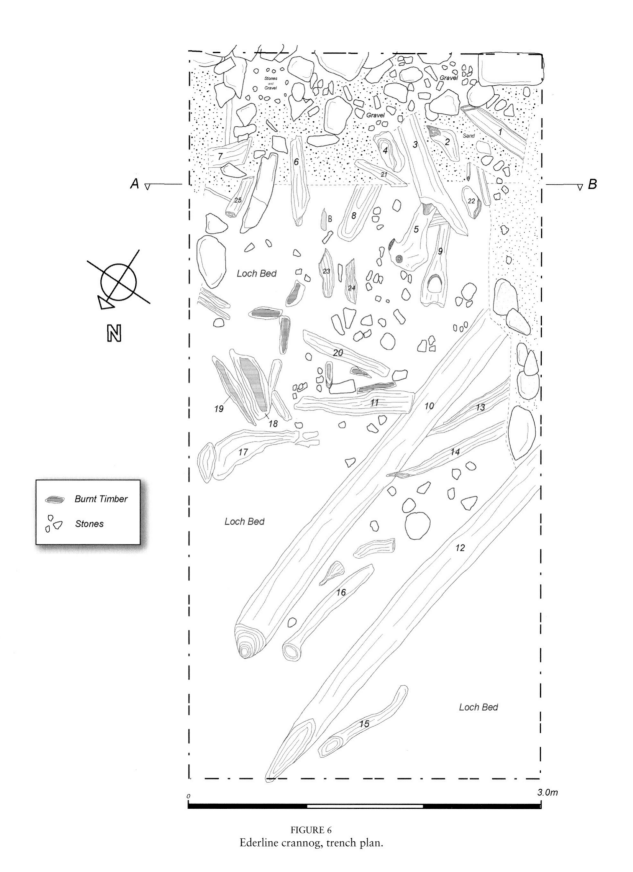

FIGURE 6
Ederline crannog, trench plan.

provided Early Iron Age dates while artefactual evidence suggested later occupation (see Cavers this volume) – is representative of the ways in which later occupation can mask earlier evidence. In some ways this is comparable with the recent recognition in Scottish broch studies that the latest, and hence surviving, occupation may not be chronologically indicative of construction and initial occupation (Harding 2005a, 169).

The long chronology view of crannogs has also created the impression that occupation at these sites was long-lived (Harding 2005b, 72). However, the dendrochronological dates from Buiston crannog in Ayrshire question this view and further reveal the complexity (and potential chronological resolution) of crannog occupation deposits (Crone 2000, 48–58). The radiocarbon determinations from Buiston span the first to the seventh centuries AD which, on a terrestrial site, would normally be interpreted as a long period of occupation. However, the dendrochronological dates reveal that the majority of the structural evidence on the site relates to a brief 80-year period of occupation in the sixth to seventh centuries AD, lasting just two generations (from AD 589 to 668). The earlier radiocarbon evidence relates to an earlier mound, built sometime in the first to second centuries AD which was abandoned and then levelled when the later occupation was established. This levelling activity also seems to have destroyed any surviving earlier *in situ* occupational deposits. Buiston has been the only crannog project which has, so far, made use of the accuracy of dendrochronological analysis. The resolution offered by such analysis allows the examination of one of the fundamental problems of archaeology, namely the dating of durations of occupation on sites (Barber & Crone 2000).

It is now clear that the validity of dating crannog sites from just one radiocarbon determination obtained from one part of the site – even if it is from recognized basal levels – can be questioned. Equally, research initiatives that claim to date the construction and form of sites from just one or two dates should be treated with caution. The detailed excavation of one site – as has been happening at Oakbank crannog since 1980 – can only ever offer a specific range of information, and given the ubiquity of crannogs in Scotland, not to mention the costs involved in total underwater excavation, it would, perhaps, be a more useful future research aim to trial trench a range of crannog sites and subject the recovered stratified structural and occupational deposits to radiocarbon and dendrochronological dating. The correlation and comparison of such

dates from stratified sequences would offer important insights into dating periods of use and re-use at crannogs. Lessons learned may then have a wider significance and affect the assumptions made in the dating of durations of occupation and re-use on terrestrial sites.

THE FUTURE OF CRANNOG RESEARCH

A more integrated approach to determining how crannog mounds were formed and what they actually represent is one way to move research forward but the significance of crannogs to Scottish archaeology and history remains much wider. Living out on the water was a major part of Scottish life, from prehistoric times up until the seventeenth century AD yet it is a practice about which we know remarkably little. If we are to improve this situation and integrate the study of crannogs into mainstream terrestrial archaeology, both in Scotland and internationally, then we need to focus on issues currently being debated in the wider archaeological arena.

A new agenda for the archaeological study of wetlands has recently been proposed by Robert Van de Noort and Aidan O'Sullivan (2006). They suggest, amongst other things, that wetland archaeology has the most to offer archaeology in debates on agency, material culture, chronology, landscape and social identity. The organic preservation seen on Scottish crannogs certainly means they should have a central role to play in debates on agency and in developing theories on the biographies and life-cycles of sites and objects. We have touched upon some of the contributions crannogs can make to chronological studies in dating the durations of occupation and identifying periods of use and re-use. As a common part of the Scottish landscape, the construction, use and re-use of crannogs was a major element in the ways that people inhabited, understood and imagined their surroundings. Investigating the re-use of crannog sites should constitute an important future research aim as we need to examine why the concept of living out in the water appears to have been of such social and cultural importance at various times in the Scottish past.

Crannogs have perhaps the biggest contribution to make in terms of reconstructing past social identities, because in addition to preserving detailed information about ancient landscapes (both structural and environmental) they preserve evidence of everyday activities carried out by various social groups through time. It is widely accepted that it was the daily, mundane activities and work tasks that fostered a sense of identity and belonging amongst communities. It could be argued that only crannog sites – given their ubiquity and wide dating horizon – offer the degree of preservation necessary to begin to fully recognize and reconstruct these identities through time. The occurrence of lake-dwellings in south-west Scotland and Argyll, for example, is of major importance in terms of perceptions of Scottish identity as they are a site type that is shared with Ireland. The influence of the Irish Dál Riada is crucial in perceptions of the formation of Scottish kingship and therefore, ultimately, in terms of perceptions of Scottish identity and the Scottish nation. Crannogs offer the closest known parallels to Irish settlement forms in Scotland but this link has never been fully investigated. In the south-west, the preponderance of Iron Age dates would appear to predate the Early Historic Irish forms, but in Argyll there is radiocarbon and artefactual evidence to suggest that crannogs may form part of the long-searched-for evidence for domestic Dál Riadic sites. Whatever the case, the investigation of lake-dwellings in both of these areas will have much to reveal about the formation of local indigenous identities in the Iron Age and Early Historic period and on the scale and impact of Irish influences at these key stages in the development of Scotland.

Ultimately, more problem-oriented research on crannogs is needed and, while a future research aim must remain the recovery of stratified sequences of crannog deposits, this data must be used to begin to address some of the wider archaeological issues highlighted above. Only when people working on crannogs have demonstrated their wider importance can we expect other researchers to integrate these iconic sites into their own period-based and wider archaeological narratives.

REFERENCES

Barber, J W & Crone, B A 2000 'The duration of structures, settlements and sites: some evidence from Scotland', in Raftery, B & Hickey, J (eds) *Recent Developments in Wetland Research*. University Monographs, 69–86. Dublin.

Campbell, E 2005 'Pottery', in Cavers, M G & Henderson, J C, 292–3.

Cavers, M G & Henderson, J C 2005, 'Underwater excavation at Ederline Crannog, Loch Awe, Argyll, Scotland', *International Journal of Nautical Archaeology* 34.2, 282–98.

Crone, B A 2000 *The History of a Scottish Lowland Crannog: Excavations at Buiston, Ayrshire 1989–90*. STAR Monograph 4. Edinburgh.

Crone, B A, Henderson, J C & Sands, R J S 2001 'Scottish crannogs: construction, conflation and collapse: problems of interpretation', in Raftery, B & Hickey, J (eds) *Recent Developments in Wetland Research*. University Monographs, 55–67. Dublin.

Dixon, T N D 1981 'Preliminary excavation of Oakbank Crannog, Loch Tay: interim report', *International Journal of Nautical Archaeology* 10.1, 15–22.

Gillespie, J E 1874 'Notice of a canoe found in Loch Lotus, Parish of New Abbey, Kirkcudbrightshire', *Proc Soc Antiq Scot* 11, 21–3.

Harding, D W 2005a 'The Iron Age in Atlantic Scotland and the Western Seaways', in Gillies, W & Harding, D W (eds) *Celtic Connections Volume Two: Archaeology Numismatics and Historical Linguistics*. University of Edinburgh Archaeological Monograph Series No 2, 166–80.

Harding, D W 2005b *The Iron Age in Northern Britain: Celts and Romans, Natives and Invaders*.

Henderson, J C 1998 'Islets through time: the definition, dating and distribution of Scottish crannogs', *Oxford Journal of Archaeology* 17, 227–44.

Henderson, J C 2004 'The Scottish Wetland Archaeology Programme: Assessing and Monitoring the Resource', *Journal of Wetland Archaeology* 4, 169–82.

Henderson, J C, Crone B A & Cavers, M G 2003 'A condition survey of selected crannogs in south-west Scotland', *Transactions of the Dumfries and Galloway Natural History and Antiquarian Society* 77, 79–102.

McArdle, C M and McArdle, T D 1973 'The Loch Awe Crannog Survey', *The Kist* 5, 2–12.

Menotti, F (ed) 2004 *Living on the Lake in Prehistoric Europe*.

Morrison, I 1982 'The crannog off Ederline, Loch Awe, Argyll', *International Journal of Nautical Archaeology* 10.4, 347–9.

Morrison, I 1985 *Landscape with Lake Dwellings*. Edinburgh.

Thomas, C 1990 '"*Gallici Nautae de Galliarum Provincis*": a sixth/seventh-century trade with Gaul, reconsidered', *Medieval Archaeology*, 34, 1–25.

Van de Noort, R & O'Sullivan, A 2006 *Rethinking Wetland Archaeology*. London.

Williams, J 1971 'A crannog at Loch Arthur, New Abbey', *Transactions of the Dumfries and Galloway Natural History and Antiquarian Society* 48, 121–4.

The complexity of crannog taphonomy: old and new evidence

GRAEME CAVERS

INTRODUCTION

One of the biggest problems facing crannog studies, for all the potential offered by organic preservation, is that it has never been absolutely clear what an occupied crannog actually looked like, or how one might have been built. Explanatory models of site construction, function and taphonomy have been based on a very small number of excavated examples, few of which have produced good evidence for superstructures, and while the traditionally cited mode of construction – a palisade revetted mound – was undoubtedly how some crannogs were built, particularly in the Early Historic period, the archaeology of crannog sites often testifies to much more complex histories of use, abandonment and reoccupation. Issues of construction and taphonomy have been reviewed by Crone *et al* (2001) who questioned the validity of interpretations of crannogs without a full understanding of taphonomy (2001, 55) and rightly stressed that different crannogs were likely to have been built in different ways. Results from recent fieldwork, however, are enhancing the picture of the variability of crannog construction techniques and contributing to a better understanding of crannogs as archaeological sites. It is becoming clear, through continued survey and excavation, that crannogs are highly diverse and complex structures, and furthermore, that this complexity is as likely to derive from changes through time and from regionality as from diversity within chronological and regional categories.

The importance of understanding crannog taphonomy is self-evident: the majority of our data for crannogs come from single dating samples and isolated finds. It is argued here that, without a proper understanding of the longevity and complexity of individual crannog sites, it can be easy to misconstrue the evidence available for these sites.

THE COMPLEXITY OF *PACKWERK* CRANNOGS

In many ways, the *packwerk* crannog is to be thought of as the archetypal lake settlement structure of the British Isles. It is probable that the majority of 'crannog' sites, as they are generally recorded, were either built in this way, or became *packwerk* mounds at some point in their history, and, while there is evidence for other structural types, it seems that *packwerk* construction can explain much of the evidence for crannog mounds as they survive today. The *packwerk* construction concept is simple: organic materials, such as brushwood, peat and turf, is piled into shallow water, weighed down with stones and held in place with vertically driven piles, through and surrounding the mound. The superstructure of the site is then built on top of the resulting mound (see Munro 1882, 1894a, 1894b).

The majority of evidence from excavated crannogs apparently supports the model of construction in this manner. The important question here, however, is whether the majority of crannogs were indeed built this way, or whether the evidence from excavated crannogs has been interpreted as representing *packwerk* construction, since this was how crannogs were 'known' to have been constructed. It has even been argued, in the past, for the Irish evidence that structures other than those of *packwerk* construction, revetted with a timber palisade, should not be thought of as 'true' crannógs (Lynn 1983, 50–1). Of course, the fact that there are closely related islet structures that were not constructed in this way argues against this viewpoint, but more importantly we should be wary of laying the path for future difficulties by establishing criteria for what does and does not constitute a 'true' crannog. Perhaps of most importance, however, is the strong possibility that some sites that have been assumed to be *packwerk* constructions in fact represent accumulations of building and rebuilding over considerable periods of time. It is possible that archaeologists have tended to assume that crannogs were built in a *packwerk* style, since this neatly explains the 'creation of an artificial island', when the truth may have involved a much more complex history of construction and taphonomy. Failing to recognize the considerable lifespans that these sites are now known to have

243

had may have further compounded this problem. Furthermore, there has been a tendency to interpret archaeobotanical and other environmental evidence in terms of this accepted taphonomic model, rather than vice versa, and there is, as yet, no developed methodology for investigating deposition processes on crannogs. For instance, it is often very difficult to distinguish between accumulated deposits of organic material resulting from occupation, which compress and degrade slowly in semi-waterlogged conditions of a drained crannog, and material which was deliberately deposited as peat for foundations (Crone *et al* 2001).

That *packwerk* crannogs are typically long-lived and complex structures is evident from the excavation reports and artefactual assemblages from many of the crannogs investigated by antiquarian and modern investigations. The site often taken as the archetypal *packwerk* crannog, at Buiston in Ayrshire (Crone 2000), was a multiphase site with two main identifiable phases – in the Roman Iron Age (RIA) and Early Historic period – separated by a period of abandonment evidenced by a sterile lake sediment layer. Very little in the way of artefactual evidence for the RIA phase was recovered during the excavation at Buiston, and the abandonment phase demonstrates not only how a substantial prehistoric site may underlie an apparently Early Historic crannog, but also that any artefactual or structural evidence of occupation on that pre-existing site may be very easily eroded away without trace in the interim period between abandonment and reoccupation. The secondary phase of occupation, commencing in the mid-sixth century AD, directly overlay the RIA occupation, with the builders consolidating the mound with brushwood and cut turf levelling deposits and retaining the mound with a replacement palisade. In the early seventh century AD the site was consolidated by the construction of a massive palisaded walkway around the perimeter of the site. Slumping of the mound was a continual problem, and may have destroyed the superstructures on the crannog on more than one occasion (Crone 2000, 26–8). When such catastrophic slumping occurred on the site, rebuilding took place on top of the previous levels, with the builders often making use of the structural remains of earlier buildings as consolidation material. Buiston, then, with seemingly unequivocal evidence for *packwerk* construction, was certainly a multiphase site, with numerous superimposed occupation layers.

The crannog excavated by Ritchie in Eaderloch, Loch Treig would also appear to be a typical example of a *packwerk* crannog. However, it seems clear from the excavation report that there were at least two phases of construction/occupation represented on the site. Ritchie himself was aware of this possibility, and noted that the appearance of the site as a stone mound was misleading, with the interior of the mound largely organic (Ritchie 1942, 20). The main structure of the crannog consisted of a rectilinear pine framework, above which was a layer of heavy stones, onto which small hut structures had been constructed (*ibid.*, 26); these upper stone layers were the context of the medieval finds from the site. However, the pine framework was built on top of a thick 'vegetable' deposit, containing large quantities of plant material and charcoal. There was also a second series of 'basal timbers', suggesting to Ritchie that there had been a primary structure on the site precursory to the later rectilinear pine framework (*ibid.*, 38–9). This earlier structure was much less regular than the upper levels, and although Ritchie envisaged a rectilinear lattice arrangement similar to the upper framework, the lower timbers are much less orderly, and Ritchie himself admitted that they were difficult to reconstruct (*ibid.*, 41). When considered in conjunction with the section through the excavated deposits, it seems very probable that there were numerous phases of construction, occupation and rebuilding on the site. Indeed, in the upper layers, probably the latest occupation on the site, there were several superimposed floors. It is unfortunate that the dating evidence for the stratigraphic layers at Eaderloch is so poor (the only datable artefacts are medieval, and come from the upper boulder levels), but on the basis of the structural evidence the repeated rebuilding of the site, possibly over an extended period of time, seems at least plausible.

Similarly the Lochend crannog at Coatbridge witnessed several phases of building, with at least two floor surfaces detected by excavation. The site consists of areas of both piling and *packwerk* structure, though within the mound of deposits the excavators were able to discern at least two phases of construction and occupation (Monteith & Robb 1937). At Milton Loch, dating for the crannog initially came from an enamelled bronze dress fastener, datable to approximately the second century AD, that came from the surface of the floor level excavated by Piggott (1953, 144–6). However, two radiocarbon determinations, one from a vertical pile and the other from the plough stilt recovered from beneath the floor (1953, 143), were both returned calibrating in the Early Iron Age (490 ± 100

BC (K-2027) and 400±100 BC (K-1394) respectively; Guido 1974, 54). The excavator's natural reaction to these radiocarbon dates was that the original interpretation of construction in the second century AD was mistaken, and that the bronze fastener represented a chance loss during use of the site 'as a suitable position from which to fish' (Guido 1974, 54), the true date of the site being the earlier horizon. However, it is important to note that neither of the radiocarbon dates were from floor timbers, and as such, could easily relate to an earlier occupation than the excavated occupation layer. The sampled vertical piles could relate to the primary construction but still have been standing and functioning in the retaining ring when the site was refurbished and reoccupied in the early first millennium AD. Indeed, both the retention ring and the walkway are on average three piles thick, suggesting that both were refurbished with replacement piles throughout the history of the site's use. Piggott's published section (1953, fig 8) clearly shows the floor layers separated from what may have been timbers of a precursory floor level close to the water-table (and so beyond the reach of the 1950s excavation). In this sense, then, there is no reason why the excavated floor level should not in fact relate to the later horizon, and simply represents the refurbishment of a pre-existing site.

CONTRASTING EVIDENCE FROM RECENT EXCAVATIONS: EDERLINE BOATHOUSE AND LOCH ARTHUR

Two sites recently investigated by the Underwater Archaeology Research Centre add to the impression of the complexity of crannog structures. A small scale excavation carried out at the crannog off Ederline Boathouse in Loch Awe yielded material that was not concurrent with a radiocarbon date obtained for a structural pile from the top of the site. The radiocarbon date, obtained by Ian Morrison in the late 1970s (Morrison 1982), was returned at 370±45 BC (UB–2415), calibrating at 400–190 BC and came from a vertical structural pile protruding from the surface of the stone mound. Excavation of the site close to the loch bed and in almost 3m of water, however, encountered redeposited midden material sealed by several tonnes of boulder capping; these deposits were given a terminus post quem in the late sixth/early seventh century AD by two sherds of E ware (Cavers & Henderson 2005). The stratigraphy of the site was therefore, apparently, inverted, with an early date from the surface of the

mound, but later dating for material recovered from the basal deposits.

This apparently inverted stratigraphy demonstrates the complexity of post-abandonment processes acting on crannog sites. The Early Historic deposits were sealed under a boulder layer comprising several hundreds of tonnes of stone and can only have been redeposited or buried after post-abandonment slumping and erosion of the crannog surface. The earlier Iron Age date for the oak timbers protruding from the surface of the crannog must have been exposed after the erosion of the later occupation levels, since it seems implausible that timbers almost a thousand years old could have functioned within the superstructure of the later crannog. The implications of this sequence are important to our interpretation of crannog archaeology more generally: it cannot, for example, be assumed that basal deposits on crannog mounds are likely to be the earliest, or that surface timbers are likely to relate to the latest occupation of the site.

The boulder layer raises its own important questions. This boulder capping at Ederline, like at Oakbank and other 'stone and timber' type crannogs, was over a metre thick and incorporated massive boulders, some of which would have presented great difficulties simply in transportation to the site. The function of these boulders – which are found on most Highland sites – has been the source of some debate in crannog studies. In the *packwerk* model of construction, it is assumed that the boulders constitute part of the make up of the mound, serving both as foundation material and as a means of weighing down the organic materials used in the construction. As the site erodes post-abandonment, the surrounding organics decay, leaving a residue of boulders that effectively caps the site and protects the underlying organic deposits (Crone 1988; Crone *et al* 2001, 61–2; Campbell & Crone 2005). This is one plausible explanation for the appearance of the boulder layer on many stone and timber sites, but it is not the only one. It is very possible, furthermore, that many stone/timber sites comprised substantial stone-built superstructures which have collapsed so completely that they are virtually impossible to detect through surface inspection. Examples of such sites, in better preserved form, have recently been recorded in Argyll and Dumfries and Galloway (Cavers 2005).

Excavations at Loch Arthur, as part of the South-West Crannog Survey, have provided information on the structure of another *packwerk* crannog in south-west Scotland. The crannog survives today as a tree-covered mound, approximately 25m in diameter above the surface, though forming a peninsula below the water with dimensions of *c* 40m by 30m. Three trenches were excavated on the crannog in 2003, two below the water level and one on the dry area of the site (Henderson & Cavers 2003 and in prep). The site was known to have witnessed at least two phases of occupation, with Iron Age dates obtained in the early 1990s from submerged vertical birch piles (Barber & Crone 1993, table 1), and medieval reoccupation represented by a small stone-footed building on top of the site (Williams 1971).

The two submerged trenches both encountered substantial *packwerk* remains, while excavation beneath the level of the medieval building on the dry area of the site encountered well-preserved horizontal timbers. Radiocarbon dating of timber samples from all of these trenches returned concurrent dates spanning the period 400–200 BC (Henderson & Cavers, in prep).

While we must always consider that the calibration ranges of radiocarbon dates in this period are large, it seems probable that much of the Loch Arthur crannog was constructed in one event; there is no obvious evidence, on the basis of the limited excavation, that the mound represents an accumulation of activity. The implications of seeing the Loch Arthur structure as a single construction are that the site must be considered a monumental structure, involving the construction of a massive artificial platform, which must imply similar demands of labour and resource control to even the most complex and ostentatious Iron Age constructions.

STONE-BUILT CRANNOGS AND STONE SUPERSTRUCTURES

One class of crannog site that may be widespread on the mainland of Scotland, but are seldom discussed, are those constructed entirely in stone. Henderson rightly considered that most apparently stone-mound crannogs turn out on excavation to comprise a substantial organic core (Henderson 1998, 237), but recent survey work has recorded sites that seem to have been entirely constructed in stone, or have very substantial stone-built superstructures. Loch Leathan crannog in mid-Argyll is one example. There is no obvious timber component to the mound, and the site seems to have been designed as a stone revetted island, with stone superstructures, including cellular buildings and harbour features built on top (Cavers 2005). Other sites in Argyll, including Loch Avich (*ibid.*) and the stone-built islets of the Inner Hebrides

(Holley 2000) also suggest that stone superstructures were common on many crannogs; Munro's description of Loch-a-Bhaillidh suggests a related site (Munro 1893, 208).

In some instances, it is possible that stone super-structures were built on islets that had organic *packwerk* foundations. At Rough Loch, Dumfries and Galloway, a substantial stone-walled roundhouse was found to be built upon a *packwerk* mound retained with vertical piling (Munro 1885, 114; Cavers 2005). A stone structure was also found to be resting on timber and brushwood, revetted by piling, in Loch a' Mhuillin, Oban (Blundell 1913, 288). Similarly, in Ashgrove Loch, a stone-walled crannog with a stone causeway was recorded, with the stone wall apparently constructed on a foundation of brushwood (Smith 1894, 57). Structures such as these must have been prone to subsidence, since the weight of the stone superstructure must have caused the foundations to compress and slump. This was certainly the case at Dun Bharabhat, Isle of Lewis, where stone structures collapsed into the loch due to the unstable foundations they were built on (Harding & Dixon 2000). As the organic substructure of stone-capped crannogs, such as Rough Loch and Ashgrove, decayed and eroded the stone superstructures would very easily have collapsed, and it is possible that in some of the more active Highland lochs where wave erosion is much more significant than in lowland lochs, stone construction could have been ruined to such an extent that it is no longer recognizable on some sites. Ruinous stone superstructures have certainly been recognized on organic *packwerk* crannogs in Ireland, as at Hackelty crannog, where a stone kerbed settlement was founded on a pile-revetted organic mound (Davies 1942, 22–3, and see esp his fig 3).

Loch Seil in Argyll contains a site that seems unparalleled by any other surveyed crannog. The site itself appears as a well-built rectangular stone revetted mound, approximately 10m by 8m and around 2.5m high. The site is in 2.5m of water, so that it is clear that the stone walling must have been built when the loch level was much lower than it is today. The loch bed around the site is littered with vertical piles and horizontal timbers, which perhaps supported superstructures surrounding the mound. Loch Seil, like Loch Coille-Bharr (which similarly makes use of stone revetting around its base), illustrates the fact that crannog structures may have frequently incorporated stone construction, which may only survive in favourable circumstances.

THE ARCHAEOLOGY OF *PACKWERK* CRANNOGS: DISCUSSION

It is clear, then, that while *packwerk* construction was certainly a widely used technique for creating a raised platform, in the majority of excavated examples there were multiple phases of building and rebuilding, so that to think of a crannog site as a single construction is, in most cases, incorrect: there has yet to be a crannog site investigated that was not likely to have been occupied and rebuilt over a considerable period of time. Even those crannog sites that have been formative in the stereotypical view of the definition of a crannog are now thought of as more complex than was originally recognized. At Lagore, Co Meath, Lynn has argued for more, and increasingly complex, occupation levels based on a reinterpretation of Hencken's excavations (1950). Lynn suggested that as a result of the need to repeatedly raise the level of the occupation surface above the water-table due to slumping and compaction (perhaps every five years or more), numerous occupation layers may become superimposed, giving the impression upon excavation of a single, complex occupation (Lynn 1986, 72). Later in this sequence, as more and more material is laid down on the site and the crannog structure stabilizes, the occupation level may need to be raised less frequently, so that there may be a natural bias towards the evidence for later periods of use (*ibid.*). Lynn was able to detect these processes of superimposition of crannog occupation layers at both Lagore and Ballinderry 1, while in Scotland, a similar process seems to have taken place through the Early Historic phases of Buiston.

The complexity of crannog construction and taphonomy can be illustrated by a schematic and hypothetical representation of the processes of deposition and erosion typical of lowland and highland *packwerk* crannogs. In the *packwerk* model typical of lowland sites (see fig 1, phase 1), the primary crannog structure is built in open water by dumping foundation materials onto the loch floor, and revetting the mound with piling and a perimeter palisade. After abandonment of the first phase (fig 1, phase 2), the primary superstructures are eroded away, while remains of the foundation deposits and structural piling are preserved to a stable level below the water level. When the site is reoccupied (fig 1, phase 3), the original mound is consolidated with new foundation material, which may incorporate elements of the structure of the original crannog, the islet is revetted with replacement piling and new superstructures are built. After the abandonment of this secondary structure (fig 1, phase 4), the mound is again eroded to below the water level, with the secondary phase material now indistinguishable from the primary structure. Hencken was troubled by this problem during his excavation of the Lagore and Ballinderry crannogs; at Ballinderry 2 the Early Christian palisade appeared to be stratigraphically below the Late Bronze Age stratum, since the tops of the piles had rotted away to a level below the layers they were driven through (Hencken 1942; Hencken 1950, 47). In our hypothetical model, as this process happens repeatedly with new consolidation material and new structure added to the site over decades or centuries (fig 1, phase x), *packwerk* sites become highly complex accumulations of multiple phases of occupation and rebuilding. Water level fall and erosion through desiccation, wave action and biological attack (Barber & Crone 1993; Crone *et al* 2001, 61) can further result in the destruction of surface deposits (fig 1, phase y), while debris relating to the history of the site is preserved beneath the water level. The result is an accumulation of archaeology that Morrison likened to a 'wet tel' (Morrison 1985, 93–4), though with the added complication that waterlogged preservation renders early construction indistinguishable from late.

'Stone and timber' crannogs may equally witness such complex sequences of occupation and reoccupation, with the added complication of the possibility of stone superstructures, as evidenced by numerous sites in Argyll. These stone structures may not only be used and reused in the same way that terrestrial roundhouses were repeatedly reoccupied, but evidence for construction and occupation, including midden material dumped into the water beside the site, may be preserved as part of the site. If a stone/timber *packwerk* crannog, such as Ederline Boathouse, was built using organic materials weighed down with stone, with superstructures built in stone in the local tradition on top of the mound, midden material and other debris may accumulate around the edges of the site during the course of occupation (fig 2, phase 1). The same sequences of abandonment and reoccupation as described above for *packwerk* crannogs may then occur, with the erosion of the mound and the slumping of boulders causing a residue of stones to cover the site (fig 2, phase 2). At this stage, early structural timbers may become exposed on the surface of the site, while later midden deposits are preserved beneath slumping boulders as the site conflates. Changes in water level may subsequently allow the site to be reoccupied (fig 2, phase 3), with stone superstructures related to medieval or later

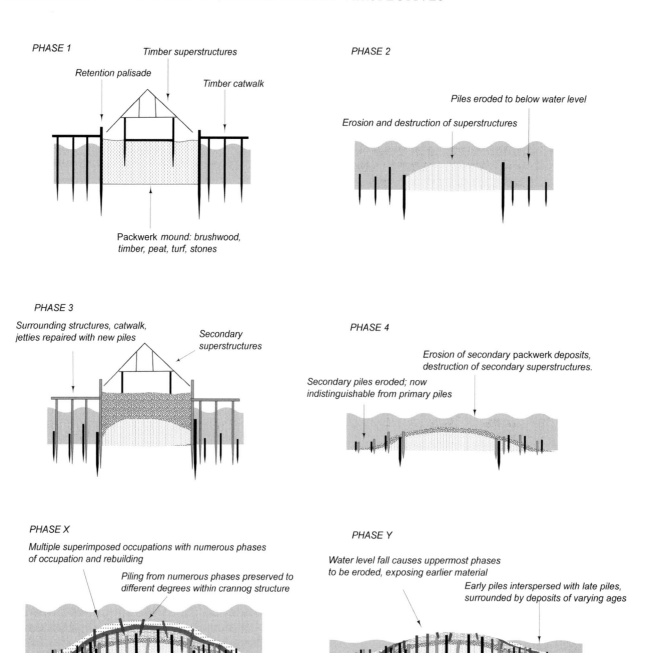

FIGURE 1

Complex taphonomy of a *packwerk* crannog. Multiple phases of use and re-use interspersed by erosive periods of abandonment combine to create a complex accumulation of activity. This model fits the evidence from the excavations at Milton Loch and Buiston.

settlement commonly found on Highland crannogs. This scenario would explain why late deposits were encountered in the trench excavated at Ederline, while an early date was obtained for a timber from the surface of the site and would also accord well with evidence from survey work in Argyll.

IMPLICATIONS FOR DATING

Understanding crannog sites as such complex accumulations of activity has clear implications for the way these structures are dated. As pointed out above, most crannogs yield evidence of a long occupation

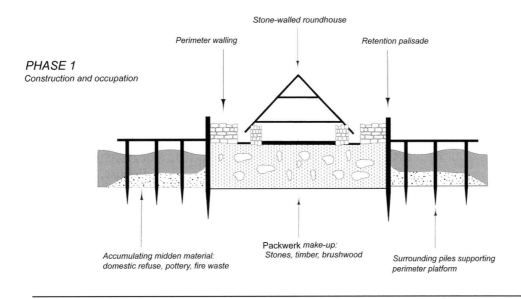

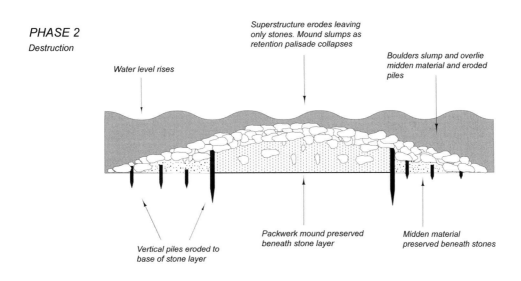

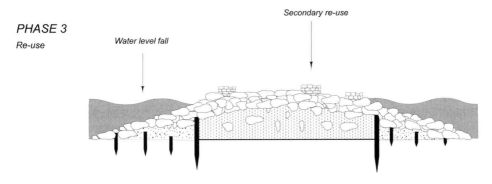

FIGURE 2

Model of complex taphonomy of a Highland 'stone and timber' crannog. Occupation levels and midden material are deposited beside the crannog and overlain by boulders as the structure erodes, collapses and slumps. Putative stone superstructures may have contributed to the boulder debris as their foundations collapsed. Secondary structures may be built on the crannog during periods of lower loch levels. This model fits the evidence from Ederline Boathouse and other Argyll crannogs.

249

sequence, often incorporating several phases of use, abandonment and re-use. Most obviously, radiocarbon dates must be viewed with caution, since they date only one phase of activity on the site, and without excavation it is difficult to be confident that the sample even relates to a major period of occupation. Crone *et al* suggested that '... the deposits of a *packwerk* structure will incorporate a large quantity of material that need have nothing to do with the use of the building and will almost certainly predate its construction' (2001, 57). While this may be true of the theoretical model of a *packwerk* crannog, it is clear that in most instances the crannog structure comprises a highly complex accumulation of construction and occupation deposits, and it cannot be assumed that what appear to be foundation deposits do not relate to occupation at the site. At Loch Arthur and Whitefield Loch, in Dumfries and Galloway, samples of the organic matrices of the sites were taken from eroding deposits beneath the water level, and were found to contain large quantities of palaeoenvironmental evidence for the domestic occupation of both sites, including cereal processing and animal excreta indicating livestock kept on the crannogs.

With these models for crannog construction and taphonomy we may contextualize the dates obtained for the crannogs recently surveyed in Argyll (table 1; Cavers 2005). At Loch Leathan, the Late Bronze Age date obtained came from a vertical pile in the loch bed adjacent to the crannog mound. The date indicates that construction began at the site in the Late Bronze Age, but does not reliably date the construction of the stone crannog mound itself. Conversely, the LBA date from Loch Avich, sampled from a vertical pile protruding from the top of the crannog mound, would indicate that the mound was constructed – or had accumulated – by the sixth century BC. Like Loch Leathan, the date from a structural pile in the loch bed at Loch Seil does not date the construction of the crannog mound, since the pile was not stratigraphically related to the stone structure. All this date can tell us is that there was building being carried out at the Loch Seil site in the Early Historic period. Interestingly, the date for the Loch Eck site, which came from an off-cut of wood extracted from the very base of the mound – from a context comparable to the deposits excavated at Ederline – is relatively late, in the medieval centuries. When compared to the late deposits from the Ederline Boathouse site and interpreted in terms of the model described in fig 2, we can contemplate that the Loch Eck date may relate to a late phase of activity, and, as such, the date of the original construction of the crannog may be considered unknown.

Considering the complexity of crannog site formation processes and the complications that they can introduce into interpreting the archaeology of crannogs, it is somewhat ironic that the one submerged *packwerk* site for which there are numerous dates from various parts of the mound – at Loch Arthur – has concurrent dates from all five samples. It is clear, then, that the *packwerk* model is valid, and some crannogs were apparently conceived and built as massive mounds of material in water. In

TABLE 1

Radiocarbon dates for selected crannogs surveyed in Argyll, with calibrated ranges at 2σ and description of the sample provenance.

Site	Lab code	Age BP	±	Cal 2σ	Sample description
Loch Avich	GU-11920	2560	50	830–510 BC	Vertical pile protruding from surface of crannog mound, below water level
Loch Leathan	GU-11921	2480	50	790–410 BC	Vertical oak pile protruding from loch bed silts beside crannog mound
Dubh Loch	GU-11924	2030	50	170 BC–AD 80	Horizontal alder timber embedded on top of crannog mound
Loch Seil	GU-11922	1500	50	430–650 AD	Vertical timber protruding from loch bed silts beside crannog
Loch Eck	GU-11923	780	50	1150–1300 AD	Worked timber off-cut removed from basal deposits of crannog mound

thinking of crannogs as long-lived settlements with complex structural histories, it is important not to lose sight of the fact that they were also monumental constructions, requiring well-organized labour and access to managed raw materials, including timber and stone.

CONCLUSION

The available evidence for crannogs points to the interpretation that most sites were long-lived settlements, often occupied repeatedly over the course of several centuries, and it is important to be aware of the taphonomic issues that may affect the type of information retrieved from crannogs during pre-excavation sampling. Wetland settlements are often thought of as archaeological 'snapshots', frozen in time and representative of a single settlement type at one chronological horizon, but the evidence from crannogs demonstrates that wetland preservation can also be misleading in the way that very long construction sequences can be compressed into what appears to be a single, very well preserved site (cf discussion by Barber & Crone 2001 and Cowley 2003). This view of Scottish prehistoric settlement, involving significant periods of abandonment and re-occupation, should not come as a surprise considering the patterns known from the terrestrial record; and the symbolic significance of the repeated occupation of dilapidated crannogs should not be overlooked, particularly when the practical considerations of rebuilding an abandoned site are taken into account (Harding 2000, 305).

This discussion has considered how crannogs should not be considered as static, unchanging sites and highlighted the importance of appreciating the provenance of dating evidence. Clear patterns are evident in the dating evidence for Scottish crannogs (eg Crone 1993; Henderson 1998), but in the absence of numerous excavated and securely provenanced dates, reliable conclusions may yet prove elusive. It is even possible that some of the anomalies in crannog dating patterns – such as the apparently complementary dating evidence for Scottish (predominantly Iron Age) and Irish (predominantly Early Historic) sites can be explained by the provenance of dating samples: dating evidence for Scottish sites comes in large part from ^{14}C samples collected from submerged areas of sites by divers, whereas the majority of Irish crannog dating evidence derives from excavations carried out on the surface of sites. However this problem may be resolved, the issue of the complexity of crannog taphonomy and strategies for interpreting samples from unexcavated sites should constitute a priority for future campaigns of crannog survey and excavation in Scotland.

REFERENCES

Barber, J W & Crone, B A 2001 'The duration of structures, settlements and sites: some evidence from Scotland', *in* Raftery, B & Hickey, J (eds) *Recent Developments in Wetland Research*, Seandálaíocht: Mon 2, Dept Archaeol, UCD and WARP Occ Paper 14. Dublin, 69–86.

Barber, J W & Crone, B A 1993 'Crannogs: a diminishing resource? A survey of the crannogs of South West Scotland and excavations at Buiston crannog', *Antiquity* 67, 520–33.

Blundell, F O 1913 'Further notes on the artificial islands in the Highland area', *Proc Soc Antiq Scot* 47, 257–302.

Cavers, M G & Henderson, J C 2005 'Underwater excavation at Ederline crannog, Loch Awe, Argyll, Scotland', *International Journal of Nautical Archaeology* 34.2, 278–94.

Cavers, M G 2005 *Crannogs and Later Prehistoric Settlement in Western Scotland*. Unpubl PhD thesis, University of Nottingham (UARC).

Cowley, D 2003 'Changing places: building life-spans and settlement continuity in northern Scotland' *in* Downes, J & Ritchie, A (eds) *Sea Change: Orkney and Northern Europe in the later Iron Age* AD 300–800. 75–81, Balgavies.

Crone, B A 1993 'Crannogs and Chronologies', *Proc Soc Antiq Scot* 123, 245–54.

Crone, B A 2000 *The History of a Scottish Lowland Crannog: Excavations at Buiston, Ayrshire, 1989–90.* STAR Monograph 4, Edinburgh.

Crone, B A, Henderson, J C, & Sands, R J S 2001 'Scottish crannogs: construction, conflation and collapse – problems of interpretation', *in* Raftery B & Hickey J (eds) *Recent Developments in Wetland Research*, 55–67. Dublin.

Crone, B A 1988 *Dendrochronology and the study of crannogs*. Unpubl PhD thesis, University of Sheffield.

Crone, B A & Campbell, E 2005 *A crannog of the first millennium* AD: *excavations by Jack Scott at Loch Glashan, Argyll, 1960.* Edinburgh.

Davies, O 1942 'Contributions to the study of crannogs in South Ulster', *Ulster Journal of Archaeology* 5, 14–30.

Guido, M 1974, 'A Scottish crannog re-dated', *Antiquity* 48, 54–6.

Harding, D W & Dixon, T N 2000 *Dun Bharabhat, Cnip: an Iron Age settlement in west Lewis.* Calanais Archaeological Research Monographs No 2, Edinburgh.

Harding, D W 2000a 'Crannogs and island duns: classification, dating and function', *Oxford Journal of Archaeology* 19, 3, 307–17.

Hencken, H O 1942 'Ballinderry crannog no 2', *Proceedings of the Royal Irish Academy* 47, C, 1–76.

Hencken, H O 1950 'Lagore crannog: an Irish royal residence of the seventh to tenth century AD', *Proceedings of the Royal Irish Academy* 53, C, 1–248.

Henderson, J C 1998 'Islets through time: the definition, dating and distribution of Scottish crannogs', *Oxford Journal of Archaeology* 17, 2, 227–44.

Henderson, J C & Cavers, M G 2003 *The South West Crannog Survey: Fieldwork and Survey, phase 3*. UARC unpubl report for Historic Scotland.

Holley, M 2000 *The Artificial Islets/Crannogs of the Central Inner Hebrides*. BAR 303, Oxford.

Lynn, C J 1983 'Some "early" ring forts and crannogs', *Journal of Irish Archaeology* 1, 47–58.

Lynn, C J 1986 'Lagore, Co Meath and Ballinderry No 1, Co Westmeath crannogs: some possible structural re-interpretations', *Journal of Irish Archaeology* 3, 69–74.

Monteith, J & Robb, J R 1937 'The crannog at Lochend, Coatbridge, with a report on the osseous remains', *Transactions of the Glasgow Archaeological Society* 9, 1, 26–43.

Morrison, I 1982b 'The crannog of Ederline, Loch Awe, Argyll', *International Journal of Nautical Archaeology* 10.4, 347–9.

Morrison, I 1985 *Landscape with Lake Dwellings*. Edinburgh.

Munro, R 1885 'The Lake Dwellings of Wigtonshire', *Archaeological and Historical Collections relating to Ayrshire and Galloway* 5, 74–124.

Munro, R 1893, 'Notice of crannogs or lake-dwellings recently discovered in Argyllshire', *Proc Soc Antiq Scot* 27, 205–22.

Munro, R 1894a 'The structural features of lake-dwellings, part I', *Journal of the Royal Society of Antiquaries of Ireland* 24, 104–14.

Munro, R 1894b 'The structural features of lake-dwellings, part II', *Journal of the Royal Society of Antiquaries of Ireland* 24, 210–21.

Piggott, C M 1953 'Milton Loch Crannog: a native house of the second century AD in Kirkcudbrightshire', *Proc Soc Antiq Scot* 87, 134–52.

Ritchie, J 1942 'The lake-dwelling or crannog at Eaderloch, Loch Treig: its traditions and its construction', *Proc Soc Antiq Scot* 76, 8–78.

Smith, J 1894 'On a stone crannog in Ashgrove Loch near Stevenston', *Archaeol Hist Collect Ayrshire Galloway* 7.

Crannog structure and dating in Perthshire
with particular reference to Loch Tay

NICHOLAS DIXON

INTRODUCTION

Crannogs from the last 2,500 years and earlier are found throughout Scotland. The appearance of the sites today is related to a number of processes. The remains of structural elements and collapsed debris from when they were inhabited, the final collapse and degradation to a level of relative equilibrium after abandonment and the long-term, mostly natural, processes that have affected them until the present time have all left evidence. The sites appear in three main forms today: drained sites; islands that project significantly above water; and totally submerged mounds. This paper examines the possibility of making useful statements about the construction of crannogs according to the visible remains, including evidence from excavations. It will also cover the substantial benefit of radiocarbon dating to the understanding of crannogs and their relationships to each other.

There are about 500 crannogs known in Scotland but there is no clear classification based on their form and function. Generally they are considered as stone mounds with, in many cases, timbers projecting from them. They have been insufficiently surveyed and examined for it to be possible to create groups that relate to each other. It has also not been possible to relate them chronologically as few dates were known. Recent survey work and the dating of a number of sites in Perthshire makes it possible to re-examine this situation to see if it is possible to create meaningful categories.

BACKGROUND

When excavations started in 1980 at the Early Iron Age site of Oakbank crannog, Loch Tay, there was nothing to indicate the form of the structure that had existed originally and how it might have developed throughout the period of its occupation. It was a mound of stones with some timbers and projecting

organic deposits. Observations of the structural elements of the site, as the excavation progressed, soon suggested that the crannog had started as a free-standing pile dwelling (clearly it did not end up as one since it appeared, like many other crannogs, as a large cairn of stones). None of the evidence from the excavations suggests that the site was not free-standing and recent work reinforces the hypothesis that it was.

The proposal that Oakbank crannog started as a free-standing structure does not accord with the ideas of other excavators whose work has led them to believe that many crannogs were constructed using a *packwerk* method, employing a solid core with the structural timbers added on (Barber & Crone 1993; Crone 2000; Crone *et al* 2001; Cavers & Henderson 2005). It is hard to understand how the elements of such a structure would be combined with a mixture of stones and timbers which do not easily lie together. One of the main questions at Oakbank was whether a free-standing structure would be a feasible method of construction and accordingly the full-sized crannog construction at the east end of Loch Tay was built to establish what was possible. That structure convinced the builders that the method was a viable proposition.

After examining many crannogs in lochs throughout the country, without sampling and excavation it is not possible to say what sort of structure existed when they were inhabited. During the period 2002–2005 the results from a number of projects gave a better understanding of a range of sites. Sampling for radiocarbon dates has brought about a closer examination of crannogs and the results of dating have put some of them in a clearer chronological context. For example, in Loch Tay, 15 of the 18 crannogs have now been dated and many of them can be related chronologically to Oakbank crannog. Radiocarbon dates have also been obtained for a number of other crannogs throughout Highland Perthshire (Dixon & Shelley 2006).

FIGURE 1
Oakbank crannog, upper floor (STUA).

OAKBANK CRANNOG

Oakbank crannog is very similar in form to many other sites that have been surveyed by the author and The Scottish Trust for Underwater Archaeology (STUA). Over 25 years underwater excavations have revealed the complexity of the structure and have led to the belief that it started life as a free-standing pile dwelling. Other sites that are similar in form may also have the same sort of construction. If they can also be shown to be contemporary with Oakbank that will add credence to a similarity of construction.

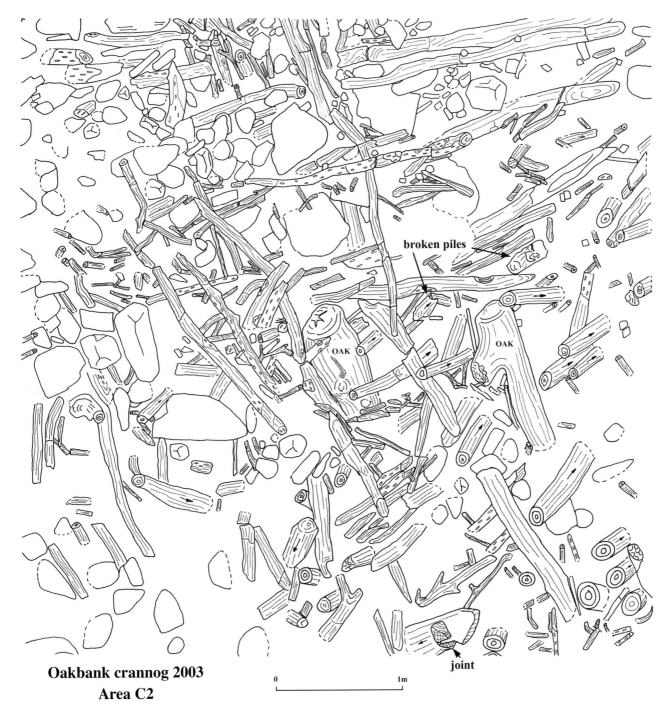

**Oakbank crannog 2003
Area C2**

0   1m

broken piles

OAK

OAK

joint

FIGURE 2
Oakbank crannog, sub-floor features showing broken piles, oaks and jointed timber (STUA).

Upper floor (fig 1)

One of the most obvious features at Oakbank was a floor discovered in 1981. The discovery was extended in 1991, and excavation took place beneath the floor in 2003. This was the latest remaining living space still preserved on the site and it had been covered with only one layer of large stones on top of the mound. What had appeared to be a substantial cairn of stones was in fact a large mound of organic material covered with a relatively thin layer of stones in the centre, although it was deeper around the periphery. If the floor had been the main floor throughout the life of the site then beneath it would be only material dumped in to bring it above water level, implying *packwerk* construction. If more coherent structural elements lay under the floor then it must overlie the remains of an earlier floor, or floors.

Upper floor foundation

Excavation showed that directly under the floor was what appeared to be foundation material made up of small branches that had been cut neatly and stripped of side branches. They were not merely brushwood but, if they were only for packing, it is not clear why the effort had been made to strip off side branches. In more than one place the sticks gave the impression of being parts of broken hurdles which would be useful packing in a sub-floor foundation and would explain the stripped branches. Cut ends on a number of branches indicated where the edge of the floor foundation had been.

There were also large stones among the foundation material and it appeared that they had been placed as packing to even-out irregularities in the underlying structure, caused by the collapse of preceding building components.

Collapsed sub-structure (fig 2)

During the excavations in 2003 and 2005, a number of features on the site that had not been observed before came to light, projecting through, and underlying, the sub-floor foundation. The tops of a number of broken piles were discovered, all leaning in basically the same direction, NW–SE, and the broken tops were still *in situ* where they had fallen and then been covered over by the later floor and sub-floor foundation. Clearly these had been structural uprights but they had no function in the house related to the floor above.

There is no obvious abandonment layer between the upper floor and the underlying collapsed structure and it seems likely that the people who built the upper floor were those who had experienced partial collapse

FIGURE 3
Oakbank crannog, joint in sub-floor timber, with timber from Hallstatt salt mines for comparison (STUA).

of their home and had taken steps to rebuild it. One of the reasons for this conclusion is that the broken piles under the floor were not eroded and the breaks were still relatively fresh with sharp broken edges.

Sub-floor features

Other structural elements also suggested that the underlying layers were part of an earlier occupation layer. Two large oak timbers were discovered that were obviously cut and shaped for a purpose, as yet unknown. They are substantial and have white fungus on them, suggesting that they were exposed in a damp place before being submerged, presumably in the collapse of that part of the structure. They have not yet been fully exposed and it is hoped that their function will become clear when they can be fully examined (fig 2).

Joints in large timbers (fig 3)

Less than 4m to the east of these oaks were two substantial timbers with joints near the end that suggested a complex purpose. The purpose of the joints is not clear but it is notable that there are a number of identical joints in timbers from the salt mines at Hallstatt, now in the museum in Vienna. A number of other structural elements in this area show that the layer beneath the sub-floor foundation was an occupation layer with well-formed features. The wide variety and number of structural timbers stratified beneath a recognizable floor layer suggests strongly that there was at least one other living floor, now collapsed down to the lower level. The fact that there are no large stones in conjunction with the lower evidence points to a free-standing structure, at least in this part of the crannog.

Possible sequence of construction at Oakbank Crannog

- Primary piles supporting the crannog are driven into the lochbed.
- Organic deposits build up under the crannog as people live there.
- Parts of the structure collapse onto the lochbed and debris collects there.
- Damage is repaired and new piles are driven into the lochbed which gives a firm foundation.
- More organic deposits build up, embedding earlier collapsed elements.

- More collapse takes place over time.
- Damage again repaired, but new piles are only driven into the organic deposit and are not well founded.
- Stones are placed around the less firm piles for support.
- Eventually too many stones make it impossible to drive new piles into the mound.
- The site is abandoned or the house is built in a different way, possibly of turf or stone.

RADIOCARBON DATING OF CRANNOGS IN LOCH TAY

Date related to form

All of the crannogs in Loch Tay have been surveyed twice, in 1979 and 2002, and have been examined less systematically on many other occasions. Usually there were insufficient resources to do more than observe them, but more recently a number of projects have allowed most of the sites to be placed in chronological context. The Ben Lawers Historic Landscape Project, run by the National Trust for Scotland, brought together a number of interested parties to look at different aspects of the Ben Lawers range. As part of the overall project, the STUA carried out a Shore and Underwater Survey from 2003 to 2005. In 2004, the Perthshire Crannog Survey was initiated, with funding support from Perth & Kinross Heritage Trust, to examine lochs in the region, and a number of radiocarbon dating projects have been carried out in conjunction with the Scottish Universities Environmental Research Centre at East Kilbride.

Some of the timber sampling projects also included sampling for environmental analysis, to try and broaden the range of information that could be acquired with minimal disturbance to the sites.

Loch Tay crannogs in the landscape

One of the main aims of the various projects was to establish whether it is possible to group sites that may be related by examining their shape, size and depth relative to water level, and comparing these features against the dates of the sites. Using the first three criteria, a simple table shows no obvious correlations between the crannogs in Loch Tay (table 1).

It is not possible to say how crannogs were constructed from observation alone. All of the crannogs in Loch Tay appear to be mounds of stone, like Oakbank crannog, but with a variety of shapes. The majority are oval or circular while Oakbank is an irregular shape but still made up of circular and oval overlapping features. The site in Kenmore Bay appears to have been deliberately or accidentally damaged so the original shape is not clear.

Comparing the sites by size does nothing to explain their construction except to say that the very large sites, such as Priory Island or Eilean Puttychan, may have started much smaller and may have been added to over time.

The depth of the crannogs in relation to the water level might seem to offer more clarity, at least in terms of a potential basic chronology. It might be concluded that the deepest sites are potentially the earliest, assuming that the loch level rose progressively over the time that the crannogs have been in existence. However, Priory Island, for example, the last inhabited artificial island in the loch, may have started its life earlier than Oakbank crannog in the Early Iron Age, but may have been

utilized and built-up over time so that it was also the latest site in the loch standing well above water level. There are other problems with this simplistic view of the temporal relationships of crannogs as related to water level (see below).

It may seem reasonable to assume that crannogs in close proximity to each other may be similar in other ways, such as date. For example, Oakbank crannog is about 100m away from the site off Fearnan Hotel. They are similar in shape, size and distance from shore and radiocarbon dates place both sites around the sixth century BC. However, the crannogs of Dall South and Dall North are similar in size and shape and are only about 25m apart. They are at significantly different depths, with Dall South about 1m higher than Dall North, and both are always submerged at all times of the year. It might be assumed that Dall North would have been abandoned by rising water level and Dall South would have taken its place. However, radiocarbon dates from both sites show that not to be the case, with Dall South apparently abandoned in the sixth

TABLE 1
Comparison of crannogs in Loch Tay by shape, size and depth (STUA).

Shape	Size	Depth
Circular 11	**Large 5 >40m**	**Islands above water 5**
Priory Island	Priory Island	Priory Island
Mary's Distaff	Eilean Breaban	Eilean Breaban
Tombreck	Eilean Puttychan	Eilean Puttychan
Milton Morenish	Acharn/Croftmartaig	Acharn/Croftmartaig
Morenish Boathouse	Spry Island	Spry Island
Morenish		
Eilean Puttychan	**Medium 10 >20m**	**Water level (summer) 4**
Firbush	Fearnan Hotel	Mary's Distaff
Dall North	Oakbank	Milton Morenish
Dall South	Mary's Distaff	Morenish Boathouse
Spry Island	Tombreck	Craggan
	Milton Morenish	
Oval/Elongated 5	Craggan	**Submerged always (just) 3**
Fearnan Hotel	Dall North	Fearnan Hotel
Eilean Breaban	Dall South	Morenish
Craggan	Old Manse	Dall South
Old Manse	Kenmore Bay	
Acharn/Croftmartaig		**Deepest**
	Small 3 <20m	Oakbank
Irregular 2	Morenish Boathouse	Tombreck
Oakbank	Morenish	Firbush
Kenmore Bay	Firbush	Dall North
		Old Manse

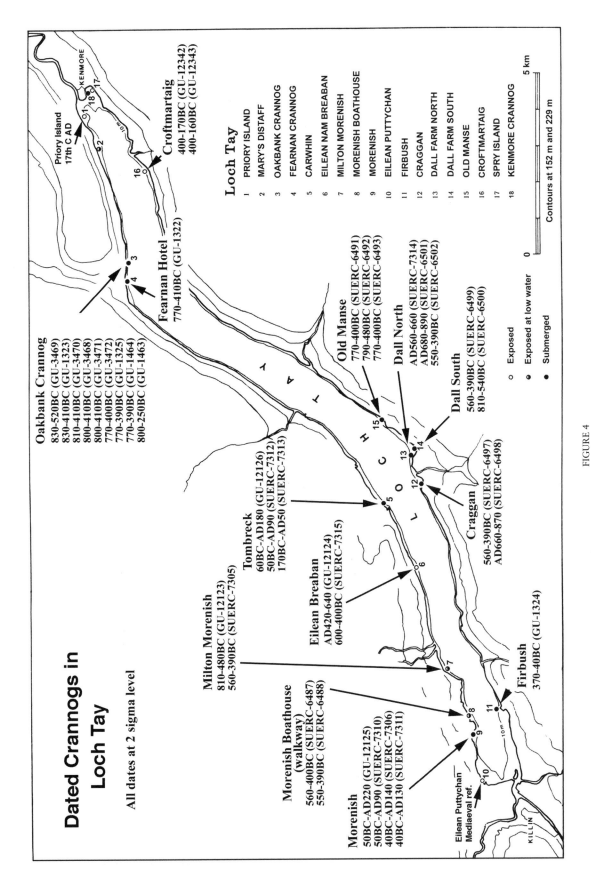

FIGURE 4
Map of Loch Tay and radiocarbon dated crannogs (STUA).

TABLE 2
Radiocarbon dates for Loch Tay crannogs (STUA).

Oakbank crannog

| Lab code | Sample mat | Yrs BP | $\delta^{13}C(‰)$ | Calibrated dates | |
				1 sigma	2 sigma
GU-1323	Wood, oak	2545±55	−25.9‰	800–550 BC	820–500 BC
GU-1325	Wood, oak	2410±60	−25.8‰	550–400 BC	670–390 BC
GU-1463	Wood	2360±60	−23.9‰		800–250 BC
GU-1464	Wood	2405±60	−24.5‰		770–390 BC
GU-3468	Wood	2490±50	−26.4‰		800–410 BC
GU-3469	Wood	2560±50	−28.8‰		830–520 BC
GU-3470	Wood	2510±50	−28.4‰		810–410 BC
GU-3471	Wood	2490±50	−28.3‰		800–410 BC
GU-3472	Wood	2450±50	−24.2‰		770–400 BC

Fearnan Hotel

| Lab code | Sample mat | Yrs BP | $\delta^{13}C(‰)$ | Calibrated dates | |
				1 sigma	2 sigma
GU-1322	Wood, oak	2475±55	−25.6‰	670–510 BC	770–410 BC

Tombreck crannog

| Lab code | Sample mat | Yrs BP | $\delta^{13}C(‰)$ | Calibrated dates | |
				1 sigma	2 sigma
GU-12126	Wood, alder	1950±50	−27.8‰	AD 0–90	60 BC–AD 180
SUERC-7312	Wood	1970±35	−26.1‰	AD 0–75	50 BC–AD 90
SUERC-7313	Wood	2040±35	−26.5‰	100 BC–AD 20	170 BC–AD 50

Eilean Breaban

| Lab code | Sample mat | Yrs BP | $\delta^{13}C(‰)$ | Calibrated dates | |
				1 sigma	2 sigma
GU-12124	Wood	1520±50	−26.0‰	AD 430–610	AD 420–640
SUERC-7315	Wood	2430±35	−24.0‰	540–410 BC	600–400 BC

Milton Morenish crannog

| Lab code | Sample mat | Yrs BP | $\delta^{13}C(‰)$ | Calibrated dates | |
				1 sigma	2 sigma
GU-12123	Wood, oak	2530±50	−24.1‰	690–540 BC	810–480 BC
SUERC-7305	Wood	2400±35	−24.4‰	520–400 BC	560–390 BC

Morenish Boathouse crannog (walkway)

| Lab code | Sample mat | Yrs BP | $\delta^{13}C(‰)$ | Calibrated dates | |
				1 sigma	2 sigma
SUERC-6487	Wood, oak	2425±35	−25.2‰	540–400 BC	560–400 BC
SUERC-6488	Wood, alder	2400±35	−27.3‰	520–400 BC	550–390 BC

Morenish crannog

| Lab code | Sample mat | Yrs BP | $\delta^{13}C(‰)$ | Calibrated dates | |
				1 sigma	2 sigma
GU-12125	Wood, alder	1940±50	−29.1‰	AD 0–130	50 BC–AD 220
SUERC-7310	Wood	1970±35	−24.0‰	AD 0–75	50 BC–AD 90
SUERC-7306	Wood	1930±35	−25.2‰	AD 45–90	40 BC–AD 140
SUERC-7311	Wood	1950±35	−25.7‰	AD 0–85	40 BC–AD 130

TABLE 2
Radiocarbon dates for Loch Tay crannogs (STUA) (*continued*).

Firbush crannog

Lab code	Sample mat	Yrs BP	δ¹³C(‰)	Calibrated dates	
				1 sigma	2 sigma
GU-1324	Wood, oak	2140±55	−26.6‰	210–90 BC	370–40 BC

Craggan crannog

Lab code	Sample mat	Yrs BP	δ¹³C(‰)	Calibrated dates	
				1 sigma	2 sigma
SUERC-6497	Wood	2420±35	−24.9‰	540–400 BC	560–390 BC
SUERC-6498	Wood	1270±35	−26.3‰	AD 690–780	AD 660–870

Dall North crannog

Lab code	Sample mat	Yrs BP	δ¹³C(‰)	Calibrated dates	
				1 sigma	2 sigma
SUERC-7314	Wood	1435±35	−26.0‰	AD 595–650	AD 560–660
SUERC-6501	Wood	1245±35	−26.0‰	AD 690–820	AD 680–890
SUERC-6502	Wood	2400±35	−25.5‰	520–400 BC	550–390 BC

Dall South crannog

Lab code	Sample mat	Yrs BP	δ¹³C(‰)	Calibrated dates	
				1 sigma	2 sigma
SUERC-6499	Wood	2420±35	−23.4‰	540–400 BC	560–390 BC
SUERC-6500	Wood	2560±35	−26.9‰	810–760 BC	810–540 BC

Old Manse crannog (SUERC-6491 & 6492 same sample)

Lab code	Sample mat	Yrs BP	δ¹³C(‰)	Calibrated dates	
				1 sigma	2 sigma
SUERC-6491	Wood	2460±35	−25.4‰	760–680 BC	770–400 BC
SUERC-6492	Wood	2485±35	−25.2‰	730–520 BC	790–480 BC
SUERC-6493	Wood	2465±35	−26.9‰	770–680 BC	770–400 BC

Croftmartaig crannog

Lab code	Sample mat	Yrs BP	δ¹³C(‰)	Calibrated dates	
				1 sigma	2 sigma
GU-12342	Wood, pile	2230±50	−27.9‰	320–200 BC	400–170 BC
GU-12343	Wood, pile	2210±50	−30.4‰	370–200 BC	400–160 BC

century BC and Dall North, *c* 1m deeper, re-occupied in the seventh century AD.

Loch Tay date map (fig 4, table 2)

There is insufficient space in this paper to analyse closely the implications of the dates for the Loch Tay crannogs but several issues are notable. Oakbank crannog used to be considered by itself but it is now clear that 13 of the sites originated in the last half of the first millennium BC. Within that group it is possible to see divisions, although it must be borne in mind that there are problems with the calibration of dates from the earlier part of the period and their use in defining occupation and construction phases. Nine sites range between *c* 830–390 BC and four of those are in the range *c* 600–390 BC suggesting that they might have origins somewhat later than the others. The site of Dall South has dates falling in both ranges.

Four sites fall in the range *c* 400 BC–AD 220 and these can also be divided into two groups consisting of those from *c* 400–40 BC and those from *c* 170 BC–AD 220. Three sites fall in the Dark Ages with Breaban *c* AD 420–640 and the other two from *c* AD 560–890. Notably, all three appear to have origins in the Early Iron Age with samples ranging from *c* 600–390 BC.

Milton Morenish is very similar to Oakbank, with many piles in the lochbed around the site. It is the same size as Oakbank and the same distance from shore; however, Oakbank is 1.5–2m deeper under the water. The dates are almost identical but an organic sample produced very much the same evidence with Spelt and Emmer wheat, wild fruits and even cloud berries, that were first noted in the early archaeological record from Oakbank. The similarities between the two sites are unmistakable. The organic sample from Milton Morenish was taken from material in which the timber sampled for radiocarbon dating was embedded, so there was no extra disturbance created by taking two samples. The extra information that came from the organic

sample more than justified the extra effort and cost, and sampling for this purpose should be considered when possible.

Eilean Breaban looks very different from most other crannogs in the loch (fig 5). Over the years it has been suggested that this might be at least a two-phase site, as there is an almost circular area above the surface sitting on a submerged oval platform that extends to the west. A date from the deeper part of the site places it at about the fifth century BC, similar to Oakbank, while the upper part dates to the fifth century AD. It would be hard, even with the early date, to suggest that the two sites were similarly constructed because Breaban is one site where there is bedrock in the foundation and it is hard to see how that might relate to a free-standing pile dwelling.

Another site where observation suggests the crannog might not have originated as a free-standing structure is Firbush crannog. There are three layers of timbers that seem to be projecting radially out

FIGURE 5
Eilean Breaban, aerial. Bedrock can be seen in submerged extension to west (STUA).

from the bottom of the site (fig 6). It is possible here that rafts of timbers may have been sunk on top of each other to create a solid foundation but it would not be easy as the timbers would want to float and it would take a substantial weight to keep them down. There are no piles obvious in the lochbed around the site, although that does not mean they are not there. Only one timber was sampled from the site (2140 ± 55 BP, GU-1324) and that work was done in 1979, so further work and more dates would be useful.

So far, five sites – Priory Island, Eilean Puttychan, Spry Island, Mary's Distaff and the submerged mound in Kenmore Bay – are the only sites not to have been radiocarbon dated. Mary's Distaff is, in appearance and depth, very similar to the other early sites in the loch but it has not yet been possible to find suitable timbers for sampling. The site in Kenmore Bay has many visible timbers but none appears to be *in situ*. Spry Island was built up to its present shape in 1841 by the Marquis of Breadalbane and no timbers have yet been noted *in situ*. Priory Island, at the east end of the loch, and Eilean Puttychan, at the west end, are both known to have been inhabited into the recent past and there are no obvious timbers at the bottom of the mounds that might relate to the date of origin.

PERTHSHIRE CRANNOG SURVEY (table 3)

In 2004 the Perthshire Crannog Survey (PCS) was initiated by the STUA to examine crannogs in a wider context. One of the aims of the project was to examine medieval and post-medieval sites as part of doctoral research being carried out by Matthew Shelley at Edinburgh University. His work on the later periods is partly derived from the historical documents and maps where crannogs are featured.

The PCS brought to light useful information relating to the later sites but also some surprising results. For example, the dates for the site in Loch Monzievaird cover construction phases from about two centuries ago and from the middle of the first millennium BC. Clearly more work is required on this site.

What became obvious, relatively quickly, was the difficulty in comparing sites merely through visual observation, as has been the case elsewhere (see above). Dating the sites has added significantly to our understanding of them but much more work is needed to back up the dates that have already been acquired and to date the other sites in the region.

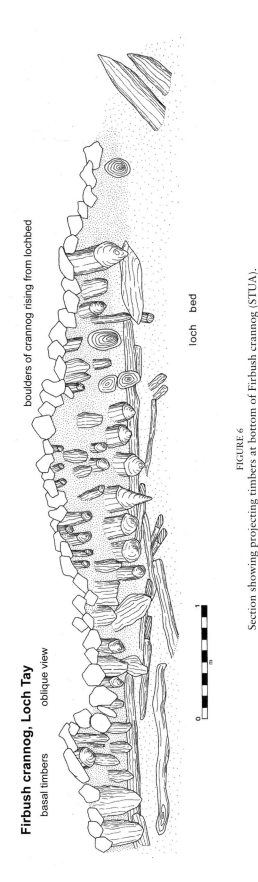

Firbush crannog, Loch Tay

basal timbers   oblique view

boulders of crannog rising from lochbed

loch bed

FIGURE 6
Section showing projecting timbers at bottom of Firbush crannog (STUA).

TABLE 3
Radiocarbon dates for crannogs sampled for Perthshire Crannog Survey (STUA).

Loch Tummel, Port an Eilean

Lab code	Sample mat	Yrs BP	δ¹³C(‰)	Calibrated dates	
				1 sigma	2 sigma
GU-12339	Wood, post	130±50	−23.9‰	AD 1800–1890	AD 1660–1960

Loch Rannoch, Eilean nam Faiolaig

Lab code	Sample mat	Yrs BP	δ¹³C(‰)	Calibrated dates	
				1 sigma	2 sigma
GU-12341	Wood	730±50	−26.6‰	AD 1240–1310	AD 1210–1330
GU-12340	Wood, oak	900±50	−27.1‰	AD 1030–1210	AD 1020–1250

Loch Earn, Edinample crannog (Eilean Craggan)

Lab code	Sample mat	Yrs BP	δ¹³C(‰)	Calibrated dates	
				1 sigma	2 sigma
GU-12344	Wood, soft	1090±50	−29.5‰	AD 890–1000	AD 810–1030

Loch Drumellie

Lab code	Sample mat	Yrs BP	δ¹³C(‰)	Calibrated dates	
				1 sigma	2 sigma
GU-12345	Wood, oak	1490±50	−27.2‰	AD 530–640	AD 430–660

Loch Monzievaird

Lab code	Sample mat	Yrs BP	δ¹³C(‰)	Calibrated dates	
				1 sigma	2 sigma
GU-12346	Wood, oak	140±50	−26.6‰	AD 1670–1950	AD 1660–1960
GU-12347	Wood, soft	2520±50	−28.0‰	700–540 BC	800–480 BC

CONCLUSIONS

Efforts have been made to group crannogs in meaningful categories since the middle of the nineteenth century when Robert Munro was the prominent researcher in the field (Munro 1879). More recently, several studies have added to the discussion (Barber & Crone 1993; Henderson 1998; Dixon 2004).

The acquisition of radiocarbon dates from crannogs in Perthshire has allowed sites to be understood in greater depth. In particular, the interpretation of crannog settlements in Loch Tay is much clearer. Of the 18 crannogs in the loch, nine started life in the Early Iron Age and some of them were re-occupied in the Dark Ages. The other sites from later in the Iron Age, and those from the modern era, show that the tradition of living on artificial islands was a part of the culture of the region for at least 2,500 years. It is now possible to formulate strategies for the examination of the crannogs of Loch Tay and elsewhere to answer specific archaeological questions.

Since 2003, the projects carried out by the STUA emphasizing the acquisition of samples for radiocarbon dating have shown a high success rate with little disturbance to sites. There is a reasonable level of confidence that the samples are from the earliest periods of construction and the latest extant phases of occupation. Timbers in the lochbed may, in most cases, reasonably be considered to date from the earlier construction phases, while samples from timbers from the very top of the site can be assumed to relate to the latest preserved phases of occupation. In a few cases, such as Monzievaird, there are timbers projecting from the site at all levels making it simple to create a relatively detailed chronological sequence for that site.

The single most useful target for the future of crannog research in Scotland would be radiocarbon dates from as many sites as possible throughout the country so that the greater understanding of the sites in Perthshire is seen as part of a nationwide programme. Along with radiocarbon dates it would be useful to gather where possible organic samples to increase the data from crannogs regarding the way of life of the people and to build up a picture of the environmental history of the site and its surroundings. Clearly, a deeper understanding of sites with the results that can be achieved from such well-preserved organic material will also contribute to the overall understanding of settlement patterns as a whole throughout the country.

ACKNOWLEDGEMENTS

The chance to acquire radiocarbon dates for the Loch Tay crannogs started with the involvement of the Scottish Trust for Underwater Archaeology in the Ben Lawers Historic Landscape Project under the auspices of the National Trust for Scotland (NTS). We would like to thank NTS co-ordinators Robin Turner and Derek Alexander, John Atkinson of Glasgow University Archaeological Research Division, and all the members of the project. Principal funders were the Heritage Lottery Fund, Historic Scotland, Scottish National Heritage and other bodies to whom we are grateful. The Perthshire Crannog Survey was initiated with a grant from Perth and Kinross Heritage Trust and the support of David Strachan was much appreciated. Thanks also to Matthew Shelley, one of the founders of the project. Several projects were initiated through the Scottish Universities Environmental Research Centre and we are grateful to Gordon Cook and his staff for their input and support.

We also thank the landowners who allowed us to dive in their lochs and walk their shores, and particularly Clive Booth of Loch Tay Highland Lodges and his staff for allowing us to use the harbour and other facilities for the duration of the Underwater and Shore Survey.

It would not have been possible to carry out the surveys and sampling without the many shore walkers, snorkellers and divers, who often worked in very cold and harsh conditions and we are very grateful for their support.

REFERENCES

Barber, J W & Crone, B A 1993 'Crannogs: a diminishing resource? A survey of the crannogs of south-west Scotland and excavations at Buiston Crannog', *Antiquity* 67, 520–33.

Cavers, M G & Henderson, J C 2005 'Underwater excavation at Ederline Crannog, Loch Awe, Argyll, Scotland', *International Journal of Nautical Archaeology* 34.2, 282–98.

Crone, B A 2000 *The History of a Scottish Lowland Crannog: Excavations at Buiston, Ayrshire 1989–90.* STAR Monograph 4, Edinburgh.

Crone, B A, Henderson, J C & Sands, R 2001 'Scottish crannogs: construction, collapse and conflation – problems of interpretation', *in* Raftery, B & Hickey, J (eds) *Recent Developments in Wetland Archaeology*, Seandálaíocht Monograph 2, Dept of Archaeol UCD and WARP Occ Paper 14, Dublin 55–67.

Dixon, T N 2004 *The Crannogs of Scotland: an Underwater Archaeology.* Stroud.

Dixon, T N & Shelley, M 2006 'Perthshire Crannog Survey 2004', *Tayside & Fife Archaeological Journal*, Vol 12, 71–81. Perth.

Henderson, J C 'Islets through time: the definition, dating and distribution of Scottish crannogs', *Oxford Journal of Archaeology* 17(2).

Crannogs and island duns: an aerial perspective

DENNIS W HARDING

Air photography has been part of the archaeologist's stock in trade for site detection and survey for nearly a century, since pioneers of military air photography like O G S Crawford realized its archaeological potential in the decades following the First World War. For many practitioners, however, archaeological air photography was synonymous with crop-mark photography and the importance of air survey as an adjunct to the detection and recording of extant earthworks in upland regions, often reduced to extremely fugitive or confusing surface patterns, has frequently been under-realized. Still more esoteric and under-valued, because restricted within Britain to Scotland, has been the contribution of air survey to the study of crannogs and island duns.

Crannogs and island duns are manifestations of essentially the same phenomenon of settlement over water or lake margins. Like the term 'dun' in terrestrial archaeology, crannogs embrace a great variety of field monuments, spanning two millennia and more of later prehistory and early history. It would be pointless being distracted into a discussion as to what constitutes a 'true crannog' in Scotland or in Ireland. The objective here is simply to examine the role of air photography in the survey of loch and lochside settlements, and to ask whether, in conjunction with water-borne or underwater survey, it can do more than simply add a few more stamps to the album.

From an early stage of the University of Edinburgh's Western Isles Research Programme the practical value of air survey became clear in a Hebridean context, both for terrestrial and wetland archaeology, where access over land and water was extremely difficult and time-consuming. There are operational constraints, of course, and more decisively there are optimum conditions for obtaining meaningful results that might seem to defy meteorological realities. First of all, to detect underwater sites requires still water, since the ripples caused by even a slight breeze will reflect into the camera and obscure underwater features. Second, it requires clear water, which will become muddied after storms through rain-wash from a loch's catchment. The action of a quite moderate wind on lochside vegetation can disturb silt and blur visibility. In the shallow lochs with deep underlying sediments of the Western Isles, the effects of wind and rain may take days to settle and clear. So all the optimistic aerial archaeologist is asking for in Highland and Island Scotland is a prolonged spell of fine, dry weather with no wind, with the bonus of falling loch levels to help to expose underlying structures.

Terrestrial, water-borne or underwater survey is an essential concomitant to air survey, if results are to be optimized. In Lewis in the 1980s the underwater programme was conducted by Dixon and Topping (1986), as a result of which the site at Dun Bharabhat, at Cnip in west Lewis, was selected for excavation.

FIGURE 1
Loch an Duna, Bragar, island broch (© D W Harding).

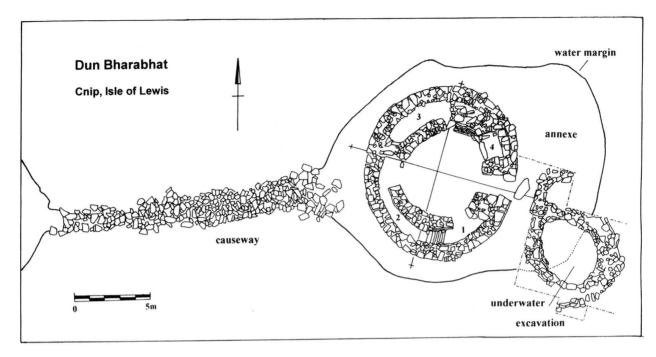

FIGURE 2
Dun Bharabhat, Cnip, plan of excavated island dun (© D W Harding).

One of the more visible among the extant island settlements is that at Bragar in the Loch an Duna (fig 1), a site whose complexity of enclosure and access might serve as a model that could be tested against the crannogs and lochside settlement of mainland Scotland. The site occupies an area significantly greater than that on which the broch itself stands: in effect, it has an enclosed annexe to the rear, loch-facing side. In this instance, the main entrance to the roundhouse is at ninety degrees to the access causeway, but in many instances in the Outer Hebrides it is diametrically opposed to the nearest shoreline, so that access from the land across a causeway, as at Dun Bharabhat (fig 2), would need a catwalk around the dun. In the case of Dun Bharabhat, this formality was obviated in the secondary phase of occupation by a breach in the landward wall of the original dun. To speak of an 'annexe', therefore, in relation to island duns, with the implication that it was behind the dun house, may be misleading: the 'annexe' at Bharabhat may, in effect, have been an extended forecourt. The crucial issue is: which direction did the occupants see their site as facing, to the shoreline or to the open water? Other features of interest at Loch an Duna (for plan see Armit, 1992, ll 5.16) and elsewhere are the lateral walls flanking the approach causeway, some of which, at any rate, may relate to

the site's later prehistoric occupation. Their purpose was presumably to reinforce control of access, though whether in a practically defensive or more socially ritualized sense, or a combination of both, is unclear.

In retrospect, I suspect, that our expectations and, more especially, our understanding of site taphonomy were too simplistic at that time, and that the factors that affected site survival may have been much more varied and complex than we appreciated. Accordingly, for example, at Loch an Duin, Shader (figs 3, 4), adjacent to the enigmatic and still undated site of Steinacleit, I inferred a threefold sequence, of which the island broch that is still substantially upstanding was the most obvious candidate for latest. The earliest, I assumed, was the least well preserved, a mound of stones underwater, only barely visible on the air photograph, but confirmed by the water-borne survey. Concealed initially by numerous algae rings, but clearly visible on the later flight, was a circular feature that appeared to have been intersected by the latest island structure, which I compared to Armit's survey of Dun Cromore (Armit 1985; 1992, ll 5.14), and regarded as an immediate predecessor to the final island broch. What now gives me some cause for second thoughts is that the narrow gap of deeper water, between the extant island and its shadow, is clearer than might be expected from arbitrary intrusion

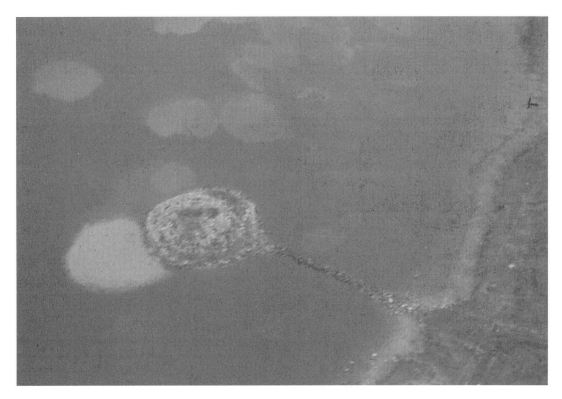

FIGURE 3
Loch an Duin, Shader, island dun with algae obscuring earlier features (© D W Harding).

FIGURE 4
Loch an Duin, Shader, showing later dun and earlier 'shadow' (© D W Harding).

across an earlier site, as if it was intended that way. What might have been the point of such a narrow channel is unclear, but at least two of the crannogs of Loch Tay, as we shall see, display similar features. Nevertheless, it is not unreasonable, as a working rule of thumb, to think that older structures will have slighter surviving remains than the more recent, not least because they may have served as a quarry for materials for subsequent building. But if this was common practice, then it follows that radiocarbon dates taken in site sampling might well be based on residual timbers from earlier sites, and might not, therefore, even guarantee that the site in question was the focus of activity at that date. This latter problem will apply even more acutely in mainland lochs like Loch Awe and Loch Tay than in the Western Isles, where timber is a more dominant constituent.

FIGURE 5
Cameron Bay, Loch Lomond, adjacent crannogs (© D W Harding).

Conditions affecting the survival of lochside settlements in deep-water mainland lochs are very different from those of the Western Isles. Recent work on the site at Ederline Boathouse in Loch Awe has served as a timely warning against simplistic interpretation (Cavers & Henderson 2005). The discovery of E ware low down in basal deposits, in contrast to the Early Iron Age radiocarbon date from upper levels, plainly indicates processes of erosion that have seemingly inverted the site's stratigraphy. Cavers is right to stress the multi-period potential of

crannogs, in parallel to the multi-period occupancy now abundantly demonstrated for the great majority of contemporary land-based settlements. In consequence, he rightly points out that sample dates probably indicate no more than the fact that there was activity on the site at the date indicated, with no assurance that this was the earliest or latest, or even the most significant phase of activity. This, of course, should not detract from the acquisition of sample dates, so long as we appreciate the potential problems of such sampling. However, it does strengthen the case for more than sample excavation of some key sites, where the prospect of recovering a fuller sequence is reasonably certain. In effect, only a complete section through the crannog would clarify the vertical stratigraphy and effects of degradation, a strategy that could impair the recovery of plans of structural phases in the horizontal plane.

One question that remains elusive is that of loch levels in antiquity, with consequential issues regarding the nature of settlements, whether over water or located on loch margins. Several sites in Loch Lomond and Loch Tay are located close by spurs of land, now underwater, from which they are separated, if at all, by a token gap. The two crannogs in Cameron Bay (fig 5) exemplify this. One is certainly separated from the underwater promontory by clear water. The other looks more complex. Here it seems that a circular mound overlaps an annexe-like extension to the underwater promontory. An eastern arm of the peninsula, off which these crannogs were built, curves away to create the effect of a lobster claw enclosing a second small bay, at the end of which a third, much fainter feature could be yet another, older crannog. Here is a clear instance where the entire underwater shoreline was potentially part of the settlement complex. The proximity of the crannog to what may have been the shoreline in antiquity is again underlined at Strathcashel Point in Loch Lomond. The same point can be made of several crannogs in Loch Tay. Tombreck (fig 6), Craggan and one of the Dall Bay crannogs (fig 7), all aligned along the southern shore of Loch Tay, are located where an underwater spur of land virtually joins the crannog to the shore, separated in some instances by what appears

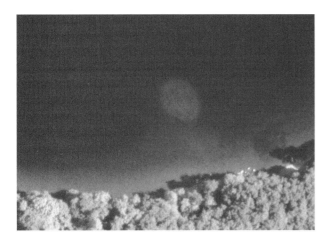

FIGURE 6
Tombreck, Loch Tay, with faint channel between crannog and old shoreline (© D W Harding).

to be a very narrow trench of water on the landward side. Graeme Cavers, in discussion, pointed to certain Irish sites where a narrow trench was deliberately dug across a projecting spur of land to create the effect of a lochside crannog, where the separation must have been largely symbolic (Fredengren 2002). A complication in interpreting the extent of the original shoreline was highlighted in the conference by the examples studied by Jon Henderson in Whitfield Loch (Henderson this volume) and in Ireland by Robert Sands at Coolure in Derravaragh Lough (O'Sullivan & Sands this volume). In both instances, there was a suggestion that the action of wave fetch might contribute to the re-deposition of sediments behind the crannog on the shoreline, thus enhancing it artificially. This indeed could be a factor in disguising whatever structures by way of wharves or buildings might originally have been part of the shore-based crannog complex.

In the case of Dall Bay, Dixon's recent radiocarbon dates show an apparent inversion of the expected sequence, in which the lesser surviving remains might be expected to be the earlier (Dixon this volume). In fact, the lesser site, designated Dall North, produced one Early Iron Age date and two in the mid- to later first millennium AD. Here, above all, the limitations of one-off sampling should be borne in mind, and until these sites are excavated, we can only recognize activity in both earlier and later Iron Ages.

In all of the instances examined, the essence of the settlement is what appears to be a single homestead, the counterpart of land-based dispersed settlement that characterizes the Northern British earlier Iron Age. Notwithstanding Morrison's attempts (1985) to relate crannogs to their landscape context, for too long crannogs have been studied in isolation from the changing patterns of terrestrial settlement, and as Cavers has rightly stressed, there is every reason to suppose that they will display a chronological sequence or structural complexity comparable to those now demonstrated for land-based settlements of the earlier and later Iron Age. Even where more than one site occurs in proximity, as at Cameron Bay, Fearnan or Dall Bay, the probability is that we are looking, in general, at a sequence, rather than an agglomeration of settlements into anything approaching village status. Other classes of Atlantic Iron Age settlement, however, such as wheelhouses, can occur in pairs, and various reasons for this could be suggested, even supposing that sites were designed essentially for a 'nuclear' family group.

The issue of orientation and direction of access is nevertheless of interest. It might be reasonable to suppose that, in the case of the major inland lochs, at any rate, water was the principal artery of communication between settlements and neighbouring territories. On this basis, the orientation might be towards the water rather than

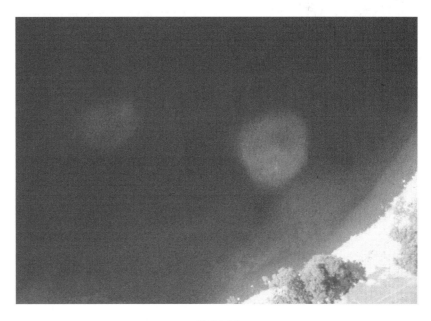

FIGURE 7
Dall Bay, Loch Tay, adjacent crannogs (© D W Harding).

271

FIGURE 8
Eilean nan Breaban, Loch Tay, crannog and shoreline (© D W Harding).

to the shore. Some of the crannogs of Loch Tay and Loch Lomond, as we have seen, are located so close to what was probably the former shoreline, that it is hard not to envisage that proximate shore as part of the settlement itself, perhaps originally with some outer protective boundary. In this case, access may have been by the shore (irrespective of whether visitors came by boat), requiring the visitor to transit a forecourt area before being admitted to the crannog itself. Comparable rites of access may be cited for early historic Ireland (O'Sullivan 2004). A comparable ritual may have controlled access at Gurness, Orkney, for example, where the approach way transits the outer court of the broch village, and whatever contemporary buildings or activity areas were located therein. Some sites, nevertheless, could have been more complex in access. Eilean nan Breaban on the north side of Loch Tay (fig 8), is located in proximity to several stony features, between which there is some evidence of interconnection. Could this have been evidence of a hierarchy of access, as is implied by the multiple approaches to Dun Sticer in North Uist?

At present, much of this remains speculation. What I hope it highlights is not simply the need for still more loch survey, including air survey, but more especially an increasing awareness of the need to undertake further research into loch levels and shorelines of the Iron Age, so that field survey may be directed more accurately at studying the location of crannogs and lochside settlements in their immediate shoreline context.

REFERENCES

Armit, I, 1985 *Later Prehistoric Defensive Structures of Lewis and Harris*. MA dissertation, University of Edinburgh Department of Archaeology.

Armit, I, 1992 *The Later Prehistory of the Western Isles of Scotland*. BAR British Series 221.

Cavers, M G & Henderson, J C 2005 'Underwater excavation at Ederline Crannog, Loch Awe, Argyll, Scotland', *International Journal of Nautical Archaeology* 34.2, 282–98.

Dixon, T N & Topping, P G 1986 'Preliminary survey of the later prehistoric artificial islands in the Isle of Lewis, Outer Hebrides', *International Journal of Nautical Archaeology and Underwater Exploration* 15.3, 189–94.

Fredengren, C 2002 *Crannogs. A study of people's interaction with lakes, with particular reference to Lough Gara in the north-west of Ireland.* Bray.

Harding, D W & Dixon, T N 2000 *Dun Bharabhat, Cnip. An Iron Age Settlement in West Lewis. Volume 1: The Structures and Material Culture.* Calanais Research Series Number 2, Edinburgh.

Morrison, I A 1985 *Landscape with Lake Dwellings, The Crannogs of Scotland.* Edinburgh.

O'Sullivan, A 2004 *The social and ideological roles of crannogs in early medieval Ireland.* Unpubl PhD thesis, NUI Maynooth.

Crannogs in south-east Scotland

ALEX HALE

INTRODUCTION

The distribution map of Scottish crannogs shows only a handful of sites (less than 10) in the south-east of the country. This paper attempts to understand whether this is a true distribution, or if it is an artefact of survey, as a result of past searches. The distribution may indeed be as a result of the removal of sites from the archaeological record, by the drainage of lochs and wetlands during the recent Improvements and reclamations schemes. A few sites that are found in the south-east of the country are explored in order to address the above questions.

If we look at a distribution map of the whole of Scotland, it shows that the presence of crannogs is heavily weighted to the west and the concentration of sites peters out towards the east, and especially towards the south-east. The question that should be asked is: how useful is this map to understanding the known sites and to identifying new locations? It contains no topographical or chronological data and, as we have seen over the past few years of crannog research, chronological data is becoming increasingly important to crannog studies (Crone 1993; Henderson 1998). Looking at the evidence from the individual sites and then using that information to provide evidence for constructing theoretical approaches to crannogs can bring together this level of detail.

BACKGROUND

This section looks at the known sites from the south-east of the country. It defines the history of crannog research in that region, identifies the characteristics of the sites, discusses their potential functions and outlines their periods of use.

Aspects of the history of wetland, in south-east Scotland appeared in print as early as the 1700s and continued sporadically through the nineteenth century, mainly as a result of landowners informing inquisitive antiquarians, and contributions to the New Statistical Account, which was published in 1845. The beginning of descriptions specifically about crannogs, however, is attributable to John Stuart, Secretary of the Society of Antiquaries of Scotland, who published a paper in volume 6 of the Proceedings of the same society. This paper entitled 'Notice of a Group of Artificial Islands in the Loch of Dowalton, Wigtownshire and of other Artificial Islands or "Crannogs" throughout Scotland', was heavily reliant on information that Stuart had gleaned from Joseph Robertson's collection. Robertson was curator of the historical and antiquarian department of the General Register House, Edinburgh and had access to a huge resource. What is clear from subsequent publications, such as Munro's 'Ancient Scottish Lake-Dwellings or Crannogs' (1882), is that despite the identification of some sites in the south-east, it did not become the 'honey-pot' for investigations, unlike the south-west.

EXISTING CRANNOGS IN THE SOUTH-EAST

There are eight known crannogs in the south-east of Scotland. Their locations, excavated remains and any diagnostic material will be outlined.

Duddingston Loch, Edinburgh (NT27SE 196)

Stuart provides us with a brief description of a series of piles protruding from the south side of the loch, at the foot of Arthur's Seat in Edinburgh, in his article in the Proceedings of the Society of Antiquaries of Scotland. They were discovered in the 1770s (Stuart 1866); however, there are no further details to identify the possible function or age of the wooden piles.

Green Knowe, Culter Parish (NT03SW 23)

This site is briefly described in the New Statistical Account (1845) as an oval mound measuring 36.6m by 27.4m and standing up to 0.9m in height. The mound comprised stones, which consolidated a timber framework. A causeway was also identified.

Nevertheless, this short account does identify typical crannog-like structures, the type of materials that were used in the construction.

Hyndford Loch, Lanark (NS94SW 10)

This crannog was excavated by Andrew Smith and overseen by Robert Munro, a retired doctor from Ayrshire (Munro 1899). We are given detailed descriptions of both structural remains and small finds and it is from these that we can begin to place a crannog from the south-east of the country into both typological and chronological frameworks. Munro had identified a single-phase structure comprising a building and multiple hearths. The structural remains at Hyndford comprised a timber platform laid directly on to the loch floor and built up in layers of brushwood, clay and timber piling. According to Munro, the single circular building on top of the platform measured about 10.4m in diameter and there was evidence of three separate hearths. As well as the hearths there were two clay floor levels. The small finds are mainly Roman and are very specific to the end of the first century AD; they have been associated with the close proximity of the Castledykes fort and temporary camps, which were occupied during both the Flavian and Antonine periods (RCAHMS 1978). However, no Antonine finds were identified from the crannog, so it has been suggested that the site was occupied during the Flavian period and fell out of use during the Antonine. In addition to the Roman finds, there were sherds of medieval ware found during the excavations.

Jordonlaw Moss, Westruther (NT64NW 3)

John Stuart provides us with information about a site found during excavations on the Spottiswoode estate, in the Borders (Stuart 1870). The site comprised a circular wooden structure, with an attendant causeway, that had been found around 1848.

Lochcote (NS97SE 3)

This site was very briefly described by John Stuart as being an island which comprised timbers. The small finds, which were probably red deer antlers, were described as 'horns' (Stuart 1866).

Lochend, Coatbridge (NS76NW 2)

Excavated between 1931 and 1932 as part of loch-deepening works, the site measured about 37m by 28m and was surrounded by wooden piles. The piles contained a platform of timbers, brushwood and clay up to 1.5m (Monteith & Robb 1937). The excavations revealed a timber foundation that supported two successive floor levels. The small finds were undiagnostic, although it has been suggested that the site was occupied over a lengthy (if not continuous) period between 500 BC and AD 500 (RCAHMS 1978, 27).

Whiteburn Bog, Westruther

Further improvements on the Spottiswoode estate in Berwickshire enabled Lady John Scott to record at least four circular structures comprising large 'roughly squared timbers', piles, interwoven sticks and causeways (Scott 1871). There also appears to have been a midden between two of the structures.

Yetholm Loch

This site has been included because it illustrates the broad range of periods during which island occupation has occurred in Scotland. Loch Tower was built on an island, reached by a causeway and was destroyed by the Earl of Surrey in 1523 (RCAHMS 1956).

TOPOGRAPHY, AN ARTEFACT OF SURVEY OR A RESULT OF THE IMPROVEMENTS?

When assessing why there are so few crannogs in the south-east we cannot cite the absence of potential locations, such as lochs, as a reason. Although the lochs of the region are smaller and most probably shallower than those in the glacially incised valleys of the Highlands, they are the part of the topography that is a prerequisite to lake-dwelling. The area to the south of the Tweed valley and to the west of Teviotdale is of particular interest, because here is an area with a concentration of water bodies, which comprises over 50 small lochs. When we consider the wetland mapping data compiled by the Macaulay Land-Use Research Institute, a further 80 wetlands, bogs or mosses could be added to the original 50 lochs.

The natural water bodies that we can search are limited to those that survive today, unlike the numerous bogs and mosses that were drained as part of the Improvements. A useful guide to previous land-use and a record of pre-Improvement landscapes is the Ordnance Survey 1st Edition maps, which were surveyed and published between the 1850s and the 1890s. They give a good indication as to the survival of potential crannog locations in a landscape that was heavily altered as a result of the extensive Improvements. For example, here are three locations where lochs which contain islands have survived to be depicted on the OS maps and could warrant further fieldwork:

(1) Faldonside Loch, S of Abbotsford (NT 505 328) contains an island on the south side of the loch.

(2) Murder Moss, just to the E of Selkirk (NT 505 284) has 'Murdermoss Island'.

(3) Hoselaw Loch, E of Kelso (NT 807 317) has a small island depicted on the map. The loch is part of a more extensive wetland, known as Din Moss.

The other consideration when assessing potential sites is landscape change and how much of the available search areas, such as bogs and lochs, have been drained during the Improvements. If we superimpose the distribution of crannogs onto a map showing land given over to both arable and improved pasture, we notice that there are virtually no crannogs surviving in the arable areas. Where we see crannogs existing in the south-east is on the margins of the improved pasture, with rough grazing. This land is the least intensively farmed and has undergone little drainage works. This is the topographical zone where we could identify potential locations that can be investigated using traditional fieldwalking techniques, with additional wetland and underwater survey.

Given the intensity of crannog research in the nineteenth century, we may expect more than eight sites to have been found in the south-east, but it would appear that work concentrated in two locations; the south-west and Highland Scotland. The first area was the domain of the doyen of crannog studies, Robert Munro, and the second was investigated by Odo Blundell, a priest who lived in Fort Augustus at the south end of Loch Ness. In both these regions the crannogs are easily identified, often protruding from the surrounding lochs and topped with verdant vegetation. This made crannog-spotting in the south-west and Highland lochs something of a relatively straightforward exercise. The shallow water bodies and mosses of the south-east would, however, have required more intensive searching. It should be remembered that archaeological excavation was a young discipline at the time these crannogs were being identified and the concept of archaeological survey had a relatively narrow definition. Rather than

survey being used as an exercise in itself, to locate new sites, it was applied as a recording tool on sites that had been previously identified and were being excavated.

SOCIAL AND RITUAL LANDSCAPES

Ian Morrison provided three chapter sub-headings in his book 'Landscape with Lake Dwellings' (1984, chapter 4), which are valuable for constructing theoretical approaches to crannog studies. They are: the immediate setting, patterns in the landscape and agriculture. To these we could add the concepts of social and ritual landscapes, and begin to explore the crannogs from the south-east in these terms.

If we look at the possible dates of the known sites we can divide them into four broad chronological horizons: Prehistoric (Duddingston Loch, Green Knowe, Jordonlaw Moss, Lochcote, Lochend and Whiteburn Bog); Roman (Hyndford); Medieval (Hyndford); and Later Medieval (Yetholm Loch). In terms of function, we are stymied by the lack of known artefacts. We can look at the various social climates that existed at times of known crannog-building phases and assess whether the south-east was influenced by societies that did not consider the construction of crannogs, and the occupation of lochs, as part of their social or ritual landscape. This approach could imply that those known crannogs were 'unusual' and had particular cultural significance.

If we look at the Prehistoric sites, searches in Duddingston Loch have produced a number of finds, such as the Late Bronze Age hoard, which comprises a fine quantity of metalwork that was ritually deposited. These deposits could be associated with the timber piles in the loch, perhaps to provide a shore-side platform for ritual ceremonies. Green Knowe, in Culter parish, South Lanarkshire, is situated immediately to the north-west of Cow Castle Iron Age fort (RCAHMS 1978). Given the absence of any dateable material from either site conclusions that can be drawn are limited. However, we could envisage a period when both sites were occupied and fulfilled complementary functions in the hierarchical, social structure of first millennium BC South Lanarkshire. Likewise, Lochcote in West Lothian lies adjacent to Bowdenhill and Cockleroy first millennium BC forts, and to the north of the earlier, ritual complex on Cairnpapple Hill. The structural remains and small finds from Lochend crannog suggest a timber-built structure that supported a dwelling site, with at least one phase of re-use, indicated by the replacement of the floor levels (Monteith & Robb 1937). The small finds are indicative of a domestic site, with evidence of pottery use, foodstuffs provided by animal remains and food preparation using the two upper quernstones. The inclusion of the remains of two human bodies in the foundation platform gives the site an additional interest. Were these bodies placed specifically within the platform structure as an offering to the water, prior to the dwelling being constructed? Unfortunately, the evidence of the five sites discovered during the drainage works of Whiteburn Bog provides little detail for further discussion.

The crannog in Hyndford Loch has been dated primarily by its artefacts (RCAHMS 1978, 108). Its location and occupancy as the predominantly Roman finds suggest, at the same time as the Roman fort, indicate a site which fills a gap in the archaeological record for crannogs as a whole. The possibility therefore exists that it was used as a trading place with the Roman neighbours. A place, which being on the loch, was perhaps of neutral territory and could be used for the exchange of goods: a mutually acceptable place to exchange goods for both Roman and local populations. If we consider that the site was in occupation during the Roman period we can attach to it a number of suppositions. For example, its date fits in with other radiocarbon dated crannogs in the region, for example, those estuarine sites in the inner Firth of Clyde, such as Dumbuck (Sands & Hale 2001) and some of the sites in the south-west: Milton Loch and Barean (Crone 1993).

By the later part of the seventh century AD, the south-east of Scotland was under the influence of the Northumbrian Angles. However, prior to that time, the native population appears to have had a limited tradition of lake-dwelling as indicated from Hyndford crannog and those further west in Lochcote and Lochend. Perhaps the re-use of these sites represents the eastern extent of the crannog tradition of the Dark Age Dál Riata nobles (Crone 2000). This social contrast between the two regions may be one reason why there is a lacuna in the south-east of Scotland. There is no evidence of lake-dwellings or a lake-dwelling tradition from south of the Border and a cursory glance into Northumbria, despite the presence of a number of lakes, confirms this. The other place to look for crannogs south of the border is Cumbria and to date no sites have been identified in the Lake District, although systematic searches have not been undertaken.

The last occupation period is the Medieval to Post-Medieval period and the example used is Yetholm Loch Tower. Given the design of tower houses, we could assume that the islands on which they are situated are at least semi-natural and have been artificially augmented. This occupation of dry ground implies the use of the water as a form of defence, a theory that has in the past been applied to prehistoric crannogs. In addition, we could suggest that water during this period was used by the island-dwellers as part of their social status. The stronghold on the island would confirm the elevated social position of the occupiers. Yetholm Loch Tower is no longer standing, however, it was situated in an extensive wetland.

FINAL REMARKS

There appears to be a thinning of crannogs towards the east of the country as a whole, and indeed towards the south-east. This does seem to represent a true distribution, which has been exacerbated by the activities of the past 250 years or so by the increased mechanization and destructive potential of agricultural practices. The best example of the total destruction of sites is the eight or so found on Whiteburn Bog, on the Spottiswoode estate. Limited, or, in some areas, no systematic survey has contributed to the low number of sites known; perhaps future research could focus on some of the surviving lochs and bogs to try and find some more. The surviving crannogs can be separated chronologically into broad categories, which, with excavation, would almost certainly need to be revised. However, the evidence from their locations and from excavation results does enable a number of social and ritual models to be proposed and explored.

ACKNOWLEDGEMENTS

With thanks to Anya Clayworth and Jon Henderson.

REFERENCES

Crone, B A 1993 'Crannogs and Chronologies', *Proc Soc Antiq Scot* 123, 245–54.

Crone, B A 2000 *The History of a Scottish Lowland Crannog: Excavations at Buiston, Ayrshire 1989–90.* STAR Monograph 4, Edinburgh.

Henderson, J 1998 'Islets through time: the definition, dating and distribution of Scottish crannogs', *Oxford Journal of Archaeology* 17.2, 227–44.

Monteith, J & Robb, J 1940 'The crannog at Lochend, Coatbridge: with a report on the osseous remains', *Transactions of the Glasgow Archaeological Society, New* 9, 1 (1937–40), 26–43.

Morrison, I 1984 *Landscape with Lake Dwellings.* Edinburgh.

Munro, R 1882 *Ancient Scottish Lake Dwellings or Crannogs.* Edinburgh.

Munro, R 1899 'Notes on a crannog at Hyndford, near Lanark, recently discovered and excavated by Andrew Smith', *Proc Soc Antiq Scot* 33 (1898–9), 373–87.

New Statistical Account 1845.

RCAHMS 1956 *An inventory of the ancient and historical monuments of Roxburghshire.* Edinburgh.

RCAHMS 1971 *Lanarkshire: An inventory of the prehistoric and Roman monuments.* HMSO.

Sands, R & Hale, A 2001 'Evidence from marine crannogs of later prehistoric use of the Firth of Clyde', *Journal of Wetland Archaeology* 1, 41–54.

Scott, J 1870 'Notes of wooden structures discovered in the Moss of Whiteburn, on the Estate of Spottiswoode, Berwickshire', *Proc Soc Antiq Scot* 8 (1868–70), 16–18.

Stuart, J 1866 'Notices of a group of artificial islands in the Loch of Dowalton, Wigtonshire, and of other artificial islands or "crannogs" throughout Scotland', *Proc Soc Antiq Scot* 6 (1864–6), 114–17.

Stuart, J 1870 'Note on Communication of Lady John Scott, descriptive of Wooden Structures at Spottiswoode, in Berwickshire', *Proc Soc Antiq Scot* 8 (1868–70), 19–20.

Monitoring *in situ* preservation on south-west Scottish crannogs

MALCOLM LILLIE, ROBERT SMITH, JANE REED and ROB INGLIS

INTRODUCTION

This paper presents an overview of the initial stages of a monitoring project aimed at assessing the nature of the depositional environments at five crannog sites in south-west Scotland. The sites considered are located between Dumfries and Stranraer. Assessments of each site included a range of parameters that directly related to both the immediate burial environment of the crannog and the off-site influences such as loch water status. As such, information on water levels, pH, redox potential, water chemistry and diatom-based biomonitoring has been generated at these locations since an initial phase of monitoring began in July 2004. Full monitoring has been undertaken at all of these locations since November 2004. Preliminary results indicate favourable environments for *in situ* preservation occurring during the winter months, with some variability in evidence that is related to seasonal trends at the locations investigated, and to external perturbations such as erosion and substrate characteristics.

A programme of monitoring has been ongoing at five crannog sites in south-west Scotland since July 2004 (fig 1). The sites investigated comprise Loch Arthur (NX90306895) and Milton Loch (NX83907192) in Dumfries, to the east, and Barlockhart (NX20505635), Whitefield Loch (Dorman's Island) (NX23775502) and Cults Loch (NX12056059) to the west, in the region of Stranraer and Glenluce. The aims of the monitoring are to investigate and identify:

- change on and around the crannogs,
- determine whether the sites are stable or decaying,
  and
- if the sites are shown to be decaying; to determine the causes of the decay as previously identified (Lillie *et al* 2003, 2)

These five crannogs were chosen for the present study as it is anticipated that the differing nature of the sites in terms of their locations, catchments and characters will facilitate comparisons of preservation status, context, burial and water conditions against which estimates of the preserving/degrading nature of the environments can be compared (Lillie *et al* 2003, 5).

Given the continued degradation of the wetland resource (eg Brunning 1999) and the advocation of preservation *in situ* as the preferred approach to burial environments containing waterlogged archaeological remains (DOE 1990, Chapman & Cheetham 2002), it is apparent that further research into the modelling and characterization of the wetland archaeological resource is an important research priority.

BACKGROUND AND METHODOLOGY

In addition to the generic parameters identified above, which are directly related to the burial environment of the crannogs, each site was chosen for study because, to date, no previous research initiatives have targeted such sites; both from the perspective of understanding preservation status and ecological setting, and with the aim of developing dedicated management strategies. Whilst crannog studies have some antiquity, as highlighted by the work of Robert Munro in 1882, it is only since the 1980s that archaeologists have investigated the Scottish crannogs in any systematic manner (Crone 1992). Using the work of Munro, Crone has identified 33 definite sites (from an original estimate of 74 reported by Munro) that remain or can be proven to exist. Of these remaining sites, only three are considered to be free from immediate threat (*ibid.*, 1992, 295).

To date, it has been assumed that a limited range of parameters, such as water-table dynamics (studied by piezometers), pH, redox potential, and occasionally microbial activity, provide a sufficiently robust data set from which characterization of a burial environment can be undertaken (Caple 1993; Caple & Dungworth 1997). Indeed, Chapman and Cheetham (2002) and Corfield (1996) have advocated saturation as the principal factor exerting an influence on preservation

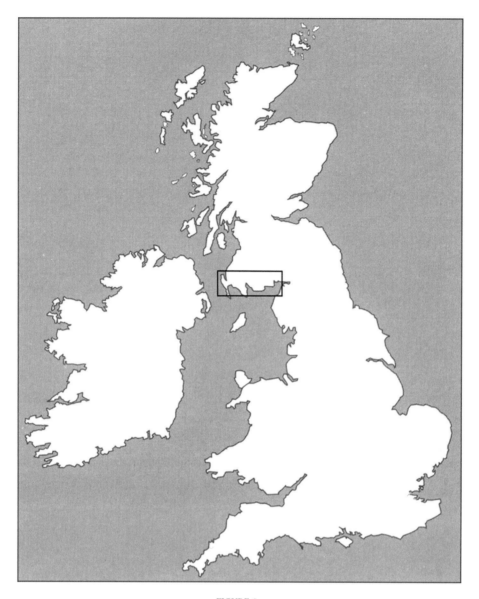

FIGURE 1
Location of the study region in south-west Scotland.

in wet environments, because saturation excludes atmospheric oxygen. However, recent research (Smith 2005) has suggested that the interactions that occur between the parameters discussed are more complex than the literature would suggest. In relation to the bacterial degradation of oak wood, the influence of dissolved oxygen, redox potential and pH in relation to the bacterial community can cause bacterial population shifts that subsequently alter the decomposition of the organic fraction in the sediment matrix. The conclusion being that a complex series of external interactions can influence the reaction of the burial environment, depending on the material contained within the waterlogged context.

In terms of the redox potential of the burial environment, research by Caple and Dungworth (1997) has suggested that, in order to maintain optimum burial conditions, redox values need to be maintained at between –100 and –400mV. Corfield (1996, 35) reported that redox potential and pH were the most useful measures in characterizing an anoxic environment, although values of between +200 to –400mV were described for anaerobic sediments.

In the current investigation, the figures provided by Patrick and Mahaptra (1968) are used to assess the preservation condition of the crannogs studied (cf Cheetham 2004, Smith 2005). They are as follows:

- Oxidized soils   =   >+400mV
- Moderately reduced   =   +100 to +400mV
- Reduced   =   −100 to +100mV
- Highly reduced   =   −300 to −100mV

The current programme aims to expand upon the earlier studies discussed above, by integrating the fundamental parameters directly related to the crannogs (redox potential, pH and water levels) with a consideration of the off-site context. These sites, by their very nature, occupy a discrete landscape context associated with the freshwater lochs of south-west Scotland. As noted by Corfield (1996, 32), 'effective preservation … requires a thorough understanding of the factors that might (promote) deterioration of the archaeological evidence'. In this respect, an understanding of site specific and landscape-wide influences is essential (Lillie & Cheetham 2002), and given the specific context of the crannogs, fundamentals of water chemistry and lake ecology are required to understand the various influences acting upon these sites.

As noted above, the principal factor influencing preservation within wet environments is the presence of saturation, which reduces the levels of oxygen accessing sediments, thereby restricting the activities of aerobic bacteria (Corfield 1996). This element has been significant in the development of management strategies for preserved sites in both the UK and abroad (cf Coles 1995).

In order to assess water-table dynamics and redox potential, monitoring points were established at each of the sites investigated. Piezometers were placed at 0.5, 1.0 and 1.5m depths through the stratigraphy of the crannog. In order to produce greater reliability in the redox potential data, a 'nest' of platinum tipped redox probes was installed. These probes have been positioned at depths within the crannogs and can therefore mirror the piezometers as these depths have been shown to have the potential to contain waterlogged archaeological materials. In addition to the deeper probes (>0.50m depth) more probes were placed at 0.10m depth in order to provide a 'control' for the assessment of redox potential with depth.

The pH analysis was undertaken at all of the sites where redox potentials have been obtained. The pH values were used to correct the redox readings to the Standard Hydrogen Electrode (SHE) (British Standards Institute 1990; Howard 1998; Cheetham 2004). As the reference electrodes used in the present study have a potential value of +222mV, a value of 222mV is added to the mean of the readings obtained from the *in situ* probes at each crannog monitoring location.

The parameters employed to assess water quality include diatom analysis, conductivity analysis, dissolved oxygen content, total phosphorus, cation and anion analysis (the latter technique is in the analysis stage at the time of writing). In general, bio-monitoring can greatly strengthen the reliability of results of aquatic monitoring programmes.

Conductivity, or specific conductance, is the measure of the water's ability to conduct an electric current. Conductivity depends upon the dissolved ionic concentration of the water. Natural fresh waters fall within the range 50–500uS cm^{-1}. In light of this, any higher conductivity values within the crannogs are likely to reflect higher biological productivity and generation of carbonates, or the increased availability of nutrients such as nitrates. In general, lowland Scottish lakes which are not heavily eutrophicated by urban waste or intense agricultural activity are likely to be oligotrophic (low in nutrients) with low conductivity.

Dissolved oxygen content (DOC) is the measure of the amount of oxygen dissolved in the water. All living organisms, except for certain types of bacteria, need oxygen to survive. The recording of DOC is one of the most frequently applied methods available for the investigation of the aquatic environment (Wetzel & Likens 1991), and is useful in distinguishing anoxic from aerobic conditions in the burial environment (Caple 1996).

DOC is indicative of the concentration of nutrients and decaying organic matter in a lake (Kegley & Andrews 1998), and, even in oligotrophic lakes, oxygen often becomes limited during the summer months. This is due to its excessive use by bacteria to degrade the increased amounts of dead organic matter being produced during the season of peak productivity by algae and plants. Parallel measurement of DOC and total phosphorus (below) provides a strong indicator of changing productivity during the annual cycle.

Total phosphorus (TP) is of direct relevance to lake productivity and eutrophication (nutrient enrichment). The main nutrients promoting algal and plant growth are nitrogen (N) and phosphorus (P). Phosphorus, in particular, is only present at very low concentrations naturally, and has been shown to be an important limiting factor on algal growth. When artificially enriched from input of phosphates, for example, from fertilizers or detergent, a lake may become eutrophic and plagued by algal blooms. SEPA (2002, 2) have shown that nutrient enrichment with phosphorus is the major threat to Scottish freshwater lochs. In general, the limits for indicating loch status range from $\leq 2.5\mu g\ l^{-1}$, which indicates ultra-oligotrophic status; $\leq 8\mu g\ l^{-1}$, which is oligotrophic; $\leq 25\mu g\ l^{-1}$, which equates to mesotrophic status; and through to $\leq 80\mu g\ l^{-1}$ which indicates a eutrophic loch status. To date, the crannog study sites have exhibited clear waters which are relatively low in nutrient content. However, measurement of total phosphorus throughout the year will provide a vital adjunct to DOC measurement and diatom-inferred TP in the accurate determination of annual fluctuations in water chemistry and limnology.

On their own, water chemistry measurements may not always reflect the true mean values of the parameters during the sampling season, since they may fluctuate widely in response to rapid events such as rain storms (Abel 1996). In a programme such as this, where continuous (daily or weekly) water chemistry monitoring is not feasible, biomonitoring provides a more robust means of assessing seasonal variation. The array of biological organisms found at a site is more likely to reflect mean conditions, and rigorous sampling for accurate results requires a lower temporal resolution than that of direct water chemistry monitoring (Chapman 1996).

In the current study, diatoms are used as indicators of pH and TP. Additional inferences concerning limnological conditions are also made based on the author's (Reed) qualitative knowledge of their modern ecology and life habits (planktonic vs shallow water, tolerance of turbidity and so on). Their state of preservation (breakage and dissolution) may also provide a useful indication of the energy of the local environment.

RESULTS

At two of the sites investigated, Whitefield and Cult's Loch, the visual assessment of context indicated that external factors, such as wave fetch and tree throw (Whitefield) and reduced water levels and swan damage (Cults), were having a detrimental impact on the crannogs. At Whitefield Loch, the preliminary diatom analyses highlighted two species in particular that would support the observations that this site is compromised. In this respect, the *Aulacoseira* genus needs high turbidity to remain afloat, and may indicate a wind-stressed environment, whilst the

abundance of small *Fragilaria* species is characteristic of shallow, unstable environments. The off-site water quality data from the diatom studies and conductivity analysis, dissolved oxygen content, total phosphorus, cation and anion analysis, are being processed at the time of writing, but preliminary observation on the diatom studies are presented below.

DIATOMS

A total of 146 diatom taxa were identified in the data-set of 13 samples from the five study sites in the initial monitoring between December 2004 and February 2005. Many samples are dominated by the cosmopolitan species, *Achnanthes minutissima*. This is a diatom with a clear preference for circum-neutral pH and well-oxygenated waters and it is common both in flowing and still-standing waters. The exception to this observation is the Milton Loch lake-centre sample, which is dominated by the planktonic species *Stephanodiscus parvus*. At Cults Loch, the samples are dominated by small *Fragilaria* taxa and the long pennate taxon, *F. capucina*, which may sometimes be found in diatom plankton. Small *Fragilaria* taxa are also common in the Barlockhart surface sediment and lake-edge samples, and the Whitefield surface sediments. These are typical 'pioneer species' of fluctuating environments and are better able than *A. minutissima* to withstand turbidity. They are renowned for being unreliable indicators of lake-water chemistry because they are tolerant of a wide range of environmental conditions in regard to parameters such as pH, TP or salinity.

In general, most of the taxa identified at this stage are characteristic of circum-neutral waters rather than highly acid waters. In this context, it is worth noting that the obligate acidophilous taxa which are typical of acidified lakes in Scotland (eg *Tabellaria quadriseptata*) are completely absent from the data set. A planktonic flora dominated none of the diatom samples studied to February 2005. Acidified lakes (pH < 5) in Scotland are extremely oligotrophic and do not support plankton. In general, plankton abundance tends to increase with productivity. The results concur with the low measured TP values obtained to February 2005 (although it should be noted that shallow waters also have a tendency towards high relative proportions of benthic taxa).

When considering the fact that this preliminary study covers the winter season of low productivity, it is interesting to note that relatively high abundances of plankton were found in some samples from

Whitefield, Milton and Cults Loch, which may prove to be the most productive as the spring/summer season data are assessed. In terms of specific diatom nutrient preferences, *Stephanodiscus* spp. and *S. hantzschii* (low abundance in Barlockhart) in particular are strong indicator species for nutrient-enriched waters.

ON-SITE MONITORING

Monitoring points were installed at each of the crannogs during July 2004. This timing proved to be rather inappropriate as the lochs were at their lowest level during this period, and subsequent water-table monitoring has shown that a vertical displacement of up to 0.35–0.50m has been experienced at these sites. The situation appears more pronounced away from the coast, in the Dumfries region at Loch Arthur and Milton Loch, but seasonal reductions in loch levels are variable, and occasionally marked, throughout the study region.

During the initial stages of the monitoring programme, the regular recording of data began in December 2004. Consequently, there is a hiatus of five months between the initial readings obtained and the onset of full monitoring. This approach was determined by a combination of factors including access, stabilization of the monitoring points, and the need to ensure that data from the wettest (winter 2004) through to the driest (summer 2005), and subsequently the wettest (winter 2005) seasons was facilitated in an attempt to generate meaningful results from all elements of the monitoring. Unfortunately, the lower loch levels in July were reversed into the winter of 2004, resulting in the complete submergence of the monitoring points at Cults Loch and Whitefield Loch. These sites were not accessible for water-table and redox potential analysis across the winter to spring of 2004–5.

The data are being processed at the time of writing, but preliminary redox values are provided for Barlockhart (in the west) and Loch Arthur and Milton Loch (in the east) for the period up to and including April 2005 (figs 2a–c). The redox data indicate that at each of the three locations studied between December 2004 and April 2005 a range of conditions from moderately reducing (+100 to +400mV) to highly reducing (–300 to –100mV) occur at all the sites investigated.

At Barlockhart (fig 2a), there is variability in the data, with the March 2005 data being similar to that for January, that is, all readings are within the reducing zone. However, in April 2005, reducing conditions continue but the surface sediments are moderately reduced (+100 to +400mV). At Loch Arthur (fig 2b), from December 2004 onwards, the surface of this crannog remained reduced, with the sediments between 0.5–1.3m depths being highly reduced (with the exception of the 0.5m depth in January 2005). This general trend remains in place between February and March 2005, although the 0.5m readings for March are considered unreliable, and in need of further analysis, with the 1.3m readings rising to reflect reducing conditions.

At Milton Loch (fig 2c), the initial redox values indicated that the surface sediments were reduced, with the sediments below this level exhibiting highly reducing conditions. These conditions are ideal for *in situ* preservation. Although no data were obtained during January 2005 (due to flooding of the crannog surface), the February data from Milton appear to suggest that the elevated water levels and heavy rainfall over this interim period had compromised the depositional sequences somewhat, with moderately reduced to reduced conditions in evidence. From March 2005, the surface and 1.5m depth deposits were reducing, and at 0.95m the deposit was highly reducing. However, the data from 0.5m depth did not follow the dominant trend and appeared unreliable. In April 2005, the data reflected highly reduced conditions throughout the profile, although there were no values obtained from 0.95m depth due to swan damage.

PRELIMINARY OBSERVATIONS

Preliminary observations in July 2004, relating to the specific contexts of the sites investigated, indicated that some external factors were actively affecting Whitefield and Cults Loch. These factors included wave fetch and wind throw at Whitefield, and swan damage and lowered loch levels due to water abstraction at Cults Loch.

The diatom data from November (2004) to February (2005) suggest that the dominance of the species *Achnanthes minutissima* reflects circum-neutral pH and well-oxygenated waters, and this is a species common both in flowing and still-standing waters. Variation occurs, with Cults, Barlockhart and Whitefield Loch (the western group of sites) having *Fragilaria* taxa in evidence. These are typical 'pioneer species' of fluctuating environments, able to withstand turbidity. An interesting observation at this stage is that the relatively high abundances of plankton found in some of the samples from Whitefield, Milton and Cults Loch may indicate that these lochs will prove to

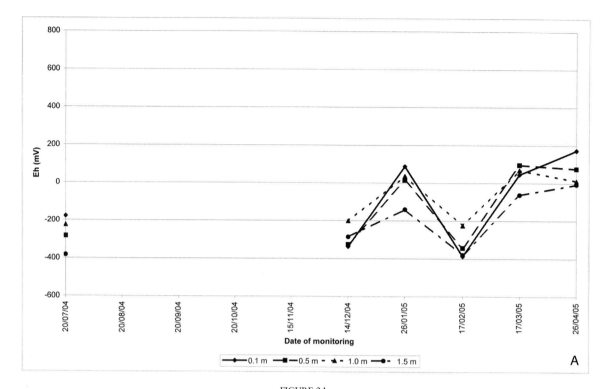

FIGURE 2A
Redox potentials for the initial Winter-Spring (2004–5) period of the monitoring programme. Barlockhart.

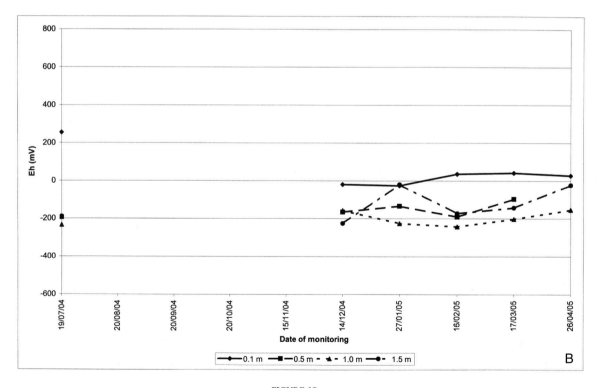

FIGURE 2B
Redox potentials for the initial Winter-Spring (2004–5) period of the monitoring programme. Loch Arthur.

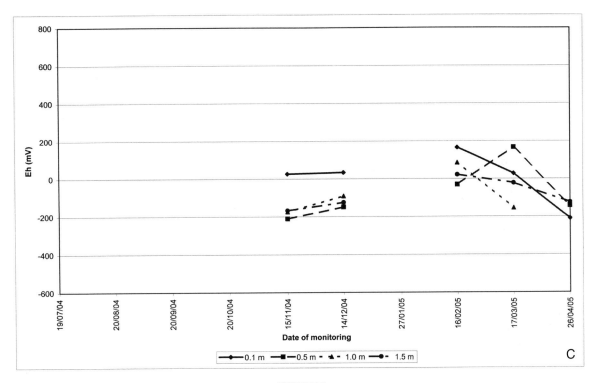

FIGURE 2C
Redox potentials for the initial Winter-Spring (2004–5) period of the monitoring programme. Milton Loch.

be the most productive as the spring/summer seasonal data are assessed.

As has been noted above, in relation to the crannog sediments themselves, it is assumed that saturation is the principal factor exerting an influence on preservation (Corfield 1996; Chapman & Cheetham 2002). This is because saturation excludes atmospheric oxygen, thereby inhibiting microbial decay. As the monitoring points at Cults Loch and Whitefield Loch have been submerged since the winter of 2004, it is suggested that saturation of the crannog sequences provides good environments for preservation.

Although the redox data are clearly variable, they suggest that even during periods of elevated rainfall and high loch water levels, the burial environment is susceptible to short-term fluctuations in redox potential. The January monitoring point at Milton Loch indicates this, where, despite flooding of the crannog surface, the redox values reflect compromised depositional environments with moderately reduced to reduced conditions in evidence. These data appear to suggest that the water inputs in January may have an elevated oxygen content when compared to those of December 2004 and February 2005. Whilst extremely tentative at this stage of the analysis, it is possible that these sites should not be considered 'stable', and that it is only through a consideration of both longer term trends and the integration of the entire corpus of monitoring data that the subtle shifts in evidence during the winter to spring of 2004–5 will be understood. In conclusion, the preliminary results presented in this paper highlight that saturation cannot be assumed *a priori* to reflect good conditions within the burial environment.

ACKNOWLEDGEMENTS

Tracy Yates processed the diatom samples; Dave Williams and Chelsea Budd assisted with the fieldwork; and Historic Scotland funded the fieldwork programme. The authors would like to thank Anne Crone and Jon Henderson for their invitation to participate in their research in this region, and Malcolm Lillie would also like to thank Jon for presenting his overview of the work at the WARP Conference in Edinburgh.

REFERENCES

Abel, P D 1996 *Water Pollution Biology*. London.

British Standard Institute (1990) *Methods of test for soils for civil engineering purposes*. Chemical and Electrochemical Tests: BS377–3. London.

Caple, C 1993 'Defining a reburial environment; research problems characterizing waterlogged anoxic environments', *in Proceedings of the 5th ICOM group on wet organic archaeological materials conference. Portland Maine*. ICOM Committee for the Conservation Working Group on WOAM: 407–21, Bremerhaven.

Caple, C 1996 'Parameters for monitoring anoxic environments', *in* Corfield, M, Hinton, M P, Nixon, T & Pollard, M (eds) *Preserving Archaeological Remains in situ*, 113–23. London & Bradford.

Caple, C & Dungworth, D 1997 'Investigations into waterlogged burial environments', *in* Sinclair A, Slater, E & Gowlett, J (eds) *Archaeological Sciences 1995: Proceedings of a conference on the application of scientific techniques to the study of archaeology*: 233–40. Oxbow Monograph 64, Oxford.

Chapman, H P & Cheetham, J L 2002 'Monitoring and modelling saturation as a proxy indicator for *in situ* preservation in wetlands – a GIS-based approach', *Journal of Archaeological Science* 29, 277–89.

Cheetham, J L 2004 'An assessment of the potential for *in situ* preservation of buried organic archaeological remains at Sutton Common, South Yorkshire'. Unpubl PhD thesis, University of Hull.

Coles, B 1995 *Wetland management – a survey for English Heritage*. Wetland Archaeology Research Project, Exeter.

Corfield, M 1996 'Preventive conservation for archaeological sites', *in* Roy, A & Smith, P (eds) *Archaeological Conservation and its Consequences*: 32–37. London.

Crone, A 1992 'Buiston Crannog', *Current Archaeology* 127, 295–7.

Howard, A G 1998 *Aquatic Environmental Chemistry*. New York.

Kegley, S E & Andrews, J 1998 *The Chemistry of Water*. California.

Lillie, M C & Cheetham, J L 2002 'Monitoring of moat ditch deposits at Knights Hospitaller's Preceptory, Beverley'. Unpubl report KHP-BEV/02–1, University of Hull.

Lillie, M, Crone, B A & Henderson, J C 2003 *South-west Crannog Survey: Phase 3. Proposal for a programme of monitoring on selected crannogs*. SWAP, unpubl report submitted to Historic Scotland.

Smith, R J 2005 'The preservation and degradation of wood in wetland archaeological and landfill sites'. Unpubl PhD thesis, University of Hull.

Wetzel, R G & Likens, G E 1991 *Limnological Analysis*. London.

Resisting decay, wind and waves:
new research on the lake-dwellings of south-west Scotland

JON C HENDERSON

INTRODUCTION

In 1989 AOC Archaeology, on behalf of Historic Scotland, carried out an assessment of the crannog resource in south-west Scotland (Barber & Crone 1993). The assumption of the survey was that the submerged crannogs in the area were relatively stable while their counterparts on drained land were rapidly decaying. While, as may have been expected, clear indications of the accelerated organic decay of sites on drained land were obtained, rather more surprisingly, it was suggested that submerged sites were also subject to decay. It was assumed that this was as a result of the infestation of underwater plant and animal life accelerating the biodegradation of organic deposits and was caused, primarily, by increased levels of nitrate run-off in affected lochs (Barber & Crone 1993, 528). This initial work resulted in the terrestrial excavation of one of the threatened drained sites – Buiston crannog (Crone 2000) – but, as is so often the case, the submerged sites were not examined further and there was no follow-up work on their state of preservation or examination of the assumptions made in the original survey.

That was until the Scottish Wetland Archaeology Programme (SWAP) was initiated in 2000, the first stated aim of which is to establish the nature, extent and condition of archaeological remains extant within the Scottish wetlands (Crone & Clarke 2001; Henderson 2004, 173). In 2002, Phase 2 of the South-West Scotland Crannog Survey was set up as part of the SWAP initiative funded by Historic Scotland. The aim of this second phase of survey is to identify crannog sites that are being subject to active biological decay, accurately survey them, and then establish effective systems of monitoring the rate of organic degradation taking place on sites located in different environments (submerged and on land). Ultimately, through a long-term monitoring programme, we hope to identify the mechanisms and causes of organic decay on crannogs throughout the south-west so that

effective preservation and management strategies can be implemented.

This paper discusses some of the results of the archaeological survey work carried out to date from 2002 to 2004, as well as some of the implications of the first pilot year of environmental monitoring (2004 to 2005). The scientific methodology and results of the monitoring work are discussed by Lillie et al in this volume. It is not my intention here to repeat this discussion, but rather offer my own observations on what the results recovered so far may indicate and how they compare with the observations made during the survey of the sites (Henderson & Crone 2002a, c; Henderson & Cavers 2003, 2004; Lillie et al 2004, 2005a, b, c, d).

THE SOUTH-WEST CRANNOG SURVEY PHASE TWO

The first phase of the South-West Crannog Survey (SWCS) identified 33 definite sites, three probable sites and 22 possible sites from the 74 sites reported by Munro and his contemporaries and subsequently listed in the National Monuments Record of Scotland (Barber & Crone 1993, 525). In the second phase, the existing survey records were examined and a desk-based assessment of the resource was carried out in an effort to select a representative sample for further work (Henderson & Crone 2002). From this study, 18 sites from a total of 14 lochs were selected for field visits to assess their suitability as monitoring sites. This included the sampling of organic deposits on crannogs and an evaluation of the surrounding landscape (ground conditions, water quality, soils, vegetation, land use) in which the sites were located (Henderson & Crone 2002c). As a group, these sites covered the full range of site locations and environments encountered in the south-west (from drained, to partly and fully submerged).

The crannogs of south-west Scotland are usually envisaged as *packwerk* mounds – made up of layers of peat, timber and brushwood to provide an artificial island for a timber superstructure – and are traditionally thought to contrast as a constructional type with the stone and boulder mounds found in the Highland regions north of the Clyde (Munro 1882, 242; Morrison 1985, 20; Henderson 1998, 236). However, the systematic surveys carried out during the SWCS have revealed that there is a far greater diversity of constructional forms present in the south-west than has previously been recognized (Henderson *et al* 2003).

While *packwerk* mounds of peat, brushwood and timber undoubtedly exist (such as at Buiston, Barlockhart, Milton Loch 1 and the Black Loch of Sanqhuar, there are also sites which feature a substantial stone element in their construction (for example at Dorman's Island in Whitefield Loch, Heron Isle in Black Loch, Cults Loch 1 and the crannog in Barean Loch) or that appear to be completely constructed out of stone with a stone superstructure on top (Rough Island in Loch Urr). The artificial island in Loch Arthur consists of two mounds of different material, the upper mound (the island) being built primarily of large boulders within a well developed soil, and the lower submerged mound of timber, brushwood and some smaller stones (Henderson & Cavers 2003; Henderson this volume).

Potential free-standing pile forms also exist. Survey of the submerged crannog in Barhapple Loch revealed a sub-rectangular plan of 144 vertical piles and 31 horizontal timbers (mainly oak with some alder) sitting directly in soft loch silts in a water depth of *c* 0.5m. The lack of any mound structure or boulder element to the site, coupled with the dense distribution of vertical timbers, may indicate that Barhapple was initially a free-standing structure that was later subject to the apparently *in situ* occupation levels recorded by Munro (Munro 1882, 182–90; 1885, 116–21). At the White Loch of Myrton, the crannog appears as a stone and timber mound with a dense concentration of over 100 vertical piles in an area some 20m by 40m occurring around the north-eastern margins of the site (Henderson *et al* 2003, fig 7, 93–4). The piles varied greatly in diameter from 0.1m to 0.4m and appeared to be regularly spaced about 1m apart. Most of the piles have decayed down to lochbed level although some still sit proud of the lochbed by about 0.2m. Soft silts surrounding the site and zero visibility conditions underwater made further examination of this site difficult, but two piles, both with axe-sharpened points, were sampled and identified as ash. Although only traceable around the north-eastern

margins of the main mound because the western and southern sides are shallower and choked with thick reeds, the location and spacing of the traceable piles suggest they were originally inserted into the lochbed in a concentric halo around the stone mound. They may therefore reflect the remains of either a site pre-dating the stone mound or of a free-standing timber superstructure contemporary with activity on the main mound.

The SWCS has also revealed the first Scottish example of a potential lakeside settlement. At Cults Loch, 16 vertical piles and one horizontal timber were found encircling a promontory which, although it did not appear artificial from surface inspection, produced charcoal on coring. These remains could indicate the presence of a crannog, though no other typical structural features were present. The site is considered more likely to be a lakeside site, perhaps related in some way to the crannog in Cults Loch. Although a worked oak stake was sampled from the site and produced a radiocarbon date of 2340 ± 50 BP (GU-12138), calibrating at 2 sigma to 550 to 200 BC, which is somewhat earlier than the date of 1790 ± 50 BP (GU-10919), calibrating to AD 120 to 390, obtained from the crannog out in the loch. Lakeside sites were previously only known from Ireland and the discovery of the site suggests that the systematic survey of lake margins may be a fruitful avenue of future research in Scotland.

The findings of the SWCS challenge simplistic definitions of crannog form and question the relevance of previously held type boundaries. Many of the sites in the south-west which feature substantial stone elements are difficult to separate on constructional grounds from the boulder mound sites of the Scottish Highlands. Furthermore, palaeobotanical studies of organic deposits from Loch Arthur crannog and Dorman's Island in Whitefield Loch (Bogaard 2004, 8–10) reveal deposits very similar in nature to those encountered at the Highland sites of Oakbank crannog in Loch Tay (Dixon 1981, 19; Miller *et al* 1998, 806) and Ederline crannog in Loch Awe (Bogaard & Hall 2005, 293–5). These deposits all feature woodchips and hazelnut shells within matrices of compressed plant matter and wooden material. The perceived differences between the Highland and south-west sites may be more attributable to the lack of underwater survey carried out nationally, as many of the key identifiable characteristics of sites noted during the SWCS can only be seen underwater. Previous surveys in the south-west have been land based and have focused on the examination of drained sites. As a result, the impression has been created in the literature that south-western sites are mounds of peat, timber and brushwood. In fact, the occurrence of peat on sites may simply be due to the circumstances of preservation as brushwood and plant matter will survive intact in submerged contexts but such deposits are more likely to decay, leading to the formation of peat on drained and periodically flooded sites. The perceived differences between Highland and south-western sites may have more to do with the widespread drainage and improvement operations in the latter area than any significant cultural, structural or chronological variation. Equally, the more widespread occurrence of exposed organics and structural timber on submerged sites in the south-west may be attributable to the smaller size and less active tidal regimes of those lochs compared to the much larger and more turbulent Highland lochs.

Some 13 radiocarbon dates have been recovered from ten crannogs during Phase 2 of the SWCS (table 1). These dates further support the view that a main phase of crannog activity occurred during the Later Prehistoric period, particularly in the second half of the first millennium BC (Henderson 1998, 235).

SITES SELECTED FOR MONITORING

The 2002 fieldwork programme identified six crannogs from six lochs as suitable candidates for

monitoring on grounds of their varied environments and perceived threats: Milton Loch; Loch Arthur; Whitefield Loch; Barhapple Loch; Cults Loch and Barlockhart (see fig 1). Their selection encompassed the full range of postulated threats to crannogs in the south-west: drainage, fluctuating water-tables, mechanical erosion, potential nitrate run-off and the effects of micro-organisms caused by active biological environments (Henderson 2004, 177–9).

High levels of biological activity were encountered in Milton Loch and Whitefield Loch, with suspended algae in particular creating poor underwater visibility ranging from 0.5m to nil. Survey revealed that all the exposed timbers on Milton Loch 1 (the site famously excavated by Piggott in 1953) and on the crannog, known locally as Dorman's Island, in Whitefield Loch were being actively degraded by aquatic plants, algae, mollusca and other wood-boring organisms. At Milton Loch 1 some 40 loose timbers were found in the water, all of which were heavily infested with wood-boring organisms and had, presumably, been eroded off the site. Exposed sections, actively eroding into the loch, were located at three points on Dorman's Island in Whitefield Loch. It is possible that the observed erosion has been caused by the impact of wave fetch in the loch. However, were this the case, it is hard to see why erosion seems to be accelerating and perhaps hard to see why the sites survive at all. All the rich organic deposits in the sections, which included structural timbers, plant matter, dung,

TABLE 1
Radiocarbon dates from the SWCS Phase 2.

Name	Sample	Lab no.	Date BP	Cal 2σ
Cults Loch	Oak; pile	GU-10919	1790±50	AD 120–390
Black Loch of Sanqhuar	Oak; pile	GU-10918	1840±50	AD 60–340
Barlockhart	Oak; woodchip	GU-11564	1980±40	60 BC–AD 130
Barlockhart	Oak; woodchip	GU-11563	1975±45	90 BC–AD 130
White Loch of Myrton	Ash; pile	GU-10921	2080±50	350–30 BC
Barhapple Loch	Oak; pile	GU-10920	2130±50	360–40 BC
Loch Arthur Tr.3	Alder; horizontal	GU-12175	2215±35	390–170 BC
Dorman's Island	Alder; pile	GU-10917	2250±50	400–190 BC
Loch Arthur Tr.1	Alder; horizontal	GU-12173	2240±35	400–200 BC
Loch Arthur Tr.2	Alder; horizontal	GU-12174	2275±35	400–200 BC
Loch Heron I	Alder; pile	SUERC-6472	2310±35	410–200 BC
Cults Loch Promontory	Oak; pile	GU-12138	2340±50	550–200 BC
Loch Heron II	Alder; pile	SUERC-6473	2390±35	760–390 BC

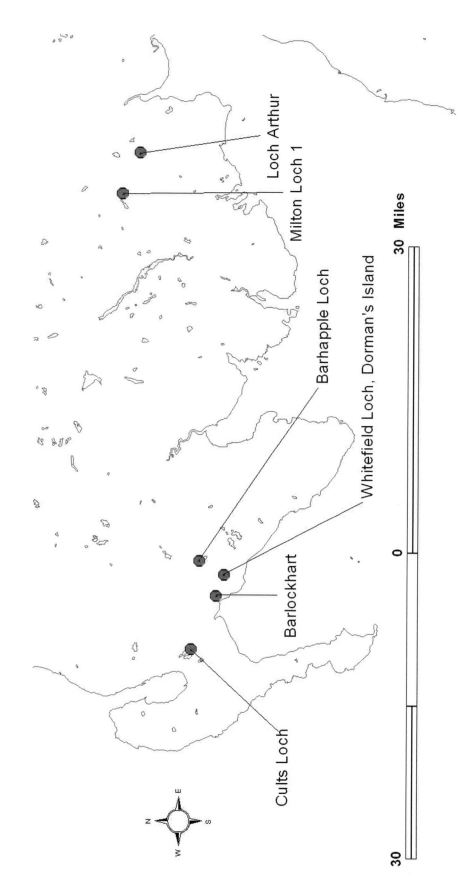

FIGURE 1
Location of SWCS monitoring sites, Dumfries and Galloway.

twigs, woodchips, charcoal and hazelnut shells, were subject to decay from the active biological regime present in the loch. The tops of timbers sampled from these sections displayed evidence of infestation by freshwater mollusca.

Biological degradation was also seen to be a cause for concern on the crannog at Loch Arthur despite the fact that the loch has very good water quality, with underwater visibility of *c* 3m, and does not suffer algal blooms, perhaps because the land around the loch is managed organically. Underwater examination revealed that organic deposits and timbers on the crannog are being actively eroded while aquatic plant growth appears to be causing the degradation of exposed timbers. Rich, sub-fossil organic deposits, consisting of bracken, twigs and comminuted plant matter, were exposed over the upper surface of the submerged mound, which lies only *c* 0.3m below the water level, while exposed areas are actively eroding around the side of the mound in depths of *c* 2–3m. The condition of the timbers on the site varies from freshly exposed timber bearing no vegetal growth, through timbers covered in vegetation, to timber in advanced stages of decay. This suggests that the degradation results from an active and, more importantly, relatively recent process.

The crannogs in Cults Loch and Barhapple appeared to be protected by silts but were being affected by fluctuating water levels. At Barhapple, the presence of exposed sapwood around the base of erosion cones on many of the *Quercus* sp. piles indicated that the silts were being actively disturbed. Sapwood, the outer few rings that still conduct water and nutrients, is very susceptible to decay and biological attack and its presence indicates that exposure was a relatively recent event. It is thought that this exposure may be caused by the shallowness of the water, allowing wave action to disturb the silts. Equally, as much of the site lies in just 0.5m of water, small changes in loch level could have drastic effects on the surviving timbers. The crannog in Cults Loch is a large stone and timber mound, protected underwater by a thick (*c* 1m) covering of silt. It was assumed that there was a low chance of active organic decay on the site due to the protective silt cover and, equally, the contour survey revealed no evidence for erosion. In this sense Cults was considered something of a control site although there was also clear evidence for a recent lowering of the water level along the lake margins in the form of recent earlier shoreline marks.

The main threats at the partially drained crannog in Barlockhart were considered to be a seasonally fluctuating water table and high levels of biological activity, including active algal blooms. As the only 'drained' crannog examined which was seen on coring to retain some level of organic deposit, it was regarded as a worthwhile candidate for monitoring.

THE PILOT MONITORING PROGRAMME (JULY 2004 TO NOVEMBER 2005)

Funding was secured from Historic Scotland for a pilot year of monitoring at the selected sites to test and refine the monitoring methodology in advance of the implementation of a longer term programme. The pilot strategy aimed to monitor the crannog burial environment over one year; directly through the measurement of the redox potential, pH and water saturation of *in situ* deposits as well as consider the effects of the wider loch environment through comparative on- and off-site diatom and water chemistry studies (Lillie *et al* 2003, 6–9; Lillie *et al* this volume). Through measuring the rate of flow of electrons in a deposit, redox potential is used to determine the reducing (ie preserving) or oxidizing (ie decaying) potential of a burial environment. Unsurprisingly, water saturation (measured using piezometers) is seen as the principal factor in wet site preservation as it excludes atmospheric oxygen (Crone *et al* 2001, 61; Chapman & Cheetham 2002). Research carried out to date suggests that measuring the key parameters of fluctuating water height, pH and redox potential provide a sufficiently robust data-set from which the preservational qualities of an environment can be assessed (Caple 1993; Caple & Dungworth 1997; Henderson & Crone 2002b). Redox probes (0.5m; 1m; 1.5m) and piezometers were established at five of the sites in July 2004 and full monitoring took place from November 2004 to November 2005 (see figs 2–6). Unfortunately, Barhapple was not part of the pilot phase assessment as it is fully submerged, but it will be included in future seasons using underwater redox probes.

For the most part, redox potentials appear to indicate reducing environments at all five sites (reducing to highly reducing over most of the year). Equally, the crannog deposits do not seem to be drastically affected by water level changes. Changes in water level of up to 0.5m have been observed at Milton Loch and Loch Arthur, which obviously impacts the redox readings from the uppermost crannog deposits. However, these changes appear to be short lived and they do not seem to have had a lasting impact on the preservative quality of

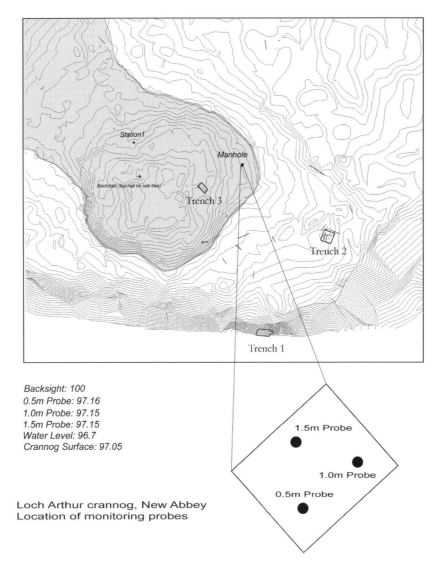

Backsight: 100
0.5m Probe: 97.16
1.0m Probe: 97.15
1.5m Probe: 97.15
Water Level: 96.7
Crannog Surface: 97.05

Loch Arthur crannog, New Abbey
Location of monitoring probes

FIGURE 2
Loch Arthur crannog, New Abbey, redox probes survey.

the deposits. The affected upper deposits quickly recover and overall the sites continue to be reducing environments although it goes without saying that a longer term study of the impact of such changes would be needed to fully assess the effects of short-term fluctuations in water heights on the preservative stability of the crannog deposits. Certainly from the five sites studied it would appear that there is nothing like the seasonal changes in water levels seen on some of the larger Highland lochs, which can often be measured in terms of metres.

In general, the lochs monitored appear to be well oxygenated and oligotrophic or mesotrophic. Only Cults Loch provided evidence for being moderately eutrophic but it was also well oxygenated. These findings are surprising in that they do not, at first glance, support the view of the lochs of the south-west as being much more biologically active (nutrient rich) than Highland lochs, which are also mainly oligotrophic in nature. However, Highland lochs tend to be acidic (due to surrounding peaty soils) and occur at much higher altitudes, factors which effectively limit the range of plant species they can support. In contrast, the south-western lochs are smaller, shallower, occur in lowland locations and tend to be pH neutral or even slightly alkaline. The lowland location and shallow nature of south-western lochs may account for the widespread occurrence of aquatic plants seen on exposed submerged crannog deposits. Although it is often assumed otherwise, submerged crannogs are not in fully anoxic environments; certainly their outer surfaces are not in hypolimnetic water. They lie in shallow water and, consequently, they are not isolated from the wind mixing of water, and are shallow enough to permit light for plant photosynthesis. Wave action may be

Milton Loch crannog I
Location of monitoring probes

1.5m Probe

1.0m Probe

0.5m Probe

N

Dry Area

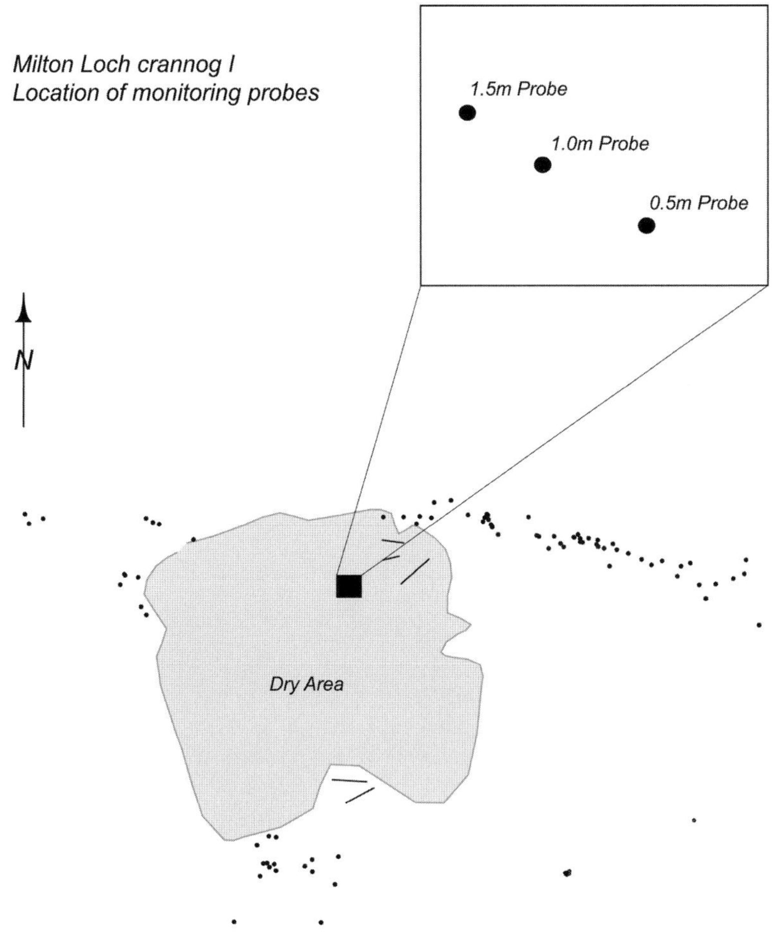

FIGURE 3
Milton Loch I: redox probes survey.

uncovering deposits on which vegetation can then develop, causing the break-up of the timbers and thus promoting aquatic plant growth and biological decay.

The view of the lochs of the south-west as stable and oligotrophic is not borne out by the experience of working and diving in them since 2002. There appears to be a wide variation in visibility due to

suspended algae in the water occurring during the summer months. While the lochs are clear during the winter, many of them are subject to algal blooms in late July, August and September. These algal blooms can be very brief and lochs can be seen to change on a week-to-week basis during the summer. It is possible that the quarterly water chemistry and bio-monitoring carried out during the pilot year was not frequent enough to fully detect these changes. That said, the diatom evidence from Barlockhart, Milton Loch and Whitefield Loch do indicate shifts from oligotrophic to eutrophic conditions occurring late in the year (Lillie *et al* 2005c, d). This correlates with the fact that algal blooms have never been noted as a problem in Loch Arthur or Cults Loch by the diving teams but have been recognized at the other three lochs. It is possible that these lochs switch from being oligotrophic to eutrophic and then back again very quickly, which in the long term could have a destabilizing influence on exposed organic deposits. This can happen when lochs are artificially enriched from an input of phosphates (most usually from fertilizers) which then quickly produce short-lived algal blooms. In fact, the Scottish Environmental Protection Agency (SEPA 2005) has identified this phenomenon as a major threat to the long-term stability of Scottish freshwater lochs – and it is something that future monitoring programmes in the south-west will have to examine in more detail.

The monitoring work has also shown that loch pH and crannog pH appear to be independent variables. The loch waters appear to be neutral to slightly alkaline, with pH values in the range of 6.5 to 8, while the deposits monitored within the crannogs provided somewhat acidic conditions, with pH values between 3 and 6. The latter conditions are certainly sufficiently acidic to inhibit biological activity and thus would promote the preservation of organic material. In other words, it would seem that the waters of the lochs do not appear to alter or otherwise affect the internal crannog sedimentary environment.

However, discussions with John Barber of SWAP have resulted in the formulation of a possible erosional mechanism involving the pH of the loch waters and crannog deposits. The pH scale of measurement is logarithmic – each unit represents one order of magnitude in the hydrogen ion concentration being measured (pH is the inverse of the log of the hydrogen concentration). The maximum difference between the lacustrine and depositional pH values is 5 units (effectively 10^5 difference in hydrogen ion concentration) while the minimum difference is 0.5 units, or a five-fold difference. This is a non-trivial gradient and where acidic humified matter in the make-up of a crannog is accessible to the waters of the loch, chemical erosion would certainly be taking place. However, the macro plant remains of structural and other wood, brushwood, reed masses, etc. exposed in the process of this erosion probably slow down the rate of erosion overall by penning in neutralized water, the product of the acid/alkali reaction (much as a wet suit pens in warm water close to the body of a diver in otherwise bitterly cold water). As noted above, wave action has been cited as a possible cause of mechanical erosion but the problem with this is that in most lochs there is probably nothing new or recent about wave action. If waves alone could account for the recent losses of material, the real research question would become: why does so much actually survive in the first place? Wave action has, however, a second effect and that is to continuously wash the exposed face of a crannog with fresh loch water, accelerating the chemical erosion by removing its neutralizing by-products. This interpretation is supported by a further observation made during this and other diving projects on crannogs. An isthmus of mineral matter, sometimes containing finds, has been observed running from the crannog towards the land. We suggest that this represents mineral matter released by the chemical erosion of humified matter on the lochside face of the crannog and moved around the sides of the crannog by wave-driven current systems to fall out of suspension in the stiller water in the lee of the crannog. In turn, this mechanism may explain the apparent concentration of archaeological finds

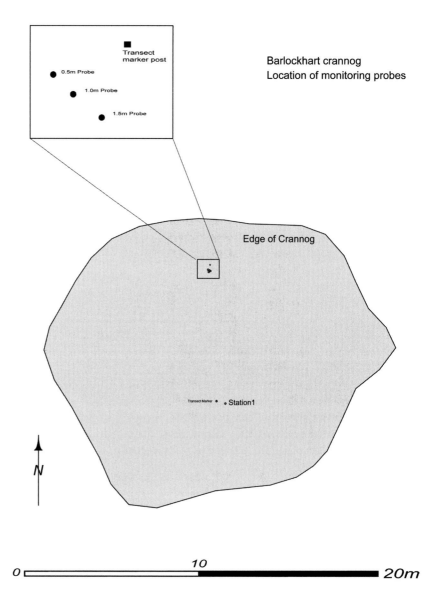

FIGURE 4
Barlockhart: redox probes survey.

in this location at several crannogs, notably at Loch Glashan in Scotland (Crone & Campbell 2005, 119–20) and Llangorse in Wales (Redknap & Lane 1994, 200).

In some lochs, mechanical damage from wave action may well be a potent erosional force. Both the monitoring and survey work have highlighted

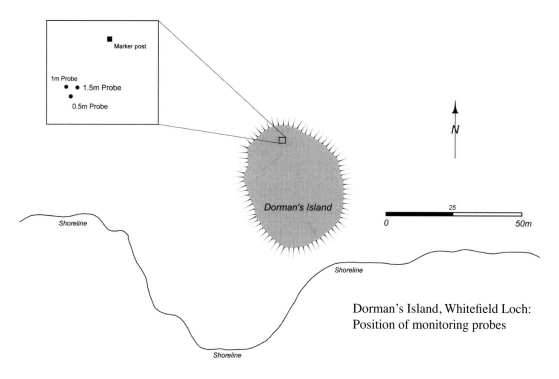

FIGURE 5
Dorman's Island, Whitefield Loch: redox probes survey.

mechanical erosion as a major factor in the exposure of deposits at Loch Arthur, Dorman's Island and, to a lesser extent, Milton Loch. It is perhaps significant that these lochs are amongst the larger lochs of the south-west and are therefore subject to larger wave fetch ranges than the other lochs examined to date. The projected effects of wave fetch are best illustrated with a case study.

CASE STUDY: DORMAN'S ISLAND, WHITEFIELD LOCH

Dorman's Island was one of the richest crannogs encountered during the South-West Crannog Survey (Henderson *et al* 2003, 94–6). Eroding sections revealed rich organic deposits of structural timbers, plant matter, dung, twigs, woodchips, charcoal and hazelnut shell. An alder pile sampled in 2002, from the northern margins of the mound, provided a date of 2250 ± 50 BP (GU-10917), which calibrates to 400–190 BC. As well as being one of the richest sites examined, Dorman's Island also displayed the most severe evidence for biological infestation and degradation. Suspended algae in the water (algal bloom) not only promoted biological activity on

exposed archaeological deposits but also resulted in low underwater visibility (less than 0.5m to zero). Along the eroding sections *in situ*, timbers were seen to be heavily infested by freshwater mollusca and other biota while the deposits themselves were affected by the very active algal regime in the loch.

Survey revealed the site is a large, oval, flat-topped boulder mound measuring 39.5m NW/SE by 31.5m SW/NE (see fig 7). The mound rises 3.2m off the lochbed, and is covered in trees and bushes. An area approximately 25m by 19m is dry all year round and it was here that the piezometer and redox probes were installed. The area of erosion, however, occurs in about 1m to 5m depth of water as a long erosional scar running along the north-west margins of the crannog mound. Changes in the condition of the eroded deposits, from freshly exposed to collapsed, were observed from June 2002 to January 2004, suggesting that the erosion is rapid and recent in origin. If the erosion was ancient then there would be little remaining to observe today.

The erosional scar is interpreted as having been formed by the effects of wave action hitting and scouring the north-western sides of the site. The recovery of diatom taxa that indicate wind-stressed

Cults Loch, Castle Kennedy
Location of monitoring probes

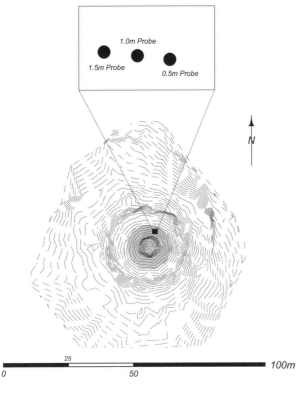

FIGURE 6
Cults Loch: redox probes survey.

water environments (*Aulacoseira* genus; Lillie this volume) further support this view. The chemical erosional model presented above may also have a role to play at this site. The location of Dorman's Island in the south-east corner of Whitefield Loch means that the site is at the receiving end of prevailing winds running along the loch from the south-west and north-west. This means the north-western sides of the site are subject to the full effects of wave fetch generated across the length of the loch. A wave's fetch is the distance through clear water over which it can run. The longer the fetch, the bigger the amplitude (or height of the wave) and, ultimately, the more destructive it will be. During the 2004 season it was observed that this activity is beginning to undermine the trees along the north-western margins of the site – one of which has now collapsed into the loch (Henderson & Cavers 2004, 4). It goes without saying that instability caused by falling trees is detrimental to the condition and preservation of the internal deposits of the mound in the affected areas.

This recent onset of wave-base erosion must relate to a shallowing out of the loch in the recent past. Further evidence of the shallowing of the loch can be seen along the southern shores where sites previously surrounded by water are now found on dry land. Fig 8 depicts a map by the Revd George Wilson of Whitefield Loch in 1871. Features described as islands in 1871, such as Tree Island (no. 7), are now on dry land while Dorman's Island (no. 17) is depicted further out from shore than is the case today. The map suggests there has been a lowering in loch level over the past 135 years by about 1.5 to 1m (ie exactly where the erosion is now occurring).

In the absence of human interference or the direct management of loch levels by use of sluices dams etc., the likely cause of level fluctuations are variations in water entering the lake as a result of climate change or as a result of changes in the lake's catchment. A large area along the northern shores of the loch was planted with conifers by the Forestry Commission in the 1960s. The afforestation, or rather the maturing of afforested areas over the past 40 years, within the catchment could, alone, account for the changing levels observed. Conifers can depress the water-table of the land on which they grow by up to 1m, and over the years would reduce the volumes of water running-off to the lake. The change in land-use from, presumably, ploughing or pasture to forestry would also have affected the sediment yields entering the loch, especially as the two main inlets to the loch are located along the steeper northern shores. These factors could have reduced the lake levels sufficiently for the wave-bases to begin the frictional erosion of the footings of the crannog.

Underwater observations and the survey suggest that erosion is maximized on the up-current/upwind side of the crannog (NW) and that deposition, or rather re-deposition, is occurring on the leeward side (SE) of the crannog (see fig 9). The re-deposition is visible as a shallow spit marked with reeds. This was previously interpreted as a possible causeway (Henderson *et al* 2003) but probing carried out in 2004 failed to reveal any coherent structure and the feature may have entirely formed as a result of the re-deposition of material from the wave-based erosion described above.

CONCLUSION

The one-year pilot monitoring programme was designed as a very broad-brush impact assessment of the conditions of the internal deposits of the

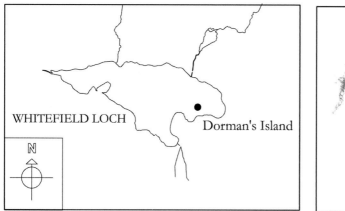

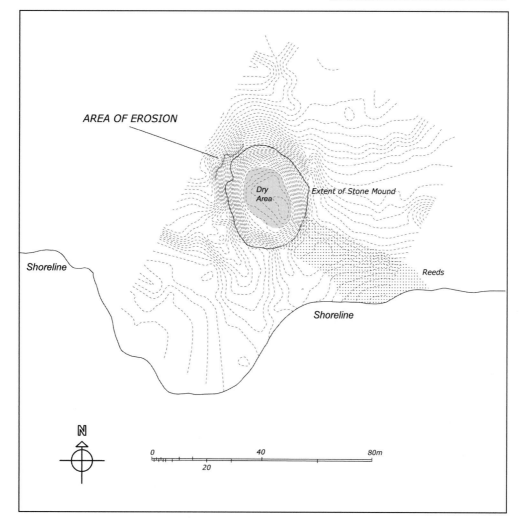

DORMAN'S ISLAND, WHITEFIELD LOCH: Contour Survey

Contours at 0.1m increments

FIGURE 7
Dorman's Island, Whitefield Loch.

selected crannogs and their wider loch environments. Longer-term studies lasting over several years would be needed to provide a robust dataset on seasonal variation and the full interaction between crannogs and their immediate environment. It is also clear that, if we are to fully understand the detail of seasonal shifts in environmental parameters on and around crannogs, a higher resolution study is required.

The pilot study redox probes indicate for the most part good reducing environments but it must be kept in mind that these data relate only to the undisturbed deposits located in the centre of the crannog mounds. The underwater surveys have revealed that deposits are being eroded at points around the sides of sites and that it is in these areas that organic deposits are being uncovered and subject to decay. It is clear that the positions of the probes do not take into account the mechanical and potentially chemical erosion occurring underwater at the sides of these sites. Using underwater redox probes located in these key areas must form an important part of future monitoring work.

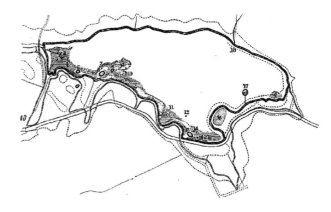

FIGURE 8
Whitefield Loch in 1871 (Wilson 1871).

The Dorman's Island case study illustrates that site specific variables of each location need to be investigated. The changes observed in the deposits at Dorman's Island appear to reflect recent land-use and environmental changes in the catchment at a synoptic

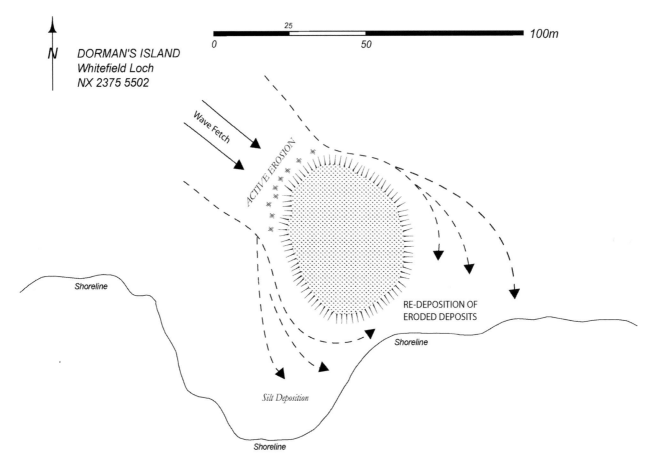

FIGURE 9
Active erosion by wave action at Dorman's Island, Whitefield Loch.

scale. The study of crannog deposits as sensitive localized environments – ie crannogs as repositories and rapid indicators of small scale environmental change – should be an important aspect of future environmental studies of these sites and, indeed, in the next phase of monitoring. By comparing longer term data recovered from the deposits on crannogs with wider local and national meteorological data it may be possible to model climate change in terms of the observable trends in crannog preservation. As such, the study of crannogs may have a role to play in future studies of the effects and impacts of global warming at a localized scale (Henderson & Cavers 2003, 8).

ACKNOWLEDGEMENTS

The fieldwork for the South-West Crannog Survey was grant aided by Historic Scotland, the Scottish Trust for Archaeological Research (STAR) and AOC Archaeology Group, and was conducted by the Underwater Archaeology Research Centre (UARC) as part of the Scottish Wetland Archaeology Programme (SWAP). Special thanks to John Barber and Anne Crone for their constant encouragement during the project and especially to Graeme Cavers for his assistance in the field. Additional thanks to Graeme for preparing the illustrations used in this paper.

REFERENCES

Barber, J W & Crone, B A 1993 'Crannogs; a diminishing resource? A survey of the crannogs of South West Scotland and excavations at Buiston Crannog', *Antiquity*, 67, 520–33.

Bogaard, A 2004 'Loch Whitefield and Loch Arthur: preliminary archaeobotanical analysis', *in* Henderson & Cavers 2004, 8–10.

Bogaard, A & Hall, A R 2005 'Archaeobotanical sample assessment', *in* Cavers, M G & Henderson, J C, 'Underwater excavation at Ederline Crannog, Loch Awe, Argyll, Scotland', *International Journal of Nautical Archaeology* 34, 293–5.

Caple, C 1993 'Defining a reburial environment; research problems characterizing waterlogged anoxic environments', *Proceedings of the 5th ICOM group on wet organic archaeological materials conference. Portland Maine.* ICOM Committee for the Conservation Working Group on WOAM, 407–21, Bremerhaven.

Caple, C & Dungworth, D 1997 'Investigations into waterlogged burial environments', *in* Sinclair, A, Slater, E & Gowlett, J (eds) *Archaeological Sciences 1995: Proceedings of a conference on the application of*

scientific techniques to the study of archaeology. Oxbow Monograph 64, 233–40, Oxford.

Cavers, M G & Henderson, J C 2005 'Underwater excavation at Ederline Crannog, Loch Awe, Argyll, Scotland', *International Journal of Nautical Archaeology* 34.2, 282–98.

Crone, B A 2000 *The History of a Scottish Lowland Crannog: Excavations at Buiston, Ayrshire 1989–90.* STAR Monograph 4, Edinburgh.

Crone, B A & Campbell, E 2005 *A Crannog of the First Millennium AD: Excavations at Loch Glashan by Jack Scott, 1960.* Society of Antiquaries of Scotland, Edinburgh.

Crone, B A & Clarke, C 2001 *Scottish Wetland Archaeology Programme: Phase 1.* Unpubl SWAP report for Historic Scotland.

Crone, B A, Henderson, J C & Sands, R 2001 'Scottish crannogs: construction, collapse and conflation – problems of interpretation, *in* Raftery, B & Hickey, J (eds) *Recent Developments in Wetland Archaeology.* Seandálaíocht Monograph 2. Dublin, 55–67.

Dixon, T N D 1981 'Preliminary excavation of Oakbank Crannog, Loch Tay: interim report', *International Journal of Nautical Archaeology* 10.1, 15–22.

Henderson, J C 2004 'The Scottish Wetland Archaeology Programme: Assessing and Monitoring the Resource', *Journal of Wetland Archaeology* 4, 61–75.

Henderson, J C & Cavers, M G 2003 *South-west Crannog Survey: Phase 3. Fieldwork and Survey 2003.* SWAP, unpubl report submitted to Historic Scotland.

Henderson, J C & Cavers, M G 2004 *South-west Crannog Survey: Phase 4. Fieldwork and Survey 2004.* SWAP, unpubl report submitted to Historic Scotland.

Henderson, J C & Crone, B A 2002a: *South-west Crannog Survey: Phase 2. Desk-based site assessment.* SWAP, unpubl report submitted to Historic Scotland.

Henderson, J C & Crone, B A 2002b *South-west Crannog Survey: Phase 2. Remote sensing systems for measuring the condition of submerged and buried organic remains.* SWAP, unpubl report submitted to Historic Scotland.

Henderson, J C & Crone, B A 2002c: *South-west Crannog Survey: Phase 2. Field assessment and evaluation of selected crannogs.* SWAP, unpubl report submitted to Historic Scotland.

Henderson, J C, Crone B A & Cavers, M G 2003 'A condition survey of selected crannogs in south-west Scotland', *Transactions of the Dumfries and Galloway Natural History and Antiquarian Society* 77, 79–102.

Lillie, M, Crone, B A & Henderson, J C 2003 *South-west Crannog Survey: Phase 3. Proposal for a programme of monitoring on selected crannogs.* SWAP, unpubl report submitted to Historic Scotland.

Lillie, M, Reed, J & Smith, R 2004 *South-west Scottish Crannogs. Monitoring of* in situ *burial environment and preservation status.* University of Hull, unpubl Report no. SWAP/04–01.

Lillie, M, Reed, J & Smith, R 2005a: *South-west Scottish Crannogs. Monitoring of* in situ *burial environment and preservation status. February 2005.* University of Hull, unpubl report no. SWAP/05–01.

Lillie, M, Reed, J & Smith, R 2005b *South-west Scottish Crannogs. Monitoring of* in situ *burial environment and preservation status. May 2005.* University of Hull, unpubl report no. SWAP/05–02.

Lillie, M, Reed, J & Smith, R 2005c *South-west Scottish Crannogs. Monitoring of* in situ *burial environment and preservation status. August 2005.* University of Hull, unpubl report no. SWAP/05–03.

Lillie, M, Reed, J, Williams, D & Budd, C 2005d *South-west Scottish Crannogs. Monitoring of* in situ *burial environment and preservation status. November 2005.* University of Hull, unpubl report no. SWAP/05–04.

Miller, J, Dickson, J H & Dixon, T N 1998 'Unusual food plants from Oakbank crannog, Scottish Highlands: cloudberry, opium poppy and spelt wheat', *Antiquity* 72, 805–11.

Munro, R 1882 *Ancient Scottish Lake-Dwellings or Crannogs.* Edinburgh.

Munro, R 1885 'The Lake Dwellings of Wigtonshire', *Archaeological and Historical Collections relating to Ayrshire and Galloway* 5, 74–124.

Redknap, M & Lane, A 1994 'The early medieval crannog at Llangorse, Powys: an interim statement on the 1989–93 seasons', *International Journal of Nautical Archaeology* 23.3, 189–205.

Scottish Environmental Protection Agency 2005: *Eutrophication Assessment of Scottish Coastal, Estuarine and Inland Waters.* Version 05/12/2005 (available online at *www.sepa.org.uk/publications/index.htm*).

Impressive, well appointed, rich and enigmatic:
Coolure Demesne crannog, Lough Derravaragh, County Westmeath

AIDAN O'SULLIVAN and ROB SANDS

INTRODUCTION

Coolure Demesne crannog, Lough Derravaragh, Co Westmeath is one of the most impressive and enigmatic archaeological sites in the Irish midlands. The excellent archaeological survival, well appointed location and the rich artefact assemblage all help to paint a picture of a structure that was, at some time, both locally and regionally important (O'Sullivan A 2004). Despite this, it has received relatively little archaeological attention. Funding from the Irish Heritage Council has allowed for

a more substantial investigation to be undertaken by the current authors and Eamonn P Kelly of the National Museum of Ireland. The full report of this work is available on the internet (O'Sullivan, Kelly & Sands 2005).

PHYSICAL FORM, SURFACE DEPOSITS AND STRUCTURAL DETAILS

Coolure Demesne is located on the northern shore of Lough Derravaragh, Co Westmeath, Ireland (figs

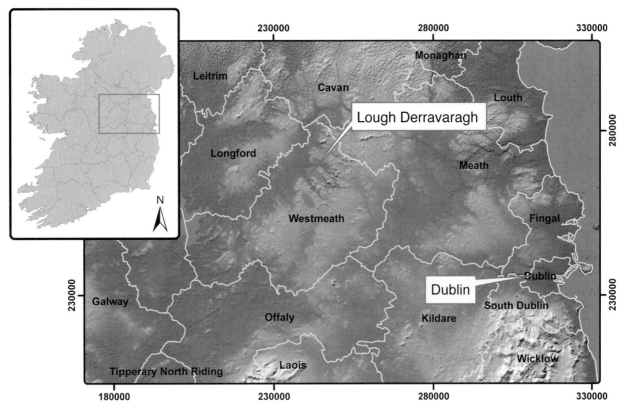

Satellite image courtesy of NASA - see http://visibleearth.nasa.gov/

FIGURE 1
Location of Lough Derravaragh.

303

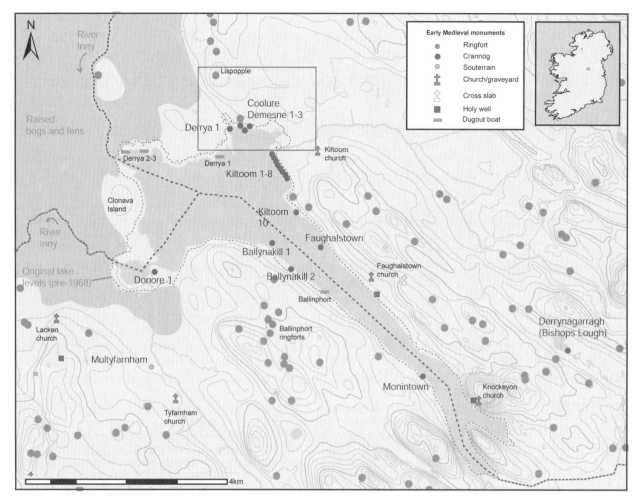

FIGURE 2
Location of Coolure Demesne crannog in Lough Derravaragh, Co Westmeath.

1 and 2). Lough Derravaragh is one of a series of midland lakes interlinked as part of the greater Shannon river catchment. It sits within the central bogland and moraine zone, with its northern end within an area of bog and its southern and eastern edges against an area of higher ground (Aalen, Whelan & Stout 1997, figs 5 and 12; O'Sullivan 1998, fig 5).

Approaching the crannog today, it appears as a tree-covered island of impressive size (fig 3). Of all of the islands on the loch, it is the largest and most visible, some 45m in diameter and 5m at its highest point. The island also commands impressive views of the lough both towards its south-eastern end and towards the extreme end of Derravaragh's south-western arm. The whole surface of the exposed crannog is covered in boulders that display no clear internal structural patterning – with the exception of

a small circular enclosure on the highest part of the site. This enclosure is of indeterminate date and might easily be duck hide constructed at some point in the last century.

The morphology revealed by the 2004 survey showed a high area of curving ground toward the northern side, creating a steep bank when viewed from the shore (fig 4). On the far side of the site, toward the south, away from the shore, the ground levels off into two lower areas. The lower of these two expands out toward the south-east, continuing below the current water line by approximately 8m, before dropping to the lochbed. The crannog as a whole corresponds to Fredengren's 'high cairn' type and the three zones identified broadly fit with the 'mid-cairn', 'plateau' and 'berm' features (Fredengren 2002, 85).

The most obvious wooden remains on the crannog are series of upright timbers that were discovered in

2004, some of which are clearly structural. These timbers can be divided into two groups (O'Sullivan, Kelly & Sands 2005, plate 27, 170):

- A series of oblong-sectioned oak uprights, mostly radially split. Currently exposed only on the southern edge of the island.

- A large number of smaller roundwood uprights, emerging as the oak uprights petered out, and extending over an area just below the water line within the south-eastern portion of the berm. Sampled timbers from this area revealed a range of species used including alder (*Alnus* sp.), yew (*Taxus baccatta*), ash (*Fraxinus excelsior*), oak (*Quercus* sp.) and hazel (*Corylus avellana*).

Samples of three of the oak uprights were taken for dendrochronological analysis and six samples from roundwood uprights were taken for radiocarbon analysis. The large oak uprights are derived from mature, long lived oak trees, felled in the fifth century AD (see below). What remains of the original structure are merely the driven ends; the extant length of the largest being approximately 2m. The width, thickness, length and depth to which these timbers have been driven must be indicative of a substantial, architecturally impressive structure. The impression this must have given to Early Medieval people viewing the island would have been very different from the rounded, slumped, tree covered mound that we see today.

SUB-SURFACE STRUCTURE AND ENVIRONMENTAL SAMPLING

While the 2004 season concentrated on surface characterization and obtaining scientific dating

FIGURE 3
Coolure Demesne crannog approached from the south-east.

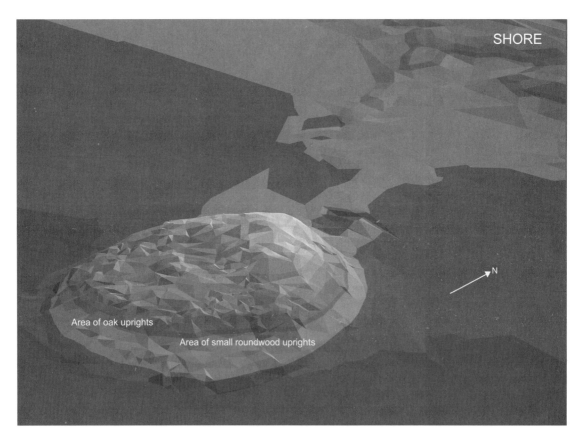

SHORE

Area of oak uprights

Area of small roundwood uprights

N

FIGURE 4
Current morphology of Coolure Demesne crannog.

material, it was considered necessary to obtain an understanding of what could be expected from sub-surface investigation. A small test pit was excavated into the surface of the berm, close to the edge of the current water line. Preliminary examination of the surface of the crannog had revealed an area of animal bone on the south-eastern side. Work during the 2004 season showed this to be very extensive, extending over much of the lower south-eastern platform. Consequently, the test pit was targeted in this area to both understand the material upon which the bone spread had been located and to assess the survival of environmental data as a basis for future investigations. Below an initial capping of larger stones (10–15cm in diameter), a series of increasingly dark organic deposits were encountered before the lake marls were reached at approximately 55cm from the ground surface. In the lower part of these deposits, three distinct, thin, brushwood layers were encountered. Dating samples were taken from bone in the upper layers and the three brushwood contexts (see below).

Bone material from the surface spread and from the test pit was examined by Vincent Butler. The conclusion of this analysis was that this assemblage broadly represented discarded waste from butchering and food consumption. The majority of the assemblage derived from cattle – with pig, sheep and goat also being well represented. There was also limited representation of horse and red deer (Butler 2005).

Environmental samples from all layers were analysed by Eileen Reilly and Penny Johnston (Reilly & Johnston 2005). Generally, the preservation was excellent, survival predominantly resulted from waterlogging, but charring was also present. Identified plant remains can be grouped into five categories:

1. Wild plants: included species such as fat hen and nettles.
2. Fruit seeds: included blackberry, elderberry and plum stones.
3. Cereal grains: included the charred remains of barley and oats.

4. Water-loving plants: included knotgrasses, buttercups and sedges.

5. Nut shells: included the fragments of hazel nut shells.

The environmental samples were also examined for insect remains. Identified species can be broadly grouped into four core ecological groups:

1. Aquatic/semi-aquatic species.
2. Woodland and wood-boring insects.
3. Decomposing and dung species.
4. Plant-feeding species.

The environmental sampling was too limited to provide detailed conclusions; however, anthropogenic activity is clearly indicated with the suggestion of the exploitation of both local wild and cultivated species. The insect remains were generally small and fragmented indicating possible bioturbation and hinting at secondary deposition. Foul conditions are indicated by the majority of beetle species recovered, which suggests the presence of human faeces and/or animal waste. The very low level of house fauna amongst the assemblage suggests that the material does not derive from within buildings on the island. The virtual absence of house fauna might also be indicative of seasonal or interrupted occupation but further, more extensive sampling, is required.

DATING

Initially dating was based on artefactual evidence that had been retrieved from the island over a number of years. The crannog was a location that was well known to local diving groups and treasure hunters, by whom it was systematically searched in the 1980s. In 1990, the crannog was the focus of National Museum of Ireland investigations when the finds came into museum care after a metal detecting amnesty. Work in 2004 included further examination of the assemblage by Eamonn P Kelly of the National Museum of Ireland. The recent study involved interviewing the treasure hunters and bringing them back on site to discuss probable original context. During this process it became obvious that nearly all finds were located close to the surface, below the upper capping of stones; the richest set of finds coming from the lower platform, with very little being found on the higher areas.

Almost one hundred objects in the National Museum of Ireland collection can be identified as having been found on Coolure Demesne crannog (Kelly 2005a, 30). Earliest in the artefactual sequence are two objects which suggest a fifth century AD date, a date that crosses the traditional boundary between the end of the Irish Iron Age and the beginning of the Early Medieval period. The earliest of these objects is a copper alloy swan's neck pin (ref E621, 93), the second is an enamelled handpin (ref 1988, 74) with *millefiori* settings, which can broadly be dated to between the fourth and sixth centuries AD (Kelly 2005b, 83). The rest of the finds span a date range which extends to, possibly, as late as the fifteenth century. The latest find in the assemblage is a small silver ring brooch (ref E499, 41) (Kelly 2005b, 89). Amongst the collection are also examples of Viking material, including silver ingots, hack silver (mostly broad-band armlets) and weight scales: these all date to between the ninth or tenth century AD. Some of this material has already been published (Sheehan 1992, 48–9) and can be considered to be the product of raid, trade or tribute and probably ultimately derive from Viking Dublin. These finds can be seen to extend the picture of a Westmeath distribution of Viking silver that concentrates to the south around Lough Ennell (Edwards 1999, fig 88, 175).

None of the objects was found in a secure context on the crannog but most seem to have been located under the stone capping and relatively close to the surface of the underlying deposits. The location of finds from different dates in such similar contexts is perhaps significant in terms of the taphonomy of the site and appears to fit with some theoretical models of crannog decay already discussed in the literature (Crone, Henderson & Sands 2001, Cavers this volume). In these models, differential erosion of soft deposits, perhaps exacerbated by slumping, lead to conflation of part of the crannog mound, ultimately leaving a uniform stone covering and concentrating certain artefactual material in a limited contextual zone. In this respect, the descriptions given of Loch Glashan crannog, Argyll, Scotland are reminiscent of Coolure Demesne (Crone & Campbell 2005, 25–7).

The 2004 season allowed for scientific dating techniques to be employed on the organic material with a secure context. Three post samples were taken for dendrochronological assessment by David Brown at the dendrochronological laboratory at Queen's University, Belfast, the results of which are presented in table 1. Crucially, one of the timbers had a surviving heartwood-sapwood boundary, which has allowed for a reasonable estimation of felling date; this provided a date of AD 402 ± 9.

TABLE 1
Results of the dendrochronological examination.

Site code	QUB code	No. of rings	Start date	End date	Estimated felling range
CD2004-T008	Q10672	234	AD 108	AD 341	After AD 373
CD2004-T015	Q10674	115	–	–	–
CD2004-T016	Q10673	264	AD 107	AD 370	AD 402 ± 9

In addition to the dendrochronological work, samples were also taken for radiocarbon analysis, again at Queen's University, Belfast. The results of this analysis and the proposed calibrated date ranges are presented in table 2. Again there is a strong mid-late first millennium AD range represented, but significantly determinations from three of the smaller roundwood posts calibrate to the ninth century BC.

Most crannog projects in Ireland have so far produced dates either in the Late Bronze Age/Early Iron Age (ie c 900–600 BC), or securely to the late sixth/early seventh century AD (at c AD 560–610), well within the Early Medieval period (Kelly 1991; Warner 1994; O'Sullivan 1998; Fredengren 2002; O'Sullivan A 2004). Consequently, the Pagan Iron Age/Early Christian transition date is one of the most exciting discoveries of the project. As mentioned above, the timbers from which these were derived are indicative of impressive substantial construction,

probably representing part of a high revetted face to the island.

COOLURE DEMESNE CRANNOG IN A PREHISTORIC CONTEXT

Approximately 1400 years before the trees used to construct the Early Medieval palisade were felled, small roundwood posts were being inserted into the marls that make up the lake bed. The bulk of any earlier structure must have been covered by later material and the small test pit, placed very close to the prehistoric posts, demonstrated that all of the build-up of organic material in that vicinity was of Early Medieval date.

With the three small posts being the only evidence for this phase, it would be difficult to make any conclusions about the nature or motivation for

TABLE 2
Results and calibrations of the radiocarbon determinations.

Lab code	Sample material	Result	$\delta^{13}C(^o/_{oo})$	1 sigma	2 sigma
Samples from wooden uprights					
UB-6357	Fraxinus excelsior	1545 ± 35	−30.8	AD 440–555	AD 421–599
UB-6358	Alnus sp.	2694 ± 35	−30.1	897–817 BC	913–805 BC
UB-6359	Quercus sp.	2741 ± 35	−29.0	919–840 BC	990–949 BC
UB-6360	Corylus avellana	2739 ± 35	−29.2	918–839 BC	988–821 BC
UB-6361	Taxus baccata	1479 ± 36	−23.6	AD 549–620	AD 532–646
Samples from test pit – ordered stratigraphically					
UB-6356	Bone	1453 ± 33	−25.0	AD 569–638	AD 546–654
UB-6355	Alnus sp.	1315 ± 32	−30.3	AD 663–689	AD 653–774
UB-6353	Fraxinus excelsior	1431 ± 33	−30.1	AD 602–649	AD 560–660
UB-6354	Alnus sp.	1550 ± 28	−26.6	AD 440–549	AD 424–569

All $\delta^{13}C$ is ± 0.2 $^o/_{oo}$ as measured by the Oxford Accelerator this construction. However, there are a number of other examples of roundwood posts that demarcate platforms in similar locations; for example, Moynagh Lough, Co Meath; Killymoon, Co Tyrone; Cullyhanna, Co Armagh; Balinderry 2, Co Offlay and Lough Eskragh, Co Tyrone (see O'Sullivan 1998, 71–96). Both O'Sullivan and Fredengren have also, quite rightly, reiterated the importance of water bodies within a Bronze Age context and the consequent symbolic significance of creating a structure within such bodies, noting a frequent association with what must have been structured deposits (O'Sullivan 1998, 96; Fredengren 2002, 190–3).

AN IRON AGE HIATUS

An Iron Age hiatus is also a feature of other lake structures in Ireland. In itself, the hiatus only demands cultural explanation if the gap is viewed as a genuine break in continuity (*contra* Fredengren 2002, 9). However, explanations do need to be sought for why one episode appears to stop and another started. The gap is also of interest when sites in Scotland are considered; here a similar hiatus is noted, but in this case it is both shorter and later, with a notable absence of dates between the third to fifth centuries (Crone & Campbell 2005, 118).

There is no absolute requirement for seeing the prehistoric phase as having anything other than an indirect influence on the later medieval construction. Its indirect influence may have been to provide an existing focus for later construction. This need not be seen as a purely practical advantage, the clear symbolic potency to such locations may have been enhanced by the existence of the physical remains of an abandoned structure about which folk memory remained or stories were told.

COOLURE DEMESNE CRANNOG IN AN EARLY MEDIEVAL LANDSCAPE

Work on crannog sites has rightly challenged the notion that all Early Medieval crannogs are high status and persisted over a long period of time (O'Sullivan 1998, 123; Fredengren 2002). However, Coolure Demesne appears to fall into the more traditional mould, being both high status and of long duration.

The beginnings of Coolure Demesne crannog, as we see it today, can largely be attributed to the start of the fifth century AD. Investigations would suggest that it is from this date that the crannog was substantially built up, signalled by the insertion of large, split, oak uprights. This constructional activity might best be seen against a backdrop of emerging power struggles. The fifth century appears to be a crucial period in the midlands, new dynastic groups, ancestral to the southern Uí Néill, were emerging, potentially displacing earlier, Iron Age tribal groups. Various annalistic and hagiographical sources would suggest that by the seventh century, and, indeed, perhaps earlier, internecine conflicts were increasing as groups vied for dominance in the Irish Midlands (O'Sullivan A 2004; Bhreathnach 2005, 373).

Dominance of this part of the midlands was gained, in the eighth century, by the Clann Cholmáin, one of the two great Southern Uí Néill dynasties (Byrne 2001, 87). Although notoriously difficult to determine with certainty (Stout 2005), three groups have been suggested to occupy the territories immediately surrounding Lough Derravaragh; the Uí Maccu Uais Mide, to the west, the Corco Róíde, to the south and the Uí Fiachrach Cúile Fobair, to the north (O'Sullivan A 2004). The crannog can be seen to fall within the conjectured territorial boundaries of the Uí Fiachrach Cúile Fobair and the latter part of this name is suggested to be represented in the townland-name Coolure (Walsh 1957, 78 note 2). Significantly, the site also lies close to the territorial boundaries of the other two groups (fig 2).

It is clear that power struggles and warfare were strong features of the midlands, particularly in the fifth to eighth centuries. Indeed, the discovery of several iron arrow heads on the shoreward side of the island might attest to Coolure crannog's active participation in these events. However, it would be wrong to see the construction of the crannog as being a simple defensive response to a shifting political climate. The rich finds from the island and its clear longevity suggest a more nuanced and complex motivation. In particular, sites like Coolure during the Early Medieval period in Westmeath should not be considered in isolation. Their presence denotes one component of a broader suite of associated sites. The immediate proximity of a ringfort on the northern shore, less than 200m away, can, with other evidence, be taken to suggest a high status complex.

Similar associations are noted elsewhere; some 16km due south of Lough Derravaragh is the suggested Royal complex at the south-western end of Lough Ennell, which links Dún na Sgiath with the crannog of Cróinis (O'Sullivan 1998, 130–1; O'Sullivan A 2004). Support for this association is found amongst the rich range of written records that survive in Ireland. Both the island and the ringfort are mentioned in poems that relate to the death of Máel Sechnaill mac Domnaill in AD 1022. His death on the island itself is referred to both in the annals and in a Middle Irish poem that concerns itself with the Kings of Meath. His association with the ringfort is strongly implied in another poem that speaks of the desolation of the locality upon the death of the king (Bhreathnach 2005, 377). It has also been suggested that a significant exclusion zone surrounded the Dún na Sgiath/Cróinis complex. This is apparently mirrored at Coolure Demesne, which is located at some significant remove from neighbouring early medieval sites (O'Sullivan A 2004; Van de Noort & O'Sullivan 2006, 72, fig 5). The nearest archaeological sites to Coolure Demesne are five ringforts about 1km to the north, situated along the townland boundaries between Ballinealoe and Mayne. There was also a ringfort at Lispopple, slightly closer at hand, 800m to the north-west.

References to Lough Ennell and other lakes clearly indicate some islands in Early Medieval Westmeath as important dwellings. Some 7km due east of Derravaragh, another such dwelling is mentioned in an account of the life of Saint Áed mac Bricc. A miracle is recounted in which Áed walks on water to plead for the life of a man held by a king on his island dwelling on Lough Lene; the king is impressed and releases the man. This tale reinforces the impression of a location infused with authority (O'Sullivan A 2004; Bhreathnach 2005, 376). In this manner, certain islands are not merely dwellings but are potent symbols of power, a symbolic impression that is heightened by their physical remove from the land.

The archaeology at Coolure Demesne both confirms and extends the impression of such sites given in the historical texts. The area, at least in its Early Medieval incarnation, fits the pattern of a Royal complex within which the crannog played a significant, intertwined, practical and symbolic role. Although there is currently no evidence of permanent occupation there is clear evidence of intensive and significant use. The quantity of animal bone uncovered during the 2004 investigation speaks of extensive feasting, as does the discovery of a metal drinking horn terminal. The importance of hospitality and feasting should not be underestimated in medieval Irish society and the conduct of such activities provides a regular theme in early Irish sources (O'Sullivan C M 2004). Similarly, the discovery of leg fetters is suggestive of another key activity; the taking of hostages, an activity spoken of on the island in Lough Lene (see above). These

observations should all be set within the context of an impressive crannog structure.

SUMMARY

The 2004 season, despite limited invasive investigation, allows for a broad developmental sequence to be painted:

1. *Late Bronze Age*: the use of roundwood posts c 1000 and 800 BC.
2. *Iron Age hiatus*: it has yet to be established whether or not this represents a genuine gap or is the product of subsequent construction masking key evidence.
3. *Iron Age/Early Christian transition*: substantial oak uprights inserted at the edge of the site in the early fifth century AD. There are two objects from the site that may date to this period.
4. *Early Medieval*: some time between the fifth century AD and the ninth century AD smaller roundwood uprights were added. During this period, at least some part of the south-eastern edge was built up with organic material. Most of the artefacts date to this period, including high-status objects such as feasting equipment, weaponry, leg fetters, pins, brooches and enamelled mounts, and evidence for trade, tribute or loot from Viking Dublin. Other activity is indicated by tools, keys and other items.
5. *Late Medieval*: including ring brooches and a bishop's seal matrix.
6. Post Medieval: meagre artefactual evidence. The island may have been largely submerged until the latter part of the nineteenth century (there were River Inny drainage programmes in both the 1860s and the 1950s).
7. *Modern period*: evidence for temporary occupation, primarily by duck hunters and fishermen. The site also held significance for local children, being used as a place for recreation.

CONCLUSION

Coolure crannog is one of the earliest dateable, protohistoric sites in the Irish midlands, and one of very few (if any) in Ireland that can be scientifically dated to this significant transition period. The large and impressive site that we see today conforms to a classic image of an Early Medieval Irish crannog. In many ways the archaeology also conforms to this image, providing evidence of a high status structure that almost certainly acted as one component in a broader Early Medieval aristocratic complex. However, this external appearance masks significant Late Bronze Age activity that might be taken to reaffirm the practical and symbolic significance of the island's location. Research continues, looking at all crannogs on the lake and placing the study firmly in a regional context.

REFERENCES

Aalen, F H A, Whelan, K & Stout, M 1997 *Atlas of the Irish Rural Landscape*. Cork.

Bhreathnach, E 2005 '"A Midhe is maith da bhámar": thoughts on medieval Mide', *in* Condit, T & Corlett, C (eds) *Above and Beyond, essays in memory of Leo Swan*. Bray.

Butler, V 2005 'The mammal bone', *in* O'Sullivan, A, Kelly, E P & Sands, R, 124–32.

Byrne, F J 2001 *Irish Kings and High Kings*, second edition. Dublin.

Crone A & Campbell, E 2005 *A Crannog of the First Millennium* AD. Society of Antiquaries of Scotland, Edinburgh.

Crone, A, Henderson, J & Sands, R 2001 'Scottish crannogs: construction, collapse and conflation: problems of interpretation', *in* Raftery, B & Hickey, J (eds) *Recent Developments in Wetland Research 55–68*. Seandálaíocht: Mon. 2, Dept Archaeol, UCD and WARP Occasional Paper 14. Dublin.

Edwards, N 1999 *The Archaeology of Early Medieval Ireland*. London.

Fredengren, C 2002 *Crannogs: A Study of People's Interaction with Lakes*. Bray.

Kelly, E P 2005a 'The antiquities from Coolure Demesne crannog', *in* O'Sullivan, Kelly & Sands (2005), 25–34.

Kelly, E P 2005b 'Catalogue of finds from Lough Derravaragh in the National Museum of Ireland', *in* O'Sullivan, A, Kelly, E P & Sands, R (2005), 60–102.

Kelly E P 1991 'Observations on Irish lake-dwellings' *in* Karkov, C & Farrell, R (eds) *Studies in Insular Art and Archaeology*. American Early Medieval Studies 1, Cornell, 81–98.

O'Sullivan, A 2004 *The Social and Ideological Roles of Crannogs in Early Medieval Ireland*, unpubl PhD thesis, NUI Maynooth.

O'Sullivan, A 1998 *The Archaeology of Lake Settlement in Ireland*, Discovery Programme Monograph 4, Dublin.

O'Sullivan A, Kelly, E P & Sands R 2005 Archaeological Investigations of a Crannog at Coolure Demesne, Co Westmeath', unpubl report for licence 04E1076 (available on-line at *www.ucd.ie/archaeology/research/*).

O'Sullivan, C M 2004 *Hospitality in Medieval Ireland*. Dublin.

Reilly, P and Johnston, E 2005 'Insect and Plant Remains', *in* O'Sullivan, A, Kelly, E P & Sands, R (2005), 133–52.

Sheehan, J, 1992 'Coiled armrings – an Hiberno-Viking silver armring type', *The Journal of Irish Archaeology* VI, 1991–2, 41–53.

Stout, M 2005 'Early Medieval Boundaries', *in* Condit, T & Corlett, C (eds) *Above and Beyond: Essays in Memory of Leo Swan*. Bray.

Walsh, P 1957 *The placenames of Westmeath*. Dublin.

Warner, R 1994 'On crannogs and kings', *Ulster Journal of Archaeology* 57, 61–9.

The lake-dwellings in Holderness, East Yorkshire, revisited: a journey into antiquarian and contemporary wetland archaeology

WILLIAM FLETCHER and ROBERT VAN DE NOORT

INTRODUCTION

The story presented in this paper began in the 1880s with the discovery of five unusual wet sites in the low-lying region of Holderness, East Yorkshire, during drainage works: West Furze, Round Hill, Barmston Drain, Gransmoor and Kelk (fig 1). The changing interpretation of the significance of these wet sites, from contemporary local accounts to their 'expert' publication early in the twentieth century (Smith 1911), contributed to the tale of the Holderness lake-dwellings, echoing the then already famous lake-dwellings of the Alpine region and elsewhere in Europe (Keller 1878). The tale of the Holderness lake-dwellings survived more recent work intact, as excavators approached the sites without challenging the preconception of these being genuine lake settlements (eg Varley 1968).

Given the sites' high wet potential, their rarity value and the prominence of these sites in the regional archaeological record, further excavations were prioritized by the English Heritage funded Humber Wetlands Project (1992–2000). Each of the five sites discovered in the 1880s was subjected to a re-examination, which included applying the range of modern techniques. An assessment of the original finds from within the stores of the British Museum has also taken place. From this work has emerged a re-affirmation of the importance of these sites but, surprisingly perhaps, the conclusion that none (or at least four of the five) of these can be considered to have been lake-dwellings or crannogs. Specifically, the site at West Furze appears to have been a trackway, with multi-period evidence spanning the Neolithic and Bronze Age (Van de Noort 1995); the Round Hill site appears to have been a Mesolithic lakeside platform, with an intriguing find assemblage; Barmston Drain was a Bronze Age settlement situated on the sediments of a Late-glacial mere or lake; Kelk was an Iron Age enclosure alongside a sinuous lake, and is one of the few sites in the region, and in the country as a whole, to have produced evidence of

bronze working from that period (Chapman *et al* 2000); and Gransmoor could not be recovered (Van de Noort 2004, 62–6).

This paper revisits the original excavations and publications, and presents their re-interpretations on the basis of recent work.

THE RESEARCH HISTORY

The original discoveries took place between 1880 and 1884, during maintenance work on the Skipsea Branch Drain and elsewhere in the low-lying region of Holderness. The geomorphology of this region was shaped by the action of ice and meltwater during the

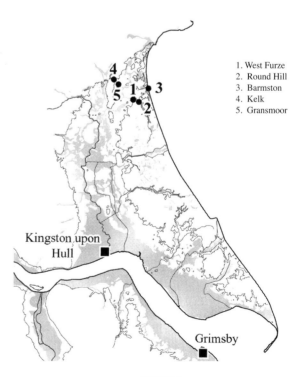

1. West Furze
2. Round Hill
3. Barmston
4. Kelk
5. Gransmoor

FIGURE 1
Map of Holderness, East Yorkshire, showing five sites
(after Van de Noort 2004).

313

Glacial and Late-glacial periods (Catt 1990), leaving an undulating till landscape. Prior to the introduction of artificial drainage in the early modern period, the landscape included many wetlands. These are known locally as 'meres' and whilst today only a single open waterbody survives in Hornsea Mere, medieval maps show over 70 such wetlands (Dinnin 1995, 27).

The archaeological discoveries were initially reported in newsprint between 1883 and 1885 by the finder, Thomas Boynton, the drainage engineer and landowner from Bridlington who oversaw the maintenance works. His article in *The Yorkshire Post* (26 July, 1883) was followed by one from T M Evans, a local journalist, in *The Standard* (20 October, 1883)

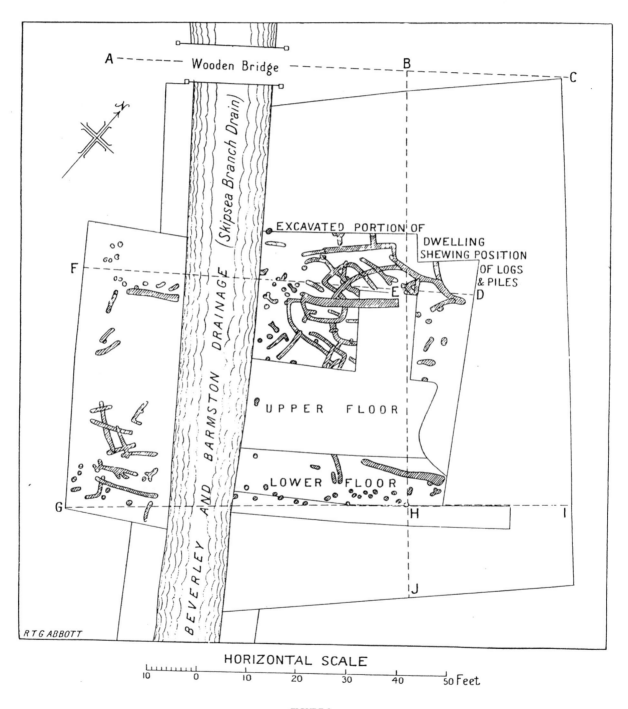

FIGURE 2
Plan of West Furze (after Smith 1911).

and another in *The Hull Quarterly and East Riding Portfolio* (1885). Reginald Smith, Keeper of Prehistoric Archaeology at the British Museum, visited Thomas Boynton and the sites of West Furze and Round Hill, probably in 1884 (the sections drawn by the British Museum draughtsman R T G Abbott are dated to 21 April 1884), but it was not until 30 years after the first find had been made that a full paper was published, under the title 'Lake-dwellings in Holderness, East Yorkshire' in *Archaeologia* (1911).

Another 50 years passed before any of the sites were investigated again, with archaeologist William Varley (1968) looking at the Barmston Drain site in more detail. A systematic analysis of the sites in a landscape context was not undertaken until 1992, with the start of the Humber Wetlands Project. The sites, although geographically close to each other, fell into two of the project's regions, and West Furze, Round Hill and Barmston Drain were investigated in 1994–5, with the results published in the Holderness monograph of the Wetland Heritage series (Van de Noort 1995), whilst Kelk and Gransmoor were researched in 1999, appearing in the Hull Valley report of the same series (Chapman *et al* 2000). This

work was brought together in a full chronological and regional framework, along with the Humber Wetlands Project archive in the synthesis (Van de Noort 2004). More recently, the British Museum has kindly facilitated access to the original finds, and this re-assessment, along with new interpretations of the sites, is presented here. This research now forms part of an ongoing collaborative project with the museum to reconsider the role of the finds from the sites and to define the chronological framework of the bone objects.

Although published in 1911, it is Reginald Smith's paper that has always been seen as the authoritative and last word on the five sites. It is here, for example, that the excavation plans and sections from West Furze and Round Hill were published for the first time (see fig 2). However, this publication was only ever a compilation of material collected over a period of about five years from the five sites. Furthermore, it was published some 30 years after the primary discovery. What characterized these five sites, in Smith's mind, was recovery of preserved archaeological wood from (former) lakes. He interpreted the worked timbers as the piles on which the lake settlements

FIGURE 3
Boynton at West Furze (after Smith 1911).

were established, undoubtedly influenced by the then already famous lake-dwellings of the Alpine region, the crannogs of Scotland and Ireland, and the Glastonbury and Meare Lake settlements in the Somerset levels (Keller 1878; Monroe 1882; Wood-Martin 1886; Bulleid 1894). Reginald Smith's interpretation of the five sites as lake-dwellings, although not challenged since the publication in 1911, was, in fact, not entirely in agreement with local opinion. Thus, T M Evans described the lower layer at West Furze as a 'causeway' (1885, 60), not a lake-dwelling, and our own assessment confirmed the accuracy of this reading of this site.

According to Evans (1885, 59), West Furze was on land belonging to Boynton himself, and the site had been more extensively uncovered by Thomas Boynton than any of the other sites. It remained open to visitors from its discovery in 1880 until (at least) sometime in 1885, and it acquired something of a celebrity status. It is also West Furze where the evocative pictures from the 1880s of the excavator Boynton standing in the trench (fig 3) were taken.

The re-assessments of the five lake-dwellings, as part of the Humber Wetlands Project, commenced with West Furze. A summary of the original interpretations of each of the sites, and our revisited interpretations, is provided in table 1.

WEST FURZE

West Furze is the best documented of the sites, including photographs, plans and sections, and the finds are currently held at the British Museum. It is located on the eastern margin of a series of elongated and sinuous meres, and depressions that characterize the local landscape in the Middle Ages, recorded as Bail Mere and Low Mere. It was, by the standards of the day, skilfully excavated by Thomas Boynton and competently recorded by R T G Abbott of the British Museum. Credit should be given to the recognition of the stratigraphy and the identification of the two 'floors' or layers, the lower layers being without pottery (and late Neolithic/Early Bronze Age in date) and the upper layers without bone tools (of Late Bronze Age date). The wooden stakes and the double alignment were also identified and recorded (including pictures of the tool marks and woodworking techniques), leading Boynton and then Evans to their conclusion that the site was likely to be a causeway or trackway, 'which appears to have reached the land at either end, thus connecting it with both shores of the narrow waters' (Evans 1885, 59–60) (fig 4).

In spite of this plausible and evidence-based interpretation, Reginald Smith concluded that the site was a lake-dwelling, as discussed above. In the recent re-assessment of the site, it became clear that very little of this site survived (Head *et al* 1995). The 1880s excavation had left the archaeological wood exposed for several years and the drainage system alongside had been efficient in its effort to drain the low-lying grounds. The Humber Wetlands Project's discovery of two barrows east of the mere-complex (from aerial photographs), and Neolithic and Early Bronze Age evidence to the west of the mere-complex (from field walking), added a different focus to the site, providing the basis for the reconstruction of the landscape context, and the re-interpretation of the site as a late Neolithic trackway and a Bronze Age log-dam or beaver lodge (Van de Noort 1995; 2004). Intriguingly, the eastern terminal of the trackway had a 'wicket' (in Smith's description) or a doorway, and the original excavations found at least three human skulls here. In the reconstruction, it has been implied that the elongated mere complex may have divided the landscape into zones. One for the living (to the west of the mere) and one for the dead (to the east), with liminal separation being provided by the wetland (see Parker Pearson 1993 for a similar explanation for prehistoric landscapes in Denmark).

Whilst the site itself may have largely desiccated, the finds provide a lasting interest. In particular, the survival of an unparalleled assemblage of bone tools or, more precisely, multiples of the same bone tools, is significant. Upwards of 15 of these tools were recovered by Thomas Boynton from the lower floor or trackway phase of the site, described as bone adzes by Reginald Smith (1911), but, in fact, resembling picks or mattocks. Nearly all are made from the distal end of *Bos Longifrons* tibia, with single hafting holes drilled into the thickest part of the joint (fig 5). They had all been used, with use-wear apparent in the breaks and cracks visible at the cutting or digging edge of the tool. These artefacts appear to have been brought together, collected and deliberately interred or cached at the site.

Does this provide an unusual example of the curation and deposition of a particular or specialized object? It is certainly the largest single collection of this type of tool from the British Isles, and to date only a few similar tools are known, including several from Skara Brae (Gordon Childe 1931), although these had been made from similar but slightly different parts of *Bos Longifrons* (Foxton 1991). The apparent care taken to curate and cache these objects at this location has drawn a parallel with Late Neolithic and Bronze

TABLE 1
Original descriptions and re-interpretation of the 'lake-dwellings' of Holderness.

	Site summary then and now	
Site	Original description and presented evidence	New information and new interpretation
West Furze (Ulrome)	Two phases were identified, separated by a layer of alluvial clay. The layers were described as 'floors' and identified as being without pottery and without bone tools. The published plan and sections from the 1880s (Smith 1911) show the lower floor as a brushwood layer with a series of upright posts, the upper floor seen as being within an alluvial matrix. Multiple finds included many *Bos Longifrons* leg bone pick axes from the lower floor and a spearhead from the upper floor. Flints, pottery and many other objects were found at the same time. Boynton/Evans in early newspaper article (*c* 1883–5) suggested it was a trackway, but Smith's later paper published the platform as a lake-dwelling. Activity at the site continued into the Roman period.	Site is situated at narrowest point where two mere systems combine, and interpretation as a trackway seems most likely, formed by the parallel posts. The brushwood layer may have been naturally occurring or associated with beaver activity (beaver bone was recorded) but still in use as a crossing (see Head *et al* 1995 and Van de Noort 1995). The bone pickaxes appear to come from a curated assemblage deposited at the site; other Late Neolithic and Early Bronze Age material has also been confirmed, among the many phases of deposition confirmed from the finds assemblage. During the Humber Wetlands Project the wider site context was investigated with the discovery of two barrows of Late Neolithic-Early Bronze Age date situated on the wetland edge.
Round Hill (Skipsea)	A section published in Smith's (1911) paper appears to be speculative and interpretative rather than real. Wooden piles were noted but the assemblage contains many multi-period finds including a human skull, pottery as well as fine objects including an amber bead and section of jet bracelet. Largely of Neolithic and Bronze Age date although some later material present.	Re-excavated in 1992; however, timber samples recovered were dated to the Mesolithic and are therefore much earlier than much of the finds assemblage (Head *et al* 1995). The evidence from topography and landscape suggest a lake-edge platform. Bulk of the assemblage may be more suited to a later period of deposition than a house/lake-dwelling site.
Barmston Drain	Wooden piles seen in drain section and recorded by Smith (1911) as evidence of lake-dwelling.	Varley (1968) identified hearths, flooring and timbers, dated to Bronze Age. He suggested that the peat developed later and covered the site. The Humber Wetlands Project re-excavated and dated the earlier peat to the Mesolithic. This showed the settlement had developed on the mere during a drier phase in the Bronze Age, and was only partially inundated by later peat growth (Head *et al* 1995). Not specifically lake settlement but settlement established on a former peat bog/lake.
Kelk	Wooden piles seen in drain section, with only a two-line description in Smith's (1911) paper.	Geophysics, field walking and excavation during Humber Wetlands Project revealed Iron Age enclosure on slope above former stream (Chapman *et al* 2000). Iron Age material had been dumped in wetland next to site and revealed in the drain cutting by Boynton.
Gransmoor	Wooden piles seen in drain section, with only a two-line description in Smith (1911).	Unpublished excavations from the 1950s revealed an extensive Iron Age settlement on adjacent low hill subsequently quarried away (see Chapman *et al* 2000). No evidence of material could be found in the Humber Wetlands Project trenches but adjacent settlement site appears to be similar to Kelk site, providing a similar interaction with the wetland.

317

Age depositional practices elsewhere in the Humber Wetlands (Van de Noort 2004). The value placed on these objects adds a layer of complexity to this site.

Comparisons could be drawn with the depositions of unfinished and unused antler barbed points at Star Carr in the nearby Vale of Pickering, interpreted as a practice that was intended to bridge

FIGURE 4
A reconstruction of the West Furze landscape in the Late Neolithic (Les Turner).

the nature–culture divide (Conneller & Schadla-Hall 2003). Whereas at Early Mesolithic Star Carr unfinished tools were returned at a striking wetland location (at the natural outflow of Lake Pickering and the source of the Hertford River), at West Furze

animal-derived tools were deposited in another striking wetland location (at the narrowest point of the elongated mere-complex) at the end of their 'lives'. Intriguingly, an example of a similar type of pick or mattock, albeit made of antler rather than bone, is included in the assemblage from Star Carr (Clark 1972).

ROUND HILL

Round Hill, located some 700m south-east of West Furze, is known from Thomas Boynton's work by a single section drawing, and a summary description of finds (Smith 1911, 605). The section appears to contradict the description somewhat, and it may be little more than a fanciful reconstruction of Boynton's description of the site. In fact, the site comprises 'logs [that] were not made to overlap, but thrown in promiscuously, and though some were of small dimensions there was no attempt to render the structure solid by means of piles' (ibid.). The finds from the site, however, form a substantial and varied assemblage, including a large flint assemblage, pottery and a circular mace-head, alongside a number of 'exotic' objects such as an amber bead and a section of jet armband or bracelet. Round Hill is, in parallel to the other sites in Holderness, described by Reginald Smith as a lake-dwelling and settlement.

The Humber Wetlands Project re-assessed the landscape context of this site (Dinnin & Lillie 1995, 74–5). Round Hill is a prominent feature in the local landscape, situated alongside Skipsea Bail Mere. This mere originated in the Late-glacial and formed part of the chain of meres that probably stretched northwards to West Furze. In prehistory, Bail Mere was probably connected to the River Hull but in the Middle Ages it only flooded seasonally.

A single timber was recovered from a small trench excavated in 1994, interpreted as a crudely hewn, somewhat desiccated stake lacking distinctive axe marks or other evidence of working. It was radiocarbon dated to 8350–7940 cal BC (9080±100 BP; GU-5451), or the early Mesolithic. This poses something of a conundrum,

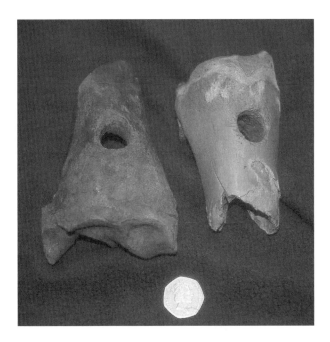

FIGURE 5
Picks or mattocks from the distal end of *Bos Longifrons* tibia,
West Furze (William Fletcher).

as the date of this single stake predates the finds
by several millennia. It is not impossible that this
prominent feature had been used and re-used on
a number of separate occasions, and that during
the Early Mesolithic a wooden platform had been
constructed on the water's edge. At some point
in the Neolithic and, again, in the Bronze Age,
renewed activity took place here, the former possibly
representing a hunting camp overlooking the mere,
providing a lookout for hunters awaiting the arrival
of larger mammals to come to the water to drink
(see Van de Noort 2004), and the latter probably
representing the ritual deposition of selected exotica
in wet places (Bradley 1990).

BARMSTON

The Barmston Drain site is, again, a different type
of site. Smith (1911) mentions little more than the
discovery of wooden piles seen in the drain section as
evidence of a lake-dwelling. William Varley, guided
by Smith's publication, excavated two trenches here
with students of Hull College of Education in 1960
and 1961, and published his work in 1968. The
excavations proved beyond doubt the existence of
a settlement, including hearths, a cobbled floor,
post-holes and cooking pits *in situ*, and radiocarbon

dates from two structural timbers (with date ranges
of 1530–810 cal BC and 1510–800 cal BC) places this
settlement in the Middle or Late Bronze Age. The peat
surrounding the posts was understood as post-dating
the settlement. Varley recognized that Barmston
was not a lake settlement, but described the site as a
'settlement of sorts within a marshy hollow' (Varley
1968, 20).

The work undertaken by the Humber Wetlands
Project closely mirrored that of Varley, down to
re-excavating his trenches and even uncovering his
labels from the sections, but by dating different
material a better picture of this site emerged.
Radiocarbon dates of the peat from where the
structural timbers had been retrieved returned
results of 10720±110 BP (GU-5449), 10190±110
BP (GU-5448) and 9300±70 BP (GU-5450, date
range 8590–8090 cal BC). In other words, the peats
at Barmston are of Lateglacial date and represent the
infill of a mere in a glacially formed depression. The
settlement was located on the dried-out surface of
the mere. Reginald Smith was thus nearly right, but
rather than a lake-dwelling Barmston is a dwelling
on a former lake.

KELK

The existence of a lake-dwelling at Kelk was referred
to by Smith in a few lines, mentioning wooden piles
and some pottery. We also investigated Kelk during
fieldwork for the Hull Valley region in 1999–2000
(Chapman *et al* 2000). Situated on a slight hill, above
a thin and sinuous peat-filled channel, field walking,
geophysics and then excavation revealed a partially
double-ditched Iron Age enclosure. Internal features
revealed both occupation and specialized industrial
activity in the form of mould fragments, slag and
crucibles from bronze casting.

This type of activity is rarely found, with only a
few well-known sites such as Gussage All Saints in
Dorset (Wainwright 1979) and Wheelsby Avenue in
Lincolnshire (Fenwick *et al* 2001). Furthermore, no
production sites had ever been located so close to the
Iron Age settlements and burials on the Yorkshire
Wolds. The way the wetland was integrated into the
site was clearly significant, but analysis of the channel
sequence suggested the wetland was not active open
water at this time. When Boynton began to canalize
the drainage some elements such as settlement debris
or a possible crossing point may have been disturbed,
leading to the report in Smith's 1911 paper. Our
own trenches into the wetland adjacent to the drain

continued to produce Iron Age material in this fashion.

GRANSMOOR

Smith had teasingly suggested that the Gransmoor lake-dwelling comprised a 'settlement extending 200–300 yards ... in the drain' (Smith 1911), which included the find of a whole 'Roman' pot. For much of the twentieth century, Gransmoor was the site of an extensive sand and gravel quarrying immediately adjacent to the stream. A small sandy hill, which survived until the 1950s, had been entirely extracted and replaced with a deep quarry pit. Prior to this destruction, the Continuing Education Department of Leeds University had undertaken several rescue excavations which hinted at the wealth of archaeology that had once existed (Copley 1953). An extensive Iron Age settlement was revealed, with up to seven hut circles, and a wealth of finds including pots, bones and a fragment of human skull. Later work on the fringes of the site revealed wet deposits (close to the Gransmoor drain) and some timbers that were thought to be providing access through the wet area (Chapman *et al* 2000). By 1999, the landscape had been comprehensively altered. Small portions of the wetland survived and trenches were excavated by the Humber Wetlands Project team, but only natural sequences were recorded.

CONCLUSION

This short paper has offered alternative explanations for the five lake-dwellings in Holderness, East Yorkshire, as originally described by Reginald Smith (1911). We have come to the conclusion that none of the sites in question resembled Alpine lake settlements, Scottish or Irish crannogs or Somerset lake settlements. In fact, West Furze was a trackway, Round Hill a platform, Barmston a settlement on the surface of a terrestrialized mere, Kelk a riverside enclosure and Gransmoor a settlement on a sandy hill.

This paper has also sought to draw attention to the importance of recognizing perceptions, paradigms or *Zeitgeiste* in our understanding of wetland archaeology. Reginald Smith believed that all wetland sites were lake-dwellings, as at the turn of that century, lake settlements were much in vogue, and alternatives were not at hand. Today, we have to recognize similar problems, and terms such as 'crannog', 'trackway' and 'votive depositions' are likely to encompass a range of sites representing activities which were perceived in diverse ways by people in the past.

ACKNOWLEDGEMENTS

We would like to thank the many members of the Humber Wetlands Project team who worked on one or more of the excavations over the years. Also, our appreciation goes to the staff of the Department of Prehistory and Europe at the British Museum (Stuart Needham and Marie-Ann Eve) who provided access to the finds assemblage and to Alan Saville for his comments on the Skara Brae objects.

REFERENCES

Bradley, R 1990 *The Passage of Arms*. Cambridge.

Bulleid, A 1892 'The Lake Village near Glastonbury', *Proceedings of the Somerset Archaeological and Natural History Society* 40, 141–51.

Catt, J A 1990 'Geology and relief', in Ellis, S & Crowther, D R (eds) *Humber Perspectives: A Region Through the Ages*. Hull.

Chapman, H, Fletcher, W, Fenwick, H, Lillie, M & Thomas, G 2000 'The archaeological survey of the Hull valley', in Van de Noort, R & Ellis, S (eds) *Wetland Heritage of the Hull Valley, an Archaeological Survey*. Hull.

Clark, J G D 1972 *Star Carr: A Case Study in Bio-archaeology*. Addison-Wesley Modular Publication, 10, Massachusetts.

Conneller, C & Schadla-Hall, T 2003 'Beyond Star Carr: The Vale of Pickering in the 10th Millennium BP', *Proceedings of the Prehistoric Society* 69, 85–106.

Copley, I B 1953 *Early Iron Age remains at Gransmoor, East Yorkshire*. Leeds.

Dinnin, M H 1995 'Introduction to the palaeoenvironmental survey', Van de Noort, R & Ellis, S (eds) *Wetland Heritage of Holderness, an Archaeological Survey*. Hull.

Fenwick, H, Van de Noort, R, Fletcher W, & Thomas, G 2001 'Introduction to the Archaeological Survey', in Van de Noort, R & Ellis, S (eds) *Wetland Heritage of the Lincolnshire Marsh, an Archaeological Survey*. Hull.

Foxton, A D 1991 *Bone, Antler, Tooth and Horn Technology and Utilisation in Prehistoric Scotland*. Unpubl PhD thesis, vol 1, University of Glasgow.

Gordon Childe, V 1931 *Skara Brae: A Pictish Village in Orkney*. London.

Keller, F 1878 *The Lake-dwellings of Switzerland and Other Parts of Europe*. London.

Kelly, T C 1967 'A series of Late-Middle Bronze Age sites, Wilde Street, Mildenhall', *Proceedings of the Suffolk Institute of Archaeology* 31, 46–59.

Head, R, Fenwick, H, Van de Noort, R, Dinnin, M & Lillie, M 1995 'The meres and coastal survey', *in* Van de Noort,

R and Ellis, S (eds) *Wetland Heritage of Holderness, an Archaeological Survey*. Hull.

Monroe, R 1882 *Ancient Scottish Lake-dwellings or Crannogs*. Edinburgh.

Parker Pearson, M 1993 'The powerful dead: archaeological relationships between the living and the dead', *Cambridge Archaeological Journal* 3, 203–9.

Smith, R A 1911 'Lake-dwellings in Holderness', *Yorkshire Archaeologia* 62, 593–610.

Van de Noort, R (1995) 'West Furze: the reconstruction of a monumental wetland landscape', *in* Van de Noort,

R & Ellis, S (eds) *Wetland Heritage of Holderness, an Archaeological Survey*. Hull.

Van de Noort, R 2004 *The Humber Wetlands: The Archaeology of a Dynamic Landscape*. Bollington.

Varley, W J 1968 'Barmston and the Holderness Crannogs', *East Riding Archaeologist* 1, 11–26.

Wainwright, G J 1979 *Gussage All Saints: An Iron Age Settlement in Dorset*. Department of Environment Archaeological Report, 10, London.

Wood-Martin, W G 1886 *The Lake-Dwellings of Ireland*. Dublin.

The lake-dwellings and lakeside settlements of Poland

ANDRZEJ PYDYN

INTRODUCTION

The paper will present the results of research and surveys conducted on the underwater and water-logged prehistoric settlements known from the North European Plain, based on examples from northern and central Poland. Lakes, bogs and swamps are relatively common features of the Polish landscape and they were intensively used by prehistoric communities. The oldest prehistoric lake-dwellings known from Poland date back to the Neolithic (c 4000 BC–1800 BC); nevertheless, these types of settlements were the most popular in the Late Bronze Age (1000–700 BC) and the Early Iron Age (750–400 BC). Wooden structures located on the shores of lakes, or directly above the water, are also known from the Early (sixth to thirteenth centuries AD) and Late Middle Ages (fourteenth and fifteenth centuries AD).

It is not really surprising that the so-called lake-dwellings and lakeside settlements can be found in the postglacial landscape of the major lake districts in Poland. One can distinguish three major regional groupings:

1. The Masuria Lake District in north-eastern Poland. The sites from this region can be compared to those known from Lithuania and Latvia.
2. Pomerania, a broad area between the lower Vistula and the lower Oder Rivers.
3. The Wielkopolska Lake District in central-western Poland.

DISCOVERIES

The majority of lake settlements have been discovered in the Masuria Lake District. To date, more than 50 sites of this type are known, either from recent archaeological surveys or from older literature. Many of them had already been located in the nineteenth century by Prussian scholars. In the 1870s and 1880s, J Heydeck excavated a number of 'palafits' (Heydeck

1874; 1889) and he accumulated a vast collection of archaeological finds. These discoveries, together with other artefacts known from cemeteries and other types of settlements, were analysed by O Tischler and other scholars (Tischler 1890). Relative chronological sequences of the Masurian lake-dwellings were established on the base of pollen analyses conducted by H Gross, in the late 1930s (Gross 1938, 126–34; 1939, 100–68). Excavations in Rybno, on Lake Piłakno, that were carried out in the early 1960s, marked the beginnings of a new wave of research on the lake-dwellings of north-eastern Poland (Bukowski et al 1964, 72–87). The most recent fieldwork on these types of sites has been conducted by G Wilke and J Gackowski (Wilke 1991; Gackowski 1995; Kola 2000). Furthermore, a number of monographs on archaeology of north-eastern Poland have been published by other authors (Okulicz 1970; Antoniewicz 1979).

In the early stages of the research, the Masurian lake-dwellings were dated to the Bronze Age. Further work indicated that this chronology should be changed, and it is generally accepted that the majority of these sites had been occupied in the period between 700 and 300 BC. Some authors have suggested that these dwellings were a dominant form of settlement for communities of the so-called West Baltic Barrow culture (Okulicz 1970, 96). This culture developed in the Early Iron Age in north-eastern Poland. Nonetheless, one has to be aware that a much broader chronology was suggested for some of the sites. As early as the nineteenth century, Neolithic and the Early Bronze Age origins were proposed for the lake settlements (Haydeck 1909, 194–202; Engel 1931, 62; Okulicz 1973, 221; Gackowski 1993a, 52). Equally, a number of artefacts suggested that some of the Iron Age lake-dwellings were used again in the Early and Late Middle Ages, but the Medieval use of the shallows is very unlikely to be directly related to the Iron Age tradition. More than half of the 50 known lake-dwellings from the Masuria region have never been properly evaluated by archaeologists. As a result, knowledge of them comes only from short notes, often dating back to the nineteenth century. Only eight settlements have been excavated and even fewer of them have been published (Gackowski 1993a, 57).

As far as the lake settlements from Pomerania are concerned, the knowledge of them is even more rudimentary than of the sites known from the Masuria Lake District. Information for about 25 sites can only be found in literature dating back to the 1860s and 1870s. The original information about unusual concentrations of wooden structures appeared as a result of major earthworks and drainage operations. This information was passed to landowners and then to amateur archaeologists fascinated by local antiquities. One of them, F W Kasiski, collected and published the first data about the now well-known sites at Lake Parsęcko (Kasiski 1869, 77–102). In 1865, Hering suggested, for the first time, direct parallels between the development of the Alpine lake-dwellings and settlements discovered in Pomerania (Hering 1866, 9–20). A fascination with an unusual form of wooden settlement was shared by R Virchow (1833–1902). He published a number of essays on Pomerania 'palafits' (Pfahlbauten), the best of which was published in 1869 (Virchow 1869, 400–16; Gackowski 1993b, 70–85). Virchow pointed out that not all wooden structures are supposed to represent typical lake-dwellings, but at the same time he was confident that a number of prehistoric lake villages were discovered in Pomerania. With the death of Virchow, research on the Pomeranian lake settlements gradually declined and only a few new sites have been discovered since. In the 1960s, 1970s and 1980s, occasional attempts were made to carry out surveys on the sites mentioned earlier. Unfortunately, the results were very limited; in many cases relocating a number of the reported wooden structures was impossible. In the early stages of research, amateur antiquarians described the majority of finds discovered on waterlogged sites as prehistoric. However, the later surveys have not confirmed this chronology. At many sites, including the recently surveyed settlement at Parsęcko, archaeological material dating back to different periods has been discovered.

The research on waterlogged sites in the Wielkopolska region in central-western Poland, has been dominated by the study of the so-called 'Biskupin type of settlements'. A significant number of these settlements developed almost simultaneously within a relatively small area of central-western Poland. Large sites between six and two hectares, often with regular streets and rows of houses, appeared at the end of the Bronze Age. They were usually located on low islands or peninsulas, completely surrounded by water (Śmigielski 1991, 23–35). Simultaneously, or more likely shortly after the collapse of the fortified settlements of the Biskupin type, other kinds of water-oriented settlements appeared in the region. A few examples of these were recently excavated on Lake Powidz, in central-western Poland. A few sites discovered along the shore of this lake were built on very wet (occasionally flooded) shorelines. The occupation took place either in the form of a small concentrated village or spread over a distance of a few hundred metres along the shore of the lake. For decades, the archaeology of this part of Poland was dominated by the research on famous fortified settlements and rich cemeteries. Further survey of lake shores and shallows will probably provide more information about prehistoric lake-dwellings. The discoveries from Lake Powidz can be dated back to the Early Iron Age and are associated with the final stages of the Lusatian culture.

There were two major factors that contributed to the discoveries and the early research carried out at lake-dwellings and lakeside settlements in Pomerania and the Masuria Lake District. The first was 'a fashion for lake settlements'. In the second half of the nineteenth century, antiquarians, as well as the general public in Europe (particularly German-speaking Europe), were very excited about the famous discoveries of lake-dwellings in the Alpine region (Kola & Wilke 1985, 15–17; Wilke 1988, 35–42). There resulted almost a race against time to discover more lake settlements among the Swiss, Austrian and German scholars. Reports on new discoveries appeared in newspapers on a regular basis. J Heydeck, R Virchow and many others were fascinated by the idea of this unusual occupation that took place on the shores and shallows of lakes in many different regions of Europe. This fascination was so intense as to make later critics comment that many of these 'palafits' could only be found in the minds of nineteenth-century German scholars (Gackowski 1993b, 81).

A new interest in an unusual form of lake-dwellings and a growing general fascination with antiquities and large-scale changes in the environment triggered many new archaeological discoveries. In the late nineteenth and early twentieth century, the Prussian Government, together with landowners, introduced changes in water management and land-use on a large scale. These changes very often resulted in a rapid drop in the water level in several lakes, and large areas of land were reclaimed from previously waterlogged bogs and marches. Many small postglacial lakes were totally drained and turned into pasture land. Never before had the wetlands of northern Poland experienced such dramatic changes. These changes were accompanied by major earthworks and the development of road and railway infrastructures. In this development-led environment, a number of wooden structures and archaeological artefacts were discovered. Many of these sites were immediately described as lake-dwellings by passionate antiquarians.

CONSTRUCTIONS

Similarities and differences in the method of construction of lake-dwellings can be a subject of lengthy discussion. The variations of types of settlements could be chronologically, geographically and technically determined. In northern Poland, regularities in lake-

dwelling construction can be found only on the sites from the Masuria Lake District. In the early stages of the research, the lake settlements from this region were already divided into *Faschinenbau* – areas built up with irregular timbers and brushwood to make artificial islands, and *Packwerkbau* – regular platforms made of a number of layers of timbers (Gackowski 1993a, 58). The first category could embrace a vast variety of sites, including the real sites built up with brushwood and irregular timbers and sites originally erected on natural small islands and later submerged, as well as the settlements with regular platforms that were badly damaged. The 'classical' site, constructed in the form of a regular platform built with layers of wooden timbers, was discovered in Orzysz. It was the most carefully documented site by J Heydeck, and remains today one of the best recorded lake settlements from the Masuria District (fig 1). The central part of the site formed a platform

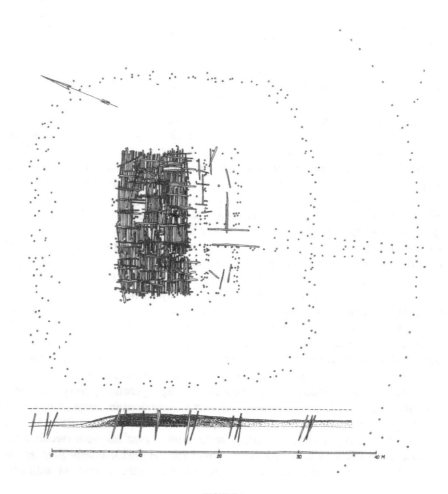

FIGURE 1
The wooden construction of the lake-dwelling at Orzysz in north-eastern Poland (after Heydeck 1909).

325

some 9 by 18m in size. This compact platform was made of layers of timber and was accompanied by an only slightly smaller platform based on rows of piles. Approximately 8m away from the edges of the platform, a regular palisade was discovered. On the southern side of the settlement, *c* 12m away from the first palisade another one was located. According to Heydeck's record, the outer fence was located only from the shore site of the settlements. The whole structure was connected to the shore with a regular bridge (Heydeck 1909, 194–202).

The site at Mołtajny on Lake Arklity represents another well-preserved example of the 'classical' platform-based lake settlement (fig 2). This site was excavated by G Wilke (1991) and later by J Gackowski (1995). The artificial island consisted of four layers of relatively young wood (mostly oak but also elm and hornbeam). Lower layers were built of thin and relatively irregular wooden branches but a top layer consisted of regular and larger timbers.

On the periphery, timbers were twisted between piles to stabilize the edges of the artificial island (Wilke 1991, 31). The settlement was joined with the shore by a bridge some 100m long. A large quantity of piles discovered along the bridge suggest that this construction had been rebuilt on many occasions. A number of piles in the construction of the palisade confirmed the same conclusion. Piles used for this fence were discovered over a large area along the island and the whole construction must have been repaired a number of times (Wilke 1991, 25–41).

The artificial platform covered the area between 460 and 500sqm (Wilke 1991, 32; Gackowski 1995, 34–5). It is very difficult to reconstruct a planning concept of the settlement. The main road through the site was 1.80m wide and had the same orientation as the bridge. This path naturally divided the settlement into a bigger northern part and a smaller southern part. The southern area could be extended in the form of a platform built on the piles that have

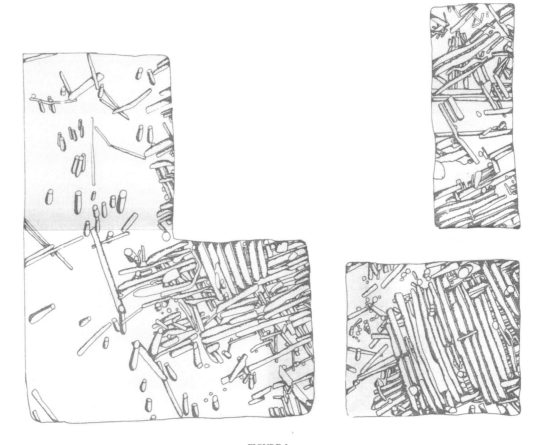

FIGURE 2
Excavated trenches with visible layers of timbers at the site in Mołtajny in north-eastern Poland (based on Gackowski 1995).

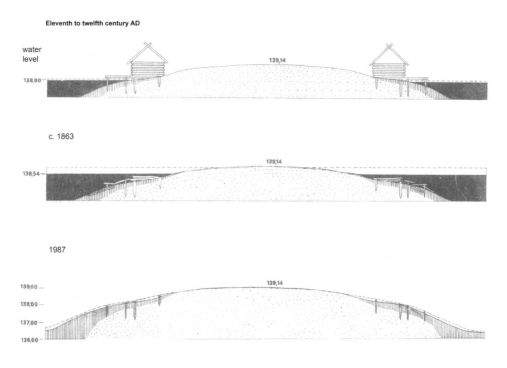

Eleventh to twelfth century AD

FIGURE 3
The reconstruction of the lake site settlement in Parsęcko in northern Poland (after Gackowski & Jabłoński 1993).

been discovered in large numbers in this part of the site. The main path through the settlement was no longer than 30m and the houses were erected along this path. Some buildings located on the edges of the settlements are supposed to be a smith's workshop and barns (Gackowski 1995, 34–5). Probably no more than five to seven houses were used at the same time on this small artificial island. The size of the houses was probably between 3.2 and 3.5m. The walls of the buildings were made of horizontal timbers and clay, and they were supported by vertical timbers driven into the wooden structure of the platform. These timbers were not very long but they were tightly wedged between compact layers of the platform. The exact construction of the walls and the roofs is still uncertain and open for interpretation.

An anthropogenic layer discovered on the Mołtajny site is relatively regular and homogeneous. This might indicate that the settlement was occupied only once at the beginning of the Iron Age. Evidence of fire was often found in the anthropogenic layer, suggesting that at least some parts of the dwelling had been destroyed and rebuilt during occupation (Gackowski 1995, 11–17). In the future, only an intensive dendrochronological dating programme will

provide information about the construction and the abandonment of the settlement. The lake-dwellings from north-eastern Poland follow the pattern of small fortified settlements that were used in the forest zone of north-eastern Europe, in the second half of the first millennium BC (Waluś 1991, 20; Gackowski 1995, 42). Both land-based fortified sites and lake-dwellings were occupied by small communities that put a lot of effort into defending their households.

The Pomeranian lake site dwellings do not follow such clear chronological or cultural pattern. Parsęcko is the most intensively researched site in this region. The site was discovered during the draining of the small lake in the nineteenth century. In the 1860s F W Kasiski published the first information about the site. He described 60 houses sized between 5.5 by 5.2m and 4.5 by 4.2m. The houses were described as having been built with horizontal timbers on a foundation of vertical piles. He also described three bridges and a fragment of the palisade. The archaeological material collected during this work dated the settlement to the period between the eleventh and thirteenth-century AD (Kasiski 1869, 77–102; 1881, 1–12). For a few years, 'palafit-like construction' of this settlement was supported or questioned by a number of scholars (fig 3). The latest archaeological and geomorphological surveys, conducted in 1987, provided not only archaeological data but also information about water-level changes that took place in this lake. Evidence of water-level fluctuation, together with new discoveries of vertical piles and horizontal timbers, suggested that houses had been built right on the shore of the lake, with some structures extending above the water. The work also confirmed that most of the wooden structures described in the nineteenth century deteriorated and can no longer be located (Gackowski & Jabłoński 1993, 115–34). The same process may have happened to the other waterlogged sites known from Pomerania.

The tradition of research on the lake-dwellings from the Wielkopolska region in central-western Poland is much shorter than on other sites of this type known from Pomerania and Masuria. The only properly researched settlements from the Wielkopolska Lake District are from Lake Powidz. This lake is the tenth largest lake in Poland and, until now, only 25 per cent of the shore of the lake has been archaeologically surveyed (Pydyn 2005). Small-scale excavations on two separate sites discovered at this lake started in the year 2000. Archaeological finds and radiocarbon dates, as well as building materials and techniques used to erect these settlements, indicate that they had been used simultaneously, probably at the end of the sixth century BC. Relatively small lake-dwellings were suitable for the decentralized communities that developed in this part of Poland after the collapse of large fortified settlements characteristic of the Late Bronze Age societies.

The variety of plant remains found on the sites indicates that lake-dwelling communities from Powidz had already used strongly anthropogenically modified environments. The region was significantly deforested. As a result, various types of wood, often younger than 30 years old, were used to construct the settlements, in clear contrast with the building materials used almost one hundred years earlier to construct the Biskupin-type settlements. To erect these fortified settlements, large oak timbers were used. The character of wooden structures from the settlements known from Masuria and Pomerania is very different from those discovered on both sites in Powidz. Horizontal wooden structures were the most popular in the Masuria, and, to some extent, in the Pomeranian Lake Districts. Vertical piles were less common. An obvious exception are the palisades known at the sites in Orzysz and Mołtajny.

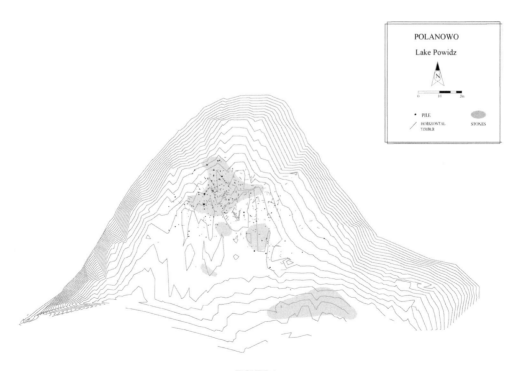

FIGURE 4
The general plan of the site in Polanowo in central-western Poland (after Pydyn & Henderson 2005).

On both settlements in Powidz, horizontal timbers frequently did not appear and the majority of wooden structures are represented by vertical and diagonal piles (Pydyn & Henderson 2005) (fig 4). At Polanowo in Lake Powidz, total station survey revealed 570 wooden elements, 383 of which were vertical piles, 45 of which were diagonal piles, while only 142 were horizontal timbers. Smaller horizontal wooden elements were probably washed away, or more likely dragged away, by ice after the collapse of the buildings. A significant number of loose timbers can be found in deeper water after the slope that limited the original settlement.

Sampled vertical piles were up to 2m long. They were perfectly sharpened and almost completely driven into the lake sediment. Originally, these piles were probably almost 4m long. Many of the diagonal piles were driven to a shallower depth and were designed to support larger vertical piles. Accumulations of two or more vertical and diagonal piles in one place might suggest that some buildings were intensively repaired. At this stage of research, it is difficult to present a full reconstruction of buildings on both settlements discovered on Lake Powidz. Houses were probably no larger than 4 by 4m. The main structures of the buildings were based on stable vertical piles. The space between the piles was filled with smaller horizontal timbers. In contrast to many late prehistoric houses, the examples from Powidz did not have any wooden floors. Clay and small pebbles were used for flooring. Hearths, in turn, were constructed with larger stones. At this stage of the excavations, it is difficult to determine if the buildings on the settlements followed any particular pattern of spatial arrangement. It is important to stress that the planning concepts of both sites were very different. At the site in Polanowo (Lake Powidz), wooden structures are concentrated in a limited area (40×60m) on a submerged peninsula. At the site in Powidz (Lake Powidz), wooden elements were located along the lake shore for a distance of 200m. Furthermore, after a short gap of another 200m they reappeared. In contrast to the settlement in Polanowo, the occupation of the site in Powidz was less concentrated and spread over a large area along a very regular lake shore.

Both dwellings discovered on Lake Powidz were built on very wet, probably, at times, flooded areas. They were located very near the water and may have been affected by seasonal water-level changes. The ground on both sites was so soft that sharpened piles were driven into floors to a depth of 2m without any digging. All wooden structures on the sites were probably not very stable and repaired a number of times. A few wooden samples taken from the settlements indicate that trees used for construction and repairs were cut in the spring. This suggests that major works took place after damage caused by the winters. The buildings on both dwellings were probably located at the very edge of the lake with some structures expanding above the water. This type of construction is similar to the settlement at Parsęcko described earlier. Despite the intensive repairs, the dwellings known from Lake Powidz were probably not used for much longer than one generation.

PRESERVATION

Lake-dwellings in Poland have been discovered in three different regions. The methods of their construction, chronology and origin are significantly different. Nonetheless, the levels of their preservation are related to a number of factors.

- The best preserved waterlogged sites, shortly after their abandonment, were flooded by the rising waters of the lakes. Some of the sites were flooded temporarily, the others permanently.

- Well-preserved sites are often covered by lake sediments. This process provides a stable environment for a long time.

- Stable water levels of lakes, or ground water levels, are crucial for the preservation of these sites. The nineteenth-century drainage works in the lake districts of northern Poland have had a devastating impact on the majority of sites. Continuous drought and dropping levels of ground water, taking place in many parts of Poland for the last 10 or 15 years, have also had a similar impact.

- Vegetation above archaeological sites often protects the wooden structures. This protection sheltered many sites from the devastating impact of wind, waves and ice.

- Public awareness is essential for the preservation and recording of the underwater and waterlogged sites. Many settlements have been destroyed without proper excavations or even without reporting to the heritage authorities. It is very disappointing that we have made little progress in comparison with the nineteenth-century Prussian local societies.

CONCLUSION

The distribution of lake-dwellings and lakeside settlements is geographically limited to the postglacial landscape of northern and central Poland. They were most common in the middle of the first millennium BC, during the transition from the Bronze Age to the Iron Age, while a number of submerged wooden structures can also be associated with the Early Middle Ages (eleventh to thirteenth centuries AD).

Lake-dwellings were characteristic of specific cultural and social settings. They usually appeared in small communities of the forest zone of north-eastern Poland. They were also known in decentralized societies of the Late Lusatian culture during the transition from the Late Bronze Age to the Early Iron Age. Living by the water was characteristic of smaller communities that managed to break free from the centralized structures. To some extent, this principle was also applicable in the Middle Ages. The lakeside dwellings appeared in societies which developed on the edges of the Early Polish Kingdom that was at that time expanding dynamically.

REFERENCES

Antoniewicz, J 1979 *Bałtowie zachodni w V w. p.n.e. – V w. n.e.* Olsztyn.

Bukowski, Z, Dąbrowski, J & Odoj, R 1964 'Sprawozdanie z archeologicznych badań podwodnych w jeziorze Piłakno, pow. Mrągowo, w 1961 r', *Sprawozdania Archeologiczne* 16, 72–87.

Engel, C 1931 'Zur Bauart und Chronologie der ostpreussischen Hügelgräber', *Mannus* 8, 41–54.

Gackowski, J 1993a 'O potrzebie przeprowadzenia systematycznych badań archeologicznych na osiedlach nawodnych w północno-wschodniej Polsce', *Acta Universitatis Nicolai Copernici, Archeologia* 21, 51–67.

Gackowski, J 1993b 'Historia i stan badań osad „palowych" na Pomorzu', *Acta Universitatis Nicolai Copernici, Archeologia* 21, 69–85.

Gackowski, J 1995 'Relikty zabudowy mieszkalno-obronnej osiedla nawodnego kultury kurhanów zachodniobałtyjskich w Mołtajnach, woj. Olsztyn (stan. 1)', *Acta Universitatis Nicolai Copernici, Archeologia* 24, 7–46.

Gackowski, J & Jabłoński, Z 1993 'Sprawozdanie z badań archeologicznych przeprowadzonych w 1987 roku na wczesnośredniowiecznej osadzie „palowej" w Parsęcku, gm. Szczecinek (stanowisko 2)', *Acta Universitatis Nicolai Copernici, Archeologia* 21, 115–34.

Gross, H 1938 'Ergebnisse der Moorgeologischen Untersuchung der vorgeschichtlichen Dörfer im Zedmar-Bruch', *Nachrichtenblatt für deutsche Vorzeit* 14, 126–34.

Gross, H 1939 'Moorgeologische Untersuchung der vorgeschichtlichen Dörfer im Zedmar-Bruch', *Sitzungsberichte der Altertumsgesellschaft Prussia* 33, 100–68.

Hering, J 1866 'Die Pfahlbauten', *Baltische Studien (Alte Folge)*, 21, 9–20.

Heydeck, J 1874 'Ueber Pfahlbauten im Geserich-See', *Schriften der Physikalisch-ökonomischen Gesellschaft zu Königsberg* 15, 14–15.

Heydeck, J 1889 'Die Pfahlbauten im Szonstag- und Tulewo-See', *Sitzungsberichte der Altertumsgesellschaft Prussia* 14, 127–37.

Haydeck, J 1909 'Pfahlbauten in Ostpreussen', *Sitzungsberichte der Altertumsgesellschaft Prussia* 22, 194–202.

Kasiski, F W 1869 'Die Pfahlbauten in den ehemaligen Parsanzig-See bei Neustettin', *Baltische Studien (Alte Folge)*, 23, 77–102.

Kasiski, F W 1881 'Der Pfahlbau in dem ehemaligen Persanzigsee bei Neustettin', in *Beschreibung der vaterländischen Alterhümer im Neustettiner und Schlochauer Kreise*. Danzig.

Kola, A (ed) 2000 *Studies in the Lake Dwellings of the West Baltic Barrow Culture*. Toruń.

Kola, A & Wilke, G 1985 *Archeologia podwodna. Część I.* Toruń.

Okulicz, J 1973 *Pradzieje ziem pruskich od późnego paleolitu do VII w. n.e.* Wrocław.

Okulicz, Ł 1970, *Kultura kurhanów zachodniobałtyjskich we wczesnej epoce żelaza.* Wrocław.

Pydyn, A 2005 'Wyniki systematycznych penetracji podwodnych w rejonie Jeziora Powidzkiego (województwo wielkopolskie)', *Fontes Archaeologisi Posnanienses* (in press).

Pydyn, A & Henderson, J C 2005 'Wykorzystanie tachimetru elektronicznego w archeologicznych badaniach podwodnych na przykładzie stanowiska 1 w Polanowie (województwo wielkopolskie)', *Wielkopolski Biuletyn Konserwatorski* (in press).

Śmigielski, W 1991 'Grody kultury łużyckiej w Wielkopolsce. Wstęp do problematyki', in *Prahistoryczny gród w Biskupinie*. Warszawa.

Tischler, O 1890 'Ostpreussische Grabhügel', *Schriften der Physikalisch-ökonomischen Gesellschaft zu Königsberg* 31, 1–37.

Waluś, A 1991 'Problemy badawcze wczesnej epoki żelaza na obszarze północno-wschodniej Polski', in *Archeologia bałtyjska. Materiały z konferencji.* Olsztyn.

Virchow, R 1869 'Die Pfahlbauten im nördlichen Deutschland', *Zeitschrift für Ethnologie* 1, 400–16.

Wilke, G 1988 'XIX-wieczna eksploracja wczesnośrednowiecznych osiedli "palafitowych" w Bogaczewie i w Szymonce w woj. olsztyńskim. Przyczynek do historii archeologicznych badań podwodnych', *in Studia nad nawodnymi formami osiedli mieszkalnych w kulturach pradziejowych i średniowiecznych Europy.* Toruń.

Wilke, G 1991 'Sprawozdanie z badań wykopaliskowych na stanowisku 1 w Mołtajnach w woj. olsztyńskim w 1986 roku na osiedlu nawodnym kultury kurhanów zachodniobałtyjskich', *Acta Universitatis Nicolai Copernici, Archeologia* 15, 25–41.

Part V
POSTERS

A wet afterlife in the Late Bronze Age

RICHARD BRUNNING

Throughout the prehistoric period from the Sweet Track (3806 BC) onwards there is a well-documented connection between ritual deposition of precious objects and/or human remains in wet contexts (eg Bradley 1990). Sometimes the objects are directly associated with wooden structures such as the metalwork, tools, and human and animal bones discovered at the famous bridges at La Téne (Vouga 1923 and De Navarro 1972) and Cornaux (Schwab 1972), the Middle Iron Age causeway at Fiskerton (Field & Parker Pearson 2003) and the Late Bronze Age bridge at Caldicot (Nayling & Caseldine 1997). The Late Bronze Age pile alignment and possible platform at Flag Fen is another well-known example for which there have been few structural parallels (Pryor 2001). Evidence from two sites in the Somerset moors suggests that ritual deposition around pile structures may have been a more common practice in a particular environmental setting.

The two sites are Greylake on King's Sedgemoor and the Harding Alignment at Harter's Hill on Queen's Sedgemoor (Brunning 1998). At the former site, a series of split oak piles had been inserted in an area of shallow, slow-moving freshwater fen, around which were disarticulated human remains (clavicle, humerus and ribs), sheep jaw bones, broken pottery, white quartz pebbles and a bronze socketed axe that appeared to have been deliberately crushed. The Harding Alignment at Harter's Hill consisted of between one and three rows of roundwood oak piles, forming a line extending for at least 140m into shallow freshwater fen from the contemporary dry land. A mass of horizontally laid cut roundwood and timber offcuts surrounded the piles along with numerous smaller vertical stakes. A bronze sword had been found in the ditch at the edge of the same field before 1940, but has subsequently been lost.

The Harding Alignment has many similarities with the Flag Fen structure although not the same density of artefacts that were found at the Power Station part of the former site. Dendrochronological analysis has been successful at both the Somerset sites and Flag Fen, demonstrating their overlapping periods of use as summarized below.

1304 BC	Earliest possible evidence of felling of trees for initial piles at the Power Station site
1259 BC	Latest date of felling of trees for initial piles in central row at Power Station site
1159 BC	Climatic disaster, possibly associated with the Hekla 3 eruption? (Baillie 2001).
1094 BC	Tree felled for pile in row 4 at Flag Fen

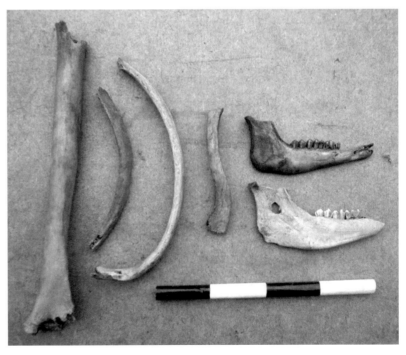

FIGURE 1
Human and sheep bones from Greylake.

FIGURE 2
The Harding Alignment at Harter's Hill looking along the rows of oak piles.

1083 BC	Tree felled for pile in row 4 at Flag Fen
1076 BC	The first trees are felled to form the pile structure at Harter's Hill
1064 BC	More piles are added to the Harter's Hill alignment until at least this date
1026 BC	Tree felled in winter for pile in row 2 at Flag Fen
1007 BC	Tree felled in spring/summer for pile in row 2 at Flag Fen
1002 BC	Tree felled for pile in row 2 at Flag Fen
989 BC	A wooden bridge is made across the river at Caldicot
983 BC	Tree felled for pile in row 2 at Flag Fen
963 BC	The pile structure at Greylake is created shortly after this date
958 BC	Tree felled in winter for pile in row 2 at Flag Fen
957 BC	Tree felled for pile in row 4 at Flag Fen
955 BC	Tree felled for pile in row 2 at Flag Fen
952 BC	More timbers are added to the Greylake site until at least this date
924 BC	Trees felled for piles for Power Station site central rows until at least this date

This evidence suggests that between 1300 BC and 900 BC there was ritual deposition taking place in southern Britain, involving deposition of metalwork, pottery and human and animal remains associated with specific types of wooden structure in particular environments. The key structural and environmental characteristics can be summarized as follows:

1. Shallow (less than 1m deep), slow-moving fresh water environments.
2. Oak piles (split or roundwood) inserted to form rows that did not support any superstructure.
3. Rows of piles added to incrementally over time and not constructed in one instance.
4. Presence of horizontal deposits of worked wood around the piles.

In each of the three sites there is evidence for the environmental setting becoming wetter just before construction of the monument. It may be that the deterioration of the climate at the end of the second millenium BC and increasing wetness of some lowland environments prompted a change in social ritual that involved the creation of oak pile structures in those environments and associated ritual deposition.

ACKNOWLEDGEMENTS

The detailed work was undertaken by a number of specialists including David Hogan (hydrology), Mark Jones (wood), Heather Tinsley (pollen), Julie Jones (plant remains), Harry Kenward (beetles), Paul Davis (snails) and the excavation team of James Brigers, Lorrain Higbee, Keith Faxon, Jan Grove and Steve Membery. Thanks are also due to Gareth Watkins, the English Heritage Project Manager.

REFERENCES

Baillie, M G L 2001 'Some things we may never know: exploring the limits of cause and effect in environmental research' in Raftery, B and Hickey, J (eds) *Recent developments in Wetland Research*. Seandálaíocht: Mon 2, Dept Archaeol, UCD and WARP Occ. Paper 14. Dublin.

Bradley, R 1990 *The Passage of Arms. An archaeological analysis of prehistoric hoards and votive deposits.* Cambridge.

Brunning, R 1998 'Two Bronze Age wooden structures in the Somerset Moors', *Archaeology in the Severn Estuary* 9, 5–8. Exeter.

De Navarro, J M 1972 *The finds from the site of La Tène, vol. 1.* London.

Field, N & Parker Pearson, M 2003 *Fiskerton, An Iron Age timber causeway with Iron Age and Roman votive offerings.* Oxford.

Nayling, N & Caseldine, A 1997 *Excavations at Caldicot, Gwent: Bronze Age paleochannels in the Lower Nedern valley.* CBA Research Report 108, York.

Pryor, F 2001 *The Flag Fen Basin. Archaeology and Environment of a Fenland Landscape.* Swindon. English Heritage.

Schwab, H 1972 'Entdeckung einer keltischen Brücke an der Zihl und ihre Bedeutung für la Tène', *Archäologisches Korrespondenzblatt* 2, 289–94.

Vouga, P 1923 *La Tène: Monographie de la Station.* Leipzig.

God-dollies? An assemblage of peg-like objects from the Pict's Knowe, Dumfries, south-west Scotland

ANNE CRONE

BACKGROUND

The Pict's Knowe is a penannular enclosure consisting of a ditch and external bank built on a small sandy knoll in the valley of the Crooks Pow stream, near Dumfries, in south-west Scotland (NGR: NX953721). It may originally have been built as a henge in the Neolithic period but it was subsequently re-used in the later prehistoric period when the ditch was extensively recut (Thomas forthcoming). The recutting of the ditch was not consistent around the circuit, some areas being dug out preferentially. As the floor of the valley has always been wet and boggy it is likely that there would have been standing water in the ditches and thus the partial recutting of the ditches would have created what were, in effect, a series of small pools or ponds.

Large quantities of waterlogged wood were retrieved from the recut ditch, particularly from the terminals and in the section opposite the entrance, at the back of the enclosure. The assemblage consisted largely of small roundwood fragments and woodworking debris such as offcuts, woodchips and several pieces of lathe-turning waste. There were also a small number of wooden artefacts including a broken keg, a small spatula, small pegs, handles and what look like tent pegs. The most unusual element of the assemblage is a group of nine peg-like objects which form the subject of this paper (the wood assemblage is described in full in Crone *et al* forthcoming). Radiocarbon dates from some of the wooden finds, including one of the peg-like objects, cluster around the second century AD (Thomas forthcoming).

DESCRIPTION

These enigmatic objects vary greatly in size but are unified by a set of distinctive characteristics. The complete examples have a distinctive head and shaft, hence the description as peg-like (fig 1). The shaft extends from the 'back' of the head and is rectangular in cross-section. Where sufficient length

survives, the shaft has been perforated by large holes, the number of holes depending on the length of the shaft. The most distinctive characteristic of the group is that they all have bulbous, domed heads, the curved surface of which is charred. The charring is restricted to and evenly distributed over the whole of the domical surface, penetrating the wood evenly to a depth of *c* 1mm. There is no charring on any of the shafts or on the flat underside of the heads, nor does there appear to have been any on the flattened rear of the heads. Such restricted and even charring can only have been deliberate and appears to have been an essential element in their design and manufacture or their use. Indeed, three of the fragments, SF333, SF808 and SF833, were in such a spongy, degraded state that it is only the charred surface which had held the wood fibres together and made their domed heads identifiable (fig 2).

In the absence of sandpapers or metal spokeshaves, it would have been difficult to produce the smooth domical surface of the head. It is possible that, after initial rough shaping with an axe, the head was repeatedly charred and the carbonized wood rubbed down (eg, with or against a suitable stone) until the smooth surface was achieved. However, if the shaped 'peg' had been simply inserted into a fire, it is difficult to explain why the base and rear of the head have suffered no charring. It seems necessary to conclude that the head was charred and shaped before the whole object was brought to its final shape. In their completed form, the rounded and blackened heads would have contrasted with the pale wood and the rectilinear outlines of the shafts and this may have been an intended feature of their design. However it was achieved, the finished objects conform to a clearly conceived plan.

The 'pegs' vary greatly in size. The largest of the complete examples, SF48 (fig 2), is 1640mm long while the smallest complete example is only 350mm long. As three of the group survive only as very incomplete head fragments, the length of the head is the only attribute available for comparison on most

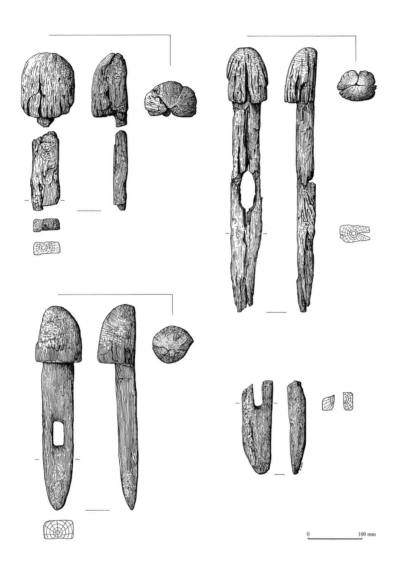

all of which are significantly smaller than the examples described above but which are roughly comparable with each other (fig 1). On these examples, the width of the shaft has been reduced at the end to a rounded, central tip and the thickness of the shaft has also been reduced at the tip. In all three cases, the shaft has been perforated roughly midway along its length by an oval hole. SF67 is a shaft fragment of similar dimensions to this group, the remnant of the oval hole visible at the broken upper end (fig 1). SF48 differs from the other 'pegs' in that it has three round holes through its shaft, the middle one of which is penetrated by a large square stake (fig 2).

Other fragments indicate that the group cannot be polarized into distinct sub-groups of small and large examples. The very fragmented head of SF833 (fig 2) and the complete head of SF862 (fig 1) are 135mm and 120mm in length respectively, and thus span the size spectrum between the very large and very small 'pegs'.

FUNCTION

The function of these objects is not immediately apparent. As their description indicates, they most resemble pegs, which would imply that they were used to secure together elements of a structure.

The tips of all the complete examples have been shaped to a rounded point and their thickness tapered down at the tip. These characteristics are suggestive of their use for insertion into some larger structure. They display none of the compression damage at the tips that would be consistent with insertion into the ground, nor do the domical heads show any sign that they were hammered. It seems most likely, therefore, that they were intended for insertion into ready-made holes in other pieces of wood. The hole/s in the shaft may have been designed for the insertion of a peg or pin that would wedge the joint tightly shut and prevent any slippage. Unfortunately, the degraded surfaces

FIGURE 1
The smaller of the peg-like objects. Clockwise from top left – SF862, SF384, SF67 and SF169.

of the examples. This ranges from 85mm to over 270mm. Although SF48 appears to be the largest of the group, because more of it has survived, there were other, larger examples. Although only fragments of the heads of SF333 and SF808 survive, their lengths (>270mm and >210mm respectively) demonstrate that they would have been in the same size spectrum as SF48 (250mm) (fig 2). Within the rest of the assemblage, there are a number of large oak timbers with rectangular cross-sections, which may be the remains of the shafts of these larger examples.

At the other end of the size spectrum are a group of three complete 'pegs', SF384, SF385 and SF169, of most of these objects means that wear marks have not survived and therefore there is no evidence to confirm or refute this suggestion. The surface of the shaft between the base of the head and the top of the hole on SF169, a distance of 110mm, appears to be a little less weathered than the rest of the shaft, suggesting that this part may have been protected, as it would have been had it been inserted into a thick plank, for example.

However, this simple functional explanation breaks down when we consider the larger examples, SF48, SF333 and SF808 (see above). Overall, it is the lack of consistency in the size of the objects, with the exception of the three complete examples, that argues against a purely structural function.

They could, however, have formed part of some kind of ritual structure, possibly an altar or a shrine. These objects have clearly been fashioned to a consistent design, albeit on different scales. It is this replication of attributes across a broad size range that brings ritual associations forcefully to mind. Ritual acts tend to be repeated acts that give rise to consistent sets of remains and the 'pegs' have clearly been fashioned with great care and consistency. The use of fire in the fashioning of the 'pegs' may have been part of that ritual activity. The 'pegs' would have been very striking in their finished form, the rounded and blackened heads contrasting with the pale wood of the rectangular shafts. We could perhaps envisage an altar or shrine consisting of a long plank raised in some way, into which these pegs would have been inserted as individual acts of supplication, the variation in the size of the pegs possibly reflecting some attribute of the individual.

The replication of attributes is also suggestive of copying from a single, perhaps evocative image. There is something vaguely anthropomorphic about the design, the proportions of the rounded head to the shaft reminiscent of a highly stylized human figure. This is, of course, a very subjective observation and may be stretching the evidence too far but representations of the human figure in prehistory are often very abstract in their interpretation of human attributes (Coles & Coles 1996, 70; van der Sanden & Capelle 2002; Stanley this volume).

The manner in which the largest complete example, SF48, was found may also have some bearing on the nature of these objects. SF48 was recovered with a stake *in situ* through the upper hole, apparently pinning it down within the recut ditch. This position

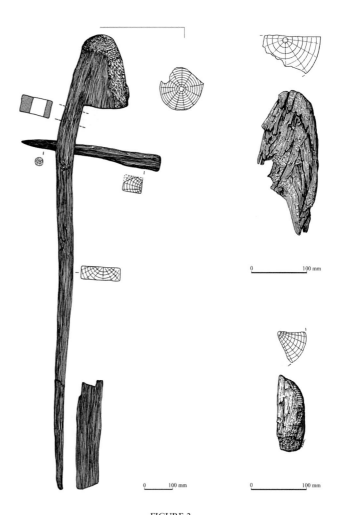

FIGURE 2
The larger of the peg-like objects. Clockwise from top left SF48, SF333 and SF833.

may simply have been fortuitous; alternatively, it could have been deliberately 'placed' and it may be that the other 'pegs' were intended to be pinned down in a similar fashion, hence the hole in all the shafts. The anthropomorphic connotations of the 'pegs' brings to mind the Bronze Age 'god-dolly' found at Ballachulish, near Fort William, Scotland, which was found lying face down in a peat bog, apparently pinned down with stakes and wickerwork (Christison 1881). Many of the wooden figures from Britain and Europe have been found in what would have been waterfilled hollows within peat bogs (van der Sanden & Capelle 2002); one might speculate whether the pools formed by the partial recutting of the henge ditch at the Pict's Knowe were deliberately created to emulate such conditions. Whilst primarily a feature of Bronze Age votive practices the deposition of wooden

341

figures in watery locations did continue into the Iron Age (Bradley 1990, 167–8) and the Pict's Knowe 'pegs' may be a local variant of this tradition.

DISCUSSION

The re-use of Neolithic monuments in later prehistory occurs frequently enough and in such a manner as to suggest that the significance of these monuments was appreciated and consciously appropriated by the Iron Age population (Hingley 1996). These sites may have been re-used as a means of establishing the legitimacy of claims to power by demonstrating ancestral lineage. In this context, the excavator has hypothesized that the henge at Pict's Knowe may have been re-used as a ceremonial centre or shrine by a locally powerful Iron Age group (Thomas forthcoming). The 'pegs' form part of the evidence which informs this interpretation. They are enigmatic objects for which no simple functional interpretation of all the observed attributes can be offered. It is possible that they were both structural and ritual at the same time, forming elements of an altar or shrine, for instance, which was dismantled and formally deposited in the ditch (Thomas forthcoming). Other elements in the artefact assemblage are also suggestive of deliberate, possibly votive, deposition in the ditch (Thomas *ibid.*).

There is certainly very little in the rest of the wood assemblage to suggest that the later prehistoric activity at Pict's Knowe was domestic in nature (Crone *et al* forthcoming). Some 55 per cent of the assemblage was woodworking debris, offcuts and woodchips from axe dressing, which consisted almost entirely of oak with a small amount of alder and a few pieces of ash. As the peg-like objects had all been fashioned by axe from branches of young, fast-grown oak with the exception of one made of alder, the woodworking debris could well be the result of their manufacture on the site. It is tempting to suggest that the 'peg-like' objects formed the focus, or were an essential element of the activities taking place on Pict's Knowe.

REFERENCES

Bradley, R 1990 *The passage of arms. An archaeological analysis of prehistoric hoard and votive deposits.* Oxford.

Christison, R 1881 'On an ancient wooden image, found in November last at Ballachulish Peat Moss, *Proc Soc Antiq Scot* 15, 158–78.

Coles, J & Coles, B 1996 *Enlarging the past. The contribution of wetland archaeology.* Edinburgh.

Crone, B A, Sands, R & Skinner, T forthcoming 'The waterlogged wood assemblage', *in* Thomas, J forthcoming.

Hingley, R 1996 'Ancestors and identity in the later prehistory of Atlantic Scotland: the reuse and reinvention of Neolithic monuments and material culture', *World Archaeology* 28(2), 231–43.

Thomas, J forthcoming *Place and Memory: Excavations at the Pict's Knowe, Holywood and Holm Farm, Dumfries and Galloway, 1994–8.* Oxford.

van der Sanden, W & Capelle, T 2002 *Götter, Götzen, Holzmenschen.* Oldenburg.

Boat and human remains from bogs in Central Norway

MERETE MOE HENRIKSEN and MORTEN SYLVESTER

INTRODUCTION

Large areas of Norway are covered by bog, and in Central Norway this accounts for 20 per cent of the total land area. The Museum of Natural History and Archaeology (Vitenskapsmuseet) in Trondheim has a large collection of archaeological artefacts recovered from these wetland areas. The artefacts are an important resource for the study of the region's prehistory. The majority of bog finds comes from the country's coastal areas and their distribution pattern arises principally from widespread peat extraction for fuel, especially in the first half of the twentieth century. Among the bog finds is what is, perhaps, the Museum's most well-known find – the ornamented Bronze Age wooden artefacts found at Høstad, near Trondheim (Marstrander 1967). Recently, two projects have been initiated at the Department of Archaeology and Cultural History at Vitenskapsmuseet, both of which take bog finds from

Central Norway as a starting point. Boat elements are being investigated by Morten Sylvester, while Merete Moe Henriksen has chosen to look more closely at human remains found in bogs.

BOATS IN BOGS

In the study of prehistoric boats in Scandinavia, both boats and parts of boats from bogs have always been an important resource, and some of the best known boat and ship finds have been recovered from this kind of context. Among these are the two Danish finds – the Hjortspring boat (c 350 BC) (Rosenberg 1937; Crumlin-Pedersen & Trakadas 2003) and the boats from Nydam bog (c AD 190–320) (Engelhardt 1865; Rieck 2003), as well as the Norwegian Kvalsund find of two boats from the period around AD 700 (Shetelig & Johannesen 1929). In addition to the well-known sites with 'intact' boats, there are many sites which

FIGURE 1
Miniature boat from Ryggaunet, probably dated to the Viking Age or the Middle Ages. (Photo: Per E. Fredriksen.)

have produced only boat parts; these have not been the focus of archaeological research to the same extent.

'Boats in Bogs' aims to seek out the more modest, less spectacular, finds from the dark reaches of the museum stores and to examine and date them so that this material can be used in archaeological research. A further goal of the project is to try to answer why and how the boat material ended up in bogs. Is it a

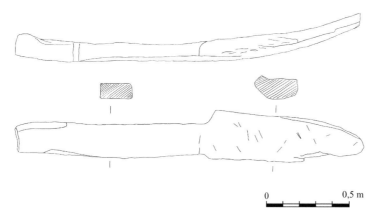

FIGURE 2
Part of a boat keel from Langmyr dated to cal AD 240–410.
(Drawing: Morten Sylvester.)

question of ritual offering or were there boat-building or technical reasons why boat parts were placed in bogs?

BOATS IN BOGS – THE MATERIAL FROM CENTRAL NORWAY

A thorough search of the Museum archives and archaeological collections has revealed a total of 29 bog sites from which boat elements have been registered, either as physical remains or as descriptions of finds where the original material no longer exists. The finds often consist of boat parts such as keels, stems, boat planks and frames. A number of miniature boats have also been found in bogs, for example, at Ryggaunet (fig 1).

Most of these discoveries were made in connection with the cutting of peat and the draining of bogs, and the finds' contextual information has come principally from local residents reporting their observations to the Museum. The finds have lain mostly unnoticed in the Museum stores. The find localities were seldom visited by archaeologists, and rarely examined by geologists or botanists.

In this project, eight finds have been ^{14}C dated, and together with finds dated previously, we now have eleven absolutely dated. These datings are all from the period 810 cal BC–cal AD 1425. For now, it seems that just one find has characteristics that suggest an interpretation as a ritual offering. For the remaining finds other explanations are more probable. A number of the boat elements are unfinished and were never incorporated into actual boats. These objects are interpreted as an expression of boat building, where partially finished items are deposited or possibly disposed of in wetlands. One example from this group is the unfinished keel from Langmyr illustrated in the drawing (fig 2).

So far, the most exciting results of the project are the datings of a find to the late Bronze Age or early pre-Roman Iron Age – two ^{14}C datings point to 810–410 cal BC. The find is the remains of the oldest plank-built boat in Scandinavia. Archaeological and paleobotanical investigations will be carried out on the find site in the autumn of 2006, funding permitting.

LAKE OF THE DEAD – HUMAN REMAINS FROM BOGS IN CENTRAL NORWAY

A number of human skeletal remains have been found in bog contexts in Norway (Sellevold & Næss 1991). However, unlike other areas of north-west Europe, we know of no bog body finds in Norway with preserved soft tissue. There are 15 documented bog skeletons, the majority of which can be dated to c 500 BC–AD 550. Men, women and children are all represented in this material. Five of these finds are from Central Norway, and are divided between four sites in the counties of North Trøndelag and Nordland. They consist of three skulls and two more complete skeletons. All of the skeletons have been sexed as female, aged 15–30 years.

Recent ^{14}C dating places four of the skeletons to the period cal AD 30–550. Preliminary examination suggests that these women were most likely deposited in open or swampy water. No artefacts were found when the sites of these discoveries were subsequently investigated. A fifth skeletal find has been dated to the Viking Age, based upon associated artefacts (Bjørn 1920). This woman was interred in bog land together with grave goods, and the find is probably an ordinary grave from a period when the bog was

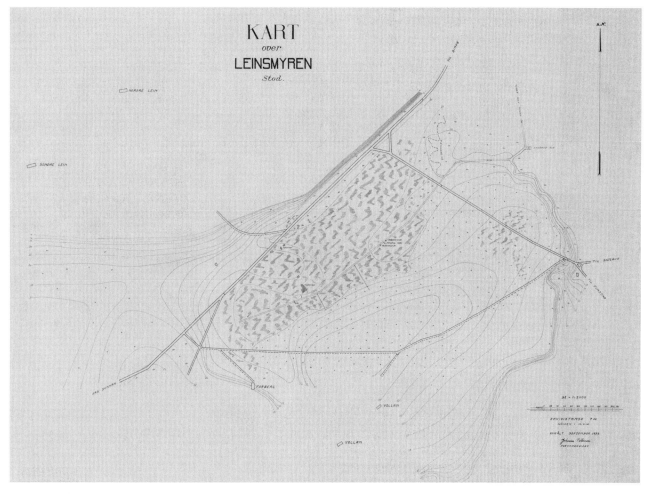

FIGURE 3
The women from Leinsmyra were most likely deposited in a pond which lay at the bottom of a steep hillside. Was this landscape feature a deciding factor for the two women to be deposited here in the Iron Age?

relatively dry. From Central Norway there are also reports of discoveries of human remains in bogs that, unfortunately, have not survived to the present day. Several places along the coast have reported finds of plaited hair, some of it reportedly found in close connection with human bones.

The deposition of humans in bogs is a practice that continued long into more recent times in Scandinavia, where it was seen, among other things, as a protection against the waking of the dead. In Central Norway, the practice continued until as late as 1681, when a man who supposedly killed 11 of his own children was buried in bog land. Is there a connection between the depositing of humans in bogs in the Middle Ages and more recent times, and the bog bodies from the Iron Age, or were Iron Age

people sacrificed, as many archaeologists propose? 'Lake of the Dead' seeks to shed light on the background for the tradition of depositing human remains in wetland areas through an analysis of the finds from Central Norway. In this study, both the environment of the find site and the features of the landscape, along with the proximity to other prehistoric sites will be mapped.

THE WOMEN FROM LEINSMYRA

In 1930 and 1931, two female skulls were found during the draining of Leinsmyra bog, North Trøndelag (figs 3 and 4). The skulls were found within 20–30m of one another, and lay 2–3m deep at

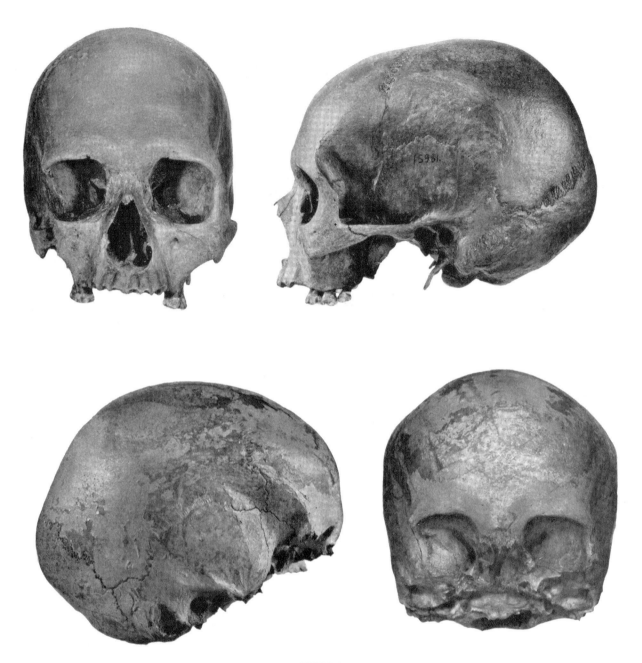

FIGURE 4
The female skulls from Leinsmyra date to cal AD 265–410 and cal AD 450–550.

the bottom of the bog. As only a limited excavation was carried out at the time of the discovery, it is possible that the associated skeletons still remain in the bog. Botanical studies on the site show that the two women were deposited into what must have been a partially overgrown pond. Based on a misinterpretation of the bog's stratigraphy, the skulls from Leinsmyra were initially dated to the Stone Age. The skulls have now been ^{14}C dated to cal AD 265–410 and cal AD 450–550. The dates show that the skulls represent two discrete events, and that the site therefore held a special relevance over a longer period of time during the Iron Age. An osteological examination of the skulls showed that the females died when approximately aged 15 and 30, but was unable to conclude the means of death.

346

REFERENCES

Bjørn, A 1920 'Nogen myrfund fra Trøndelagen', *Det Kgl Norske Videnskabers Selskabs Skrifter* 4, 4–12. Trondheim.

Crumlin-Pedersen, O & Trakadas, A (eds) 2003 'Hjortspring. A Pre-Roman Iron-Age Warship in Context', *Ships and Boats of the North 5*, The Viking Ship Museum in Roskilde.

Engelhardt, C 1865 *Nydam Mosefund 1859–1863*. Copenhagen.

Marstrander, S 1967 'Fra bronsealderens treskjærerkunst', *Viking – Tidskrift for norrøn arkeologi* 31, 5–46. Oslo.

Rieck, F 2003 'Skibene fra Nydam Mose', *in* Jørgensen, L Storgaard, B & Thomsen, L G (eds), *Sejrens triumf – Norden i skyggen af det romerske Imperium*, 296–309. Copenhagen.

Rosenberg, G 1937 *Hjortspringfundet,* Nordiske Fortidsminder III. Copenhagen.

Shetelig, H & Johannesen, F 1929 *Kvalsundfundet og andre norske myrfund av fartøier*. Bergen Museums Skrifter, 2. Bergen.

Sellevold, B J & Næss, J R 1991 'Mennesker i myr', *in* Wik, B (ed) 'Sentrum-periferi. Sentra og sentrumsdannelser gjennom førhistorisk og historisk tid', *Gunneria* 64, 2, 429–42. Trondheim.

Talking about wetlands in the past

KATRIN THIER

ARCHAEOLOGY AND LANGUAGE

Language is as much an identifying feature of human societies as material culture, but one that is far less durable. While large assemblages of material remains can survive in the ground over long periods of time, the spoken word is lost as soon as it has been uttered.

Language survives in the form of writing, and our knowledge is heavily dependent on the time at which a group of people chose to write, and the way in which they acquired this knowledge. Historical linguistics is essentially the archaeology of the spoken word. From written records, attempts are made to understand the speech of the time, recognize development patterns and reconstruct missing material. Methods used are very similar to typology, taking account of both the sound and the meaning of the word, and relative as well as absolute chronologies can be extrapolated. Just like material culture, languages are periodized in different ways in different regions. The sound of language can be reconstructed to a certain extent from written sources, by careful comparison of evidence and through understanding of spelling conventions. Particular pieces of evidence can be anchored in time if they occur in datable manuscripts or on archaeological finds (eg rune staves).

Words can tell much about the way people see their environment, through their choice of word, the number of words available for a concept and their origin. An old word is likely to indicate long-term familiarity with a concept, while new concepts from other cultures are often adopted along with their names. The further back one goes in time, the more difficult it is to interpret the ever-diminishing evidence.

The immediate linguistic prehistory of northern Europe is the Late Iron Age, up to around AD 500 (fig 1). What we know about the languages of the area at this time is recognized only through analysis of classical (ie non-native) and later evidence. There is little Celtic and even less Germanic writing in this area before AD 500, although the few existing pieces

of dated evidence (eg inscriptions) can help in pinning down developments otherwise only seen through reconstruction (cf eg Sims-Williams 2003; page 1999).

In Scandinavia and in the Baltic Sea area, a Germanic language was probably spoken, although the languages we now know as North Germanic (Icelandic, Norwegian, Danish, Swedish) are not attested until the Viking period. There is evidence that there was contact with Baltic languages (now eg Lithuanian and Latvian, but in the Late Iron Age also spoken much further west) (Udolph 1994, 48–9). Germanic speakers from the south coast of the Baltic Sea migrated south, and one of their languages is preserved in the fourth-century Gothic bible translation (East Germanic) (Green 1998, 164–81). On the continental North Sea coast (and further inland), West Germanic languages were spoken (now eg English, Frisian, Dutch and German). These were first written down in any quantity after c AD 700 (eg Old English) (cf Robinson 1992). West of this area, in modern-day Belgium and Northern France, Gaulish, a group of Celtic dialects, survived into the first half of the first millennium AD. Other Celtic languages were spoken in Britain, British (now eg Welsh and Cornish), and Pictish. The earliest known language of Ireland is Old Irish, ancestor of Irish, Scottish Gaelic and Manx, first attested in a corpus of inscriptions of the first half of the first millennium AD (cf McManus 1991). Celtic and Germanic languages are thought to descend from a common Indo-European language, probably at some time in the Neolithic, although almost everything about this language is debated.

Many of the speakers of Germanic and Celtic languages inhabited the North European plains, the British Isles and Scandinavia, which between them constitute a geographical zone with the right conditions for the formation of extensive wetlands, especially peat bogs (van der Sanden 1996, 21–37). The main geographic division within this area is probably east of the Elbe, where glacial moraines characterize the landscape. As forms of these wetlands dominated people's environment,

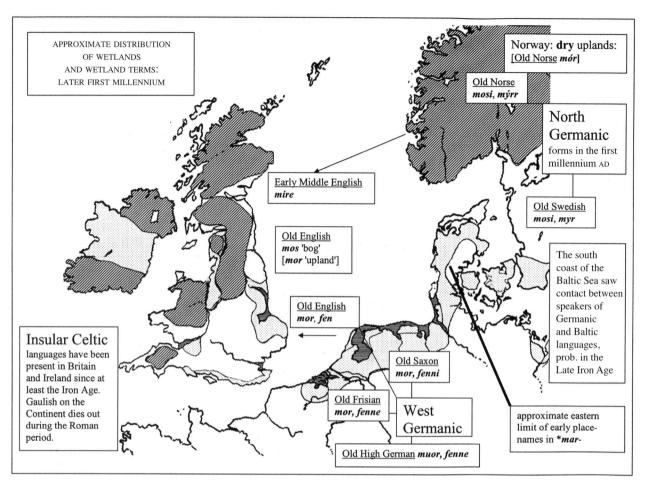

FIGURE 1

Approximate distribution of uplands, wetlands and wetland terms in northern Europe in the second half of the first millennium AD. Legend: diagonal hatching: uplands (predominantly wet except in Norway); horizontal hatching: mudflats; stipples: low-lying wetlands and coastal salt-marshes.

similar technologies as well as cultural expressions developed in the area. Wooden trackways, for instance, are found at various periods, constructed in different ways but serving the same purpose. Their presence is an example of similar problems inspiring similar solutions. Contacts and traditions probably play a role in their development, but they are not a necessary factor. On the other hand, this same geographical area shows several distinctive cultural features, which show strong similarities without any practical necessity and regardless of language boundaries. One example is the extraordinary treatment of bog bodies. While a large number of these are perhaps merely victims of accidents, there are a few which appear to have been specially treated, probably ritually. These include examples from Denmark, which was almost certainly Germanic-

speaking, as well as Celtic-speaking Britain (cf van der Sanden 1996). Another example might be the wooden effigies, which date from all periods, from as early as the Bronze Age, and have three main types (round, forked and flat); these types, however, are not grouped either by date or region and occur in the entire area (van der Sanden & Capelle 2002, 71).

MODERN ENGLISH, AND BACK

English has a variety of words for wetlands. Many of these are old and can be traced back to Indo-European, for example, *moor*, *marsh*, *moss*, *fen*, all of which are known from the Old English period onwards (see below). Others were borrowed later, such as *mire* (thirteenth century, from Old Norse,

OED3 (2002)) and *bog* (sixteenth century, from Irish and Scottish Gaelic, OED2). Some terms are known in Old English and often later, but have now disappeared or become rare (eg *hope*, *slade*). *Swamp*, on the other hand, is an old Germanic term, which only became common in the seventeenth century, when a new term was needed for wetlands of unfamiliar kind in Virginia. The neutral term *wetland* first appears in eighteenth-century North America; it starts its life as a descriptive phrase (*wet land*) and gradually develops into the modern compound noun (OED2).

This is just a selection of the breadth of terms available to English speakers, past and present, suggesting close familiarity with different kinds of wetlands. Since many seem to go back beyond written records, it is fair to assume that this familiarity goes back equally far. Different terms were probably used for different kinds of wetland, according to consistency, topography or land-use, although these senses can be hard to trace. Specializations as well as generalizations of senses are in constant flux, and the speakers' view of the world shapes these distinctions. Words and senses will also have differed in different regions.

A WORD FOR A WET PLACE WITH M?

Fig 2 shows the approximate distribution of wetland terms across Europe in the later first millennium AD. A number of Germanic and Celtic words for wetlands begin with M-, although they are not all related. One group derives from an Indo-European term for a body of water, reflected in English *mere*. In common Germanic, this would have been **mar-*. This root is well attested not only in Germanic, but also in the Celtic, Baltic and Slavonic languages as well as in Latin and its descendants. It is absent from Greek, Albanian and the Indo-European languages of Asia (eg Hittite, Iranian and Indic languages) (Pokorny 1959, 748). Old place-names containing this Germanic root **mar-* are quite common west of the Elbe and also occur in Britain and Jutland, but are very rare east of this area (Udolph 1994, 374–5). Only the West Germanic languages formed a derivative from this root with a second element **-isc-* (cf modern English *-ish*): 'land associated with or belonging to water, lakes or the sea', that is, 'wetland'. This formation spawned a complex set of terms including *marsh*, *marish* and *morass* (OED3 2000, 2002). These words appear to have been mainly used for low-lying land liable to flooding, such as meadows, riverbanks and seashores. On the continental North Sea coast, the term has now become specialized to mean a salt-marsh; this did not happen in English (there is still a need to specify *salt-marsh*), perhaps because of Britain's different coastal topography. Germanic **marisc-* was also borrowed into Latin (*mariscus*), whence it came back into English via French *marais* in the Middle Ages. The result was *marish*, which had the same sense as *marsh*. This duplication eventually led to the disappearance of *marish*, except in some dialects and in the literary language. The same French word was also loaned into Middle Dutch, where the vowel was changed by analogy with *moor* to give *morasch* (now *moerass*). The latter term was in turn borrowed into English as *morass*.

A completely different origin has been reconstructed for the word *moss*, which derives from an Indo-European root meaning 'damp, wet' (OED3 2002). This appears in two forms, **mus-* and **meus-* (Pokorny 1959, 742). Like the root **mar-* 'body of water', **mus-* is attested in Germanic, Slavic and Baltic languages as well as Latin (though not Celtic in this case). It has chiefly given rise to words denoting a peat-forming plant (*muscus*, *sphagnum*), but in several languages (eg Old High German, English) the word also has (or had) the sense 'wetland'. Given its frequency, even in the earliest period, it is likely that the plant sense was original, but with the important role mosses play in peat formation, the link between the sense of 'moss (the plant)' and 'bog' is very close. Where the 'wetland' sense exists in early Germanic languages, the word is ambiguous. It is only in the later development of the Scandinavian languages that a complete split is achieved (cf Danish *mos* 'moss (the plant)', *mose* 'wetland'). Significantly, this split happened in the areas where the words *moor* and *marsh* were originally rare or absent.

The variant **meus-* in the West Germanic languages developed into a group of words nearly exclusively denoting the plant; most of which are now rare (such as English *mese*), having lost out to *moss* (etc.). However, in Scandinavia this lengthened root became Old Norse *mýrr*, a term apparently exclusively denoting wetlands, never plants (de Vries 1961, 398). English *mire* can only have come from Old Norse *mýrr*, since there are no parallels in the West Germanic languages. This means it would have been introduced to Britain by the Vikings, and the largely northerly distribution of the term supports this view. Unlike most other terms, *mire* was used in literary contexts early on, often in figurative senses (OED3 2002).

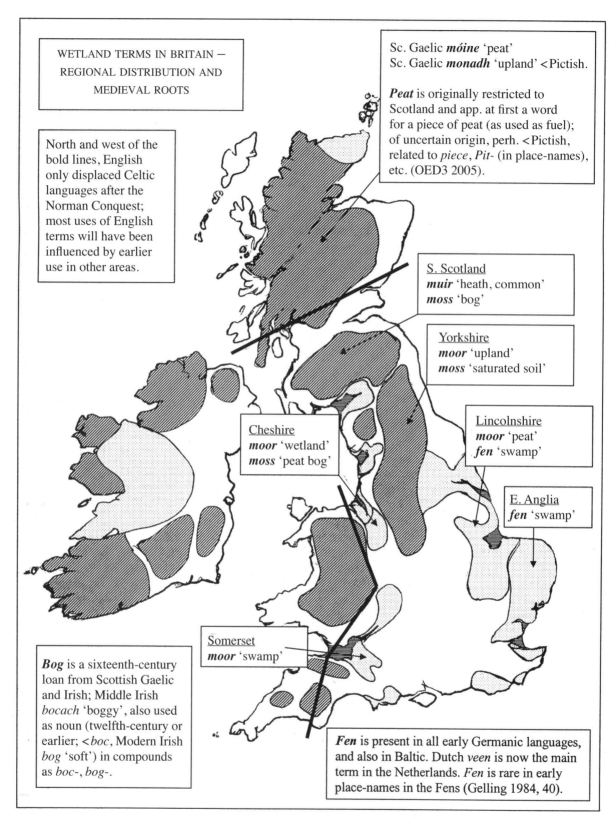

FIGURE 2
Geographical distribution of wetland terms in contemporary Britain, reflecting medieval developments.

It is unfortunate in this context that the only East Germanic language known to any extent almost exclusively survives in a translation of the Gospels, stories set in a hot dry climate, which do not feature wetlands. Therefore, despite the former presence of related languages on the Baltic Sea coast, it is difficult to assess their contribution to these developments.

A group of similar-sounding Celtic terms exists in Britain and Ireland. The Old Irish word for 'peat' and hence 'peat bog' is *móin*, related to Welsh *mawn* 'peat' but otherwise of unknown origin. In Scottish Gaelic *mòine* 'peat, bog' co-exists with the similar-looking *monadh* 'mountain, (upland) moor', which is in fact unrelated and of Pictish origin. Not originally a wetland term, it is parallel to Welsh *mynydd* 'mountain' and comes ultimately from the same root as English *mountain* (OED3 s.v. *mounth* 2002). The old place-name *Mona*, used both for Anglesey (Welsh *Ynys Môn*) and the Isle of Man (Manx *Ellan Vannin*), comes ultimately from the same root, despite its superficial similarity to the Irish peat-word (Room 1988, 10, 230).

The semantic link between uplands and wetlands here seems to have its source in the topography, where uplands are often covered by bogs. This may have encouraged the Celtic words to influence each other. It is also likely to have caused a further development.

WHAT'S IN A MOOR?

Moor (Old English *mor*, OED2 2002, cf Gelling 1984, 54–6) is originally a term for a wetland, possibly but not certainly derived from a variant of the root of *mere* and *marsh* (see above) and restricted to West Germanic. The use of *moor* meaning 'upland' is unique to Britain. Its origins lie both in the geography of Britain and in the more recent history of settlement, towards the end of the first millennium AD. In the south of England, *moor* has retained its original sense of 'wetland'. Much of this area consists of downs and lowlands, and wetlands tend to be of the low-lying kind (eg the Somerset Levels). It was also outside the Viking sphere of influence.

A large part of northern England and southern Scotland, by contrast, consists of unforested upland where large tracts of blanket bog have developed. The region also has a certain amount of low-lying lands, wet and dry, mostly near the coast. There are therefore two fundamentally different types of wetlands here, which deserve distinction in their terminology. This is where the Vikings settled; here Old English and Old Norse languages met and, on account of their relative similarity, had a strong impact on each other.

The Vikings brought with them the term *mór* meaning 'upland', a word entirely unrelated to, but sounding exactly like Old English *mor* 'wetland', the descendant of the West Germanic word discussed above. Its ultimate etymology is unknown, but it is related to a number of Scandinavian terms for dry land (eg Swedish *mo* 'chalky soil'), and was also borrowed into Finnish and Estonian at an early date (de Vries 1961, 392). The *-r* in this word is in fact a grammatical ending, but since the equivalent ending had disappeared from Old English by that time, speakers in England may not have realized this. The identical sound of Old English and Old Norse words, together with the overlap in sense provided by upland bogs, allowed the words to merge. So while in the south Old English *mor* remained the term for a low-lying wetland, in the north its sense shifted to upland bog, leaving low-lying wetlands without a distinct term. To fill this gap, English in the north used the ambiguous term *moss* (Old English *mos*), which denotes both the plant and a wetland, reinforced by the sense 'wetland' of Old Norse *mosi* (contrasting with Old Norse *mór*). In English, *moss* also remained the word for the plant, which is now the main sense, but especially in the north the word is still ambiguous. This ambiguity can be sustained, because usually the sense is clear from the context.

The distribution of these senses of *mor* (and *mos*) is already distinguishable in the Old English written evidence, and they also survive into modern English regional use. Fig 2 shows their distribution with some examples from key dialects.

CONCLUSIONS

The belt of wetland stretching across Northern Europe is home to people speaking distinctly different languages at least as early as the late Iron Age. The areas these languages are spoken in are not necessarily the same as those of archaeological groupings. Although our knowledge of the early stages of language is vague, some non-essential practices associated with wetlands can be observed both in clearly Celtic- and Germanic-speaking areas. A certain dividing line can be observed along the Elbe, which seems to reflect geographical more than cultural factors.

Language is shaped by the environment, and Germanic in particular has a variety of words for wetlands. Several of these sound similar, even where they are unrelated. It is likely that such terms have influenced each other over time. This phenomenon also overlaps with some insular Celtic terms, although it is uncertain to what extent this is coincidence.

A case-study for the way language adapts to its surroundings has shown how words for uplands and wetlands have merged in English *moor*, while one root, probably originally denoting a peat-forming plant, split into words for the plant and a wetland. A similar split occurred in Scandinavia. This shows that language is a dynamic system able to adapt to changing circumstances. It also serves to stress the importance of the landscape in the people's view of the world; language had to change to accommodate new environments because it was vital to have an appropriate set of vocabulary at all times.

REFERENCES

de Vries, J 1961 *Altnordisches Etymologisches Wörterbuch*. Leiden.

Gelling, M 1984 *Place-Names in the Landscape*. London.

Green, D H 1998 *Language and History in the Early Germanic World*. Cambridge.

McManus, D 1991 *A Guide to Ogam*. Maynooth.

OED2: Simpson, J & Weiner, E 1989, *Oxford English Dictionary*, 2nd edn (20 vols). Oxford.

OED3: [individually dated] *Oxford English Dictionary Online*, www.oed.com.

Page, R I 1999 *An Introduction to English Runes*, 2nd edn, Woodbridge.

Pokorny, J 1959 *Indogermanisches Etymologisches Wörterbuch*. Bern.

Robinson, O W 1992 *Old English and its Closest Relatives*. London.

Room, A 1988 *Dictionary of Placenames in the British Isles*. London.

Sims-Williams, P 2003 *The Celtic Inscriptions of Britain*. Oxford.

Udolph, J 1994 *Namenkundliche Studien zum Germanenproblem*. Berlin.

van der Sanden, W 1996 *Through Nature to Eternity*. Amsterdam.

van der Sanden, W & Capelle, T 2002 *Götter, Götzen, Holzmenschen*. Oldenburg.

This essay is dedicated to the memory of my father, of whose death I learned during the conference.

Modelling the archaeological potential of a Scottish wetland: a case study from the Mòine Mhór, Argyll

RUPERT A HOUSLEY, CIARA CLARKE and EWAN N CAMPBELL

INTRODUCTION

The Scottish Wetland Archaeology Programme (SWAP) was established in 1998 to promote coherent research projects concerned with the investigation, preservation and management of the Scottish wetland resource (Crone & Clarke 2001). The Mòine Mhór Cultural Heritage Project began in 2002 and is concerned with the development of methods to establish the location and extent of wetland archaeology deposits in Scotland using predictive modelling techniques and other non-invasive methods of detection (Henderson 2004, 169).

Despite having approximately 72 per cent of the British peat resource (Lindsay 1995), peatland archaeology in Scotland has been characterized by chance finds and only the occasional discovery of structural remains (Crone 1993a; Ellis *et al* 2002). The paucity of the Scottish peatland record is in marked contrast to the more dramatic finds from fen peats and raised bogs in other parts of Britain and Continental Europe. As Henderson (2004, 170) has pointed out, this may be due to the nature of the Scottish peatland resource – mostly upland blanket peat – but alternatively could be the result of the fact that there has been a lower level of commercial peat extraction in Scotland in recent years, with a concomitant lower probability for discovery, in comparison to other parts of Europe. As others have shown (eg Ritchie *et al* 1974; Newell 1988; Crone 1993b; Quartermaine *et al* this volume), whilst both upland blanket peats and lowland mires may sometimes preserve pre-peat archaeological landscapes, such horizons are not wetland archaeology in the usual sense of the term, that is, organic archaeological remains preserved by the inhibition of decay due to the presence of anaerobic conditions. Furthermore, although Tipping *et al* (this volume) are right to warn us that not all of Scotland's blanket peats are sited in remote inhospitable upland areas far from human habitation, the fact remains that the probability of discovering humanly worked organic remains must increase if one focuses on the lowland raised bogs and mires that are likely to have been closer to possible centres of past population. It is for these reasons that SWAP set out to model the wetland archaeological potential of a lowland peat mire in an area of high archaeological potential, and thus the Mòine Mhór Cultural Heritage Project was born.

Developing a strategy for the management of Scotland's peatland archaeology depends on being able to establish, from the surface, the location of archaeological remains within peatlands. Whilst it is conceded that single artefact finds are generally serendipitous and their location unpredictable, structures relating to settlement, the movement of people and their livestock, or economic activity will be predicated by variables such as topography or geomorphology, while their survival will involve factors like the hydrology and land-use history of the catchment. By modelling these and other variables we have sought to accurately predict likely areas for archaeological deposits within the study area.

PREDICTIVE MODELLING OF HUMAN ACTIVITY IN PEATLANDS

The foundation of predictive modelling techniques is generally to relate a modelled version of the physical environment to known statistics based on recorded archaeological sites (Cavers 2006, 19–20). In terms of physical geographical data, a combination of Ordnance Survey terrain models and river/water body mapping can be used in conjunction with soil and peat cover maps to derive physical environments most conducive to the presence of wetland archaeology. Attribute data relating to location and environment of known wetland sites should also be incorporated into predictive modelling techniques, and this information can come from wetland sites located in any country or region where similar conditions to those found in the study area in question have been encountered.

Archaeological resource management has often used predictive modelling to deal with archaeological records and areas that are incomplete, unreliable or unsupported by field survey data (eg see Sebastian & Judge 1988; van Leusen 1995). The aim of such approaches is generally to identify areas with a high probability of archaeology being present in order to help with the planning process. The basic strategy of predictive models is to use known patterns or relationships to periods, locations or environments that are either only partially, or poorly, known. As Wheatley and Gillings (2002, 165) have explained, the purpose of such an approach is efficiency, that is, the desire to reduce

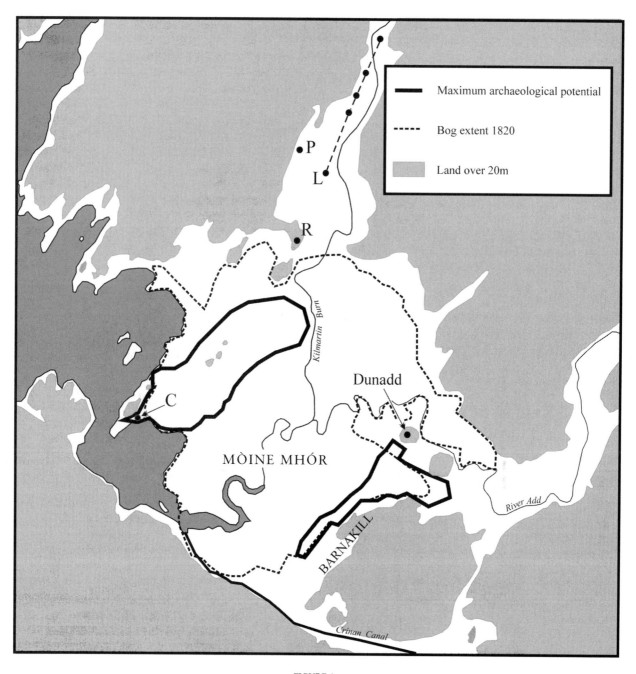

FIGURE 1
Kilmartin area showing the pre-improvement extent of the Mòine Mhór, and areas of identified maximum archaeological potential.
R – Rownfield; P – Poltalloch; C – Crinan Ferry; L – linear cemetery. (Source: authors.)

the amount of effort needed to identify areas of high archaeological significance.

Using these methodologies, a GIS system was set up for the Mòine Mhór, with a database of all known archaeological sites (Campbell & Housley 2002). The approach adopted here has been to identify areas with a high potential for the preservation of the remains of past human activity that have been preserved through the presence of anaerobic conditions and which can be tested in the field by geophysical prospection. In the case of peatlands, the development and spread of a mire is an important variable since the likely sites of human activity have almost certainly varied with time (Chapman & Geary 2002, 85) and so it is important to take the palaeoenvironmental history of the wetland into consideration. But in instances where detailed palaeoenvironmental and chronological data are lacking, as is the case with

the Mòine Mhór in Kilmartin Glen, a degree of imprecision is inevitable.

CASE STUDY: KILMARTIN AND ITS ARCHAEOLOGY

Kilmartin Glen in Argyll (fig 1) is a relatively sheltered part of west mainland Scotland, which is known for its wealth of archaeology dating from prehistoric and historical times (Ritchie 1997; RCAHMS 1999; Butter 2000). Monuments such as the stone and timber circle at Temple Wood, the linear cemetery which includes the cairn at Nether Largie, together with a number of standing stone and rock art sites attest to intense activity in Neolithic and Early Bronze Age times (RCAHMS 1988). Later prehistoric activity is less prominent

FIGURE 2
Photograph showing the rocky knoll (left foreground) upon which Dunadd is sited, and the surrounding lowland raised mire of the Mòine Mhór (foreground) set against a backdrop of the hills of Argyll. (Source: Kilmartin House Museum.)

in Kilmartin, being confined to small enclosures, hut circles and hilltop duns. The historical era saw occupation of the craggy hill of Dunadd, which became an important fortified royal centre of the Dalriadic Scots in the seventh to ninth centuries AD (Lane & Campbell 2000), whilst the establishment of Christianity is marked by the presence of early Christian and medieval stone grave slabs in the parish graveyard (RCAHMS 1992). The wealth and visibility of the archaeology from many periods suggested that Kilmartin Glen had been a significant centre of population in the past and so was a good area in which to apply modelling techniques for predicting the location of wetland archaeology.

THE MÒINE MHÓR

The Mòine Mhór (Great Moss or Big Bog) is a large expanse of low-lying raised bog that dominates the southern Kilmartin valley and surrounds the rocky knoll upon which the historic site of Dunadd sits (fig 2). Today, the Mòine Mhór encompasses around 1200 hectares with peat deposits up to 4.1m in thickness. At its maximum extent, the bog may have occupied up to 1800 hectares (Campbell & Housley 2002, 16 & fig 8). Based on partial pollen diagrams, the oldest waterlogged horizons probably date from at least 7,000–8,000 years ago and overlie marine and estuarine sediments that were deposited within the former Lateglacial embayment of Loch Crinan (Haggart & Sutherland 1992). Various statutory UK and European nature conservation designations (SSSI, NNR and SAC) protect the natural habitat of the flora and fauna on the Mòine Mhór, and some of the dry land archaeological sites are protected as scheduled ancient monuments. There are no recorded organic artefacts from the moss (SWAD: Clarke *et al* 2001), although the wooden effigy from Ballachulish moss in Lochaber gives some idea of what may await discovery in the Mòine Mhór.

The only natural undisturbed margins of the Mòine Mhór are to be found on the south-eastern margin where it abuts the wooded upland of the Barnakill ridge. The southern margin was lost when the Crinan Canal was built in the early nineteenth century; the western margin grades into salt marsh and mud flats; and the northern edge of the bog was lost to peat-cutting, extraction and wastage attributable to agricultural developments from the mid-eighteenth century. Therefore, the only places where undisturbed wetland archaeology is likely to occur adjacent to drier ground are along the south-eastern border near

Barnakill and around the rocky knolls or sand/gravel islands that project above the peat-filled valley floor.

PREDICTING THE WETLAND ARCHAEOLOGY POTENTIAL OF THE MÒINE MHÓR

MESOLITHIC

There is potential for pre-agricultural Mesolithic activity to exist in the Kilmartin Glen (Wickham-Jones 1994) although none has so far been discovered. Beyond the confines of Kilmartin there are a number of rock shelters around the coastline, for example, at Crinan Ferry and Duntrune, some of which have produced midden material and burials which have been claimed to be Mesolithic in age (Lacaille 1954, 197–9). Recently, unpublished Mesolithic dates have been recorded from pits underlying the important timber circle site at Upper Largie (Clare Ellis pers comm). There are well-known sites around the postglacial shorelines of Argyll (Tolan-Smith 2001) and islands such as Islay (Mithen 2001), so one would expect similar sites in the Kilmartin area.

One problem is the lack of detailed work on the postglacial sea-levels, though there is some information on late glacial events (Haggart & Sutherland 1992). However, isostatic uplift data suggest that any surviving Mesolithic remains in this area should be at similar levels to those around Oban, where the main Flandrian marine limit was 13m OD. This suggests that they should all be found above the 10m OD contour, since Haggart & Sutherland (1992) suggest a level of 11–11.5m OD at Kilmartin.

The types of area where Mesolithic activity would be expected can be divided into two categories. The first is steep south-facing bluffs overlooking salmon rivers such as the River Add. The second is estuarine peninsulas and islands within the Crinan embayment. Only the second of these is likely to lie within the area covered by the Mòine Mhór, which nowhere rises above 13m OD. The likeliest settings for Mesolithic exploitation are therefore the rocky knolls, which protrude through the peat, as these would represent possible islands in the Mesolithic period. Most of the areas of these which lie around the 10m contour are above the peat surface, for example, around the Crinan Ferry knoll. Only in the area to the south of Dunadd are there rock outcrops, which are covered with peat around the 10m contour, where the intact south-eastern edge of the bog butts the Barnakill ridge. Furthermore, only at the northern end of this boundary, where the ridge lowers and runs under the bog to Dunadd, is it likely to have possessed the characteristics of an estuarine peninsula. This, then, is one possible area of Mesolithic remains. The area in the centre of the northern bog may be at sufficient elevation to cover open-air Mesolithic sites, but the depth of peat here (over 4m) means it is unlikely to be ever available for study, at least in the foreseeable future.

NEOLITHIC AND BRONZE AGE

These periods have the main concentration of upstanding monuments in the valley and include standing stones, cairns and stone circles. These are concentrated on the lower fluvio-glacial terraces of the River Add and, in greater numbers, of the Kilmartin Burn. The higher terraces of marine origin tend to have cist burials, the henge and cursus monuments. The relationship between the peat and these monuments is not well understood at present, as there is no chronology for the development of the bog. However, it is clear that some of the lower-lying monuments were covered by spreading peat at some point after their construction, as they either protrude from the moss today or are recorded in the past as being covered before the drainage in the late eighteenth century (eg Nether Largie standing stones).

Indications as to the location of possible sites can be gained from the detailed study of the topographic situation of the known monuments (Abernethy 2001). These often appear to be sited on 'islands' of slightly higher elevation within the terraces. In the past they may have been surrounded by floodwater at some times of the year. As already mentioned, the topography of the valley includes a number of rocky knolls, which protrude through the superficial deposits of the valley floor. These are aligned NE–SW due to the grain of the meta-morphic rocks of the Dalriadan Assemblage (Hill 1905; Peach & Kynaston 1909; Whittow 1977). The summits of these knolls include Dunadd itself, and a number of smaller hillocks, but there are also others buried in the peat. One buried ridge of bedrock runs from Barnakill to Dunadd, and then across the Add. Here it forms a rock barrier, which has resulted in the creation of two separate meander belts, one above the ford, and one below. Another major line of hillocks, which indicate a buried ridge, can be observed running from Rowanfield to Crinan Ferry. This is a very significant ridge as it lies on the line of the famous Kilmartin linear cemetery. This line of Bronze Age burial cairns possibly

overlies an earlier Neolithic alignment (Abernethy 2001), and may include rock-art sites. Fieldwork by Abernethy has suggested that one unrecorded complex lies on the hillock at Rownfield, and there are other standing stones and cists further south. The area around these hillocks is a prime site for the existence of buried early prehistoric wetland archaeology but unfortunately it is not currently accessible.

IRON AGE AND EARLY HISTORIC

The Iron Age and early historic periods are dominated by the hilltop settlements characteristic of Argyll, the duns and forts. Only one of these classes of monuments falls within the study area – the important stronghold of the kings of Dál Riata at Dunadd. This site was occupied from at least the early Iron Age (Lane & Campbell 2000), but its location and very low elevation is unusual in this area for a fort or dun. There may well have been undefended occupation on the gravel terraces at this time, but the only recorded site is at Bruach an Druimein (Poltalloch), where an Ogham stone and other early medieval material has been found.

As the bog was likely to have been at its widest extent during this period, there is little prospect of sub-peat remains being encountered. The only exceptions are possible trackways which would have cut across the moss. Such trackways (or *toghers*) are common in Ireland, and, in the early historic period, a system of roadways was developed throughout the boggy areas of central Ireland (Raftery 1996; 1999). The most likely location for such structures would be for access to the important sites of the period, particularly Dunadd. There are two lines of access from the south across the bog to Dunadd. One runs from Dunamuck to the unnamed hillock south-east of Dunadd, whilst the other follows the Barnakill ridge across the bog via a series of small rocky knolls. The latter has the most potential for the survival of wetland archaeology as the peat in this area is unaffected by later drainage. It is also a likely routeway, as an important inscribed early Christian cross was originally located near Barnakill, possibly marking an important burial site.

Any other archaeological finds of these periods would probably consist of stray finds dropped during visits to the bog, or artefacts that were ritually deposited, and are only likely to be found during commercial peat-cutting. Rather surprisingly, no such artefacts were reported from the extensive cuttings of the nineteenth and early twentieth centuries from this area.

FIGURE 3
Map from Clarke (2003, fig 2) showing the area surveyed by ground penetrating radar to the south-west of Dunadd.
(Source: AOC Archaeology Group.)

TARGET AREAS IDENTIFIED BY PREDICTIVE MODELLING

Modelling of known sites and the past extent of the Mòine Mhór identified two areas of high archaeological potential:

1. To the west, a series of buried hillocks continue the alignment of the Kilmartin linear cemetery and provide a promising setting for wetland deposition in the Neolithic and Early Bronze Age.
2. To the east, a buried ridge extends south-westerly from Dunadd, forming a natural line of communication to the site.

Due to reasons of access, it was decided to investigate the second of these two areas, between Dunadd and the Barnakill ridge, and the method adopted was to use ground penetrating radar (GPR).

GPR AND SURFACE TOPOGRAPHIC SURVEY OF THE SELECTED AREA

A number of previous investigations (eg Clarke *et al* 1999; Ellis *et al* 2002; Schou Jørgensen 1997) had demonstrated the value of GPR as a method for investigating sub-peat archaeology and so a similar approach was adopted at the Mòine Mhór. In June 2003, the area between the bottom of Dunadd and the second rock outcrop to the south-west of the hillfort, between Dunadd and the Barnakill ridge, was surveyed using GPR (fig 3). The study covered an area of 28,500m² and was undertaken using Utsi Electronics' Groundvue 2, with the radar equipment harnessed to the rear of an Agrocat (fig 4).

The survey successfully demonstrated that GPR was suitable for defining the morphology of the basin at the Mòine Mhór, for a clear signal was obtained of the interface between the peat and the sand, silt and gravel sub-peat strata (Clarke 2003; Utsi this volume). The survey also produced an accurate estimate of peat depth when compared to the 1959 Soil Survey of Scotland (Scottish Peat Survey 1965, 175–92). However, in terms of detecting archaeological features below the peat, the June 2003 GPR survey was inconclusive (Clarke 2003). While it is acknowledged that the sub-peat ridges may respect ancient crossing point(s) between the present day rocky knolls, the GPR data did not show clear surviving evidence of anthropogenic modification or enhancement of these sub-peat features – the anomalies that were recorded may simply be natural geological phenomena. No linear arrangement was observed that could represent a track or pathway. This is not to dismiss this area as a possible approach route across the moss to Dunadd for, in antiquity, it may have been possible to traverse the area without the need for extensive anthropogenic modification. Alternatively, waterlogged structures may be present below the peat along this routeway but if they comprise structures made only from timber and other organic materials then such features are unlikely to have shown up clearly or coherently in the radar survey. Only further investigations, probably of an intrusive nature, will resolve this matter.

CONCLUSIONS AND AVENUES FOR FUTURE RESEARCH

Further GPR survey of the Mòine Mhór has the potential to provide a more detailed understanding of the peat basin morphology and could also be used to test hypotheses in other areas of high archaeological

FIGURE 4
Photograph showing the ground penetrating radar survey being undertaken in June 2003. The Agrocat is pulling the GPR system across the Mòine Mhór between Dunadd and the Barnakill ridge. (Source: AOC Archaeology Group.)

potential in the bog. A limited programme of coring and radiocarbon dating would provide information on the chronological development of the mire. Such investigations would provide a further check on the peat depths as defined by the radar and would also facilitate investigations of the relationship between radar signal clarity at the peat/mineral deposit boundary.

New radar work targeted at archaeological hypotheses on other Scottish peatlands would improve the development and application of the technique, which at present provides the only non-invasive method of subsurface wetland survey. In future, it would be desirable to select wetland areas where invasive works would be permitted so that indicative peat depths and anomalies could be verified and investigated. Recently the Black Moss of Achnacree in Argyll has been identified as a good candidate on which to undertake such work as its archaeological potential in this context has been demonstrated (Inglis & Housley 2006), and invasive work is unlikely to be opposed since the area has suffered disturbance as a consequence of recent economic development pressures. The desk-based assessment has identified a three-phase strategy for investigation, involving mapping the peat and sub-peat basin morphology and establishing a chronology for the development of the moss in antiquity through a programme of systematic augering and radiocarbon dating of the major lithological horizons. Within the Moss of Achnacree there exists a microcosm of wetland environments (raised bog, alluvium and lacustrine lochs) and likely areas of high archaeological potential have been identified, including one where wetland structures have already been reported (Smith 1873). The Moss of Achnacree is one of a number of areas identified by SWAP as worthy of further investigation in the next few years (Cavers 2006, 72–3) and further developments are to be anticipated.

ACKNOWLEDGEMENTS

We are grateful to Historic Scotland for their financial assistance for this study; to Scottish Natural Heritage for access to the study area and for providing valuable assistance in kind during the fieldwork; Lorraine McEwan for preparing fig 1; and to Erica Utsi for providing the expertise and equipment needed to make the radar survey.

REFERENCES

Abernethy, D 2001 *Prehistoric Monumentality in the Kilmartin Glen, Mid Argyll*. Unpubl MLitt thesis, University of Glasgow.

Butter, R 2000 *Kilmartin: A Guide to Scotland's richest prehistoric landscape*. Kilmartin.

Campbell, E N & Housley, R A 2002 *The Wetland Archaeology Potential of the Mòine Mhór*. Unpubl report to Historic Scotland for STAR.

Cavers, G 2006 *The Scottish Wetland Archaeology Programme: Setting a Research Agenda*. Unpubl report to Historic Scotland for SWAP.

Chapman, H P & Geary, B R 2002 'Archaeological predictive modelling in raised mires – concerns and approaches for their interpretation and future management', *Journal of Wetland Archaeology* 2, 77–88.

Clarke, C 2003 *The cultural heritage of Mòine Mhór: 2003 radar and topographic survey*. Unpubl report to Historic Scotland for AOC Archaeology Group.

Clarke, C, Ellis, C, Gittings, B M & Newton, A J 2001 *Scottish Wetlands Archaeological Database*, www.geo.ed.ac.uk/swad/

Clarke, C, Utsi, E & Utsi, V 1999 'Ground penetrating radar investigations at North Ballachulish Moss, Highland, Scotland', *Archaeological Prospection* 6(2), 107–21.

Crone, A 1993a 'A wooden bowl from Loch a'Ghlinna Bhig, Bracadale, Skye', *Proc Soc Ant Scot* 123, 245–54.

Crone, A 1993b 'Excavation and survey of sub-peat features of Neolithic, Bronze Age and Iron Age date from Bharpa Carinish, North Uist, Scotland', *Proceedings of the Prehistoric Society* 59, 361–82.

Crone, A & Clarke, C 2001 *Scottish Wetland Archaeology Programme: Phase 1*. Unpubl report to Historic Scotland for SWAP.

Ellis, C, Crone, A, Reilly, E & Hughes, P 2002 'Excavation of a Neolithic Wooden Platform, Stirlingshire', *Proceedings of the Prehistoric Society* 68, 247–56.

Haggart, B A & Sutherland, D G 1992 'Mòine Mhór', in Walker, M J C, Gray, J M & Lowe, J J (eds) *The Southwest Scottish Highlands*, 143–52. Cambridge.

Henderson, J C 2004 'The Scottish Wetland Archaeology Programme: assessing and monitoring the resource', *Journal of Wetland Archaeology* 4, 169–82.

Hill, J B 1905 *The Geology of Mid Argyll*. Memoirs of the Geological Society of Scotland (explanation to sheet 37).

Inglis, R & Housley, R A 2006 *The Wetland Archaeology Potential of the Moss of Achnacree: Desk-based Assessment and Field Reconnaissance*. Unpubl report to Historic Scotland for SWAP.

Lacaille, A 1954 *The Stone Age in Scotland*. Oxford.

Lane, A & Campbell, E 2000 *Excavations at Dunadd: an early Dalriadic capital.* Oxford.

Lindsay, R 1995 *Bogs: the ecology, classification and conservation of ombrotrophic mires.* Edinburgh.

Mithen, S (ed) 2001 *Hunter-gatherer Landscape Archaeology: The Southern Hebrides Mesolithic Project, 1988–1998.* Cambridge.

Newell, P J 1988 'A buried wall in peatland by Sheshader, Isle of Lewis', *Proc Soc Ant Scot* 118, 79–93.

Peach, B N & Kynaston, H 1909 *The Geology of the Seaboard of Mid Argyll.* Memoirs of the Geological Survey of Scotland (explanation to sheet 36).

Quartermaine, J, Cook, J, Druce, D & Huckerby, E forthcoming 'The trials and tribulations of Upland Peat: results of investigations into the archaeological potential of the higher peatlands', *in this volume.* Edinburgh.

Raftery, B 1996 *Trackway excavations in the Mountdillon Bogs, Co Longford, 1985–91.* Irish Archaeological Wetland Unit Transactions 3. Dublin.

Raftery, B 1999 'The Milling Fields' *in* Coles, B, Coles, J & Jorgensen, M S (eds) *Bog Bodies, Sacred Sites and Wetland Archaeology,* 191–202. Exeter.

RCAHMS 1988 *Argyll. An Inventory of the Ancient Monuments* Volume 6 *Mid Argyll & Cowal, Prehistoric & Early Historic Monuments.* Edinburgh.

RCAHMS 1992 *Argyll. An Inventory of the Ancient Monuments* Volume 7 *Mid Argyll and Cowal, Medieval and Later Monuments.* Glasgow.

RCAHMS 1999 *Kilmartin: Prehistoric and early historic monuments.* Edinburgh.

Ritchie, A, Ritchie, G, Whittington, G & Soulsby, J 1974 'A prehistoric field-boundary from the Black Crofts, North Connel, Argyll', *Glasgow Archaeological Journal* 3, 66–70.

Ritchie, G (ed) 1997 *The Archaeology of Argyll.* Edinburgh.

Schou Jørgensen, M 1997 'Looking into the landscape', *Aarhus Geoscience* 7, 157–66.

Scottish Peat Survey 1965 'Mòine Mhór, Argyllshire, surveyed 1959' *in Scottish Peat Surveys, Volume 3: Central Scotland,* 175–92. Edinburgh.

Sebastian, L & Judge, W 1988 'Predicting the past: correlation, explanation and the use of archaeological models', *in* Judge, W & Sebastian, L (eds) *Quantifying the Present and Predicting the Past: Theory, Method and Application of Archaeological Predictive Modelling.* Denver.

Smith, R A 1873 'A descriptive list of antiquities near Loch Etive, Argyllshire, consisting of vitrified forts, cairns, circles, crannogs, etc.; with some remarks on the growth of peat', *Scotland* 9 (1870–2), 87.

Tipping, R, Ashmore, P, Davies, A, Haggart, A, Moir, A, Newton, A, Sands, R, Skinner, T & Tisdall, E forthcoming 'Peat, pine stumps and people: interactions behind climate, vegetation change and human activity in wetland archaeology at Loch Farlary, northern Scotland', *in this volume.* Edinburgh.

Tolan-Smith, C 2001 *The Caves of Mid Argyll: An Archaeology of Human Use.* Edinburgh.

Utsi, E forthcoming 'Wetlands viewed through the antennas of a Ground Penetrating Radar', *in this volume.* Edinburgh.

van Leusen, P M 1995 'GIS and archaeological resource management: a European agenda' *in* Lock, G & Stancic, Z (eds) *Archaeology and GIS: a European perspective,* 27–42. London.

Wheatley, D & Gillings, M 2002 *Spatial Technology and Archaeology: the archaeological applications of GIS.* London.

Wickham-Jones, C 1994 *Scotland's first settlers.* Edinburgh.

Whittow, J B 1977 *Geology and Scenery in Scotland.* Harmondsworth.